FOUNDATIONS OF ELASTICITY THEORY

INTERNATIONAL SCIENCE REVIEW SERIES

Edited by Lewis Klein
National Bureau of Standards

VOLUME I

Lewis Klein, Dispersion Relations and the Abstract Approach to Field Theory

VOLUME II

Harry L. Morrison, The Quantum Theory of Many-Particle Systems

VOLUME III

D. McIntyre and F. Gornick, Light Scattering from Dilute Polymer Solutions

VOLUME IV

N. N. Bogoliubov, The Theory of Superconductivity

VOLUME V

P. K. Kabir, The Development of Weak Interaction Theory

VOLUME VI

M. E. Rose, Nuclear Orientation

VOLUME VII

P. H. Meijer, Group Theory and Solid State Physics
(In Two Volumes)

VOLUME VIII

Part 1: C. Truesdell, The Mechanical Foundations of Elasticity and Fluid Dynamics (In Preparation)

Part 2: C. Truesdell, The Rational Mechanics of Materials

Part 3: C. Truesdell, Foundations of Elasticity Theory

Part 4: C. Truesdell, Problems of Non-Linear Elasticity

Additional Volumes in Preparation

FOUNDATIONS OF ELASTICITY THEORY

Edited by

C. TRUESDELL

The Johns Hopkins University

GORDON AND BREACH, Science Publishers, Inc.

New York London Paris

Library of Congress Catalog Card Number: 65-16956

For Great Britain and Europe:

Gordon and Breach, Science Publishers, Ltd.
171 Strand
London W. C. 2, England

Printed in the United States of America

PREFACE TO THE COLLECTION

This volume of reprints is one of four designed to reflect the resurgence of continuum mechanics in the past few years. Nothing published earlier than 1945 is included, and nothing later than 1961. The contents of the four volumes are connected, sometimes loosely and sometimes closely, with each other, so that the division is somewhat arbitrary.

The prefaces to the several papers are intended to help the reader understand and place the research presented in them. Since a detailed exposition of the field as it now stands, along with full references to the sources, is given in the treatises CFT and NFTM (see the list of abbreviations on p. vi), no attempt is made to render the present collection complete either in coverage or in documentation. Rather, these volumes are meant to show the **ideas and methods** of the creators of the modern theories, along with a fair sample of the results they found.

Like other new fields in the past, the new continuum mechanics attracted little notice at first. The forty-nine papers reprinted here are by only eighteen authors, of whom six are responsible for thirty-six of the papers. While some important authors have been left, with regret, unrepresented, and some important papers omitted, the group active in the field before 1961 was by any estimate a small one, so that a sample of ideas and methods should give more than usual help to the beginner.

C. T.

TABLE OF ABBREVIATIONS
FOR TITLES OF WORKS FREQUENTLY CITED

MF — C. Truesdell, **The Mechanical Foundations of Elasticity and Fluid Dynamics,** Journal of Rational Mechanics and Analysis, Volume 1, pp. 125-300 (1952); Corrections and Additions, ibid., Volume 2, pp. 593-616 (1953). Reprinted, with corrections inserted, and with a special preface and appended notes, in the International Science Review Series, Gordon and Breach, New York, 1965.

RMM — **The Rational Mechanics of Materials,** International Science Review Series, Gordon and Breach, New York, 1965.

FET — **Foundations of Elasticity Theory,** International Science Review Series, Gordon and Breach, New York, 1965.

PNE — **Problems of Non-linear Elasticity,** International Science Review Series, Gordon and Breach, New York, 1965.

CFT — C. Truesdell & R. Toupin, **The Classical Field Theories,** with an appendix by J. L. Ericksen, **Invariants,** Flügge's Encyclopedia of Physics, Vol. 3, Part 1, pp. 226-858 (1960).

NFTM — C. Truesdell & W. Noll, **The Non-linear Field Theories of Mechanics,** Flügge's Encyclopedia of Physics, Vol. 3, Part 3, to appear in 1965.

PREFACE TO
FOUNDATIONS OF ELASTICITY THEORY

The contents of this volume and of PNE are closely related. Here are collected studies of the concept of elasticity in the broader sense, while the papers in PNE concern more specific problems in the classical theory.

No. 1 in this volume, by REINER, is the first to study concretely the concept of finite elastic strain divorced from energetic concepts. No. 2, by RICHTER, introduces simple methods of algebra, distinct from components and expansions. BAKER & ERICKSEN's note (No. 3) proposes some general inequalities, and in No. 4 CAPRIOLI gives a work principle sufficient that an elastic material be hyperelastic.

The next three papers concern hypo-elastic materials, defined as those in which the stress is built up linearly in response to infinitesimal increments of strain. No. 13, by BERNSTEIN, attacks the problem of finding the relation between elasticity and hypo-elasticity, initiated by NOLL in No. 5 of RMM, and obtains a definitive condition to be satisfied by the stress field.

Nos. 8, 9, and 11, returning to the classical theory of finite elasticity, attempt to determine inequalities sufficient to ensure physically reasonable response. In No. 11, in particular, COLEMAN & NOLL succeed in extending to elastic materials arguments of the type presented by GIBBS a century earlier for fluids.

TOUPIN in No. 10 formulates in classic simplicity a theory of the interaction between elasticity and electrostatics. In No. 12, a prize-winning essay, KRÖNER attempts to formulate the theory of "dislocations" in a properly invariant fashion; his analysis refers mainly to the geometrical foundations of the theory, leaving the constitutive equations unspecified.

The volume closes with a paper by COLEMAN & NOLL, closely connected with No. 15 of RMM, in which BOLTZMANN's accumulative theory of visco-elasticity is given a rational place as an approximation for slightly deformed simple materials with fading memory.

C. T.

CONTENTS

CONTENTS

No. 1

ELASTICITY BEYOND THE ELASTIC LIMIT.

M. Reiner

American Journal of Mathematics, Volume 70, pp. 433-446 (1948).

This paper is in character transitional between the older type of research on the foundations of elasticity and the modern, to which the volume is devoted. The older work usually included a good deal of talk about physical phenomena that was never rendered concrete in the mathematical theory. Section 1 is of this kind. The idea that only the "recoverable" part of the strain is "elastic" or "reversible" is an old one that has never led to any definite mathematical solutions of specific problems except in the very case when all of the strain is recoverable; to this case, all papers in the volume are devoted, and it is to this case, despite its title, that this paper makes a contribution. In Section 2 GREEN's assumption of a stored-energy function is abandoned, and instead CAUCHY's definition of an elastic material is laid down as Eq. (2. 2). That equation, however, is neither self-consistent nor invariant except for an isotropic material and for a strain tensor $\epsilon_r{}^S$ that is itself an invertible isotropic function of CAUCHY's tensor **c** (cf. MF, Section 17), taken with respect to an "undistorted state" (cf. NFTM, Section 47). REINER in effect assumes isotropy at Eq. (4. 1), which is far more special than (2. 2). The representation theorem (4. 4), formally analogous to one he had derived earlier for a non-linearly viscous fluid (cf. RMM, No. 1), emerges.

The main importance of the paper lies in Sections 5-6, where it is indicated that Eq. (4. 4) gives a theory **independent of the measure of strain** (within the class of what are called spatial strain measures in MF, Section 14) and that, in effect, **no less general definition of elasticity** has that property, obviously a necessary one for an unprejudiced theory. Note also the indication in Section 5 that there is **no** theory of finite strain of an isotropic material that does **not** predict normal-stress effects in simple shear. Cf. the simultaneous treatment of simple shear by RIVLIN in No. 1 of PNE. The rest of the paper concerns mainly the naming of coefficients; also typical of the older studies on "rheology," this part has not proved useful.

REINER's theory was criticized in Section 46 of MF for resting on nothing more than the concept of isotropy. While the criticism was just, CAUCHY's definition of elasticity can in fact be based on a clear physical concept and expressed easily in invariant form for materials of arbitrary symmetry, as is shown in the next paper in this volume and also in Sections 43-50 of NFTM. On the basis of this theory, the problems of simple shear, uniform dilation, and simple extension are treated in Sections 54-55 of NFTM. Cf. also the discussion of the equivalence of strain measure in Section 32 of CFT. While the results in this paper should have put an end forever to fancies about the virtues of one or another strain measure, these furnish a popular literary subject even today. As shown by the development in Chapter D of NFTM, it is not necessary to define or discuss "strain" at all.

For a modern treatment of the distinguishing properties that follow from existence of a stored-energy function (as is always assumed in what REINER in Section 2 calls "the classical theory," now called "hyperelasticity,"), see Sections 79-85 of NFTM.

ELASTICITY BEYOND THE ELASTIC LIMIT.*

By M. Reiner.

1. Theories of elasticity have so far presupposed the existence of what Love (Art. 76) called a "state of ease" of "perfect elasticity" in which "a body can be strained without taking any set"; that state ranging between an "initial," "unstressed" and "unstrained" state (Art. 64) on one hand and the "elastic limit' on the other. Recent technological progress has gradually reduced, absolutely and, still more, relatively, the field in which this assumption holds good. Not only has increased accuracy of measurements of permanent sets lowered the elastic limit until in many cases as, for instance, annealed copper, it has nearly disappeared. More important, in materials which *do* show a definite elastic limit as, for instance, mild steel, deformations in most practical applications go *beyond* that limit. In addition, one has to consider elastic materials such as bitumen or cement-stone showing creep: their elastic potential gradually disappears through relaxation. Finally, there are such materials as rubber which can be caused to undergo very large deformations, a certain part of which will always be non-recoverable. It therefore becomes necessary to consider elasticity beyond the elastic limit. If we define elasticity with Love as "the property of recovery of an *original* size and shape," there would in all these cases be no question of elasticity because the *original* size and shape is not recovered. However, *some* of the deformation is *always* recovered: but *which* part of it is recoverable, becomes apparent only when all external forces, gravity included, *have been removed.* We may denote as the *ground-position* that position of the body which is then reached. To every deformation there corresponds a ground-position of its own, which generally will not be the *initial* position from which the deformation started. Let us denote by *deformation* a change of size and of shape in general, whether recoverable or not, and by *strain* that part of it which is recovered when all external forces have been removed. Generally, the strain will differ from the deformation not only in magnitude, but also in the orientation of the principal axes.

The ground-position is accordingly an unstrained and unstressed state, but it is not an *undeformed* state. A general theory of elasticity, then, has to relate the strain as now defined to (i) the stress produced by it and (ii) the

* Received October 12, 1947.

external forces necessary to equilibrate the stresses in the body in accordance with d'Alembert's principle; while the classical theory of the "state of ease" refers to the special case when the strain is identical with the deformation. The considerations of the present paper are, however, also applicable in the latter case.

2. The classical theory was brought to completion by Murnaghan when considering finite strain. He derived the relation between the stress tensor T^{rs} and the strain tensor ϵ_{rs} from a formula connecting the elastic potential ϕ with the stress tensor.[1] That formula itself was derived by considering the virtual work of the stresses across a closed boundary of a portion of the material. This method is inapplicable in our case. If we write the fundamental law of thermodynamics for isothermal processes in the form of the Gibbs-Helmholtz equation

$$\delta w = \rho \delta \phi + \rho \delta \psi \tag{2.1}$$

where w is the strainwork per unit volume, ϕ the intrinsic free energy-density and ψ the bound energy-density (compare Weissenberg, 1931), not only will ψ in our general case not vanish, but what is more remarkable, as Taylor and Quinney have shown in a metal which is subjected to cold working, part of the free energy is "latent" and not recoverable mechanically. We therefore must apply that other method used in the classical theory for the derivation of the stress-strain relation (e. g. by Stokes) which is a generalization of Hooke's law, writing

$$T_s{}^r = f(\epsilon_s{}^r) \tag{2.2}$$

and developing the function f by means of tensor analysis, as was done by Reiner in the analogous case of viscosity. The equation will then express a law of elasticity if ϵ indicates the strain defined above as the recovered part of the deformation and if the relation connecting $T_s{}^r$ and $\epsilon_s{}^r$ is unequivocal. From the last condition there follows, that we can also write

$$\epsilon_s{}^r = \mathfrak{f}(T_s{}^r). \tag{2.3}$$

In the experimental determination of the relation one would have in principle to proceed as follows: Subject a material to external forces and let it undergo a process of deformation of a certain type,[2] arrest the deformation and record

[1] We shall use in the present paper wherever possible Murnaghan's notation.

[2] For "type" compare Love (Art. 73).

the magnitude of stress; [3] mark a sphere of unit radius in the material around some selected point; remove all external forces: this will induce relative displacements in the material changing the sphere into an ellipsoid called the reciprocal strain ellipsoid; wait until this movement dies out; measure the axes of the ellipsoid: they will provide a measure of strain; repeat this experiment reaching different magnitudes of the same type of deformation in a gradually increasing or decreasing order; record the strain, as determined, against the stress: provided the relaxation of the stress is negligible, the result is an empirical relation for (2.3) depending upon the type of deformation.[4] For instance, in the usual tensile test for metals in the work-hardening range, when the volume of an element of the material can be assumed as constant and the deformation has axial symmetry, only one axis of the ellipsoid need be measured *viz.,* either along or across the test piece and the empirical formula relates the axial traction p_{zz} to the axial strain ϵ_{zz}.

3. In the first stage of our investigation we need not fix the *measure* of strain. Denoting the three axes of the above mentioned ellipsoid by l_i (i running over 1, 2, 3) or, what is sometimes more convenient, the axes of the strain ellipsoid by $\lambda_i = 1/l_i$ "one may use (as Weissenberg (1946) pointed out) any function of the elongation ratios (λ_i) in the direction of the main axes choosing the function to suit the particular field of investigation." One would, naturally, require that all these functions are reduced for infinitesimal strain to the Cauchy measure $\lambda_i - 1$. This is the case with the Kirchoff-measure which is based upon $\frac{1}{2}[(\lambda_i)^2 - 1]$ and the Murnaghan-measure based upon $\frac{1}{2}[1 - (l_i)^2]$; it is also so with the measure $ln\ (\lambda_i) = - ln(l_i)$ originally proposed by Roentgen for rubber and, since systematically introduced by Hencky, now widely in use. We may also mention the measure $(\lambda_i - l_i)$ proposed by Wall. All these measures comply also with a second requirement, *viz.* that the strain vanishes for $\lambda_i = 1 = l_i$. It is clear that a linear stress-strain relation in one measure will be non-linear in every other and the desire for linearity is often one of the motives behind the introduction of one or the other of the measures mentioned, our enumeration being far from complete.

4. Starting from (2.2) or (2.3), we follow the reasoning applied by Reiner, as has already been mentioned, in the analogous case of viscous

[3] It is necessary first to arrest the deformation as, generally, part of the stress will be due to viscous resistance, depending upon the velocity of deformation.

[4] "If . . . the stress-strain relations can be found experimentally, the strain-energy function can be calculated" (Sokolnikoff, p. 89).

resistance. We note that on the left side there stands a mixed tensor of rank two. Then in a development of either function f or $\mathfrak{f}$ all terms on the right side must also be mixed tensors of rank two. The right side can therefore consist only of sums of mixed tensors of rank two multiplied by scalars and of inner products of such tensors which again are reduced to tensors of rank two. The general term of a development of the function f will therefore be of the form $\epsilon_a{}^r\epsilon_\beta{}^a\epsilon_\gamma{}^\beta \cdots \epsilon_s{}^\lambda \cdot f(I)$, where $f(I)$ is a function of the three invariants: and we can therefore write

$$(4.1) \qquad T_s{}^r = f_0\delta_s{}^r + f_1\epsilon_s{}^r + f_2\epsilon_a{}^r\epsilon_s{}^a + f_3\epsilon_a{}^r\epsilon_\beta{}^a\epsilon_s{}^\beta + \cdots.$$

This would mean an infinite number of such terms. However, in view of the Cayley-Hamilton equation of matrix theory, the following relation holds good [5]

$$(4.2) \qquad \epsilon_a{}^r\epsilon_\beta{}^a\epsilon_s{}^\beta = \delta_s{}^r III - \epsilon_s{}^r II + \epsilon_a{}^r\epsilon_s{}^a I$$

where I, II and III are the first, second and third invariants respectively.

Therefore

$$(4.3) \qquad \begin{aligned} \epsilon_a{}^r\epsilon_\beta{}^a\epsilon_\gamma{}^\beta\epsilon_s{}^\gamma &= \delta_a{}^r\epsilon_s{}^a III - \epsilon_a{}^r\epsilon_s{}^a II + \epsilon_a{}^r\epsilon_\beta{}^a\epsilon_s{}^\beta I \\ &= \delta_s{}^r I \cdot III + \epsilon_s{}^r(III - I \cdot II) + \epsilon_a{}^r\epsilon_s{}^a(I^2 - II) \end{aligned}$$

and similarly with respect to higher terms. This enables us to write

$$(4.4) \qquad T_s{}^r = F_0\delta_s{}^r + F_1\epsilon_s{}^r + F_2\epsilon_a{}^r\epsilon_s{}^a$$

and analogously

$$(4.5) \qquad \epsilon_s{}^r = \mathfrak{F}_0\delta_s{}^r + \mathfrak{F}_1 T_s{}^r + \mathfrak{F}_2 T_a{}^r T_s{}^a$$

where the F are functions of the three invariants I_ϵ, II_ϵ and III_ϵ of the strain-, and the $\mathfrak{F}$ functions of the three invariants I_T, II_T and III_T of the stress-tensor. Prager has recently derived equations built up in a manner similar to (4.4) and (4.5), but subject to specializations due to certain simplifying assumptions. Our equations are general and express nothing more than that both stress and strain are tensors of rank two, the principal axes of which coincide; and that the functions F and $\mathfrak{F}$ are scalars. We may call a material in such a state *isotropic*.

However, we also require that in the ground-position, when the stress is removed, the strain should also vanish, and *vice versa*. Therefore

[5] These developments are entirely analogous to those of Reiner for the viscous liquids, but it was thought desirable to make the present paper self-contained.

(4. 6) $$F_0 = F_{01} I_\epsilon + F_{02} II_\epsilon + F_{03} III_\epsilon$$

(4. 7) $$\mathfrak{F}_0 = \mathfrak{F}_{01} I_T + \mathfrak{F}_{02} II_T + \mathfrak{F}_{03} III_T$$

where the new F and $\mathfrak{F}$ are again, in general, functions of all three invariants I, II and III.

The functions F are *moduli* of elasticity, the functions $\mathfrak{F}$ *coefficients* of elasticity; the latter, generally, *not* the reciprocals of the former. There are therefore, generally, five of each kind, each one possessing ∞^3 values in accordance with the values which the invariants may have in every particular case. In the expressions for F and $\mathfrak{F}$ as functions of the invariants, there will appear a number of parameters, which are the elastic "constants" of the material. The F and $\mathfrak{F}$ may, of course, themselves be constants; in special cases some of them may vanish, in other cases they may not be independent; and this would reduce their number from five to less.

The F and $\mathfrak{F}$ can be given physical interpretations only when a definite measure of strain is assumed and we shall examine what consequences the adoption of any such measure may have.

5. Before dealing with the problem in a general way, it will be useful to examine the special case of simple shear dealt with by Love in Art. 37. This is given kinematically by the equations

(5. 1) $$x_1 = x + sy; \qquad y_1 = y; \qquad z_1 = z.$$

Putting

(5. 2) $$s = 2 \tan \alpha,$$

Love calculates

(5. 3) $$\lambda_1 = \frac{1 - \sin \alpha}{\cos \alpha}; \qquad \lambda_2 = \frac{1 + \sin \alpha}{\cos \alpha}; \qquad \lambda_3 = 1$$

and he proves that the directions of the principal axes of strain are the bisectors of the angle $(\pi/2) + \alpha$ with the x-axis, and the angle through which the principal axes are turned is the angle α. The stress caused by the strain will have the principal components T_1, T_2, T_3 which from (4. 4) and (4. 6) are

(5. 4) $$T_i = F_{01} I + F_{02} II + F_{03} III + F_1 \epsilon_i + F_2 \epsilon_i^2.$$

The components of stress with respect to the system x, y, z will be from Love's equations, Art. 49:

$$
(5.5)\quad
\begin{aligned}
T_{xx} &= \tfrac{1}{2}(T_1 + T_2) - \tfrac{1}{2}(T_1 - T_2)\sin\alpha \\
T_{yy} &= \tfrac{1}{2}(T_1 + T_2) + \tfrac{1}{2}(T_1 - T_2)\sin\alpha \\
T_{zz} &= T_3 \\
T_{xy} &= -\tfrac{1}{2}(T_1 - T_2)\cos\alpha; \qquad T_{yz} = T_{zx} = 0.
\end{aligned}
$$

Introducing the expressions for the principal stresses from (5.4) into (5.5) gives

$$
(5.6)\quad
\begin{aligned}
T_{xx} &= F_{01}I + F_{02}II + F_{03}III + \tfrac{1}{2}\{F_1[(\epsilon_1 + \epsilon_2) - (\epsilon_1 - \epsilon_2)\sin\alpha] \\
&\qquad + F_2[(\epsilon_1^2 + \epsilon_2^2) - (\epsilon_1^2 - \epsilon_2^2)\sin\alpha]\} \\
T_{yy} &= F_{01}I + F_{02}II + F_{03}III + \tfrac{1}{2}\{F_1[(\epsilon_1 + \epsilon_2) + (\epsilon_1 - \epsilon_2)\sin\alpha] \\
&\qquad + F_2[(\epsilon_1^2 + \epsilon_2^2) + (\epsilon_1^2 - \epsilon_2^2)\sin\alpha]\} \\
T_{zz} &= F_{01}I + F_{02}II + F_{03}III \\
T_{xy} &= -\tfrac{1}{2}[F_1(\epsilon_1 - \epsilon_2) + F_2(\epsilon_1^2 - \epsilon_2^2)]\cos\alpha.
\end{aligned}
$$

We now assume definite measures of strain. If l_0 is a length extended in simple elongation by Δl to l, the measure of the extension may relate Δl to either l_0 or l, or it may relate an element of elongation dl to the instantaneous length l. These three possibilities correspond to the Kirchhoff-measure.

$$(5.7)\qquad \epsilon_i^K = \tfrac{1}{2}(\lambda_i^2 - 1)$$

the Murnaghan-measure

$$(5.8)\qquad \epsilon_i^M = \tfrac{1}{2}(1 - l_i^2) = \tfrac{1}{2}(1 - 1/\lambda_i^2)$$

and to the logarithmic or Hencky-measure

$$(5.9)\qquad \epsilon_i^H = ln\lambda_i = -\,lnl_i.$$

Introducing the expressions λ_i from (5.3), we find the principal strain-components, the strain-invariants and the stress-components in the x, y and z directions as entered in the following Table:

ϵ_i	$\frac{1}{2}(\lambda_i^2 - 1)$	$ln\lambda_i$	$\frac{1}{2}(1 - 1/\lambda_i^2)$
ϵ_1	$-\tan\alpha \dfrac{1-\sin\alpha}{\cos\alpha}$	$ln \dfrac{1-\sin\alpha}{\cos\alpha}$	$-\tan\alpha \dfrac{\cos\alpha}{1-\sin\alpha}$
ϵ_2	$\tan\alpha \dfrac{\cos\alpha}{1-\sin\alpha}$	$ln \dfrac{\cos\alpha}{1-\sin\alpha}$	$\tan\alpha \dfrac{1-\sin\alpha}{\cos\alpha}$
ϵ_3	0	0	0
I_ϵ	$2(\tan\alpha)^2$	0	$-2(\tan\alpha)^2$
II_ϵ	$-(\tan\alpha)^2$	$-(ln \dfrac{\cos\alpha}{1-\sin\alpha})^2$	$-(\tan\alpha)^2$
III_ϵ	0	0	0
T_{xx}	$(\tan\alpha)^2[2F_{01} - F_{02} + 2F_1 + F_2(1 + 4\tan^2\alpha)]$	$ln \dfrac{\cos\alpha}{1-\sin\alpha}[(F_2 - F_{02}) ln \dfrac{\cos\alpha}{1-\sin\alpha} + F_1 \sin\alpha]$	$-(\tan\alpha)^2(2F_{01} + F_{02} - F_2)$
T_{yy}	$(\tan\alpha)^2(2F_{01} - F_{02} + F_2)$	$ln \dfrac{\cos\alpha}{1-\sin\alpha}[(F_2 - F_{02}) ln \dfrac{\cos\alpha}{1-\sin\alpha} - F_1 \sin\alpha]$	$-(\tan\alpha)^2[2F_{01} + F_{02} + 2F_1 - F_2(1 + 4\tan^2\alpha)]$
T_{zz}	$(\tan\alpha)^2(2F_{01} - F_{02})$	$-(ln \dfrac{\cos\alpha}{1-\sin\alpha})^2 F_{02}$	$-(\tan\alpha)^2(2F_{01} + F_{02})$
T_{xy}	$\tan\alpha(F_1 + 2F_2\tan^2\alpha)$	$ln \dfrac{\cos\alpha}{1-\sin\alpha} F_1$	$\tan\alpha(F_1 - 2F_2\tan^2\alpha)$

In infinitesimal strain we may neglect $(\tan\alpha)^2$ and introducing $\tan\alpha=\alpha=s/2$ all three measures give the same $\epsilon_2=-\epsilon_1=s/2$, $T_{xy}=F_1 s/2$, while normal tractions T_{xx}, T_{yy} and T_{zz} vanish. In this case simple shear is accompanied by a shearing stress only. In finite strain such a simple relation is not possible, whatever the values of the elastic moduli. We may in the Kirchhoff measure make $F_{02}=2F_{01}$ and T_{zz} vanishes. We may in addition make $F_2=0$ and T_{yy} will vanish. But there *must* remain a tension in the direction x which is $T_{xx}=2F_1(\tan\alpha)^2$ and we cannot put $F_1=0$ because then T_{xy} also would vanish. Alternately, we may put $F_2=-2F_1/[1+4(\tan\alpha)^2]$ which would make T_{xx} vanish, but leave a pressure $T_{yy}=-2F_1(\tan\alpha)^2/[1+4(\tan\alpha)^2]$. Conditions are similar in other measures. In an isotropic material finite simple shear is accompanied by either a tension in the direction of the displacement or compression in the direction of its gradient or both. Weissenberg (1947) has demonstrated the existence of such stresses in elastic liquids in a series of striking experiments.

6. The present theory is distinguished from the usual theory of elasticity of finite strains mainly by the appearance of the modulus F_2. In the usual theory, Equation (5.4) would be

$$T_i=F_0+F_1\epsilon_i \tag{6.1}$$

which constitutes three equations with two unknowns, *viz.*, the moduli F_0 and F_1. In order that these equations should be consistent, certain relations between T_i and ϵ_i must be satisfied. The matrix of the coefficients is of rank two. The augmented matrix

$$K=\left\|\begin{matrix}1 & \epsilon_1 & T_1\\ 1 & \epsilon_2 & T_2\\ 1 & \epsilon_3 & T_3\end{matrix}\right\| \tag{6.2}$$

must therefore also be of the rank two. This requires the determinant

$$\begin{vmatrix}1 & \epsilon_1 & T_1\\ 1 & \epsilon_2 & T_2\\ 1 & \epsilon_3 & T_3\end{vmatrix}=0 \tag{6.3}$$

or

$$\frac{T_1-T_2}{\epsilon_1-\epsilon_2}=\frac{T_2-T_3}{\epsilon_2-\epsilon_3}=\frac{T_3-T_1}{\epsilon_3-\epsilon_1}=F(I_\epsilon, II_\epsilon, III_\epsilon, I_T, II_T, III_T). \tag{6.4}$$

Equation (6.4) has been proposed by Weissenberg (1947) as a law of elasticity. As has, however, been shown here, it is not general enough and is not independent of the *measure* of strain. For instance, should experiments show that simple shear is accompanied by a tension in the direction of displacement, the Murnaghan measure could not be used. On the other hand, should experiments show that it is accompanied by compression in the direction of the gradient of the displacement, the Kirchhoff measure could not be used. In the form of Equation (5.4) the law of elasticity is independent of the measure and does not prejudice the outcome of experiment.

7. Considering that, by including the modulus F_2 (or the coefficient $\mathfrak{F}_2$), we are independent of the measure of strain, we may for our further investigation assume any measure. We shall select the Hencky-measure for two reasons:

(i) Because of $\epsilon_i = ln\lambda_i$, $\dot{\epsilon}_i = \dot{\lambda}_i/\lambda_i$. Denoting by e_i the principal "velocity-extension" of hydrodynamics, we accordingly get $e_i = \dot{\epsilon}_i$, provided the principal axes do not rotate. Therefore in *pure* strain, in the Hencky-measure, to use Murnaghan's words "the variation of the strain tensor (is equal) to the space derivative of the virtual displacement vector." This is of advantage, especially if we consider that it may be possible in many cases to arrange "the removal of the external forces" (compare **2** and **3** above) in such a way that the axes do not rotate and the strain is acordingly pure.

(ii) Secondly, from

$$V/V_0 = \lambda_1 \cdot \lambda_2 \cdot \lambda_3, \tag{7.1}$$

there follows

$$\epsilon_v = ln(V/V_0) = ln\lambda_1 + ln\lambda_2 + ln\lambda_3 = \epsilon_1 + \epsilon_2 + \epsilon_3 = I_\epsilon. \tag{7.2}$$

Therefore, in the Hencky measure, and only in that measure, the cubical dilation is equal to the first invariant of the strain tensor.[6] Accordingly, only in this measure has the resolution of the tensor in an isotropic and a deviatoric component physical significance.

8. By carying out the resolutions

$$T_s{}^r = T\delta_s{}^r + T'_s{}^r; \qquad \epsilon_s{}^r = \epsilon\delta_s{}^r + \epsilon'_s{}^r \tag{8.1}$$

where

$$T_a{}^a = 3T, \quad \epsilon_a{}^a = 3; \qquad T'_a{}^a = \epsilon'_a{}^a = 0 \tag{8.2}$$

we get from (4.4) and (4.6)

[6] This is, of course, also the case in infinitesimal strain.

$$T = F_{01} + F_{02} + II'_\epsilon + F_{03}III'_\epsilon \tag{8.3}$$
$$T'^{\ r}_{s} = F_1\epsilon'^{\ r}_{s} + F_2(\epsilon'^{\ r}_{a}\epsilon'^{\ a}_{s} + 2II'_\epsilon/3 \cdot \delta_s^r)$$

and from (4.5) and (4.7)

$$\epsilon = \mathfrak{F}_{01}T + \mathfrak{F}_{02}II'_T + \mathfrak{F}_{03}III'_T \tag{8.4}$$
$$\epsilon'^{\ r}_{s} = \mathfrak{F}_1T'^{\ r}_{s} + \mathfrak{F}_2(T'^{\ r}_{a}T'^{\ a}_{s} + 2II'_T/3 \cdot \delta_s^r)$$

where the accents indicate the deviator and the F and $\mathfrak{F}$ are now functions of the invariants of the deviator, different from the functions F and $\mathfrak{F}$ appearing in (4.4) to (4.7).

If we introduce $\epsilon'^{\ r}_{s}$ from (8.4) into (8.3), considering that δ_s^r, $T'^{\ r}_{s}$ and $T'^{\ r}_{a}T'^{\ a}_{s}$ stand for the zero, first and second powers in the stress components, we find

(8.5) [7]
$$F_1 = \frac{\mathfrak{F}_1^2 + II'_T/3 \cdot \mathfrak{F}_2^2}{\begin{vmatrix} \mathfrak{F}_1 & [\mathfrak{F}_2III'_T - 2II'_T/3 \cdot \mathfrak{F}_1]\mathfrak{F}_2 \\ \mathfrak{F}_2 & \mathfrak{F}_1^2 + II'_T/3 \cdot \mathfrak{F}_2^2 \end{vmatrix}}$$

$$F_2 = \frac{\mathfrak{F}_2}{|\text{ as above }|}.$$

The moduli of elasticity F are therefore generally not the reciprocals of the coefficients of elasticity $\mathfrak{F}$.

We now carry out in imagination a series of experiments such as mentioned at the end of Section 2.

(i) Firstly, we apply a uniform hydrostatic pressure; here the stress tensor is a scalar tensor

$$T_s^r = -p\delta_s^r \tag{8.6}$$

where p is what is commonly called "pressure" and the stress invariants are

$$T = -p, \qquad II'_T = III'_T = 0 \tag{8.7}$$

$T'^{\ r}_{s}$ and $T'^{\ r}_{a}T'^{\ a}_{s}$, therefore, vanish and the second of (8.4) gives $\epsilon'^{\ r}_{s} = 0$, while the first yields

$$\epsilon = -p\mathfrak{F}_{01}(T, 0, 0). \tag{8.8}$$

This defines a *coefficient of volume elasticity*

$$k' = -3\epsilon/p = 3\mathfrak{F}_{01}. \tag{8.9}$$

[7] For the derivation compare Reiner.

Considering that II'_ϵ and III'_ϵ vanish, the first of (8. 3) gives

(8. 10) $$T = -p = \epsilon \mathfrak{F}_{01}.$$

This defines the *modulus of compression*

(8. 11) $$k = -p/3\epsilon = F_{01}/3$$

and $k' = 1/k$.

(ii) In the second experiment we apply a tangential stress

(8. 12) $$T_s{}^r = \left\| \begin{matrix} 0 & T_{xy} & 0 \\ T_{xy} & 0 & 0 \\ 0 & 0 & 0 \end{matrix} \right\| = T'_s{}^r$$

so that

(8. 13) $$T = 0; \qquad II'_T = -T_{xy}{}^2; \qquad III'_T = 0$$

and

(8. 14) $$T'_a{}^r T'_s{}^a = T_{xy}{}^2 \left\| \begin{matrix} 1 & 0 & 0 \\ 0 & 1 & 0 \\ 0 & 0 & 0 \end{matrix} \right\|.$$

This makes (8. 4)

(8. 15)
$$\epsilon = -T_{xy}{}^2 \mathfrak{F}_{02}(0, II'_T, 0)$$
$$\epsilon'_s{}^r = \mathfrak{F}_1(0, II'_T, 0) T_{xy} \left\| \begin{matrix} 0 & 1 & 0 \\ 1 & 0 & 0 \\ 0 & 0 & 0 \end{matrix} \right\| + \mathfrak{F}_2(0, II'_T, 0) \frac{T_{xy}{}^2}{3} \left\| \begin{matrix} 1 & 0 & 0 \\ 0 & 1 & 0 \\ 0 & 0 & -2 \end{matrix} \right\|$$

and defines three coefficients of elasticity, *viz.*

(8. 16)
$$\delta' = -\epsilon/II'_T = -\mathfrak{F}_{02}$$
$$\mu' = 2\mathfrak{F}_1$$
$$\alpha' = -2\mathfrak{F}_{2/3}.$$

The coefficient $\mathfrak{F}_1$ connects shearing stress with shearing strain and is accordingly a generalized *coefficient of shear elasticity* or *of rigidity*. The isotropic component of the strain, ϵ, is a measure of the cubical dilation. If δ' does not vanish, a simple shearing stress will produce an increase (or decrease for negative δ') of the volume measured by $\delta' T_{xy}{}^2$.[8]

---

[8] It is remarkable that Sir William Thomson (Lord Kelvin) should have foreseen in 1875 the possible existence of such a phenomenon on purely theoretical grounds, *vide* the following quotation: "It is possible that a shearing stress may produce in a truly isotropic solid condensation or dilatation in proportion to the square of its value; and it is possible that such effect may be sensible in india-rubber or cork, or other bodies susceptible of great deformations or compressions with persistent elasticity." Footnote p. 34, *Math. & Phys. Papers*, Vol. III, London, 1890. Weissenberg has observed negative elastic dilatancy in porous rubber (not yet published).

Accordingly, δ' may be termed the *coefficient of* (elastic) *dilatancy* (compare Reiner). Should δ' vanish, but not α', then a simple shearing stress will produce (in the case of a positive α') an extension normal to the plane of shear (in our case the z-direction) which is equal to $\alpha' T_{xy}^2$, together with two lateral contractions equal to $\alpha'/2 \cdot T_{xy}^2$, so that the volume is not changed. If δ' should not vanish, there will be superposed a change of volume. We may call α' the *coefficient of cross-elasticity.*

(iii) If we force upon the material a tangential strain, we shall similarly find three moduli of elasticity

(8.17) [9]
$$\delta = -F_{02}/4$$
$$\mu = F_1/_2$$
$$\alpha = -F_2/6$$

of which μ is a generalized *shear modulus* or *modulus of rigidity.* δ, the *modulus of dilatancy,* will measure a hydrostatic tension necessary to maintain simple shear; and α, a *modulus of cross-elasticity,* measures a stress produced by simple shear, in the direction normal to its plane.

(iv) Simple pull, in infinitesimal elasticity employed to determine Young's modulus and Poisson's ratio, gives us

(8.18)
$$T_s{}^r = \begin{Vmatrix} 0 & 0 & 0 \\ 0 & 0 & 0 \\ 0 & 0 & T_{zz} \end{Vmatrix}$$

so that

(8.19)
$$T = T_{zz}/3\,;\, T'_s{}^r = \frac{T_{zz}}{3} \begin{Vmatrix} -1 & 0 & 0 \\ 0 & -1 & 0 \\ 0 & 0 & 2 \end{Vmatrix};\, T'_a{}^r T'_s{}^a = \frac{T_{zz}{}^2}{9} \begin{Vmatrix} 1 & 0 & 0 \\ 0 & 1 & 0 \\ 0 & 0 & 4 \end{Vmatrix}$$

and

(8.20)
$$II'_T = -T_{zz}{}^2/3; \qquad III'_T = 2T_{zz}{}^3/27.$$

This makes

(8.21)
$$\epsilon_s{}^r = T_{zz}/3(k'/3 + T_{zz}\delta' + (2T_{zz}{}^2/9)\mathfrak{F}_{03}) \begin{Vmatrix} 1 & 0 & 0 \\ 0 & 1 & 0 \\ 0 & 0 & 1 \end{Vmatrix}$$
$$+ (T_{zz}/6)(\mu' - \alpha' T_{zz}) \begin{Vmatrix} -1 & 0 & 0 \\ 0 & -1 & 0 \\ 0 & 0 & 2 \end{Vmatrix}$$

---

[9] Note that a simple shear is measured traditionally by twice the tangential component of the strain-tensor.

and defines a generalized Youngs' modulus

$$(8.22) \quad E^{-1} = \epsilon_{zz}/T_{zz} = -\tfrac{1}{3}[k'/3 + \mu' + T_{zz}(\delta' - \alpha') + (2T_{zz}^2/9)\mathfrak{F}_{03}]$$

and a generalized Poisson-ratio

$$(8.23) \quad \sigma = -\epsilon_{xx}/\epsilon_{zz} = -\frac{k'/3 - \mu'/2 + T_{zz}(\delta' + \alpha'/2) + (2T_{zz}^2/9)\mathfrak{F}_{03}}{k'/3 + \mu' + T_{zz}(\delta' - \alpha') + (2T_{zz}^2/9)\mathfrak{F}_{03}}.$$

Either E or σ can be used to determine a further coefficient of elasticity

$$(8.24) \quad \beta' = 2\mathfrak{F}_{03}/9.$$

Summarizing, we can now write (8.4) as follows:

$$(8.26) \quad \begin{aligned} \epsilon_v &= -k'p - 3\delta' II'_T + (27/2)\beta' III'_T \\ \epsilon'_s{}^r &= (\mu'/2)T'_s{}^r - 3(\alpha'/2)(T'_a{}^r T'_s{}^a + 2II'_T/3 \cdot \delta_s{}^r) \end{aligned}$$

and (8.3) as follows:

$$(8.27) \quad \begin{aligned} p &= -k\epsilon_v + 4\delta II'_\epsilon - (9\beta/2) III'_\epsilon \\ T'_s{}^r &= 2\mu\epsilon'_s{}^r - 6\alpha(\epsilon'_a{}^r \epsilon'_s{}^a + 2II'_\epsilon/3 \cdot \delta_s{}^r) \end{aligned}$$

where p is the hydrostatic pressure and ϵ_v the cubical dilatation, $\epsilon'_s{}^r$ the deviator of strain and $T'_s{}^r$ the deviator of stress, k, δ, β, μ, α moduli of elasticity and k', δ', β', μ', α' coefficients of elasticity. These are generally functions of all three invariants of stress and strain respectively, but may also degenerate to constants. A hydrostatic tension will cause a cubical dilation and *vice versa*; but a cubical dilatation may also be caused in the absence of a hydrostatic tension by either simple shearing stress or traction. Likewise, a hydrostatic pressure may be required to maintain simple shear or a volume-constant simple extension. Finally, a simple shearing stress may not only produce a corresponding shearing strain, but also "sideways" a volume-constant extension. Likewise simple shear may require for its maintenance not only a corresponding shearing stress but also "sideways" a traction. The general elastic body has accordingly three additional properties absent in classical elasticity, namely dilatancy of two kinds, (shear- and tractional dilatancy) and cross-elasticity. It is not so much the property of dilatancy predicted by Kelvin as early as 1875 and observed as a permanent set by Reynolds as early as 1885, which is challenging, but the cross-elasticity, which is connected with the functions $\mathfrak{F}_2$ and F_2 respectively. We, therefore, consider this property again from a different aspect.

9. Let n be the normal to an element of interface in the interior or of surface on the boundary of the body under consideration. Let the traction

T_n be resolved into three orthogonal components T_{nq} where q runs through n, t and c; t being the direction parallel to the face and c the direction crosswise to n and t, so that

$$T_{nc} = 0. \tag{9.1}$$

Let ϵ_n be resolved in the same directions. We find, then, from the second of (8.4)

$$\epsilon'_{nc} = \mathfrak{F}_2 T'_{na} T'_{ac} \tag{9.2}$$

the term following within brackets disappearing because $r \neq s\,(n \neq c)$. Now

$$T'_{na}T'_{ac} = T'_{nn}T'_{nc} + T'_{nt}T'_{tc} + T'_{nc}T'_{cc}. \tag{9.3}$$

As (9.2) is not affected by an isotropic stress component, T'_{nc} vanishes also and this reduces (9.3) to

$$T'_{na}T'_{ac} = T'_{nt}T'_{tc}. \tag{9.4}$$

Now on the right side of (9.4) T'_{nt} does not vanish, by definition; and if one imagines in the standard cube which defines T_{xx} etc., x, y, z replaced by n, t, c, it is clear that T'_{tc} will, in general, not vanish. Therefore ϵ'_{nc} is finite. This brings out very strikingly a consequence of the existence of $\mathfrak{F}_2$ and supports the designation "cross-elasticity." We have, however, shown that $\mathfrak{F}_2$ (or F_2) can generally not be omitted without prejudicing experimental results.

TEL AVIV, PALESTINE.

BIBLIOGRAPHY.

Hencky, H., *Annalen der Physik* (5), vol. 2 (1929), p. 617.
Love, A. E. H., *Mathematical Theory of Elasticity*, Cambridge, 1906.
Murnaghan, F. D., *American Journal of Mathematics*, vol. 59 (1937), p. 235.
Prager, W., *Journal of Applied Physics*, vol. 16 (1945), pp. 837-840.
Reiner, M., *American Journal of Mathematics*, vol. 67 (1945), p. 35.
Roentgen, *Annalen der Physik*, vol. 159 (1876), p. 601.
Sokolnikoff, I. S., *Mathematical Theory of Elasticity*, New York, 1946.
Stokes, G. G., *Transactions of the Cambridge Philosophical Society*, vol. 8 (1849), p. 287.
Taylor, G. I. and Quinney, H., *Proceedings of the Royal Society*, A., vol. 143 (1934), p. 307.
Wall, F. T., *Journal of Chemical Physics*, vol. 10 (1942), p. 132.
Weissenberg, K., *Akademie der Wissenschaften*, Berlin, 1931.
Weissenberg, K., *British Rheologist's Club Conference*, London, 1946.
Weissenberg, K., *Nature*, vol. 159 (1947), p. 310.

No. 2

ON THE THEORY OF FINITE ELASTIC DEFORMATION

H. Richter

(Zur Elastizitätstheorie endlicher Verformungen),
Mathematische Nachrichten, Volume 8, pp. 65-73 (1952).

This paper is the first to apply the concepts of modern linear algebra to the mechanics of continua. It had strong influence on the work of NOLL, represented by No. 11 in this volume but more particularly by Nos. 5 and 12 in RMM.

Stress and deformation are envisaged directly as linear transformations of vectors, independent of co-ordinates and components. Eq. (2.1) is, in effect, CAUCHY's definition of an elastic material, subjected to the requirement later called the "principle of isotropy of space," "principle of material indifference," etc. The polar decomposition theorem is introduced in (2. 2), from which, effortlessly, follows as Eq. (2. 3) the explicit dependence of the stress vector on the finite rotation, while dependence on the right stretch tensor remains arbitrary. In terms of the stress tensor, the result appears as Eq. (3. 6), specialized to (3. 6 iso) and (3. 7 iso) for isotropic materials. The simplicity, directness, and generality of the purely algebraic reasoning is to be contrasted not only with the more elaborate and less general and specific calculation in REINER's paper, preceding in this volume, but even more with the classical and far more special argument recapitulated in MF, Section 37.

The remaining contents are essentially classical and may be found also in MF, Sections 38-41.

The paper closes with a wholesome reminder that there is no logical ground for preferring any particular set of variables or co-ordinates in elasticity. It must be recalled that even in 1952 there was still a widespread belief, growing from numerous obscure papers by "specialists," that different theories of finite elasticity had been proposed. This short note, along with MF, showed that all these theories, to the extent they were not wrong or "approximate," are identical.

ON THE THEORY OF FINITE ELASTIC DEFORMATION

H. Richter in Haltingen (Kr. Lörrach)

(Translation of **Zur Elastizitätstheorie endlicher Verformungen,** Mathematische Nachrichten, Volume 8, pp. 65-73 (1952))

Dedicated to Mr. Georg Hamel in veneration on his 75th birthday
(Received June 6, 1952)

Section 1. Introduction

The following development is in part not new, to the extent that the relations derived here have been proved from other standpoints and by other methods, some of them in earlier works of the author, some in other pertinent works, as especially in the textbooks of Mr. Hamel. Rather, the emphasis here lies upon uniting the various known results from a unified geometric standpoint. This desire arose in an extended correspondence between Mr. Hamel and the author, who is grateful to comply with the suggestion of the Jubilee in this regard by publishing his development of that period — so much the more grateful, since this exposition was influenced essentially by the course of the above-mentioned discussion.

Section 2. Intuitive Consideration of the State of Stress and Strain.

If an initially unstressed elastic medium suffers a static strain that does not vary too rapidly in space — with regard, say, to the distance between defects or to the size of the grains — it may be regarded as a continuum in which the stresses generated at each point depend only upon the affinity $\mathfrak{A}$ that specifies the strain in an infinitesimal neighborhood. Hence we shall consider only homogeneous, direct, affine, static strains $\mathfrak{A}$, where this symbol at first shall stand for a transformation of vectors $\mathfrak{x}$ in space, in the sense of pure Euclidean geometry, with no reference to any particular co-ordinate system. The affinity inverse to $\mathfrak{A}$ will be denoted by $\mathfrak{A}^{-1}$; let $\mathfrak{E}$ be the identity mapping; the letter $\mathfrak{R}$ shall stand for an orthogonal transformation, and $\mathfrak{S}$ for a pure stretch in three mutually orthogonal directions with positive stretch ratios. The $\mathfrak{A}$'s form a group, in which $\mathfrak{B}\mathfrak{A}$ means that first $\mathfrak{A}$ is applied, then $\mathfrak{B}$. Also $\mathfrak{A}+\mathfrak{B}$ is defined by $(\mathfrak{A}+\mathfrak{B})\mathfrak{x} = \mathfrak{A}\mathfrak{x}+\mathfrak{B}\mathfrak{x}$ and $\lambda\mathfrak{A}$ by $(\lambda\mathfrak{A})\mathfrak{x} = \lambda\cdot\mathfrak{A}\mathfrak{x}$, for numbers λ.

Let the stresses, also, be visualized: For every direction $\mathfrak{n}$ in space we think of the plane $E(\mathfrak{n})$ orthogonal to n at the material point under consideration in the medium deformed by $\mathfrak{A}$. By the stress $\mathfrak{p}(\mathfrak{n};\mathfrak{A})$ we understand the force per unit area of $E(\mathfrak{n})$ of such magnitude and direction as to replace the material "outside" $E(\mathfrak{n})$ as far as concerns the preservation of equilibrium. For every $\mathfrak{n}$, $\mathfrak{p}$ is represented also by a vector.

We ask how the vector function $\mathfrak{p}(\mathfrak{n};\mathfrak{A})$ depends upon $\mathfrak{A}$. If to this end we regard the material strained in accord with $\mathfrak{A}$ and then subjected to the rotation $\mathfrak{R}$, then $\mathfrak{p}$ and $\mathfrak{n}$ are both rotated with $\mathfrak{R}$; thus

$$\mathfrak{p}(\mathfrak{n};\mathfrak{R}\mathfrak{A}) = \mathfrak{R}\mathfrak{p}(\mathfrak{R}^{-1}\mathfrak{n};\mathfrak{A}). \tag{2.1}$$

Now every $\mathfrak{A}$ may be represented uniquely in the form

$$\mathfrak{A} = \mathfrak{R}_l\mathfrak{S}_r \quad \begin{pmatrix}\mathfrak{S}_r = \text{right stretch component of } \mathfrak{A},\\ \mathfrak{R}_l = \text{left rotation component of } \mathfrak{A}\end{pmatrix}, \tag{2.2}$$

so that (2.1) yields

$$\mathfrak{p}(\mathfrak{n};\mathfrak{A}) = \mathfrak{R}_l\mathfrak{p}(\mathfrak{R}_l^{-1}\mathfrak{n};\mathfrak{S}_r). \tag{2.3}$$

Hence follows:

In an arbitrary anisotropic material, the right stretch component determines the thermodynamic quantities completely but the stresses only to within orientation; for complete calculation of the stresses, also the rotation component of the strain must be given.

If, however, the material is isotropic, then it makes no difference if an additional rotation is effected before $\mathfrak{A}$. In this case the analogue of (2. 1) is

(2. 1 iso) $$\mathfrak{p}(\mathfrak{n}; \mathfrak{A}\mathfrak{R}) = \mathfrak{p}(\mathfrak{n}; \mathfrak{A}).$$

If we form the unique decomposition analogous to (2. 2):

(2. 4) $$\mathfrak{A} = \mathfrak{S}_l \mathfrak{R}_r,$$

then follows

(2. 3 iso) $$\mathfrak{p}(\mathfrak{n}; \mathfrak{A}) = \mathfrak{p}(\mathfrak{n}; \mathfrak{S}_l).$$

Since $\mathfrak{S}_l \mathfrak{R}_r = \mathfrak{R}_r(\mathfrak{R}_r^{-1}\mathfrak{S}_l\mathfrak{R}_r)$, comparison of (2. 2) with (2. 4) yields at once

(2. 5) $$\mathfrak{R}_l = \mathfrak{R}_r = \mathfrak{R}, \quad \mathfrak{S}_r = \mathfrak{R}^{-1}\mathfrak{S}_l\mathfrak{R};$$

That is, the rotation components of $\mathfrak{A}$ are identical, and the stretch parts differ from one another only in the orientation of the direction of stretch. From (2. 3 iso) and (2. 3) then follows at once

$$\mathfrak{p}(\mathfrak{n}; \mathfrak{S}_l) = \mathfrak{p}(\mathfrak{n}; \mathfrak{A}) = \mathfrak{R}\mathfrak{p}(\mathfrak{R}^{-1}\mathfrak{n}; \mathfrak{R}^{-1}\mathfrak{S}_l\mathfrak{R}),$$

or for an isotropic material in general

(2. 6 iso) $$\mathfrak{p}(\mathfrak{n}; \mathfrak{R}\mathfrak{S}\mathfrak{R}^{-1}) = \mathfrak{R}\mathfrak{p}(\mathfrak{R}^{-1}\mathfrak{n}; \mathfrak{S}).$$

Thus we have:

In an isotropic material the thermodynamic quantities and the stresses depend only on the left stretch component, $\mathfrak{S}_l$. If the axes of stretch of $\mathfrak{S}_l$ are subjected to a rotation $\mathfrak{R}$, so is $\mathfrak{p}$.

Hence it follows in particular by use of a rotation through 180° that for the directions of stretch $\mathfrak{s}$ of $\mathfrak{S}_l$ we have $\mathfrak{p}(\mathfrak{s}; \mathfrak{S}_l) \parallel \mathfrak{s}$.

Our considerations give us at the same time information about the number of parameters in the general elastic law for finite deformations: In a general anisotropic material the principal stretches and the situation of $\mathfrak{S}_r$ with respect to the crystal axes are essential; thus the elastic energy and the entropy involve 6 parameters, which determine the stresses to within orientation, which follows, in turn, from $\mathfrak{R}$. In an isotropic material, by (2. 3 iso) and (2. 6 iso) only the three principal stretches are essential, and these are determined by $\mathfrak{S}_l$ alone; if $\mathfrak{S}_l$ is used, $\mathfrak{R}$ is not essential. On the other hand, while $\mathfrak{S}_r$ yields the three parameters in the isotropic case, it does not yield the orientation and is to this extent less convenient.

The above considerations presume that $\mathfrak{p}(\mathfrak{n})$ is determined by $\mathfrak{A}$. Such is the case if the temperature or entropy is prescribed for the initial and end states or if special changes such as isothermal or adiabatic strains are considered. In the general case, temperature or entropy appears as a further parameter in the elastic law.

Section 3. Matrix Notation.

Doubtless the most elegant version of the theory of finite elastic deformations is that which employs tensors in an arbitrary co-ordinate system. However, it has its unattractive side in the continual regard for the vanishing of the curvature tensor and the difficulty of attributing directly to tensors the above simple geometric relations; indeed, the usual too quick construction of the "strain tensor" so as to get genuine tensors conceals important relations. Since afterward the conversion to an arbitrary co-ordinate system is easily possible in matrix calculus, without use of Ricci-calculus, for simplicity we here lay down a Cartesian co-ordinate system, in which the vector of the typical point of the initial state is given by a column matrix:

(3. 1) $$\hat{\mathfrak{x}} = \begin{pmatrix} \hat{x}_1 \\ \hat{x}_2 \\ \hat{x}_3 \end{pmatrix}$$

nd the vector of the corresponding point in the deformed state by

3. 2) $$\mathfrak{x} = \begin{pmatrix} x_1 \\ x_2 \\ x_3 \end{pmatrix}$$

nd the affinity $\mathfrak{A}$ is characterized by a square matrix, which is denoted by the same ymbol, so that

3. 3) $$\mathfrak{x} = \mathfrak{A}\hat{\mathfrak{x}}$$

n a homogeneous affine strain. Matrices of the type of $\mathfrak{R}$ or $\mathfrak{S}$ are characterized by the onditions

3. 4) $$\mathfrak{R}\mathfrak{R}' = \mathfrak{E} \text{ and } \mathfrak{S} = \mathfrak{S}',$$

espectively, where $\mathfrak{A}'$ denotes the transpose of $\mathfrak{A}$ (reflection through the main diagonal). qs. (2. 3), (2. 4), and (2. 5) are unchanged. In addition,

3. 5) $$\mathfrak{A}\mathfrak{A}' = \mathfrak{S}_l^2 \text{ and } \mathfrak{A}'\mathfrak{A} = \mathfrak{S}_r^2,$$

vhere $\mathfrak{S}_l$ and $\mathfrak{S}_r$ are uniquely determined as positive-definite square roots. If we denote y $|\mathfrak{A}|$ the determinant formed from $\mathfrak{A}$, then the fractional increase in volume is given y $|\mathfrak{A}| = |\mathfrak{S}_l| = |\mathfrak{S}_r|$.

As is well known, from the equilibrium of forces and moments it can be proved that n Cartesian co-ordinates $\mathfrak{p}(\mathfrak{n})$ may be represented in terms of a matrix $\mathfrak{P}$, the stress ensor, as follows:

$$\mathfrak{p}(\mathfrak{n}) = \mathfrak{P}\mathfrak{n}, \qquad \mathfrak{P} = \mathfrak{P}'.$$

Our equations (2. 3), (2. 3 iso), and (2. 6 iso) now take the forms

(3. 6) $$\mathfrak{P}(\mathfrak{A}) = \mathfrak{R}\,\mathfrak{P}(\mathfrak{S}_r)\,\mathfrak{R}^{-1},$$

(3. 6 iso) $$\mathfrak{P}(\mathfrak{A}) = \mathfrak{P}(\mathfrak{S}_l),$$

(3. 7 iso) $$\mathfrak{P}(\mathfrak{R}\mathfrak{S}\mathfrak{R}^{-1}) = \mathfrak{R}\,\mathfrak{P}(\mathfrak{S})\,\mathfrak{R}^{-1}.$$

The transformation property (3. 7 iso) is characteristic for isotropic material, ince (3. 6 iso) follows from (3. 7 iso) together with (3. 6) and (2. 5). For an anisotropic naterial $\mathfrak{P}(\mathfrak{S}_r)$ is thus not an affinely or even an orthogonally invariant matrix function; ather, it consists of six functions as yet unrelated to one another.

ection 4. Strain Tensors and Modified Stress Tensors.

By a "strain tensor $\mathfrak{B}$ of $\mathfrak{A}$ for $\mathfrak{P}$" we understand, leaving out of account the tensor roperty, here inessential, a matrix $\mathfrak{B}$ with the properties:

a) $\mathfrak{B}$ is a function of $\mathfrak{A}$ only: $\mathfrak{B} = \mathfrak{B}(\mathfrak{A})$.

b) If $\mathfrak{B}(\mathfrak{A}) = \mathfrak{B}(\mathfrak{B})$, then $\mathfrak{P}(\mathfrak{A}) = \mathfrak{P}(\mathfrak{B})$ for every material.

c) The manifold of all $\mathfrak{B}$ is of dimension as little less than nine as possible.

Then every one-to-one matrix function of $\mathfrak{B}$ is a strain tensor. This property may be used so as to normalize the strain tensor. From the considerations of Section 2 it follows that

In a general anisotropic material there exists no strain tensor for $\mathfrak{P}$. In an isotropic material the strain tensors are the one-to-one functions of $\mathfrak{S}_l$.

Since, by (3.6), $\mathfrak{S}_r$ determines $\mathfrak{P}$ only to within orientation, it is natural to introduce a modified stress tensor:

(4. 1) $$\mathfrak{P}_1 = \mathfrak{R}^{-1}\,\mathfrak{P}(\mathfrak{A})\,\mathfrak{R} = \mathfrak{P}(\mathfrak{S}_r).$$

Another combination of this kind is

(4. 2) $$\mathfrak{P}_2 = |\mathfrak{A}| \cdot \mathfrak{A}^{-1}\,\mathfrak{P}(\mathfrak{A})\,\mathfrak{A}'^{-1},$$

which, with the aid of (2. 2), (3. 6) and the fact that $|\mathfrak{A}| = |\mathfrak{S}_r|$, may be written

(4. 3) $$\mathfrak{P}_2 = |\mathfrak{S}_r| \cdot \mathfrak{S}_r^{-1}\,\mathfrak{P}(\mathfrak{S}_r)\,\mathfrak{S}_r^{-1}.$$

Therefore,

for the modified stress tensors $\mathfrak{P}_l$ and $\mathfrak{P}_2$, in any anisotropic material, any one-to-one function of $\mathfrak{S}_r$ is a strain tensor.

On the other hand, $\mathfrak{P}_1$ and $\mathfrak{P}_2$ yield the stresses in space only if $\mathfrak{R}$ is known as well. Since $\mathfrak{P}$ is symmetric, and because of (3. 4), $\mathfrak{P}_1$ and $\mathfrak{P}_2$ are both symmetric. Moreover, $\mathfrak{P}_1$ has the same invariants as $\mathfrak{P}$; in particular, the trace of $\mathfrak{P}_1$ equals thrice the hydrostatic pressure. This property, however, as we shall see in a moment, does not carry over to $\mathfrak{P}_2$, commoner in the literature.

The connection between the stress and strain tensors introduced by us with those introduced elsewhere in the literature is very easy to see. Starting from (3. 3), one forms in the usual way the expression $\frac{1}{2}(|\mathfrak{x}|^2 - |\hat{\mathfrak{x}}|^2)$ and regards it as a quadratic form in $\mathfrak{x}$ with a symmetric coefficient matrix $\mathfrak{T}$, or in $\hat{\mathfrak{x}}$ with matrix $\hat{\mathfrak{T}}$. Then from (3. 3) we have

$$|\mathfrak{x}|^2 - |\hat{\mathfrak{x}}|^2 = \mathfrak{x}'(\mathfrak{E} - (\mathfrak{A}\mathfrak{A}')^{-1})\mathfrak{x} = \hat{\mathfrak{x}}'(\mathfrak{A}'\mathfrak{A} - \mathfrak{E})\hat{\mathfrak{x}}$$

and hence, with use of (3. 5), the following "strain tensors" $\mathfrak{T}$ and $\hat{\mathfrak{T}}$:

(4. 4) $$\mathfrak{T} = \tfrac{1}{2}(\mathfrak{E} - \mathfrak{S}_l^{-2}) \text{ and } \hat{\mathfrak{T}} = \tfrac{1}{2}(\mathfrak{S}_r^2 - \mathfrak{E}).$$

Thus $\mathfrak{T}$ and $\hat{\mathfrak{T}}$ are particular analytic functions of the stretch components $\mathfrak{S}_l$ and $\mathfrak{S}_r$, the prototypes of strain tensors, with corresponding restrictions: $\mathfrak{T}$ is a strain tensor only for isotropic materials, and for $\mathfrak{P}$. $\hat{\mathfrak{T}}$ is always a strain tensor, but only for $\hat{\mathfrak{P}}_r$ or similarly formed quantities. One may equally well use other functions of the stretch components, among which the "natural strain tensors,"

(4. 5) $$\mathfrak{L} = \log \mathfrak{S}_l \text{ and } \hat{\mathfrak{L}} = \log \mathfrak{S}_r$$

have proved especially suitable and in particular through the ordinary formation of deviators allow a separation of change of shape from change of volume.

In the literature, mainly in connection with the Lagrangean standpoint, is introduced a modification, $\hat{\mathfrak{P}}$, of the stress tensor, defined as follows:

a) Application of $\hat{\mathfrak{P}}$ to a surface element $d\hat{\mathfrak{f}}$ of the initial state yields the force on the corresponding surface element $d\mathfrak{f}$ of the deformed state;
b) The force acting upon $d\mathfrak{f}$ is specified in the co-ordinate system deformed by means of $\mathfrak{A}$.

The connection of $\hat{\mathfrak{P}}$ with $\mathfrak{P}$ is easy to perceive. Namely, if we denote the force acting upon $d\mathfrak{f}$ in the Cartesian system by $d\mathfrak{k}$ and in the affinely deformed system by $d\hat{\mathfrak{k}}$, we have the relations

(4.6) $$d\mathfrak{k} = \mathfrak{P}d\mathfrak{f}, \quad d\hat{\mathfrak{k}} = \hat{\mathfrak{P}}d\hat{\mathfrak{f}}, \quad d\mathfrak{f} = |\mathfrak{A}| \cdot \mathfrak{A}'^{-1}d\hat{\mathfrak{f}}, \quad d\mathfrak{k} = \mathfrak{A}d\hat{\mathfrak{k}},$$

from which follows at once

(4. 7) $$\hat{\mathfrak{P}} = |\mathfrak{A}| \cdot \mathfrak{A}^{-1}\mathfrak{P}(\mathfrak{A})\mathfrak{A}'^{-1}.$$

Thus $\hat{\mathfrak{P}}$ is just the $\mathfrak{P}_2$ introduced and defined above.

Section 5. The Elastic Energy.

Let a unit volume of the stress-free initial state be subjected to the deformations $\mathfrak{A}(t)$, which depend continuously on the parameter t (e. g., the time) and satisfy $\mathfrak{A}(0) = \mathfrak{E}$. At the "time point" t let the internal energy be $u(t)$; the entropy, $s(t)$); the absolute temperature, $\Theta(t)$; and the work done by the material, $A(t)$. Then

(5.1) $$dA + du - \Theta ds = dA + d(u - \Theta s) + s d\Theta = 0.$$

The external work stored in the element of volume is often called "the elastic potential." We see that this potential for isentropic strains is the internal energy, u; for isothermal ones, the free energy, $f = u - \Theta s$.

u is assumed to be a function of $\mathfrak{A}$ and s:

(5. 2) $$u = \psi(\mathfrak{A}, s).$$

Since in isochoric processes $dA = 0$, it follows that

(5. 3) $$\Theta = \frac{\partial \psi}{\partial s}$$

and hence from (5. 1)

(5. 4) $$dA + (d\psi)_{s=\text{const}} = 0.$$

Hence we may restrict ourselves to isentropic processes; that is, we regard s as a free parameter, left unwritten. ψ is a function of the components a_{ik} of $\mathfrak{A}$.

If we subject a finite volume V with bounding surface F to the infinitesimal affinity $\mathfrak{B} = \mathfrak{E} + d\mathfrak{B}$, and if in V there is a homogeneous state of stress, $\mathfrak{P}$, then the work done by V is given by

$$dA_1 = -\iint_F (\mathfrak{P}\, d\mathfrak{f})' d\mathfrak{B}\,\mathfrak{r} = -\iint_F (\mathfrak{P}' d\mathfrak{B}\,\mathfrak{r})' d\mathfrak{f} = -\iiint_V \operatorname{div}(\mathfrak{P}' d\mathfrak{B}\,\mathfrak{r})$$

or, since $\mathfrak{P} = \mathfrak{P}'$, by

(5. 5) $$dA_1 = -V \cdot \{\mathfrak{P}\, d\mathfrak{B}\},$$

where (as henceforth) the sign { } denotes the trace of a matrix. In our case $V = |\mathfrak{A}|$, and $\mathfrak{B} = \mathfrak{E} + d\mathfrak{B}$ is the affinity that leads from $\mathfrak{A}(t)$ to $\mathfrak{A}(t+dt) = \mathfrak{A}(t) + d\mathfrak{A}$; thus $\mathfrak{A} + d\mathfrak{A} = (\mathfrak{E} + d\mathfrak{B})\,\mathfrak{A}$, and thence

(5. 6) $$d\mathfrak{B} = d\mathfrak{A} \cdot \mathfrak{A}^{-1}.$$

From (5. 4) and the general rule $\{\mathfrak{A}\mathfrak{B}\mathfrak{C}\} = \{\mathfrak{C}\mathfrak{A}\mathfrak{B}\}$ we thus obtain

(5 . 7) $$|\mathfrak{A}| \cdot \{\mathfrak{A}^{-1}\mathfrak{P}(\mathfrak{A})\, d\mathfrak{A}\} = du = d\psi(a_{ik}).$$

Section 6. The General Law of Elasticity.

If for any matrix $\mathfrak{M}$ we use the obvious notation $\mathfrak{M} = (m_{ik})$, $m_{ik} = (\mathfrak{M})_{ik}$, then (5. 7) may be written thus:

$$|\mathfrak{A}| \sum_{i,k} (\mathfrak{P}(\mathfrak{A})\,\mathfrak{A}'^{-1})_{ik}\, da_{ik} = \sum_{i,k} \frac{\partial\psi}{\partial a_{ik}}\, da_{ik},$$

whence follows at once

(6. 1) $$\mathfrak{P}(\mathfrak{A}) = |\mathfrak{A}|^{-1}\Psi\,\mathfrak{A}' \quad \text{with} \quad (\Psi)_{ik} = \frac{\partial\psi}{\partial a_{ik}}.$$

Nevertheless, $\psi(a_{ik})$ is not an arbitrary function, since $\mathfrak{P} = \mathfrak{P}'$. This condition yields for ψ the partial differential system

(6. 2) $$\sum_{\nu=1}^{3}\left(\frac{\partial\psi}{\partial a_{i\nu}}\, a_{k\nu} - \frac{\partial\psi}{\partial a_{k\nu}}\, a_{i\nu}\right) = 0 \quad \text{for} \quad (i, k) = (1,2), (1,3), \quad \text{and} \quad (2,3),$$

the general solution of which reads

(6. 3) $$\psi = \varphi(\gamma_{ik}) \quad \text{with} \quad \gamma_{ik} = \sum_{\nu=1}^{3} a_{\nu i}\, a_{\nu k} = (\mathfrak{A}'\mathfrak{A})_{ik} = (\mathfrak{S}_r^2)_{ik}.$$

Thus the internal energy depends on $\mathfrak{S}_r$ only, in agreement with the intuitive results of Section 2. So as to verify by calculation as well that $\mathfrak{S}_r$ in an arbitrary material is a strain tensor for the modified stress tensor, $\widehat{\mathfrak{P}}$, by the aid of (2. 2) and (4. 7) we transform (5. 7) into

$$du = \{\widehat{\mathfrak{P}}\,\mathfrak{S}_r\, d\mathfrak{S}_r\} + \{\mathfrak{S}_r\,\widehat{\mathfrak{P}}\,\mathfrak{S}_r\,\mathfrak{R}'\, d\mathfrak{R}\}.$$

By use of the rule $\{\mathfrak{A}\mathfrak{B}\} = \{\mathfrak{A}'\mathfrak{B}'\}$ and the fact that $\widehat{\mathfrak{P}} = \widehat{\mathfrak{P}}'$ we see that

$$2\{\mathfrak{S}_r\widehat{\mathfrak{P}}\mathfrak{S}_r\mathfrak{R}'\, d\mathfrak{R}\} = \{(\mathfrak{S}_r\widehat{\mathfrak{P}}\mathfrak{S}_r)(\mathfrak{R}'\, d\mathfrak{R})\} + \{(\mathfrak{S}_r\widehat{\mathfrak{P}}\mathfrak{S}_r)(d\mathfrak{R}'\cdot\mathfrak{R})\} = \{(\mathfrak{S}_r\widehat{\mathfrak{P}}\mathfrak{S}_r)\, d(\mathfrak{R}'\mathfrak{R})\} = 0,$$

so that on account of (4. 4) we obtain

(6. 4) $$\{\widehat{\mathfrak{P}}\, d\widehat{\mathfrak{T}}\} = du.$$

Moreover, by (6.3) u is a function of the γ_{ik}, and thus may be written as a function of the six quantities $\widehat{t}_{ik}$ with $i \leq k$. Thus from (6.4) follows

$$(6.5) \qquad \widehat{\mathfrak{P}} = \left(\frac{\partial u}{\partial \widehat{t}_{ik}}\right),$$

where before differentiation $\widehat{t}_{ik}$ is to be replaced by $\frac{1}{2}(\widehat{t}_{ik} + \widehat{t}_{ki})$. $\mathfrak{P}$ itself then follows by use of (4.7).

Formulae (6.1) and (6.5) are valid generally, in any anisotropic material. By transformation of (5.7) one can get further formulae of this kind, of which we mention only the one that corresponds to use of $\mathfrak{B} = \mathfrak{A}^{-1}$ instead of $\mathfrak{A}$, as suggests itself when the Eulerian standpoint is adopted. Since

$$0 = d(\mathfrak{A}\mathfrak{A}^{-1}) = d\mathfrak{A} \cdot \mathfrak{A}^{-1} + \mathfrak{B}^{-1} d\mathfrak{B} \quad ,$$

from (5.7) follows first

$$\{\mathfrak{P}\mathfrak{B}^{-1} d\mathfrak{B}\} = -du \cdot |\mathfrak{B}|$$

and hence

$$(6.1^*) \qquad \mathfrak{P} = -|\mathfrak{B}| \cdot \left(\frac{\partial u}{\partial b_{ik}}\right) \mathfrak{B}.$$

The symmetry requirement $\mathfrak{P} = \mathfrak{P}'$ leads back to (6.3) again; indeed, u may depend only on $\mathfrak{B}\mathfrak{B}' = (\mathfrak{A}'\mathfrak{A})^{-1}$.

In the special case of an isotropic material the relations obtained become particularly simple. Here $\mathfrak{P}$ is coaxial with $\mathfrak{S}_l$, and $\mathfrak{P}_2$ and $\widehat{\mathfrak{P}}$, on account of (4.3), is coaxial with $\mathfrak{S}_r$: $\mathfrak{P}\mathfrak{S}_l = \mathfrak{S}_l\mathfrak{P}$, $\widehat{\mathfrak{P}}\mathfrak{S}_r = \mathfrak{S}_r\widehat{\mathfrak{P}}$. u depends only upon the invariants of $\mathfrak{S}_l$ or $\mathfrak{S}_r$ or any other strain tensor. If we use as invariants the $\widehat{J}_\nu = \{\widehat{\mathfrak{T}}^\nu\}$ for $\nu = 1, 2, 3$ and on account of coaxiality set $\widehat{\mathfrak{P}} = \sum_{\nu=0}^{2} \lambda_\nu \widehat{\mathfrak{T}}^\nu$, then by equating coefficients we obtain at once from (6.4)

$$(6.6) \qquad \widehat{\mathfrak{P}} = \frac{\partial u}{\partial \widehat{J}_1}\mathfrak{E} + 2\frac{\partial u}{\partial \widehat{J}_2}\widehat{\mathfrak{T}} + 3\frac{\partial u}{\partial \widehat{J}_3}\widehat{\mathfrak{T}}^2 \quad \text{with} \quad \widehat{J}_\nu = \{\widehat{\mathfrak{T}}^\nu\}.$$

If in (5.7) we substitute $\mathfrak{A} = \mathfrak{S}_l\mathfrak{R}$, we are led to

$$|\mathfrak{A}|^{-1} du = \{(\mathfrak{S}_l^{-1}\mathfrak{P}\mathfrak{S}_l)(d\mathfrak{R} \cdot \mathfrak{R}')\} + \{\mathfrak{S}_l^{-1}\mathfrak{P}\, d\mathfrak{S}_l\}.$$

The conclusion, analogous to that carried through in the derivation of (6.4), that the first summand vanishes is possible only if $\mathfrak{S}_l^{-1}\mathfrak{P}\mathfrak{S}_l$ is symmetric, which requires $\mathfrak{P}\mathfrak{S}_l = \mathfrak{S}_l\mathfrak{P}$ and isotropy; this corresponds to the fact that only for isotropic materials does $\mathfrak{P}$ have a strain tensor. Then we have

$$|\mathfrak{A}|^{-1} du = \{\mathfrak{P}\mathfrak{S}_l^{-1} d\mathfrak{S}_l\},$$

which by (4.4) we may write as

$$(6.7) \qquad |\mathfrak{A}|^{-1} du = \{\mathfrak{P}\, d\mathfrak{L}\} \quad \text{or} \quad |\mathfrak{S}_l|^{-1} du = \{\mathfrak{P}\mathfrak{S}_l^2\, d\mathfrak{T}\}.$$

In analogy to (6.6), it follows by aid of (4.4) and (4.5) that

$$(6.8) \qquad \mathfrak{P} \cdot e^{j_1} = \frac{\partial u}{\partial j_1}\mathfrak{E} + 2\frac{\partial u}{\partial j_2}\mathfrak{L} + 3\frac{\partial u}{\partial j_3}\mathfrak{L}^2 \text{ with } j_\nu = \{\mathfrak{L}^\nu\}$$

and

$$(6.9) \qquad \mathfrak{P} = |\mathfrak{E} - 2\mathfrak{T}|^{\frac{1}{2}} \left(\frac{\partial u}{\partial J_1}\mathfrak{E} + 2\frac{\partial u}{\partial J_2}\mathfrak{T} + 3\frac{\partial u}{\partial J_3}\mathfrak{T}^2\right)(\mathfrak{E} - 2\mathfrak{T}) \text{ with } J_\nu = \{\mathfrak{T}^\nu\},$$

which by aid of the Cayley-Hamilton theorem is easily transformed into a polynomial of degree 2. Further transformations of the law of elasticity are easy to carry through, but for anisotropic materials nothing will lead to a formula expressing $\mathfrak{P}$ through a strain tensor in analogy to (6.1) and (6.5). It is equally impossible, even in an isotropic material, to represent $\mathfrak{P}$ in terms of $\widehat{\mathfrak{T}}$ or $\widehat{\mathfrak{P}}$ in terms of $\mathfrak{T}$.

Section 7. Lagrangean and Eulerian Standpoint.

The above developments and formulae obtained are completely independent of whether, in the construction of the theory of elasticity, one wishes to adopt the Eulerian or the Lagrangean standpoint, since only matrices and thermodynamic invariants as functions of the matrix components appear. It does not follow — as is often claimed — that the Lagrangean standpoint necessarily leads to $\widehat{\mathfrak{P}}$ and $\widehat{\mathfrak{T}}$, the Eulerian, to $\mathfrak{P}$ and $\mathfrak{T}$. Such an impression is usually the result of a construction too special from the very start, and in particular, of a representation in components. To be sure, the functional matrix $\mathfrak{F}$ is $\mathfrak{A}$ for the Lagrangean standpoint and $\mathfrak{A}^{-1}$ for the Eulerian (moreover, this fact, along with (5.6), leads directly to Jaumann's equations of conversion), so that in the former case $\widehat{\mathfrak{T}} = \frac{1}{2}(\mathfrak{F}'\mathfrak{F} - \mathfrak{E})$ and in the latter $\mathfrak{T} = \frac{1}{2}(\mathfrak{E} - \mathfrak{F}'\mathfrak{F})$ are especially simple to form. This, however, is a circumstance of economy in calculation and not of logic. From the physical standpoint, the sole essential one, only the following demonstrated fundamental distinctions are important:

In the anisotropic case $\mathfrak{P}$ has no strain tensor. Thus one must consider $\widehat{\mathfrak{P}}$ and, necessarily (or some other function of $\mathfrak{S}_r$) as the strain tensor belonging to it, and the thermodynamic potentials depend only on this latter. Nevertheless, it must be observed that $\widehat{\mathfrak{P}}$ does not yield the stresses in space without knowledge of the entire $\mathfrak{A}$.

In the isotropic case, on the other hand, $\mathfrak{P}$ has the strain tensor $\mathfrak{T}$ (or any other one-to-one function of $\mathfrak{S}_l$), which determines the thermodynamic potentials as well. Use of $\mathfrak{P}$ and $\mathfrak{T}$, therefore, is desirable.

Above all its is important, though often disregarded, that one should reach entire clarity as regards the intuitive and physical meaning of the tensors used, toward which these considerations are wished to make a contribution.

No. 3

INEQUALITIES RESTRICTING THE FORM OF THE STRESS-DEFORMATION RELATIONS FOR ISOTROPIC SOLIDS AND REINER-RIVLIN FLUIDS

M. Baker & J. L. Ericksen

Journal of the Washington Academy of Sciences, Volume 44, pp. 33-35 (1954)

This paper refers to isotropic elastic materials as defined by REINER & RICHTER in the two previous papers and to viscous fluids as defined by REINER and RIVLIN in RMM, Nos. 1 and 2. For both these substances a representation of the form (4) is valid. Forms are found for the requirement that the corresponding proper numbers of the two tensors A and B shall be ordered alike. In the context of elasticity, with a proper choice of B, this means that the greater principal stress shall always occur in the direction of the greater principal stretch; in the Reiner-Rivlin theory of fluids, that the greater principal stress shall always occur in the direction of the greater principal stretching. The former requirement has since been named the **Baker-Ericksen inequalities**. For hyperelasticity, these inequalities take the form (12). For incompressible materials, they reduce to inequalities proposed for a different reason by TRUESDELL in Section 41 of MF and interpreted in the context of wave propagation by ERICKSEN in No. 7 of PNL. The equivalent form (9) is expressed directly in terms of the coefficients in the representation (5), which is the one most commonly used in solution of specific problems of finite elasticity.

Reprinted from JOURNAL OF THE WASHINGTON ACADEMY OF SCIENCES
Volume 44, No. 2, February, 1954
Printed in U.S.A.

MATHEMATICS—*Inequalities restricting the form of the stress-deformation relations for isotropic elastic solids and Reiner-Rivlin fluids.* M. BAKER and J. L. ERICKSEN, Naval Research Laboratory. (Communicated by Horace M. Trent.)

According to the natural state theory of elasticity, the principal values t_1, t_2, t_3 of the stress tensor for an isotropic, perfectly elastic material are given in terms of the principal extensions δ_1, δ_2, δ_3 by[1]

$$t_i = \frac{2\rho}{\rho_0}\left[\left(II\frac{\partial\Sigma}{\partial II} + III\frac{\partial\Sigma}{\partial III}\right) + \frac{\partial\Sigma}{\partial I}(1+\delta_i)^2 - III\frac{\partial\Sigma}{\partial II}\frac{1}{(1+\delta_i)^2}\right], \quad (1)$$

if the material is compressible, and by

$$t_i = -p + 2\frac{\partial\Sigma}{\partial I}(1+\delta_i)^2 - 2\frac{\partial\Sigma}{\partial II}\frac{1}{(1+\delta_i)^2}, \quad (2)$$

if the material is incompressible. Here, Σ the strain energy, is a function of $I \equiv (1+\delta_1)^2 + (1+\delta_2)^2 + (1+\delta_3)^2$, $II \equiv (1+\delta_1)^2(1+\delta_2)^2 + (1+\delta_3)^2(1+\delta_1)^2 + (1+\delta_2)^2(1+\delta_3)^2$ and $III \equiv (1+\delta_1)^2(1+\delta_2)^2(1+\delta_3)^2$, p is an arbitrary hydrostatic pressure, ρ is the density in the deformed state, and ρ_0 the density in the undeformed state. The condition for incompressibility is $III = 1$ so that $\Sigma = \Sigma(I, II)$ in (2).

Truesdell[2] has given a physical argument which shows that, for an incompressible material, the inequalities

$$(1+\delta_i)^2\frac{\partial\Sigma}{\partial II} + \frac{\partial\Sigma}{\partial I} > 0 \quad (3)$$

should always be satisfied. Rivlin[3] derived a special case of this inequality and used it to obtain qualitative information about the Poynting effect. These inequalities also gave information concerning the propagation of waves in such materials.[4]

By considering general isotropic functions, we shall deduce certain inequalities which follow from conditions imposed on the eigenvalues of the tensors involved. We shall then discuss the significance of these conditions as applied to elastic solids and viscous fluids, and determine the form which these inequalities assume in the different physical situations. In particular, we shall see that inequality (3) should hold for both incompressible and compressible materials.

Suppose that the 3 × 3 real symmetric matrix **A** is an isotropic analytic function of the 3 × 3 real symmetric matrix **B**. We then have[5]

$$\mathbf{A} = f_0\mathbf{1} + f_1\mathbf{B} + f_2\mathbf{B}^2, \quad (4)$$

where the scalars f_j are functions of the three principal invariants of **B**.

Now, if $\mathbf{B}^{-1}$ exists, we can also write **A** in the form

$$\mathbf{A} = g_0\mathbf{1} + g_{-1}\mathbf{B}^{-1} + g_1\mathbf{B}, \quad (5)$$

where the scalars g_i are also functions of the three principal invariants of **B**. Equation (4)

[1] See, e.g., TRUESDELL, C. A., *The mechanical foundations of elasticity and fluid dynamics*, Journ. Ratl. Mech. and Anal. **1**: 173–182. 1952.
[2] TRUESDELL, C. A., op. cit.: 181–182.
[3] RIVLIN, R. S., and SAUNDERS, D. W., *Large elastic deformations of isotropic materials VII. Experiments on the deformation of rubber*, Phil. Trans. Roy. Soc. London (A) **243**: 251–288. 1951.
[4] ERICKSEN, J. L., *On the propagation of waves in isotropic, perfectly elastic materials*, Journ. Ratl. Mech. and Anal. **2**: 329–337. 1953.
[5] TRUESDELL, C. A., op. cit.: 131–132.

implies that the eigenvalues a_1, a_2, a_3 of **A** are related to the eigenvalues b_1, b_2, b_3 of **B** by

$$a_i = f_0 + f_1 b_i + f_2 b_i^2, \tag{6}$$

while (5) yields

$$a_i = g_0 + g_{-1}/b_i + g_1 b_i. \tag{7}$$

We want to determine necessary and sufficient conditions that the inequality $a_i > a_j$ hold whenever $b_i > b_j$. Let us first consider (6), which yields

$$a_i - a_j = (b_i - b_j)[f_1 + f_2(b_i + b_j)].$$

Thus a necessary and sufficient condition that $b_i > b_j$ imply $a_i > a_j$ is that

$$f_1 + f_2(b_i + b_j) > 0, \tag{8}$$

whenever $b_i > b_j$. Since (8) is unaltered if b_i and b_j are interchanged, this inequality must hold unless $b_i = b_j$ $(i \neq j)$, in which case (8) is replaced by the weaker inequality $f_1 + f_2(b_i + b_j) = f_1 + 2f_2 b_i \geqq 0$. This latter condition follows from the fact that **A** is a continuous function of **B**. Similarly, from (7), we obtain, as an alternative necessary and sufficient condition,

$$g_1 > g_{-1}/b_i b_j, \tag{9}$$

unless $b_i = b_j$, and $g_1 \geqq g_{-1}/b_i b_j = g_{-1}/(b_i^2$ if $b_i = b_j$ $(i \neq j)$.

Let **T** denote the stress tensor in a continuous medium. At any point P, each of the three perpendicular planes whose normal vectors are eigenvectors of **T** has the property that the stress vector acting on it at P is normal to it. These normal forces (per unit area) are the eigenvalues t_1, t_2, t_3 of **T**. A positive eigenvalue corresponds to a tension, a negative eigenvalue to a pressure. We assume the eigenvalues ordered so that $t_1 \geqq t_2 \geqq t_3$.

In an isotropic, perfectly elastic body, the principal directions of **T** coincide with the directions of principal extension. We restrict our attention to these directions. For such a material, it is reasonable to suppose that the greatest (least) tension occurs in the direction corresponding to the greatest (least) extension. Expressing these conditions analytically, we obtain

$$t_i > t_j \text{ whenever } \delta_i > \delta_j. \tag{10}$$

It may be possible to get further conditions by comparing forces and extensions in other directions. One might, for example, compare normal stresses and extensions normal to an arbitrary pair of perpendicular planes. However, because of the fact that a pure shearing stress acting on a plane may give rise to extensions normal to this plane, the validity of results obtained from such a comparison is questionable. Comparing (1) and (7), we see that (10) implies (9) with $b_i = (1 + \delta_i)^2$, $g_1 = 2(\rho/\rho_0)\,\partial\Sigma/\partial I$, $g_{-1} = -2(\rho/\rho_0)\,III\,\partial\Sigma/\partial II$. Since $\rho/\rho_0 > 0$, we have for $i \neq j$,

$$\left.\begin{aligned} &\frac{\partial\Sigma}{\partial I} + \frac{III}{(1+\delta_i)^2(1+\delta_j)^2}\frac{\partial\Sigma}{\partial II} > 0 \text{ if } \delta_i \neq \delta_j, \\ &\frac{\partial\Sigma}{\partial I} + \frac{III}{(1+\delta_i)^2(1+\delta_j)^2}\frac{\partial\Sigma}{\partial II} \geqq 0 \text{ if } \delta_i = \delta_j, \end{aligned}\right\} \tag{11}$$

for a compressible material. Since $III = (1 + \delta_1)^2(1 + \delta_2)^2(1 + \delta_3)^2$, the inequalities (11) become

$$\left.\begin{aligned} &\frac{\partial\Sigma}{\partial I} + (1+\delta_i)^2\frac{\partial\Sigma}{\partial II} > 0 \\ &\qquad \text{if } \delta_j \neq \delta_k \ (i, j, k \neq), \\ &\frac{\partial\Sigma}{\partial I} + (1+\delta_i)^2\frac{\partial\Sigma}{\partial II} \geqq 0 \\ &\qquad \text{if } \delta_j = \delta_k \ (i, j, k \neq). \end{aligned}\right\} \tag{12}$$

Comparing (7) with (2), we see that (10) implies (9) with $b_i = (1 + \delta_i)^2$, $g_1 = 2\partial\Sigma/\partial I$, $g_{-1} = -2\partial\Sigma/\partial II$. Using the incompressibility condition $III = 1$, one can show that the resulting inequality reduces to (12), which is in agreement with Truesdell's result (3). Results of a number of experiments on rubber,[6] which is virtually incompressible, show that $\partial\Sigma/\partial I > 0$, $\partial\Sigma/\partial II > 0$ for a wide range of values of I and II so that (12) certainly holds in this case.

Now, in the classical linear theory of elasticity, the stress tensor **T** is given in

[6] Rivlin, R. S., and Saunders, D. W., op. cit.

terms of the infinitesimal strain tensor **E** by $\mathbf{T} = \lambda\, \mathbf{1} + 2\mu\mathbf{E}$, where λ and μ are the Lamé constants. Application of the above analysis to this expression for **T** leads immediately to the condition $\mu > 0$, which is certainly true for all materials which are adequately described by this theory.

According to the theory of compressible, highly viscous fluids proposed by Reiner,[7] the stress **T** is an analytic isotropic function of the rate of deformation **D**, so that

$$\mathbf{T} = f_0\mathbf{1} + f_1\mathbf{D} + f_2\mathbf{D}^2, \tag{13}$$

where the scalars f_i are functions of the three principal invariants of **D**. In terms of the eigenvalues d_1, d_2, and d_3 of **D**, these invariants are $d_1 + d_2 + d_3$, $d_1d_2 + d_2d_3 + d_3d_1$, and $d_1d_2d_3$. Rivlin's theory[8] differs from this only in that **D** is assumed to satisfy the condition of incompressibility, $d_1 + d_2 + d_3 = 0$, and $-f_0$ is replaced by an arbitrary hydrostatic pressure p. That is,

$$\mathbf{T} = -p\mathbf{1} + f_1\mathbf{D} + f_2\mathbf{D}^2. \tag{14}$$

At a given point P at a given time, the rate of increase of distance between the material particle at P and particles lying on a sphere of fixed radius r about P will take on stationary values for certain particles on this sphere. The directions determined by drawing the radius vector from P to these particles approach the principal directions of **D** as r tends to zero. In first approximation, the stationary values mentioned above are obtained by multiplying the appropriate eigenvalue of **D** by r. Let us restrict our attention to the principal directions of **D** which, in a Reiner-Rivlin fluid, are simultaneously principal directions of **T**. It seems reasonable to suppose that, at a point P in such a material, the greatest (least) tension will be exerted across a plane whose normal is in the direction in which the rate of increase of distance between the particle at P and particles equidistant from P is greatest (least). That is, we should have

$$t_i > t_j \text{ whenever } d_i > d_j. \tag{15}$$

It then follows from (6), (8), and (13) that, for a compressible material,

$$\left.\begin{aligned} &f_1 + f_2(d_i + d_j) > 0 \quad \text{if } d_i \neq d_j, \\ &f_1 + f_2(d_i + d_j) \geqq 0 \quad \text{if } d_i = d_j\, (i \neq j). \end{aligned}\right\} \tag{16}$$

From (6), (8), and (14) it follows that (16) must also hold for incompressible materials. In this case one can, using the incompressibility condition $d_1 + d_2 + d_3 = 0$, write (16) as

$$\left.\begin{aligned} &f_1 - f_2 d_i > 0 \qquad \text{if } d_j \neq d_k\, (i,j,k \neq), \\ &f_1 - f_2 d_i \geqq 0 \qquad \text{if } d_j = d_k\, (i,j,k \neq). \end{aligned}\right\} \tag{17}$$

For a plane motion of an incompressible fluid, $d_2 = 0$ and $d_3 = -d_1$, so that (17) becomes

$$\left.\begin{aligned} &f_1 > 0, f_1 > f_2 d_1, f_1 > -f_2 d_1 \quad \text{if } d_1 \neq 0, \\ &f_1 \geqq 0 \qquad\qquad\qquad\qquad\quad \text{if } d_1 = 0. \end{aligned}\right\} \tag{18}$$

If $d_1 = 0$, then $d_2 = d_3 = 0$, so the motion is instantaneously rigid. From (18),

$$\left|\frac{f_1}{f_2 d_1}\right| > 1, \tag{19}$$

except perhaps when $d_1 = 0$, in which case the ratio on the left may be indeterminate. It has been shown[9] that, in such a motion, the equation $f_1 + f_2 d_1 \cos 2\varphi = 0$ determines two characteristic directions for the equations (14). According to (19), there exists no real angle φ for which this equation is satisfied.

In the classical theory of isotropic viscous fluids, $f_2 = 0$ and $f_1 = 2\mu$, where μ is the coefficient of viscosity. Since μ is always positive, (16) holds for materials to which this theory applies.

[7] REINER, M., *A mathematical theory of dilatancy*, Amer. Journ. Math. **65**: 350–362. 1945.

[8] RIVLIN, R. S., *Hydrodynamics of non-Newtonian fluids*, Nature **160**: 611–613. 1947.

[9] ERICKSEN, J. L., *Characteristic surfaces of the equations of motion for non-Newtonian fluids*, Zeitschr. für Angew. Math. u. Physik **4**: 260–267. 1953.

No. 4

ON A CRITERION FOR THE EXISTENCE OF THE STORED-ENERGY FUNCTION

L. Caprioli

(Su un criterio per l'esistenza dell'energia di deformazione), Bolletino della Unione Matematica Italiana, Series 3, Volume 10, pp. 481-483 (1955).

This paper distinguishes those elastic materials for which a stored-energy function exists – in the terminology of MF, the materials elastic in the sense of CAUCHY that are elastic in the sense of GREEN, or, in the presently used terminology, those elastic materials that are hyperelastic. Elastic materials are called "elastoplastic" by CAPRIOLI in Section 1. The simple argument is contained entirely in Sections 2-3 and footnote 7. The theorem may be stated as follows: If, for an elastic material, there exists a configuration κ such that the work done in every deformation process from κ is non-negative, then the material is hyperelastic.

In Section 83 of NFTM this theorem is related to other work theorems of hyperelasticity, and it is shown also that the stored-energy function must take on its absolute minimum in κ, and that κ must be a natural state, i. e., the stress vanishes in κ. This fact shows that CAPRIOLI's theorem does not characterize hyperelastic materials, since the mere existence of a stored-energy function does not ensure the existence of a natural state for the material.

The work of CAPRIOLI grew from a discussion of a paper by UDESCHINI held in GRAFFI's seminar in Bologna.

ON A CRITERION FOR THE EXISTENCE OF THE STORED-ENERGY FUNCTION

L. Caprioli

(Translation of "Su un criterio per l'esistenza dell' energia di deformazione," Bollettino della Unione Matematica Italiana, Series III, Volume 10, pp. 481-483 (1955)).

Abstract: the third paragraph of Section 1.

In a particularly interesting paper[1] published some years ago, which, among other things, obtained an expression of the stress-deformation law for an elastic-plastic body, P. UDESCHINI observed that in an elastic continuum, even if anisotropic, for which Hooke's Law holds, the existence of a stored-energy function is subordinate to the single hypothesis that the work necessary to deform a body be always positive (it being presumed that Hooke's law still holds), starting from the natural undeformed state.

Now, this observation of UDESCHINI is much broader: in fact, below it will be shown by a simple mathematical lemma, of easy proof (Section 2), how to recover the result of UDESCHINI and to prove it valid also when Hooke's law does not hold (and, in particular, for an elasto-plastic body.)

More precisely, it will be proved (Section 3) that for the existence of a stored-energy function in a solid, even one not elastic, which is loaded in such a way that the corresponding deformations may be regarded as infinitesimal[2], two hypotheses suffice: that the work necessary for the deformation be always non-negative[3] when the deformation is begun from the natural, undeformed state; that the stress tensor depend only on the corresponding deformation tensor[4].

As another example of the validity of the criteria shown, it will be proved at the end (Section 4) that an electrostatic energy exists in a dielectric of conductivity zero, without hysteresis, and not necessarily isotropic, provided only the electric vector be a function, even if a non-linear one, of the displacement vector alone[5]; and, analogously, that a magnetostatic energy exists in a possibly anisotropic ferromagnetic substance without hysteresis, provided the magnetic vector be a function, even if a non-linear one, of the magnetic induction alone[6].

2. Consider the linear differential form $\delta\dot{F} = \Sigma_i A_i \, \delta x_i$ in the n variables x_i, and let the quantities A_i be functions of the variables x_i **alone**; let these functions be defined and continuous in a domain $\mathcal{D}$ of an n-space, which we shall regard as referred to a system of Cartesian axes x_i. That is, the A_i can be considered as the components along the axes x_i of a vector A, which we shall call the **position vector** in $\mathcal{D}$. It is easy to prove the following lemma:

If in $\mathcal{D}$ there exists a point P such that the integral of the form δF along any curve l issuing from P be of definite sign (i.e., independently of l it shall be, e.g., non-negative); and if A is the position vector in the sense just specified, then the form δF is an exact differential in $\mathcal{D}$.

To this end, note that the integral of δF along any closed curve c_p in $\mathcal{D}$ passing through P is zero; and, likewise, so is the integral around an arbitrary closed curve in $\mathcal{D}$ which does not pass through P[7].

3. This much settled, consider a deformable solid, even one that is not perfectly elastic and not necessarily isotropic, and assume that the work needed to produce an arbitrary infinitesimal deformation in any element of the body, starting from its natural and undeformed state[8], be non-negative. That is, if p_{ik} and ξ_{ik} are the tensors of stress and deformation, let the integral of the form $\Sigma_{ik} \, p_{ik} \, \delta\xi_{ik}$ along any curve starting from the orgin $\xi_{ik} \equiv 0$ in the space of the ξ_{ik} be non-negative. Furthermore, assume that in

the space of the ξ_{ik} there exists a neighborhood $\mathcal{D}$ of the point $\xi_{ik} \equiv 0$ in which the p_{ik} are functions, possibly non-linear, of the ξ_{ik} alone. Then the lemma of Section 2 holds for the form $\Sigma_{ik}\, p_{ik}\, \delta\xi_{ik}$, which is, accordingly, an exact differential in $\mathcal{D}$, whence follows at once the existence of a stored-energy function. Since, obviously, this result is valid also when the body obeys Hooke's law, the assertions of Section 1 have been proved.

4. Extensions of the criteria to other fields of physics, already noted, are now almost immediate. Among the numerous ones which might be listed here, the following, drawn from electrostatics and magnetostatics, may be of some interest.

Consider the dielectric which we spoke of in Section 1, and assume, following common experience, that the work needed to polarize the dielectric in any way, starting from polarization zero, be non-negative. That is, if we denote by E_i and D_i the Cartesian components of the electric vector and the polarization, let the integral of the differential form $\Sigma_i E_i \delta D_i$ along any line starting from the origin $D_i \equiv 0$ in the space of the D_i be assumed non-negative.

By the lemma of Section 2, the differential form $\Sigma_i E_i \delta D_i$ is exact, and thus the existence of the electrostatic energy of the dielectric is proved.

With obvious changes in the meansings of the symbols, the procedure followed here, under hypotheses altogether analogous to those just listed for dielectrics, serves to prove the existence of energy of magnetization in a ferromagnetic substance satisfying the conditions stated in Section 1.

FOOTNOTES

[1] P. UDESCHINI, "Sull'energia di deformazione," Rend. Ist. Lombardo Sci. Lett. (3) **76** (1942/3).

[2] It is not excluded that the considerations forming the object of this note can hold also in the case of finite deformations.

[3] As is well known, this proposition, which is normally assumed as a principle in the theory of deformable continua (cf. UDESCHINI, op. cit.), expresses the fact, never contradicted by common experience, that in order to deform a body from its undeformed state, work must be done.

[4] That is, phenomena of dissipative type are excluded.

[5] If we exclude dielectric hysteresis, these conditions may be regarded as verified in practice in the substances called "ferroelectric," which are widely used in engineering (cf., e.g., W. P. MASON & R. R. WICK, "Ferroelectrics and the dielectric amplifier," P.I.R.E. **42**, no. 11, 1954). Further, the hypothesis that there is no hysteresis may be regarded as acceptable for these materials, particularly for working frequencies that are not extremely high.

[6] Here, too, the hypothesis that there is no hysteresis squares well enough with experience, as follows from the frequent use, otherwise not possible, of ferromagnetic core transformers and impedances with extremely low losses (Permalloy, etc.) in modern amplifiers (even for very high frequencies) and in magnetic amplifiers.

[7] Indeed, by hypothesis the curve c_p is supposed to be traversed in an assigned sense: $\oint_{cp} \delta L \geq 0$, but, by the same hypothesis, this inequality must still hold if c_p is traversed in the opposite sense. Since A is a position vector, the sign of $\oint_{cp} \delta L$ changes with the sense in which c_p is traversed. It follows thus that $\oint_{cp} \delta L = 0$. Given a closed curve c in $\mathcal{D}$ not passing through n, consider the closed curve c' consisting of c broken off at a point Q and of an arbitrary curve QP traversed twice in opposite senses. By what has been said just above, $\oint_{c'} \delta L = 0$, but then obviously $\oint_{c'} = \int_P^Q + \oint_c + \int_Q^P = \oint_c$;

[8] Conditions analogous to those presented in the text could be repeated, with obvious changes, in case the deformation were effected from a state of forced equilibrium.

No. 5

THE SIMPLEST RATE THEORY OF PURE ELASTICITY

C. Truesdell

Communications on Pure and Applied Mathematics,
Volume 8, pp. 123-132 (1955).

The antecendents of hypo-elasticity are described in MF, Sections 55-56, where a theory of only slightly less generality is proposed. The paper reprinted here contains the text of a lecture delivered in the spring of 1954. Hypo-elasticity was designed to stand "alongside the finite strain theory;" the two theories were to represent "two essentially different ideas of spring," and the hypo-elastic body of grade zero was vaunted as "introducing no new empirical constants besides those of the classical theory." Both intentions were defeated, the former by a theorem of NOLL in No. 5 of RMM, and the latter by the gradual understanding that it can make absolutely no difference which invariant stress flux one chooses in formulating a rate theory, while the difference between two such fluxes is of grade 1 in the velocity gradient (cf. the footnote indicated by "||" on p. 95 of Paper No. 7 in this volume, and CFT, Sections 147-151).

Despite its failure in both its main objectives, this paper is reprinted as an example of the way a rate theory may be studied: The aim is to find by integration stress-strain relations corresponding to a particular initial stress.

A simpler but more general treatment of the kinematical problem of Section 2 and the existence theorem in Section 3 is given in Section 28 of NFTM. A more general solution, not restricted to accelerationless motions, was obtained and discussed by A. E. GREEN, **Simple extension of a hypo-elastic body of grade zero,** Journal of Rational Mechanics and Analysis, Volume 5, pp. 637-642 (1956). While interpretation of the results seems to remain somewhat a matter of taste, it appears that the validity of the quasi-static approximation (4.6) depends strongly on the particular sequence of deformations to which it is supposed to apply.

COMMUNICATIONS ON PURE AND APPLIED MATHEMATICS, VOL. VIII, 123–132 (1955)

The Simplest Rate Theory of Pure Elasticity*

By C. TRUESDELL
Graduate Institute for Mathematics and Mechanics, Indiana University

1. *The Hypo-elastic Body of Grade Zero*

The classical linear theory of elasticity is defined by the constitutive equation

(1.1) small stress $=$ f (small strain from an unstressed state).

Here, as henceforth, we are taking twice the shear modulus μ for the particular material as the unit of stress. The usual form of the classical finite strain theory extends (1.1) by the more general constitutive equation

(1.2) stress $=$ f (strain from an unstressed state).

While the last few years have brought physical confirmation to the finite strain theory for rubber, there remain many physical materials which are linearly elastic under small enough strain but which in large strain behave in a fashion the finite strain theory is not intended to represent. Now the linear theory need not be regarded as an approximation to the finite theory only. The concept of elasticity embodied in (1.2), while in one sense more general, in another is far more restrictive than that employed in (1.1). It asserts that no matter how violent the distortion, the body responds to it only with reference to the unstressed state. The body has a memory for its initial state only, being utterly oblivious of all intermediate stages. This is true of the linear theory, too, but with the restriction that the initial state must be a very near one. It is much less to expect of a material that it remember where it has just been than where it was long ago. Thus we may prefer to generalize (1.1) by

(1.3) stress increment $=$ f (small strain from the immediately preceding state).

When the immediately preceding state is unstressed, (1.3) reduces to (1.1). Thus (1.3) and (1.2) represent two essentially different ideas of spring, both yielding as a common first approximation the classical linear theory for small strains from an unstressed state.

When we come to realize (1.3) mathematically, it is natural to begin with

(1.4) rate of stress $=$ f (rate of deformation).

By "rate of deformation" we mean the tensor

$$d_{ij} \equiv v_{(i,j)} , \tag{1.5}$$

*This paper was written under a joint contract with the Office of Naval Research and the Office of Ordnance Research, United States Army.

v_i being the velocity vector. (We do not wish to use any measure of the rate of change of finite strain, since our theory is not to involve any "natural state" or other preferred state of the body.)

But what is meant by "rate of stress"? It cannot mean simply the material derivative,

$$\dot{s}^{ij} \equiv \partial s^{ij}/\partial t + s^{ij}_{,k} v^k, \tag{1.6}$$

for then our proposal would imply that the stress tensor remains constant for each particle in a rigid motion. This is dynamically absurd: when a bar in simple tension is rotated rigidly through a right angle, any reasonable theory must change the stress from $s^{xx} = k \neq 0$, $s^{yy} = 0$ into $s^{xx} = 0$, $s^{yy} = k$. Not only the stress tensor but also the stress vector must change in a rigid motion. Rather, the stress vector in a rigid motion must remain *vectorially* invariant. Now an absolute contravariant vector B^α is invariant under the motion $x^i = x^i(X^\alpha, t)$ if and only if it is carried at time t into

$$b^i = x^i_{,\alpha} B^\alpha. \tag{1.7}$$

Put

$$b^{i\prime} \equiv \dot{b}^i - v^i_{,j} b^j. \tag{1.8}$$

Then equivalent to (1.7) is $b^{i\prime} = 0$ for all t. Applying (1.8) to the contravariant stress vector[1] $s^{ij} da_j$, where da_j is an element of area, yields

$$(s^{ij}\, da_j)' = \mathring{s}^{ij}\, da_j, \tag{1.9}$$

where

$$\mathring{s}^{ij} \equiv \dot{s}^{ij} - s^{ik} v^j_{,k} - s^{kj} v^i_{,k} + s^{ij} v^k_{,k}. \tag{1.10}$$

Thus it seems reasonable, and it is at least consistent with the principles of dynamics, to take for the "rate of stress" in (1.4) the tensor $\mathring{s}^{ij}$ defined by (1.10).

In the simplest case of our new idea of elasticity the tensor $\mathring{s}^{ij}$ will depend upon the rate of deformation in the same way that stress depends upon strain in the classical theory:

$$\mathring{s}^i_j = \frac{\nu}{1 - 2\nu} d^k_k \delta^i_j + d^i_j, \tag{1.11}$$

where the constant ν is the classical Poisson ratio.

---

[1]Had we applied the same line of reasoning to the covariant stress vector, we should have obtained a formula different from the covariant equivalent to (1.10). The mathematical reason for the difference lies in there being no invariant metric for the motion $x^i = x^i(X^\alpha, t)$, so that covariant and contravariant vectors with respect to it are different and in general unrelated entities. The mechanical reason for arguing in terms of the contravariant rather than the covariant stress vector is that the stress vector is a force field and hence to be regarded ultimately as a field of line elements rather than a field of plane elements.

More general relations are possible, but in the present work we shall not consider them. The ideal material defined by (1.11) we shall call the *isotropic hypo-elastic body of grade zero.* The full system of differential equations for it is

$$\frac{\partial \rho}{\partial t} + (\rho v^i)_{,i} = 0,$$

$$(1.12) \qquad 2\mu s^{ij}_{,j} + \rho f^i = \rho\left(\frac{\partial v^i}{\partial t} + v^i_{,j} v^j\right),$$

$$\frac{\partial s^i_j}{\partial t} + s^i_{j,k} v^k - s^{ik} v_{j,k} - s^k_j v^i_{,k} + s^i_j v^k_{,k} = \frac{\nu}{1 - 2\nu} v^k_{,k} \delta^i_j + \tfrac{1}{2} (v^i_{,j} + v_j{}^{,i}).$$

Since the extraneous force f^i is taken as given, there are ten unknown quantities (s^i_j , v^i, ρ) to be obtained by integrating these ten equations, of which all but one are non-linear. Thus, using a concept which for small strain from an unstressed state reduces to the usual idea of linear elasticity, and introducing no new empirical constants besides those of the classical theory (μ and ν), we have constructed a non-linear field theory which has meaning and is dynamically admissible for strains and rotations of any magnitude. This theory is a natural extension of the classical one and as such is worthy to be studied alongside the finite strain theory. So as certainly to avoid misunderstanding, I repeat that this new theory does not employ any concept of strain. To be sure, stress-strain relations will emerge, but only as the outcome, not the assumption of the theory, and moreover these will vary from problem to problem. The system (1.12) together with appropriate boundary and initial conditions define the theory. No additional assumptions, whether or not whitened as "approximations," are to be employed.

2. *Homogeneous Deformation Compatible with Equilibrium Stress Systems*

We turn now to a problem of general continuum mechanics: what is the most general motion compatible with an equilibrium stress system? Plainly it is necessary and sufficient that the acceleration be zero; equivalently, in such a motion each particle travels in a straight line at uniform speed. It is not easy, however, to describe all such motions of a continuum in a useful way, and several attempts toward this end have been published. Here we content ourselves with the special case of a homogeneous deformation:

$$(2.1) \qquad v_i = a_{ij} x^j + b_i, \qquad a_{ij} = a_{ij}(t), \qquad b_i = b_i(t).$$

In order for the acceleration field to vanish it is necessary and sufficient that the matrices $\mathbf{a}(t)$ and $\mathbf{b}(t)$ satisfy the matrix equations

$$(2.2) \qquad d\mathbf{a}/dt + \mathbf{a}^2 = 0, \qquad d\mathbf{b}/dt + \mathbf{ab} = 0.$$

To solve $(2.2)_1$, let $\mathbf{A}$ be a constant matrix. Then

$$\frac{d}{dt}[(\mathbf{1} + \mathbf{A}t)\mathbf{a}] = \mathbf{A}\mathbf{a} + (\mathbf{1} + \mathbf{A}t)\frac{d\mathbf{a}}{dt} = [\mathbf{A} - (\mathbf{1} + \mathbf{A}t)\mathbf{a}]\mathbf{a}. \tag{2.3}$$

Both sides vanish if

$$(\mathbf{1} + \mathbf{A}t)\mathbf{a} = \mathbf{A}, \tag{2.4}$$

whence it appears that $\mathbf{A} = \mathbf{a}(0)$. Thus if (2.4) can be solved for $\mathbf{a}$, it gives near $t = 0$ the general solution of the initial value problem for $(2.2)_1$. If $\mathbf{a}(0) = 0$, from the uniqueness theorem for differential equations follows $\mathbf{a}(t) = 0$. If $\mathbf{A} = \mathbf{a}(0) \neq 0$, the condition for solving (2.4) is $\det(\mathbf{1} + \mathbf{A}t) \neq 0$, and for sufficiently small t this condition is always satisfied. We may write the solution of (2.4) symbolically as

$$\mathbf{a} = \mathbf{A}/(\mathbf{1} + \mathbf{A}t). \tag{2.5}$$

If $\mathbf{A}$ has positive (negative) real proper numbers, write the largest (smallest) as $-1/t_-(-1/t_+)$; otherwise, write $t_- = -\infty$ $(t_+ = +\infty)$. Then (2.5) exists and is a differentiable function of t in the interval $t_- < t < t_+$. Moreover, if m is the largest among the absolute values of all the proper numbers of $\mathbf{A}$, then (2.5) is analytic for $|t| < 1/m$.

To solve $(2.2)_1$, we have by (2.4)

$$(\mathbf{1} + \mathbf{A}t)(d\mathbf{b}/dt) + \mathbf{A}\mathbf{b} = 0. \tag{2.6}$$

Hence

$$(d/dt)[(\mathbf{1} + \mathbf{A}t)\mathbf{b}] = \mathbf{A}\mathbf{b} - \mathbf{A}\mathbf{b} = 0, \tag{2.7}$$

so that

$$(\mathbf{1} + \mathbf{A}t)\mathbf{b} = \mathbf{B}, \tag{2.8}$$

where $\mathbf{B} = \mathbf{b}(0)$. If $\mathbf{B} = 0$, then $\mathbf{b} = 0$. If $\mathbf{B} \neq 0$, then the conditions for solving (2.8) for $\mathbf{b}$ are the same as those already worked out for (2.4). Hence, symbolically,

$$\mathbf{b} = \mathbf{B}/(\mathbf{1} + \mathbf{A}t). \tag{2.9}$$

The results (2.5) and (2.9) furnish the general solution of (2.2).

It might be thought that these motions, in which every particle travels in a straight line at uniform speed, would be rather dull. That such they need not be is shown by the following example of simple extension:

$$\mathbf{d} = k \left\| \begin{matrix} -\sigma & 0 & 0 \\ 0 & -\sigma & 0 \\ 0 & 0 & 1 \end{matrix} \right\|, \qquad a_{ij} = a_{ji} = d_{ij}, \qquad b_i = 0, \tag{2.10}$$

where $k(t)$ and $\sigma(t)$ are functions to be determined. The condition (2.5) yields

$$(2.11) \qquad k(t) = \frac{k_0}{1 + k_0 t}, \qquad \sigma(t) = \sigma_0 \frac{1 + k_0 t}{1 - k_0 \sigma_0 t},$$

where σ_0 and k_0 are arbitrary constants. If the initial motion is stretching and thinning, we have $k_0 > 0$, $\sigma_0 > 0$, and our solution is valid until $t = 1/(\sigma_0 k_0)$. Figure 1 shows some of the features of this motion, in the plane $y = 0$ and for the case $\sigma_0 = \frac{1}{3}$. The less useful case of stretching with thickening corresponds

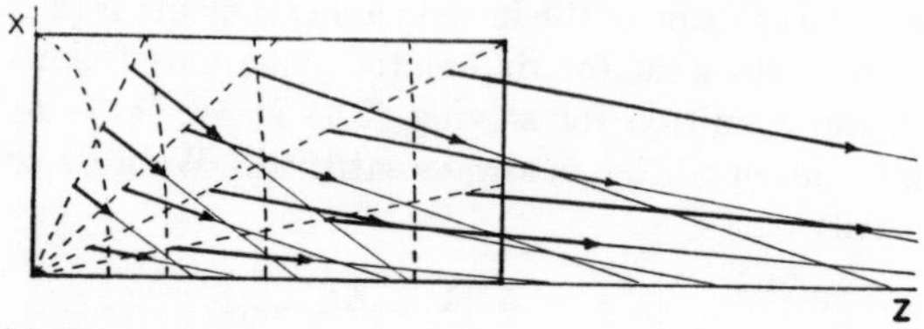

(a) The undeformed block. The arrows are the velocity vectors of the particles; the light lines are their paths; the dashed straight lines are loci of particles whose velocities are parallel; the dashed ellipses are loci of particles having the same speed.

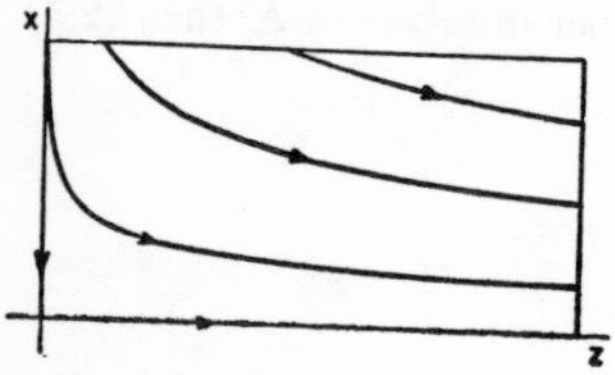

(b) Stream-lines when $\tau = 0$.

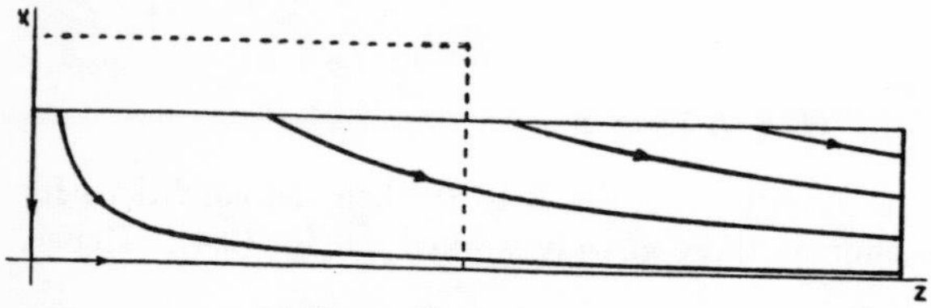

(c) Stream-lines when $\tau = 1$.

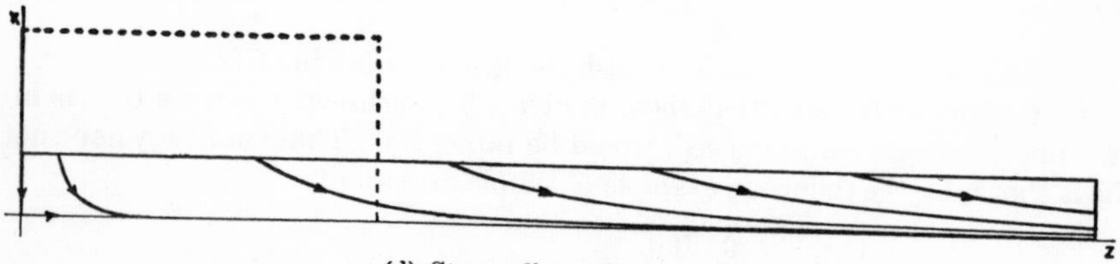

(d) Stream-lines when $\tau = 2$.

FIG. 1. Simple extension without acceleration, in the case $\sigma_0 = 1/3$. The parameter $\tau = k_0 t$ is the longitudinal extension. When $\tau = 3$ the bar has contracted to a wire.

to $k_0 > 0$, $\sigma_0 < 0$, and the solution is valid for all $t = 0$. For contracting and thickening $k_0 < 0$, $\sigma_0 > 0$, and the motion becomes singular at $t = -1/k_0$. Finally, if both $k_0 < 0$ and $\sigma_0 < 0$, our solution is valid only until $t = \min(-1/k_0, 1/(k_0\sigma_0))$.

In all cases the path of the particle (X, Y, Z) is the straight line

$$\frac{z - Z}{Z} = -\frac{1}{\sigma_0}\cdot\frac{x - X}{X} = -\frac{1}{\sigma_0}\frac{y - Y}{Y} = k_0 t. \tag{2.12}$$

Thus all particles initially situate upon a common ray through the stationary particle (0, 0, 0) travel in a common direction. To visualize the motion it is enough to consider the plane $y = 0$. The angle θ of the velocity with the direction of extension is related to the inclination Θ of the ray by

$$\tan \theta = \frac{v_x}{v_z} = -\sigma_0 \frac{X}{Z} = -\sigma_0 \tan \Theta. \tag{2.13}$$

The speed of $(X, 0, Z)$ is given by

$$v_x^2 + v_y^2 = k_0^2\sigma_0^2\left(X^2 + \frac{Z^2}{\sigma_0^2}\right). \tag{2.14}$$

Thus all particles initially situate upon an ellipse whose center is the stationary particle, whose axes are parallel to the principal axes of extension, and the length of whose axis in the direction of the extension is σ_0 times that in the perpendicular direction, move with a common speed. The stream-lines in the $y = 0$ plane are the curves

$$zx^{1/\sigma} = \text{const.}, \tag{2.15}$$

where σ is given by $(2.11)_2$. A rectangular block with one vertex at the stationary particle, with faces parallel to the axes of extension, and of dimensions X, Y, Z is carried at time t into another such, of dimensions x, y, z given by (2.12). Its volume becomes

$$xyz = XYZ(1 + k_0 t)(1 - k_0\sigma_0 t)^2. \tag{2.16}$$

Hence the singularities we noticed above occur when the volume of this typical block has been reduced to zero. The volume varies according to the following scheme:

$k_0 > 0$,	$\sigma_0 \geq \frac{1}{2}$	volume decreases steadily.
$k_0 < 0$,	$\sigma_0 \leq \frac{1}{2}$	
$k_0 > 0$,	$\sigma_0 \leq 0$	volume increases steadily to ∞ as $t \to \infty$.
$k_0 > 0$,	$0 < \sigma_0 \leq \frac{1}{2}$	volume increases until at time $k_0 t = (1 - 2\sigma_0)/(3\sigma_0)$ it attains $4(1 + \sigma_0)^3/(27\sigma_0)$ times its initial value, then decreases to zero.
$k_0 < 0$,	$\sigma_0 > \frac{1}{2}$	

(These facts are reflected in a familiar conclusion of the geometry of infinitesimal strain: in extension a body contracts, retains its same volume or expands according as its Poisson modulus exceeds, equals, or falls short of $\frac{1}{2}$.)

3. *Homogeneous Stress and Deformation in the Hypo-elastic Body: Existence and Uniqueness of Solution*

For motions without acceleration, such as those just studied, the dynamical equations $(1.12)_2$ are satisfied by any homogeneous (i.e., spatially constant) stress s^{ij}. To obtain a solution, all that remains is to satisfy the constitutive equations $(1.12)_3$. Now when any homogeneous deformation (2.1) is substituted into $(1.12)_3$, for homogeneous stress we get simply the ordinary differential system

$$d\mathbf{s}/dt = \mathbf{f}(\mathbf{s}, \mathbf{a}(t), \mathbf{b}(t)), \tag{3.1}$$

where the matrix function $\mathbf{f}$, which may be calculated explicitly from $(1.12)_3$, is an analytic function of the components of $\mathbf{s}$, $\mathbf{a}$, and $\mathbf{b}$.

If we follow the common practice of neglecting the inertia of the material, we may assign $\mathbf{a}$ and $\mathbf{b}$ arbitrary values as functions of t; for example, constant values. If $\mathbf{a}$ and $\mathbf{b}$ are analytic for $|t| < C$, it follows then from the general theorems on differential equations that there exists a unique stress field $\mathbf{s}(t)$ taking on an arbitrary value $\mathbf{s}_0$ when $t = 0$, satisfying (3.1), and analytic for $|t| < C$.

If, however, we are to satisfy the dynamical equations exactly, we obtain in place of (3.1)

$$\frac{d\mathbf{s}}{dt} = \mathbf{f}\left(\mathbf{s}, \frac{\mathbf{A}}{1 + \mathbf{A}t}, \frac{\mathbf{B}}{1 + \mathbf{A}t}\right). \tag{3.2}$$

For an arbitrary constant matrix $\mathbf{A}$ and an arbitrary vector $\mathbf{B}$ we now get a unique stress field $\mathbf{s}(t)$ taking on an arbitrary value $\mathbf{s}_0$ when $t = 0$, satisfying (3.2) and analytic for $|t| < 1/m$. In the rigorous theory, then, *initial* stress, rate of deformation, and vorticity may be prescribed arbitrarily, but their subsequent course, if they are to remain homogeneous, is uniquely determined thereafter by the theory itself.

Comparison of the results of the two foregoing paragraphs shows that the additional freedom gained by neglecting the inertial terms permits a gross overdetermination of the problem. In practice in other parts of continuum mechanics such an overdetermination usually consists in assuming a special form for $\mathbf{s}$ as well as for $\mathbf{a}$ and $\mathbf{b}$, rather than for $\mathbf{A}$ and $\mathbf{B}$ only, as required by the rigorous theory. Whether or not such an overdetermination leads to results more or less in accord with the rigorous theory depends only on "physical intuition" or other psychological factors.

4. *Extension*

To complete our illustration of the simplest ideas of this new theory, we now determine a homogeneous stress field which can produce the extensile motion discussed at the end of §2. For a solution,

$$\mathbf{s} = \left\| \begin{matrix} -Q & 0 & 0 \\ 0 & -Q & 0 \\ 0 & 0 & T \end{matrix} \right\| \tag{4.1}$$

will be general enough, since a stress-system initially of this type must remain ever so. Putting (2.10) into the constitutive equations $(1.12)_3$ yields

$$\begin{aligned} \frac{1}{k}\frac{dT}{dt} &= (1 + 2\sigma)T + \frac{1 - \nu - 2\sigma\nu}{1 - 2\nu}, \\ \frac{1}{k}\frac{dQ}{dt} &= -Q + \frac{\sigma - \nu}{1 - 2\nu}. \end{aligned} \tag{4.2}$$

Now in order for a solution of this system to satisfy the dynamical equations also it is necessary and sufficient that k and σ be given by (2.11). If we choose to overlook this fact (i.e., to neglect the effect of the inertia of the material), we may leave k and σ arbitrary and put $Q = 0$ for all t. Then $(4.2)_2$ yeilds

$$\sigma = \nu: \tag{4.3}$$

the contraction ratio is Poisson's ratio, just as in the classical theory. At the same time, since $k = \overline{\log z}^{\,\cdot}$, from $(4.2)_1$ follows

$$\log \frac{z}{z_0} = \int_{T_0}^{T} \frac{d\xi}{(1 + 2\nu)\xi + 1 + \nu}, \tag{4.4}$$

or, if we take

$$\tau \equiv \frac{z}{Z} - 1 = k_0 t \tag{4.5}$$

as a measure of strain,

$$T = T_a \equiv T_0 + \frac{1 + \nu + (1 + 2\nu)T_0}{2\nu + 1}\left[(1 + \tau)^{2\nu+1} - 1\right]. \tag{4.6}$$

While results such as these have appeared recently in the literature, they are wrong, at least as far as the present theory is concerned. It is obvious that when the dynamically correct values (2.11) for k and σ are put into the right hand sides of (4.2), no solution with $Q = 0$ is possible. This is only what experience in other parts of non-linear continuum mechanics would suggest: tensile stress alone is insufficient to produce simple extension. This result does not contradict the consistency of our theory with ordinary elasticity when the strain is small. Indeed, if $Q = 0$ when $t = 0$ we get from (4.2)

$$\left.\frac{dQ}{d\tau}\right|_{\tau=0} = \frac{\sigma_0 - \nu}{1 - 2\nu}. \tag{4.7}$$

Thus if we choose the initial contraction ratio $\sigma_0 = \nu$, Poisson's ratio, the cross stress Q will at first rise more slowly than for any other initial ratio. That is for small strains Q will be very nearly zero, as in the classical theory.

Now let us put $\sigma_0 = \nu$ and put (2.11) into (4.2), thus getting the correct differential equations of our problem:

$$(4.8)\quad \begin{aligned} (1+\tau)(1-\nu\tau)\frac{dT}{d\tau} &= (1 + 2\nu + \nu\tau)T + \frac{1+\nu}{1-2\nu}(1 - 2\nu - \nu\tau), \\ (1+\tau)(1-\nu\tau)\frac{dQ}{d\tau} &= -(1-\nu\tau)Q + \frac{\nu(1+\nu)}{1-2\nu}\tau. \end{aligned}$$

The general solution satisfying the conditions $T = T_0$, $Q = Q_0$ when $\tau = 0$ is*

$$(4.9)\quad \begin{aligned} T &= \frac{1+\tau}{(1-\nu\tau)^2}\left\{T_0 + \frac{1+\nu}{1-2\nu}\left[\frac{\tau(1+\nu^2\tau)}{1+\tau} - 2\nu\log(1+\tau)\right]\right\}, \\ Q &= \frac{1}{1+\tau}\left\{Q_0 + \frac{1+\nu}{1-2\nu}\left[\frac{1}{\nu}\log\frac{1}{1-\nu\tau} - \tau\right]\right\}. \end{aligned}$$

Since $T(\nu^{-1}) = +\infty$, to annul the volume by pulling requires infinite tension, but the length may be reduced to zero by the *critical pressure* $P_c = (1-\nu)/(1-2\nu)$. For $\nu = \frac{1}{3}$ we find $P_c = 2$, a very large value. If $Q_0 = 0$ we find Q very small when the extension is small, but for large extensions Q grows rapidly and increases in magnitude beyond all bounds: $Q(\nu^{-1}) = +\infty$, $Q(-1) = -\infty$. Pulling and pushing are quite different, however: in pulling $Q/T \to 0$ as $\tau \to \nu^{-1}$, while in pushing $Q/T \to \infty$ as $\tau \to -1$. Thus in pushing the cross-stress Q soon becomes the dominant factor.

While there are some qualitative features in common between the true solution (4.9) and the quasi-static result (4.6), in quantity they are entirely different. In the quasi-static treatment there is no reason to limit the range of τ; we should then conclude that $T_q \to \infty$ as $\tau \to \infty$. For shortening to zero length there is a critical pressure $P_{cq} = (1+\nu)/(1+2\nu)$, never so great as the true value P_c: *e.g.*, if $\nu = \frac{1}{3}$ we have $P_{cq} = \frac{4}{5}$ instead of the correct value $P_c = 2$. If we compare (4.6) and (4.9) over the entire range of τ we find that the quasi-static theory represents the body as far softer than it really is. Of course, it is the cross-stress Q which must be applied in order to effect the assumed homogeneous and accelerationless deformation that has the effect of stiffening the body.

Let it be noticed that none of the usual conversation regarding slow rates of deformation or long experimental times has the least relevance here, nor can it in any theory where no time constant is present. While our theory is put in terms of rates, there is no standard of comparison by which these can be said to be great or small. Thus in any end result, as is illustrated by the above

* Eq. $(4.9)_1$ is printed here as corrected by A. C. ERINGEN, Section 80 of Nonlinear theory of continuous media, New York, McGraw-Hill, 1962.

example, the rate and the time must cancel one another. The formulae (4.6) and (4.9) are determinate relations between stress and extension. Except for small extensions, they do not agree at all. *Whatever the rates or times involved*, the solution (4.6), obtained as is usual in the literature of plasticity theory by neglecting the inertia of the material, is simply wrong as soon as the *extension* grows appreciable. This is not to say that our rigorous solution (4.9) gives correct answers for any specific physical material, but only that it is a dynamically possible solution, so that there is at least some reason in trying to check its predictions by an experiment so controlled that the motion actually conforms to (2.10) and (2.11).

NOTE: The reader is assumed to be familiar with *The mechanical foundations of elasticity and fluid dynamics*, J. Rational Mech. Anal., Vol. 1, pp. 125–300 (1952), and Vol. 2, pp. 593–616 (1953), where references to related earlier work may be found.

NOTE ADDED IN PROOF, DECEMBER 20, 1954: Since the present work was completed, its ideas have been developed further in *Hypo-elasticity*, J. Rational Mech. Anal., Vol. 4, No. 1, January, 1955.

Received June 30, 1954.

No. 6

HYPO-ELASTICITY

C. Truesdell

Journal of Rational Mechanics and Analysis,
Volume 4, pp. 83-133, 1019-1020 (1955).

Of the two criticisms of hypo-elasticity mentioned in the preface to the previous paper, the former is obviated in this paper, which deals almost exclusively with bodies of grade 1 or 2. What are called "bodies of grade zero" on p. 48 are only certain particular, in no way preferred, bodies of grade 1, and references to them throughout the paper should be ignored. In regard to the second criticism, it should be emphasized that the overlap with elasticity theory, mentioned in Section 3, is more apparent than real for the problems treated here, as is explained in the two final sentences of Section 3.

The considerations in Section 2, based on the old-fashioned vague concept of isotropy stated in the first sentence of that section, are misleading. The correct view, which was just then being formed, is sketched in footnote 1 of Section 2. In fact, all hypo-elastic materials are isotropic. For a general treatment of the relation between elasticity and hypo-elasticity, correcting some wrong ideas still current, see Section 100 of NFTM.

Eq. (2. 5) is not a correct constitutive equation for incompressible materials; it should be replaced by Eq. (14. 5) in the paper by NOLL, No. 5 of RMM.

The main value of the paper lies in showing the various qualities of response that can result from a rate theory, treated exactly. For this reason it has not seemed worthwhile to insert in the reprint all the corrections of detail listed in the note at the end, since these do not alter the general picture.

Reprinted from JOURNAL OF RATIONAL MECHANICS AND ANALYSIS
Vol. 4, No. 1, January, 1955
Printed in U.S.A.

Hypo-elasticity

C. TRUESDELL

Graduate Institute for Mathematics and Mechanics, Indiana University, Bloomington, Indiana*

CONTENTS

1. Definition of the hypo-elastic bodies. In the paper called *The mechanical foundations of elasticity and fluid dynamics*[1] I drew attention toward the concept

---

* This paper was written for the Applied Mathematics Branch, Naval Research Laboratory, Washington, D. C. The numerical calculations and the figures drawn from them were prepared by Messrs. HARRISON HANCOCK and B. G. ZIMMERMAN of the Computer Section; the final drawings were made by the Graphic Arts Division.

[1] See Chapter IV–D as revised, pp. 603–609 of Vol. 2 of this *Journal* (1953). The present memoir is to be taken as correcting in some respects and especially as simplifying and broadening the ideas of the passage quoted. The ground thought has been explained more fully in a note called *The simplest rate theory of pure elasticity*, presented at the Second Ordnance Symposium, Chicago, April, 1954. This preliminary note, which concerns only what are here called *bodies of grade zero* (§4), is to appear in the *Communications on Pure and Applied Mathematics N. Y. U.*, Vol. **8**, No. 1, January, 1955.

of elasticity embodied in the principle

$$\text{rate of stress} = f(\text{rate of deformation}). \tag{1.1}$$

Here I begin a thorough search of the theory which rests upon it.

As I have shown, for a dynamically sound theory "rate of stress" shall mean the tensor $\tilde{s}^{ij}$ defined by

$$\tilde{s}^{ij} \equiv \dot{s}^{ij} - s^{ik} v^j{}_{,k} - s^{kj} v^i{}_{,k} + s^{ij} v^k{}_{,k}, \tag{1.2}$$

where s^{ij} is the spatial stress tensor referred for convenience to twice the shear modulus as the unit of stress, the dot denotes the material derivative, the comma denotes the covariant derivative, and v^i is the velocity. The "rate of deformation", as usual, is

$$d_{ij} = \tfrac{1}{2}(v_{i,j} + v_{j,i}). \tag{1.3}$$

Finally, it makes for economy to replace (1.1) by a still more general concept of elasticity, according to which the response to deformation may be moderated by the magnitude of the reigning stress field. Thus we propose to study the ideal material defined by the constitutive equation

$$\tilde{\mathbf{s}} = \mathbf{f}(\mathbf{d}, \mathbf{s}). \tag{1.4}$$

(As is usual in continuum mechanics, quantities distinguishing any preferred directions with which we may wish to endow the body are understood to enter (1.4) without being written explicitly. Also, if it is desired to include dependence on the temperature θ as well, the ratio θ/θ_0, where θ_0 is a reference temperature, may be inserted.)

In the way I introduced into continuum mechanics some years ago, we now render the functional form of $\mathbf{f}$ in (1.4) more explicit by applying dimensional analysis. The stress tensor $\mathbf{s}$, being related to the usual stress tensor $\mathbf{t}$ by

$$\mathbf{s} \equiv \frac{\mathbf{t}}{2\mu}, \tag{1.5}$$

is dimensionless. Hence not only $\mathbf{d}$ but also $\tilde{\mathbf{s}}$ is of the dimension T^{-1}, where T is a unit of time.

At this point we add another constitutive restriction: just as in the classical theory, *no modulus of our ideal material shall carry a dimension independent of the dimension of stress.* The dimensional moduli may be tensors rather than scalars, as must indeed be the case for materials endowed with no symmetries; our restriction asserts that the physical components of these tensors must carry dimension $[\text{stress}]^\alpha$, for some α. In particular, the absence of a modulus of dimension T makes what are usually called "relaxation effects" impossible in our present theory. From (1.5) and the above assumption we conclude that the function $\mathbf{f}$ in (1.4) must be of dimension T^{-1} and that for its specification only *dimensionless* parameters in addition to its explicit arguments **d** and **s** may occur. Finally, we add the restriction that **f** must be an *analytic* function of the components $d^i{}_j$ and $s^i{}_j$ for all values of these components and in all co-ordinate systems. For dimensional invariance it is then necessary that (1.4) shall reduce to a relation which is homogeneous of degree 1 in the $d^i{}_j$:

$$\mathring{s}^i{}_j = A^{i\,k}_{\;j\;l}\, d^l{}_k, \tag{1.6}$$

where the tensor $A^{i\,k}_{\;j\;l}$ is a dimensionless function of the components $s^m{}_n$.

That our easy inferences may not pass as merely facile, I pause to assert with vehemence that the definitive form (1.6) has fallen to us only by our stated assumptions: for a material possessing a time constant, or for a relation (1.4) which is not at least differentiable with respect to $d^i{}_j$ near $\mathbf{d} = 0$, nothing so simple as (1.6) can be expected even for sufficiently small values of **d**. But for the ideal material we define here the constitutive equation (1.6) is in no sense an approximation: for all types of motion, it expresses our concept and is consistent with the principles of mechanics. We shall name the class of ideal materials defined by (1.6) *hypo-elastic bodies*.

Now I shall be asked what physical materials are to be regarded as hypo-elastic. I answer, if we are to discard this theory on physical grounds, let us at least wait until we have first learned what it predicts. To this I add only what must be obvious from the derivation: a hypo-elastic body is a material which may soften or harden in strain but in general has neither preferred state nor preferred stress; in its response to deformation it is, analytically speaking, entirely smooth. I repeat, moreover, that the definition of the hypo-elastic bodies differs from most employed in plasticity theory in that it is dynamically sound. It is at least possible to ask how a hypo-elastic body behaves under large strains, large rotations, or quick stress changes, with some chance of getting an answer which is a theorem rather than an opinion. In this same spirit will we pursue its theory, seeking only exact solutions.

2. Isotropic hypo-elastic bodies. An ideal material is said to be *isotropic*[1] if its constitutive equations are expressed by isotropic functions. One way of

---

[1] At the present writing the invariance principles of general continuum mechanics furnish a field of vigorous and earnest research. In particular, concepts of isotropy broader than that in the *Mechanical foundations* have been introduced by RIVLIN & ERICKSEN and by NOLL, who have proposed also additional restrictions upon all constitutive equations. According to these new restrictions, a relation of type (1.4) must always reduce to (2.1), or, in other words, the definition of hypo-elastic bodies given here is appropriate *only* to the isotropic case, unless we add to the arguments of (1.4) quantities specifying the local rotation from a preferred initial state. More generally, it appears from these new restrictions that anisotropy is a concept appropriate only to materials which have a preferred state. See W. NOLL, *On the continuity of the solid and fluid states*, preceding in this issue, and R. S. RIVLIN & J. L. ERICKSEN, *Stress-deformation relations for isotropic materials*, to appear in the next issue.

delimiting the special class of functions **f**(**d**, **s**) which are isotropic is to say that no quantities specifying preferred directions shall enter the list of arguments of **f**. That is, the function symbol is to be taken almost literally: the components of **f** are to be functions *only* of the components of **d** and **s** and unspecified scalars, and the relation is to be tensorially invariant.

The concept of an isotropic function, while introduced by CAUCHY, is neglected in algebra, and only recently has there been an attempt to construct the general theory. Using an unduly restricted definition of an isotropic function, some years ago[2] I concluded that an analytic isotropic relation $\tilde{\mathbf{s}} = \mathbf{f}(\mathbf{d}, \mathbf{s})$ between symmetric 3 × 3 matrices $\tilde{\mathbf{s}}$, **d**, **s** must necessarily be expressible in the form

$$\tag{2.1} \begin{aligned} \tilde{\mathbf{s}} = \mathfrak{g}_0 \mathbf{1} &+ \mathfrak{g}_1 \mathbf{d} + \mathfrak{g}_2 \mathbf{d}^2 \\ &+ \mathfrak{g}_3 \mathbf{s} + \mathfrak{g}_4 \mathbf{s}^2 + \tfrac{1}{2}\mathfrak{g}_5(\mathbf{ds} + \mathbf{sd}) \\ &+ \tfrac{1}{2}\mathfrak{g}_6(\mathbf{ds}^2 + \mathbf{s}^2\mathbf{d}) + \tfrac{1}{2}\mathfrak{g}_7(\mathbf{sd}^2 + \mathbf{d}^2\mathbf{s}) \end{aligned}$$

where the $\mathfrak{g}_\Gamma$ are analytic scalar functions of **d** and **s**. Since then RIVLIN & ERICKSEN[3] have given an adequate definition and have proved that (2.1) is fully general.[4] For an isotropic hypo-elastic body (1.6) and (2.1) must be consistent. Hence, since the $\mathfrak{g}_\Gamma$ are power series in the components of **d**, we must have $\mathfrak{g}_2 \equiv \mathfrak{g}_7 \equiv 0$; $\mathfrak{g}_1$, $\mathfrak{g}_5$, and $\mathfrak{g}_6$ must be independent of **d** and so functions of **s** only; while $\mathfrak{g}_0$, $\mathfrak{g}_3$, and $\mathfrak{g}_4$ must be of degree 1 in the components d_{ij}. Write

$$\tag{2.2} \delta \equiv d^k{}_k, \qquad M \equiv s^i{}_j d^j{}_i, \qquad N \equiv s^i{}_j s^j{}_k d^k{}_i.$$

Then, since the $\mathfrak{g}_\Gamma$ must also be power series in **s**, our result is

$$\tag{2.3} \begin{aligned} \tilde{\mathbf{s}} = \delta g_0 \mathbf{1} &+ g_1 \mathbf{d} + \delta g_2 \mathbf{s} + M g_3 \mathbf{1} \\ &+ \tfrac{1}{2} g_4(\mathbf{ds} + \mathbf{sd}) + \delta g_5 \mathbf{s}^2 + M g_6 \mathbf{s} \\ &+ N g_7 \mathbf{1} + \tfrac{1}{2} g_8(\mathbf{ds}^2 + \mathbf{s}^2\mathbf{d}) + M g_9 \mathbf{s}^2 + N g_{10} \mathbf{s} + N g_{11} \mathbf{s}^2, \end{aligned}$$

where the g_Γ are dimensionless analytic functions of the three principal invariants of **s**:

$$\tag{2.4} \begin{gathered} g_\Gamma = g_\Gamma(I, II, III), \\ I \equiv s^k{}_k, \qquad II \equiv \tfrac{1}{2}\delta^{ij}_{kl} s^k{}_i s^l{}_j, \qquad III \equiv \tfrac{1}{6}\delta^{ijk}_{lmn} s^l{}_i s^m{}_j s^n{}_k. \end{gathered}$$

---

[2] See §26 of "A new definition of a fluid. II. The Maxwellian fluid," *J. math. pures appl.* (9) **30**, 111–158 (1951).

[3] *Op. cit. ante.*

[4] It does not follow from the work of RIVLIN & ERICKSEN that our assumed analyticity of (1.6) implies that the $\mathfrak{g}_\Gamma$ also are necessarily analytic. However, Dr. ERICKSEN has shown me an independent argument which proves that in the case considered here, *viz.*, $\mathfrak{g}_2 \equiv \mathfrak{g}_7 \equiv 0$, the remaining $\mathfrak{g}_\Gamma$ are indeed analytic. Thus (2.3) with analytic g_Γ is fully general for the present theory. The case when (1.6) is not analytic near $\mathbf{d} = 0, \mathbf{s} = 0$ is far from devoid of interest but will not be considered in this paper.

The equations (2.3) are the constitutive equations of the isotropic hypo-elastic body.

In an isochoric motion, $\delta = 0$. An incompressible body is one susceptible only of isochoric motions. We might require (2.3) to hold for incompressible bodies also, but in so doing we should lose the possibility of its being consistent with a variational principle or of including conservative deformations as a special case. It seems better, asserting analogy to other models of incompressible bodies in continuum mechanics, to replace (2.3) in the incompressible case by

$$\overset{\circ}{\mathbf{s}}' = \mathfrak{g}_1\,\mathbf{d} + \tfrac{1}{2}\mathfrak{g}_4(\mathbf{ds} + \mathbf{sd}) + M_{\mathfrak{g}_6}\,\mathbf{s} + \tfrac{1}{2}\mathfrak{g}_8(\mathbf{ds}^2 + \mathbf{s}^2\mathbf{d}) + M_{\mathfrak{g}_9}\,\mathbf{s}^2 + N_{\mathfrak{g}_{10}}\,\mathbf{s} + N_{\mathfrak{g}_{11}}\,\mathbf{s}^2, \tag{2.5}$$

where $\mathbf{s}' \equiv \mathbf{s} + p\mathbf{1}$, p being an arbitrary hydrostatic pressure.

The full set of differential equations of hypo-elasticity is obtained by adding to (2.3) or (2.5) the definition (1.3) and the usual equations of mass and motion:

$$\dot{\rho} + \rho v^k{}_{,k} = 0, \tag{2.6}$$

$$2\mu s^{ij}{}_{,j} = \rho(\dot{v}^i - f^i), \tag{2.7}$$

where ρ is the density and where f^i, the field of extrinsic force, is to be regarded as given. Thus if we eliminate $\mathbf{d}$ by (1.3), we obtain a system of ten non-linear equations for ten unknowns. For compressible bodies the unknowns are ρ, s^{ij}, and v^i; for incompressible bodies they are p, s^{ij}, and v^i.

It would seem natural to employ in hypo-elasticity the same boundary conditions, referring to stress, displacement, or both, as in elasticity. A displacement condition is complicated because it requires integration of the velocity field $\mathbf{v}$, however, and in many cases it will be equally natural to prescribe $\mathbf{v}$ instead. The main analytical difference from elasticity theory comes in the appearance of $\partial\mathbf{s}/\partial t$ in addition to $\mathbf{s}$ in the differential equations. Thus, beyond boundary conditions such as are usual in elasticity, we may expect to be able to satisfy the condition of *arbitrary initial stress*: $\mathbf{s} = \mathbf{S}$, say, when $t = 0$, where $\mathbf{S}$ is any solution of (2.7) consistent with whatever boundary conditions are employed.

In this paper we make no attempt to prove a general theorem of existence and uniqueness. A special theorem is obtained in §6.

3. Relation to the theory of elasticity. In a displacement $\mathbf{u}$ which is sufficiently small, sufficiently nearly irrotational, and sufficiently nearly homogeneous, we may employ the approximations

$$\overset{\circ}{\mathbf{s}}\,dt \approx \mathbf{s}(t + dt) - \mathbf{s}(t), \qquad \mathbf{u} \approx \mathbf{v}\,dt, \tag{3.1}$$

thus in the case $\mathbf{s}(t) = 0$ recovering the classical infinitesimal theory of elasticity. *That is, the equations of the theory of hypo-elasticity reduce to those of the classical linear theory of elasticity under the assumptions usual in formulating that theory.*

There is no obvious connection between the classical theory of finite strain and the theory of hypo-elasticity. Indeed, it was originally my intention to find a new concept of elastic behavior, mutually exclusive with the theory of finite strain except in the linearized case. However, Dr. WALTER NOLL[1] has announced a proof that *every isotropic elastic body is also an isotropic hypo-elastic body*. Thus hypo-elasticity is a generalization of the classical theory of finite strain.

Beyond this greater generality, there are two important differences. First, for the elastic case the coefficient functions in (2.3) will have special forms. The hypo-elastic theory for these special cases is not equivalent to elasticity, however, since in elasticity only a special class of initial stresses, those obtainable by elastic strain from the natural state, are admissible, while in hypo-elasticity any initial stress satisfying the equations of motion may be employed. Thus even for bodies whose response to strain from an unstressed state is elastic, the theory of hypo-elasticity offers the possibility of a more liberal treatment of initially stressed configurations.[2]

Second, if the strain energy in the elastic case has an especially simple form, no particularly simple form of the resulting hypo-elastic coefficients in (2.3) is to be expected. More important, the especially simple hypo-elastic bodies to be defined in the next section will generally fail to fall within the elastic special case. Thus the theory of hypo-elasticity offers some simple models for elastic behavior in large deformation which are not included in the classical theory of finite strain.

4. Some special hypo-elastic bodies. To include the classical linear theory as a special case in first approximation, we take (*cf.* (1.5))

$$(4.1)\qquad \mathfrak{g}_1(0, 0, 0) = 1, \qquad \mathfrak{g}_0(0, 0, 0) = \frac{\lambda}{2\mu} = \frac{\nu}{1 - 2\nu},$$

where λ and μ are the usual Lamé constants and ν is the usual Poisson modulus.

We shall say a hypo-elastic body is of *grade zero* if the right hand side of (2.3) or (2.5) is independent of $\mathbf{s}$:

$$(4.2)\qquad \mathfrak{g}_0 \equiv \frac{\lambda}{2\mu}, \qquad \mathfrak{g}_1 \equiv 1, \qquad \mathfrak{g}_2 \equiv \mathfrak{g}_3 \equiv \cdots \mathfrak{g}_{11} \equiv 0, \qquad \text{for all } \mathbf{s};$$

of *grade one* if

---

[1] In a colloquium at Indiana University in May, 1954. After hearing this result, I realized that equation (55.4) in *The mechanical foundations* gives a strong hint of it in the case when there is a strain energy. The proof is given in §15b of NOLL's paper cited in §2 above.

[2] It now seems to me that the theory of the hypo-elastic body of grade zero, with the inertial terms in the equations of motion neglected, is what CAUCHY intended by his much misunderstood theory of initial stress (see §55 of *The mechanical foundations*).

$$
(4.3)\qquad
\begin{aligned}
&g_0 \equiv \frac{\lambda}{2\mu} + \alpha_0 I, \qquad g_1 \equiv 1 + \alpha_1 I,\\
&g_2 \equiv \alpha_2, \qquad g_3 \equiv \alpha_3, \qquad g_4 \equiv \alpha_4,\\
&g_5 \equiv g_6 \equiv \cdots g_{11} \equiv 0, \qquad \text{for all } \mathbf{s},
\end{aligned}
$$

where the α_Γ are dimensionless constants; of *grade two* if

$$
(4.4)\qquad
\begin{aligned}
&g_0 \equiv \frac{\lambda}{2\mu} + \alpha_0 I + \beta_0 I^2 + \beta_0' II,\\
&g_1 \equiv 1 + \alpha_1 I + \beta_1 I^2 + \beta_1' II,\\
&g_2 \equiv \alpha_2 + \beta_2 I, \qquad g_3 \equiv \alpha_3 + \beta_3 I, \qquad g_4 \equiv \alpha_4 + \beta_4 I,\\
&g_5 \equiv \beta_5, \qquad g_6 \equiv \beta_6, \qquad g_7 \equiv \beta_7, \qquad g_8 \equiv \beta_8,\\
&g_9 \equiv g_{10} \equiv g_{11} \equiv 0, \qquad \text{for all } \mathbf{s},
\end{aligned}
$$

where the β_Γ are dimensionless constants; *etc.* If we think of our theory as extending the classical linear one, the grades we have defined would suggest a perturbation scheme with respect to a slightly stressed state. However, no such view is necessary. Each special choice of the functions g_Γ in (2.3) or (2.5) defines a special hypo-elastic body, consistent with the principles of mechanics for deformations and stresses of any magnitude whatever. According to this view (4.2), (4.3), and (4.4) merely represent interesting simple kinds of hypo-elastic body.

5. Some properties of $\mathring{\mathbf{s}}$. It simplifies solutions in special cases to notice that the affine connection need not be known in order to calculate $\mathring{\mathbf{s}}$: in all co-ordinate systems we have

$$
(5.1)\qquad \mathring{s}^{ij} = \partial_t s^{ij} + v^k \partial_k s^{ij} - s^{ik}\partial_k v^j - s^{kj}\partial_k v^i + (s^{ij}/\sqrt{g})\partial_k(\sqrt{g}\, v^k),
$$

where ∂_t denotes $\partial/\partial t$ with x^k held constant, ∂_k denotes $\partial/\partial x^k$, and $g \equiv \det g_{ij}$, the g_{ij} being the covariant metric components.

Now we shall solve the equation

$$
(5.2)\qquad \mathring{\mathbf{s}} = 0
$$

for a given velocity field $\mathbf{v}$. Let the motion be $x^i = x^i(X^1, X^2, X^3, t)$, where the X^α are any three independent functions of the initial co-ordinates. (In other words, let the functions x^i be any three independent integrals of the system $dx^i = v^i\,dt$.) Then $v^i = \partial x^i/\partial t$. Let $\mathbf{c}^{-1}$ be the reciprocal of Cauchy's deformation tensor calculated from the configuration X^α:

$$
(5.3)\qquad (c^{-1})^{ij} = G^{\alpha\beta} x^i_{,\alpha} x^j_{,\beta},
$$

where the $G^{\alpha\beta}$ are the contravariant components of any second order tensor field depending only on **X**. Then it is easy to show that[1]

$$\text{(5.4)} \qquad \overline{(c^{-1})^{ij}}^{\,\bullet} = (c^{-1})^{ik} v^{j}_{,k} + (c^{-1})^{kj} v^{i}_{,k}.$$

Hence

$$\text{(5.5)} \qquad \overline{\rho(c^{-1})^{ij}}^{\,\bullet} = \rho[(c^{-1})^{ik} v^{j}_{,k} + (c^{-1})^{kj} v^{i}_{,k} - (c^{-1})^{ij} v^{k}_{,k}].$$

Comparison with (1.2) shows that $\rho(c^{-1})^{ij}$ is a solution of (5.2). Since the X^{α} are arbitrary independent functions of the initial coordinates, the quantities $x^{i}_{,\alpha}$ at time $t = 0$ are not necessarily Kronecker deltas but may take on arbitrary values. Hence the quantities $\rho(c^{-1})^{ij}$ take on arbitrary initial values, and thus furnish a solution of the initial value problem for (5.2). Since (5.2) is linear in **s**, this solution is unique. Hence

$$\text{(5.6)} \qquad s^{ij} = \rho(c^{-1})^{ij}$$

is the general solution of (5.2).

For bodies of grade zero we can separate the boundary value problem from the initial value problem. For, as Dr. ERICKSEN has remarked, if **s** satisfies the constitutive equation (1.6) in the case when $A^{i\,k}_{\,j\,l}$ is independent of **s**, then so does $\mathbf{s} + {}_0\mathbf{s}$, where ${}_0\mathbf{s}$ is any solution of (5.2). But, as we have just seen, (5.6) provides a solution of (5.2) satisfying arbitrary initial data. Let **s** be a function which satisfies

1. The constitutive equations;
2. The equations

$$\text{(5.7)} \qquad 2\mu s^{ij}_{,j} = \rho(f^{i} - 2\mu_0 s^{ij}_{,j} - \dot{v}^{i});$$

3. The boundary conditions

$$\text{(5.8)} \qquad s^{ij} n_j = b^{i} - {}_0s^{ij} n_j,$$

where n_j is the unit normal and b^{i} is the prescribed surface traction; and

4. The initial condition $s^{ij} = 0$.

Then $\mathbf{s} + {}_0\mathbf{s}$ satisfies the original combined problem.

From (5.6) it is evident that a solution of $\tilde{\mathbf{s}} = 0$ which satisfies the equations of motion (2.7) at $t = 0$ will generally fail to do so subsequently. This fact is reflected in the foregoing analysis by the appearance of ${}_0s^{ij}_{,j}$ as an effective extrinsic force in (5.7). If, however, we have a particular motion and a particular initial condition such that (5.6) yields ${}_0s^{ij}_{,j} = 0$, then we can formulate a superposition principle: if **s** satisfies all the differential equations of the theory, so does $\mathbf{s} + {}_0\mathbf{s}$.

---

[1] Use $\mathbf{c}\mathbf{c}^{-1} = \mathbf{1}$ and the special case $\mathbf{r} = 0$ of eq. (22.3) in *The mechanical foundations*. Note that for the present argument $G^{\alpha\beta}$ need not be a metric tensor of space.

In the equation (2.5), appropriate to incompressible bodies, appears the quantity $\mathbf{s}' \equiv \mathbf{s} + p\mathbf{1}$. Our solution (5.6) of the equation $\tilde{\mathbf{s}} = 0$ shows that any deformation $\mathbf{x} = \mathbf{x}(\mathbf{X})$ such that $(c^{-1})_i{}^j{}_{,j} = p_{,i}$, for some p, yields a solution $\mathbf{s}' = \mathbf{c}^{-1} - p\mathbf{1}$ of the equation $\tilde{\mathbf{s}}' = 0$. Among such deformations are all those which can be produced by suitable surface loads in any incompressible elastic body and all those similarly possible in RIVLIN's "neo-Hookean" material.[1] If one of these is a solution for an incompressible hypo-elastic body of grade zero, and if $\mathbf{s}$ is any possible stress in such a body, then $\mathbf{s} + \alpha(\mathbf{c}^{-1} - p\mathbf{1})$ for arbitrary α is also a solution for that body.

6. Homogeneous stress. We recall[2] that a linear velocity field

$$\mathbf{v} = \mathbf{a}\mathbf{x} + \mathbf{b}, \tag{6.1}$$

where $\mathbf{a}$ is a square matrix and the co-ordinate $\mathbf{x}$ is rectangular Cartesian, corresponds to a motion without acceleration if and only if $\mathbf{a}$ and $\mathbf{b}$ have the forms

$$\mathbf{a} = \frac{\mathbf{A}}{\mathbf{1} + \mathbf{A}t}, \qquad \mathbf{b} = \frac{\mathbf{B}}{\mathbf{1} + \mathbf{A}t}. \tag{6.2}$$

The constant matrix $\mathbf{A}$ and vector $\mathbf{B}$ are the initial values of the velocity gradient and the velocity at the origin. Among the linear velocity fields (6.1) it is only these which can correspond to a system of stresses and forces under which equilibrium is possible.

In particular, consider a state of homogeneous stress $\mathbf{s}(t)$ subject to no extrinsic force. For a velocity field satisfying (6.1) and (6.2), the dynamical equations (2.7) are satisfied, and the constitutive equations (1.6) reduce to an ordinary differential system:

$$\dot{\mathbf{s}} = \mathbf{g}\left(\mathbf{s}, \frac{\mathbf{A}}{\mathbf{1} + \mathbf{A}t}\right), \tag{6.3}$$

where $\mathbf{g}$ is analytic in its arguments. The second argument exists and is continuously differentiable in the interval $t_- < t < t_+$, where $-1/t_+(-1/t_-)$ is the least negative (greatest positive) proper number of $\mathbf{A}$, or, if there is no such, $t_+ = +\infty\,(t_- = -\infty)$. The second argument is analytic for $|\,t\,| < t_0$, where $1/t_0$ is that among the absolute values of the proper numbers of $\mathbf{A}$ which is not surpassed by any other. From the general theory of ordinary differential equations follows then the

Existence and uniqueness theorem for homogeneous stress. *Consider the class of linear accelerationless motions given by* (6.1) *and* (6.2), $\mathbf{A}$ *being the initial velocity gradient and* $\mathbf{B}$ *the initial velocity of the origin. Then, whatever is* $\mathbf{B}$, *to each* $\mathbf{A}$ *and to arbitrary homogeneous initial stress* $\mathbf{S}$ *there corresponds for any given*

[1] See §54 of *The mechanical foundations*.

[2] These results are proved in the note cited in §1.

hypo-elastic body, a unique homogeneous stress system $\mathbf{s}(t)$ *in* $t_- < t < t_+$. *For* $|t| < t_0$ *this stress system* $\mathbf{s}(t)$ *is an analytic function of* t.

In proving the foregoing theorem, we have considered only the compressible case. For incompressible bodies we may assign $p(t)$ as an arbitrary continuously differentiable or analytic function, and the argument in the two cases goes through in just the same way. The presence of this arbitrary pressure enables us to satisfy boundary conditions more easily in the incompressible case.

Most of the remainder of this paper will consider special examples of the class of solutions just obtained. It is interesting and important to notice the occurrence of movable singularities. The numbers t_-, t_+, t_0 are determined by $\mathbf{A}$, the matrix of *initial velocity gradients*. Thus a homogeneous stress distribution exists for a certain time for any linear motion; how long it continues to exist, while not influenced by the initial stress, depends on how the motion is started.

7. Hydrostatic stress. We begin with the simplest possible case: $d^i{}_j = (\delta/3)\delta^i{}_j$, $s^i{}_j = -\varpi\delta^i{}_j$, where δ and ϖ are functions of time only. Such a solution is not dynamically possible unless the acceleration field vanishes. Hence the density ρ must satisfy

$$\rho = \frac{\rho_0}{(1 + k_0 t)^3}, \tag{7.1}$$

where k_0 is an arbitrary constant. Since $\delta = -d \log \rho/dt$, the constitutive equation (2.3) yields

$$\log \frac{\rho}{\rho_0} = \int_{\varpi_0}^{\varpi} \frac{d\xi}{f(\xi)},$$

$$\begin{aligned} f(\varpi) \equiv {} & g_0 + \tfrac{1}{3}g_1 + \varpi(\tfrac{1}{3} - g_2 - g_3 - \tfrac{1}{3}g_4) \\ & + \varpi^2(g_5 + g_6 + g_7 + \tfrac{1}{3}g_8) - \varpi^3(g_9 + g_{10}) + \varpi^4 g_{11}, \end{aligned} \tag{7.2}$$

where the arguments of the g_Γ are -3ϖ, $3\varpi^2$, $-\varpi^3$. Thus if the pressure is applied in such a way that (7.1) holds, or, equivalently, the volume V shall satisfy $V/V_0 = (1 + k_0 t)^3$, there is then the definite relation (7.2) connecting pressure $p = 2\mu\varpi$ with density ρ, determinate to within a pair of arbitrary initial values ϖ_0, ρ_0.

The amount of pressure required to produce a given condensation will generally differ from the amount of tension required for a rarefaction of equal magnitude. Moreover, to satisfy the physical requirement $d\rho/d\varpi \geqq 0$ we must have

$$f(\varpi) \geqq 0, \tag{7.3}$$

a restriction upon the class of admissible coefficient functions g_Γ, upon the range of admissible pressures, or upon both.

When $\varpi > 0 (\varpi < 0)$ we shall say the body *hardens* or *softens* according as the curve of ρ against ϖ is curved downward or upward (upward or downward). Thus, for example, only if the curvature changes sign at $\varpi = 0$ can the body harden both in pressure and in tension. Since

$$(1/\rho)d^2\rho/d\varpi^2 = \frac{1 - f'}{f^2}, \tag{7.4}$$

the hardening or softening of a body can be determined from the sign of $1 - f'$, except possibly at points where $\rho = 0$ or $d\rho/d\varpi = \infty$.

For bodies of grade zero, one, or two we have

$$\begin{aligned} f(\varpi) &= \kappa + \alpha_p \varpi + \beta_p \varpi^2, \\ \kappa &\equiv \frac{\lambda + \frac{2}{3}\mu}{2\mu} = \frac{k}{2\mu} > 0, \\ \alpha_p &\equiv \tfrac{1}{3} - 3\alpha_0 - \alpha_1 - \alpha_2 - \alpha_3 - \tfrac{1}{3}\alpha_4, \\ \beta_p &\equiv 9\beta_0 + 3\beta_0' + 3\beta_1 + \beta_1' + 3\beta_2 + 3\beta_3 + \beta_4 + \beta_5 + \beta_6 + \beta_7 + \tfrac{1}{3}\beta_8. \end{aligned} \tag{7.5}$$

For a body of grade zero, $\alpha_p = \frac{1}{3}$ and $\beta_p = 0$; grade one, $\alpha_p \neq \frac{1}{3}$ and $\beta_p = 0$; grade two, $\beta_p \neq 0$. In all cases the sign of $1 - \alpha_p - 2\beta_p \varpi$ determines hardening or softening, except possibly at a root of $(7.5)_1$ or where $\rho = 0$.

For a body of grade zero $(7.2)_2$ becomes

$$\frac{\rho}{\rho_0} = \left(\frac{\kappa + \frac{1}{3}\varpi}{\kappa + \frac{1}{3}\varpi_0}\right)^3. \tag{7.6}$$

This body softens in compression but hardens in tension. As $\varpi \to \infty$, so does ρ, but at the tension $\varpi = -3\kappa$ the density vanishes. In an application to a given physical material, we must expect rupture or yield before such a tension is obtained. For a material whose Poisson modulus is $\frac{1}{3}$, this tension is 4, a very large value indeed.

For a body of grade one we have hardening (softening) or softening (hardening) in compression (tension) if $\alpha_p > 1 (\alpha_p < 1)$; (7.6) is to be replaced by

$$\frac{\rho}{\rho_0} = \begin{cases} \left(\dfrac{\kappa + \alpha_p \varpi}{\kappa + \alpha_p \varpi_0}\right)^{1/\alpha_p}, & \alpha_p \neq 0, \\ \exp \dfrac{\varpi - \varpi_0}{\kappa}, & \alpha_p = 0. \end{cases} \tag{7.7}$$

In compression (tension) there is hardening or softening (softening or hardening) according as $\alpha_p > 1$ or $\alpha_p < 1$; if $\alpha_p = 1$, (7.7) reduces to the classical linear formula. If $\alpha_p > 0$ there is a tension $\varpi = -\kappa/\alpha_p$ at which $\rho = 0$. Negative values of the α_Γ tend to reduce the magnitude of this tension from the value $\varpi = -3\kappa$ which is appropriate to the body of grade zero. If $\alpha_p < 0$ there is a pressure

$\varpi = \kappa/(-\alpha_p)$ at which $\rho = \infty$, suggesting that such a body will collapse under pressure but not under tension. Thus physical application for the case $\alpha_p > 0$, especially when $\alpha_p \geqq 1$, is more likely than for $\alpha_p < 0$. Figure 7.1 shows our results concerning bodies of grade zero and grade one for various values of α_p in the case $\varpi_0 = 0$, $\kappa = \frac{4}{3}$.

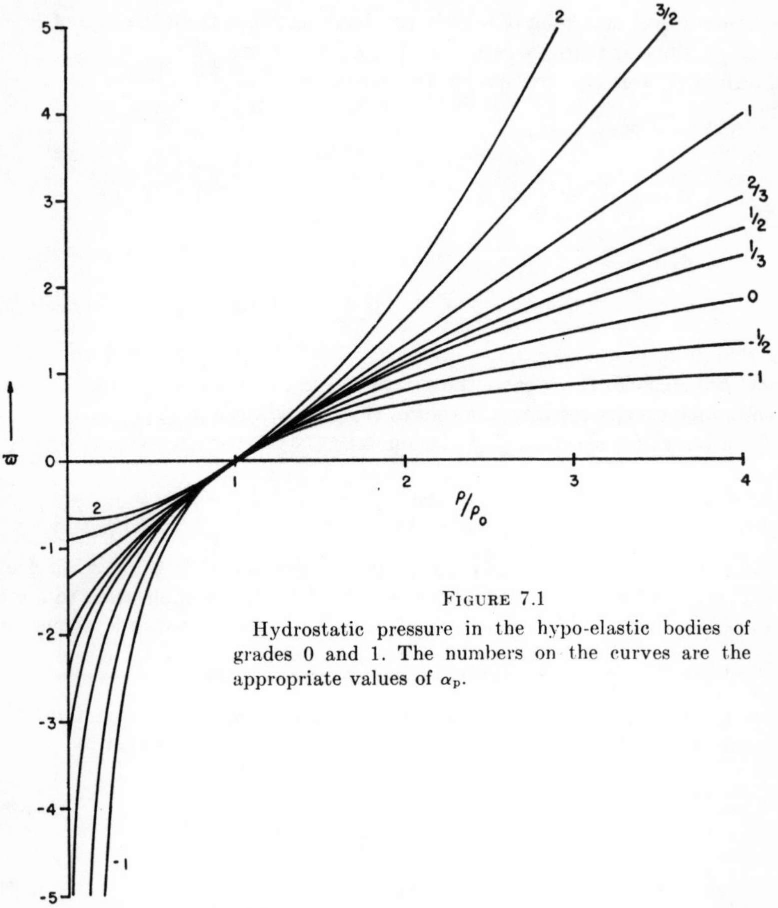

FIGURE 7.1

Hydrostatic pressure in the hypo-elastic bodies of grades 0 and 1. The numbers on the curves are the appropriate values of α_p.

For the bodies of grade two, put

$$\bar{\beta} \equiv +\sqrt{|\,\alpha_p^2 - 4\kappa\beta_p\,|}. \tag{7.8}$$

Then, formally,

$$
(7.9)\qquad \frac{\rho}{\rho_0} = \begin{cases} \left[\dfrac{2\beta_p\,\varpi + \alpha_p - \bar{\beta}}{2\beta_p\,\varpi + \alpha_p + \bar{\beta}}\cdot\dfrac{2\beta_p\,\varpi_0 + \alpha_p + \bar{\beta}}{2\beta_p\,\varpi_0 + \alpha_p - \bar{\beta}}\right]^{1/\bar{\beta}}, \\[2ex] \exp\left[\dfrac{4\kappa(\varpi - \varpi_0)}{(2k + \alpha_p\,\varpi_0)(2\kappa + \alpha_p\,\varpi)}\right], \\[2ex] \exp\left[\dfrac{2}{\bar{\beta}}\left(\operatorname{Arctan}\dfrac{2\beta_p\,\varpi + \alpha_p}{\bar{\beta}} - \operatorname{Arctan}\dfrac{2\beta_p\,\varpi_0 + \alpha_p}{\bar{\beta}}\right)\right], \end{cases}
$$

according as $4\kappa\beta_p \lesseqgtr \alpha_p^{\,2}$. A large variety of possible behavior is included in this result. The fourteen essentially different cases are delimited and shown in Figure 7.2 for typical values of α_p and β_p when $\varpi_0 = 0$ and $\kappa = \frac{4}{3}$. In all graphs the light line is the result from the classical linear theory. Dashed lines are asymptotes; circles locate points of inflection. At one extreme lie the very soft bodies of types 6–10, which must give way easily either in pressure or in tension; at the other, the extremely hard bodies of types 12–14, which approach a limit density as $\varpi \to \infty$ and which yield in tension only after very great stress is applied. Between these extremes lie bodies which yield both in pressure and in tension, with greater or lesser ease, or in one but not in the other. In some, such as types 1 and 10, the body first hardens in compression and then softens after sufficient pressure has been applied. In these results we see for the first time pressure-density relations which are qualitatively like those of many actual materials yet emerge as rigorous solutions in a dynamically possible theory of continuum mechanics.

Thus far in our examples we have supposed $\varpi_0 = 0$. Since the internal pressure in a test specimen is unknown, and since in any case our assumed homogeneity of the pressure field will in a test situation be at best an idealization, it is possible that ϖ_0 might be left in some cases a parameter to be adjusted to fit the experimental data. If, however, a definite value for ϖ_0 is known in advance, we can determine the effect of initial pressure or tension in a simple way. From (7.2) we have

$$
(7.10)\qquad \log\frac{\rho}{\rho_0} = \int_0^{\bar{\varpi}-\bar{\varpi}_0}\frac{d\eta}{g(\eta)}, \qquad g(\eta) \equiv f(\eta + \varpi_0);
$$

i.e., the density increment corresponding to a pressure increment $\varpi - \varpi_0$ from initial pressure ϖ_0 in the body defined by $f(\varpi)$ is the same as that corresponding to an equal pressure increment from an unstressed state in the body defined by $g(\varpi) \equiv f(\varpi + \varpi_0)$. For example, in the bodies of grade zero, one, and two we have

$$
(7.11)\qquad \begin{gathered} g(\varpi) = \kappa^* + \alpha^*\,\varpi + \beta^*\,\varpi^2, \\ \kappa^* \equiv \kappa + \alpha_p\,\varpi_0 + \beta_p\,\varpi_0^2, \qquad \alpha^* \equiv \alpha_p + 2\beta_p\,\varpi_0, \qquad \beta^* \equiv \beta_p. \end{gathered}
$$

For a body of grade zero we get the same result as in the classical theory of elasticity: initial hydrostatic pressure ϖ_0 has the effect of raising the dimensionless

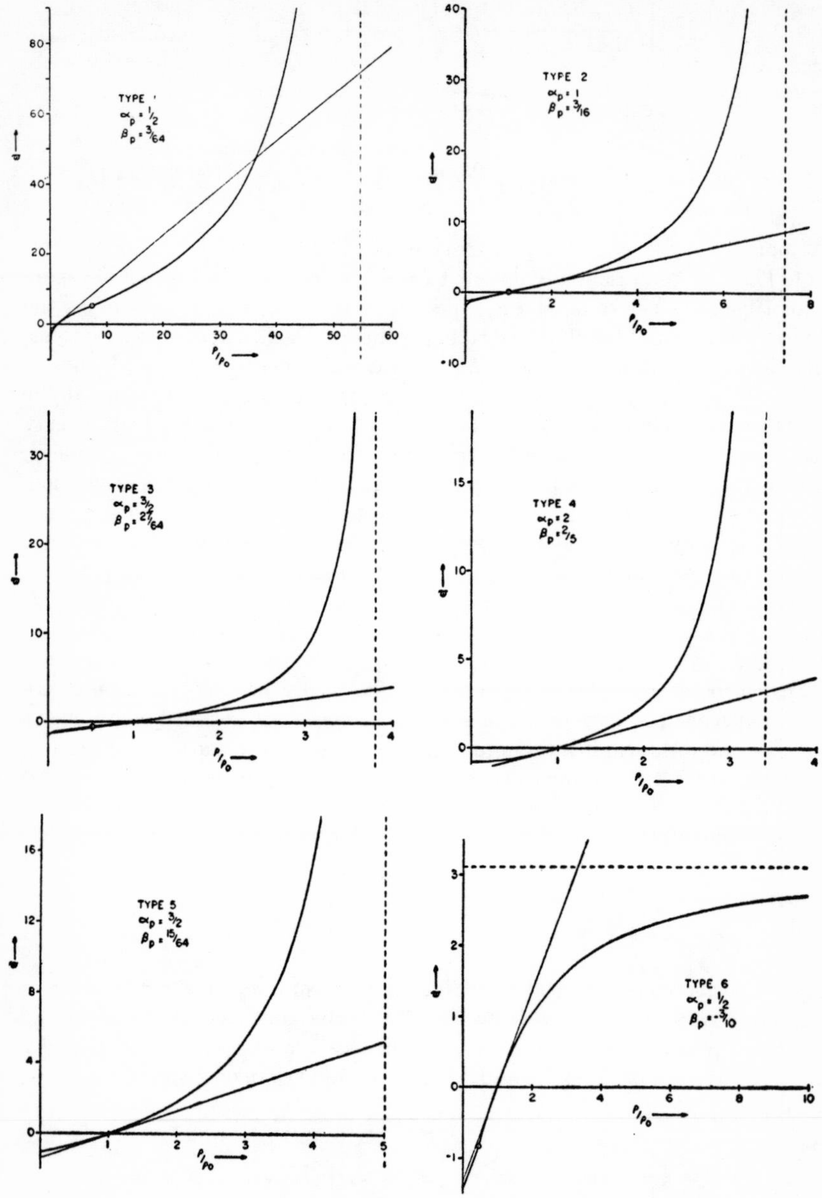

FIGURE 7.2, Types 1–6
Hydrostatic pressure in typical hypo-elastic bodies of grade 2

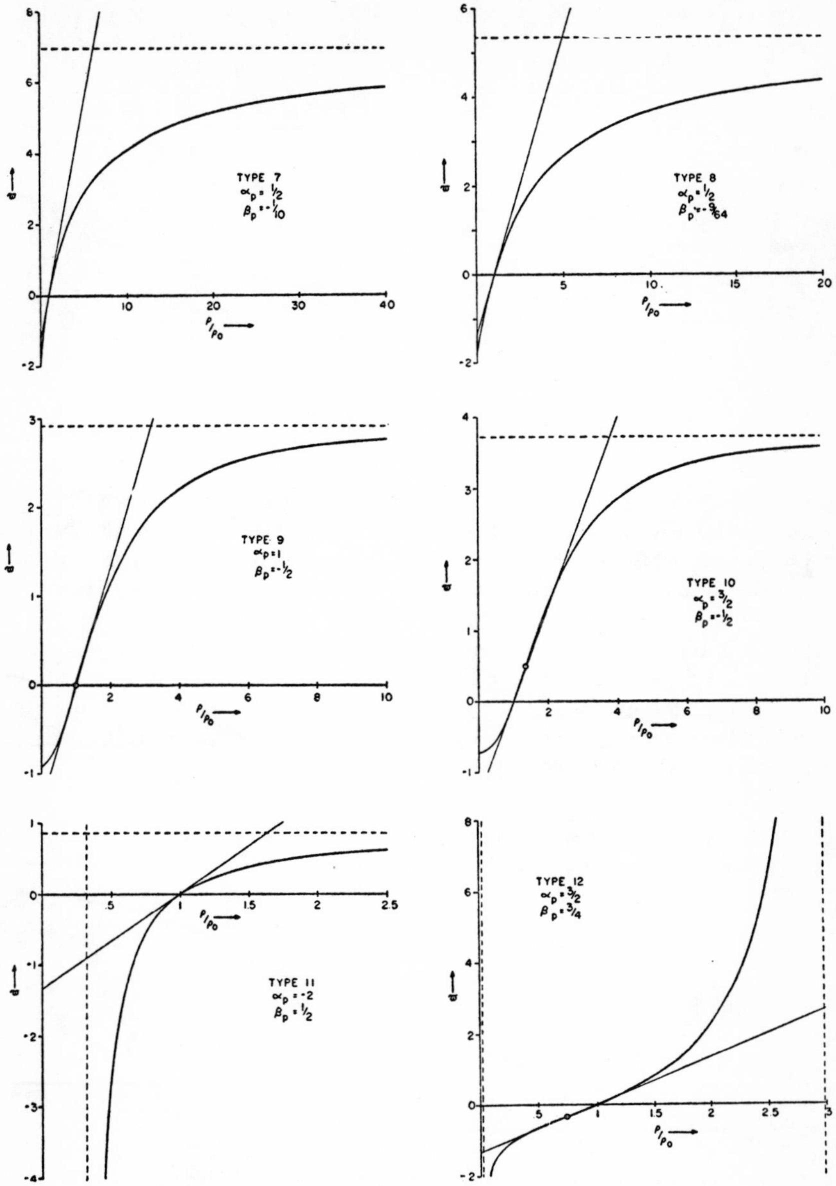

FIGURE 7.2, Types 7–12

Hydrostatic pressure in typical hypo-elastic bodies of grade 2

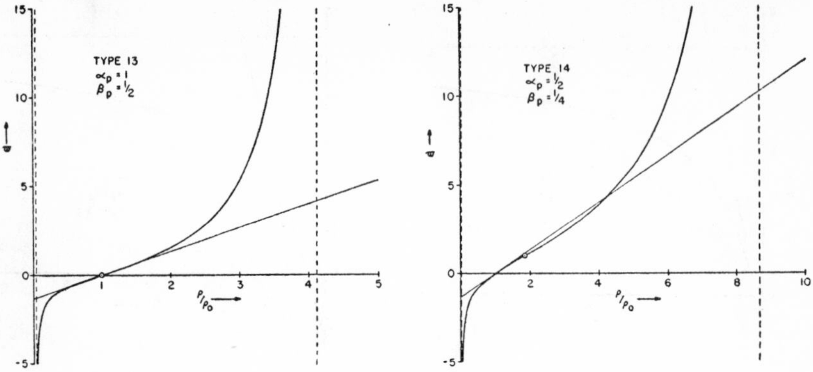

FIGURE 7.2, Types 13–14
Hydrostatic pressure in typical hypo-elastic bodies of grade 2

compressibility by the amount $\frac{1}{3}\varpi_0$. For a body of grade two in which $\beta_p > 0$ any sufficiently large initial pressure or tension increases the effective compressibility, while for grades zero and one initial pressure and tension must necessarily have opposite effect on the response of the body. Further results concerning the effect of initial pressure can be read off by substituting $(7.11)_2$–$(7.11)_4$ into the conditions defining the fourteen types illustrated in Figure 7.2. Figure 7.3 gives some examples. For bodies of grades zero and one initial pressure affects only the quantity, not the quality of the response, while for a body of grade two sufficiently large initial pressure converts the response of the body into a form typical of another of the fourteen basic types.

8. Simple shear of compressible bodies.* Another case evidently compatible with homogeneous stress is simple shear, where

$$v_x = 2ky, \qquad v_y = v_z = 0, \qquad k = \text{const.} \tag{8.1}$$

If we put

$$\tau \equiv kt, \qquad \theta \equiv \text{Arctan}\ \tau, \tag{8.2}$$

then θ is the angle through which a plane initially normal to the x-axis has been rotated at time t, and τ is a convenient dimensionless measure of the shear. Guided by the analogous problem in finite elasticity theory, we seek as a solution a stress field such that $s_{xz} = s_{yz} = 0$. The constitutive equations (2.3) then

*** See the list of corrections to Section 8 reprinted at the end of the paper.**

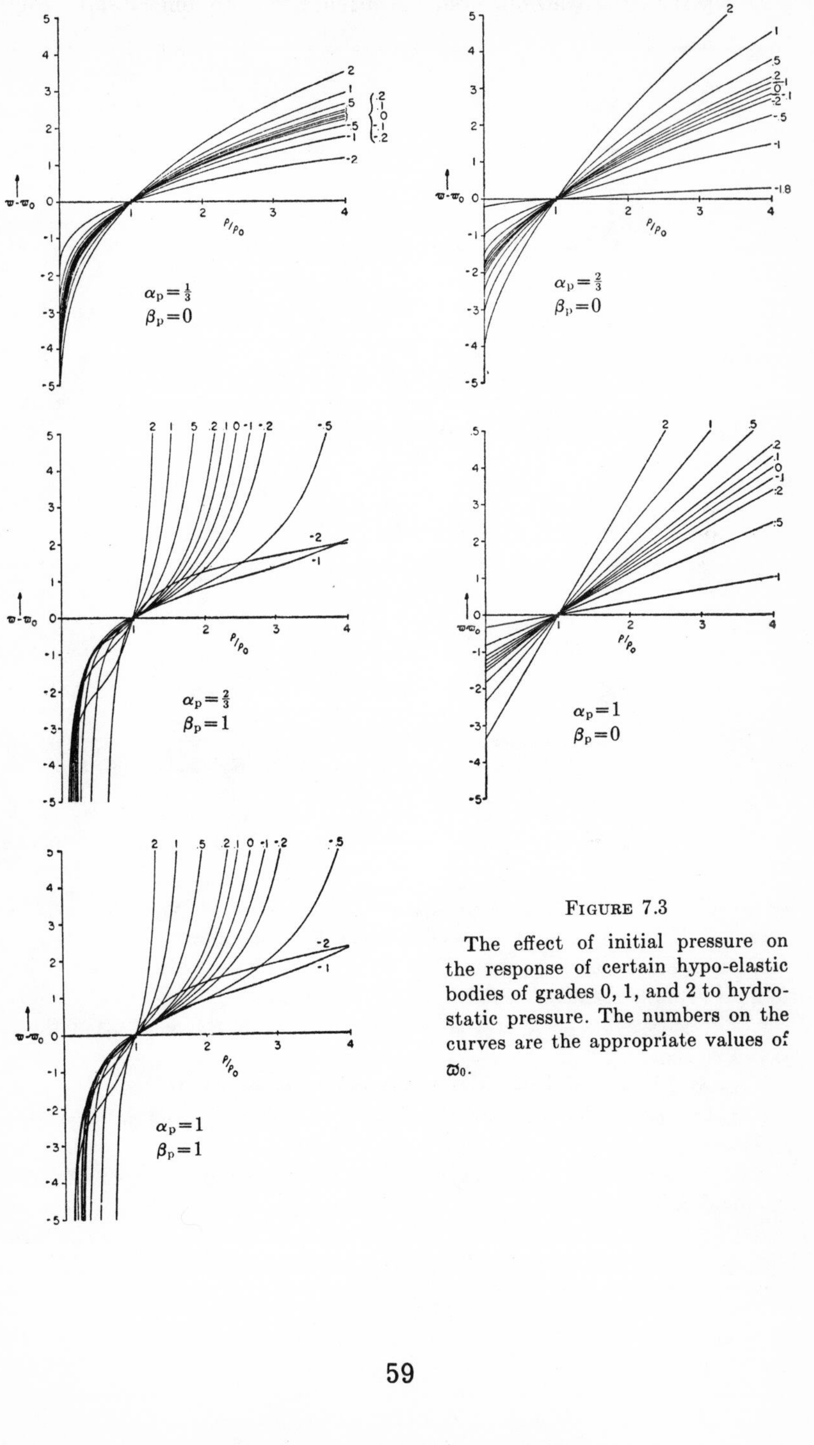

FIGURE 7.3

The effect of initial pressure on the response of certain hypo-elastic bodies of grades 0, 1, and 2 to hydrostatic pressure. The numbers on the curves are the appropriate values of ϖ_0.

yield the following system of four ordinary differential equations:

$$
\begin{aligned}
\frac{d}{d\tau}\left\|\begin{array}{ccc} s_{xx} & s_{xy} & 0 \\ \cdot & s_{yy} & 0 \\ \cdot & \cdot & s_{zz} \end{array}\right\| &= \left\|\begin{array}{ccc} 2s_{xy} & -s_{xy} & 0 \\ \cdot & 0 & 0 \\ \cdot & \cdot & 0 \end{array}\right\| + g_1 \left\|\begin{array}{ccc} 0 & 1 & 0 \\ \cdot & 0 & 0 \\ \cdot & \cdot & 0 \end{array}\right\| \\
&+ 2s_{xy}[g_3 + (s_{xx} + s_{yy})g_7]\left\|\begin{array}{ccc} 1 & 0 & 0 \\ \cdot & 1 & 0 \\ \cdot & \cdot & 1 \end{array}\right\| \\
&+ g_4 \left\|\begin{array}{ccc} s_{xy} & \frac{1}{2}(s_{xx} + s_{yy}) & 0 \\ \cdot & s_{xy} & 0 \\ \cdot & \cdot & 0 \end{array}\right\| \\
&+ 2s_{xy}[g_6 + (s_{xx} + s_{yy})g_{10}]\left\|\begin{array}{ccc} s_{xx} & s_{yy} & 0 \\ \cdot & s_{yy} & 0 \\ \cdot & \cdot & s_{zz} \end{array}\right\| \\
&+ g_8 \left\|\begin{array}{ccc} s_{xy}(s_{xx} + s_{yy}) & \frac{1}{2}(s_{xx}^2 + s_{yy}^2) + s_{xy}^2 & 0 \\ \cdot & s_{xy}(s_{xx} + s_{yy}) & 0 \\ \cdot & \cdot & 0 \end{array}\right\| \\
&+ 2s_{xy}[g_9 + (s_{xx} + s_{yy})g_{11}]\left\|\begin{array}{ccc} s_{xx}^2 + s_{xy}^2 & s_{xy}(s_{xx} + s_{yy}) & 0 \\ \cdot & s_{yy}^2 + s_{xy}^2 & 0 \\ \cdot & \cdot & s_{zz}^2 \end{array}\right\|,
\end{aligned}
\tag{8.3}
$$

where the arguments of the g_Γ are $s_{xx} + s_{yy} + s_{zz}$, $s_{xx}\, s_{yy} + s_{yy}\, s_{zz} + s_{zz}\, s_{xx} - s_{xy}^2$, $(s_{xx}\, s_{yy} - s_{xy}^2)s_{zz}$. A number of results follow by inspection:

1. As in finite elasticity theory, shearing stress alone is always insufficient to maintain simple shearing.
2. The coefficients g_0, g_2, and g_5 have no influence on the response of the body to simple shear.
3. $s_{zz} = 0$ is a possible solution if and only if $g_3 \equiv g_7 \equiv 0$.
4. $s_{yy} = 0$ is a possible solution if and only if $g_3 \equiv g_4 \equiv g_7 \equiv g_8 \equiv g_9 \equiv g_{10} \equiv g_{11} \equiv 0$.

A body of grade zero satisfies both the conditions 3 and 4. For it we get the extremely interesting result

$$
s_{xy} - S_{xy} = \tau, \qquad s_{xx} - S_{xx} = \tau^2 + 2\tau S_{xy},
\tag{8.4}
$$

where the capital letters denote initial stresses. For an initially unstressed specimen, *the classical law of proportionality between shear stress and shear strain continues to hold precisely with* τ *as the measure of shear, but in addition a normal tension equal to the square of the shear stress must be supplied on the* x = const. *planes*. For an initially rectangular block with faces parallel to the co-ordinate planes, the stresses which must act upon the faces inclined at angle $\frac{1}{2}\pi - \theta$ to the shearing planes are:

$$
\begin{aligned}
n &\equiv \text{Normal tension} = \frac{s_{xx} - 2\tau s_{xy} + \tau^2 s_{yy}}{1 + \tau^2}, \\
&= -\frac{\tau^2}{1+\tau^2} = -\sin^2\theta; \\
s &\equiv \text{Shearing stress} = \frac{(s_{xx} - s_{yy})\tau + s_{xy}(1 - \tau^2)}{1 + \tau^2}, \\
&= \frac{\tau}{1+\tau^2} = \tfrac{1}{2}\sin 2\theta.
\end{aligned} \tag{8.5}
$$

Thus as the shearing proceeds the shear stress on these slanted faces builds up to the value $\frac{1}{2}$ when $\theta = \frac{1}{4}\pi$ but falls off thereafter to 0, while the normal stress is a pressure which increases steadily to 1. A similar phenomenon in the finite strain theory of elasticity is called "the Poynting effect."

For a body of grade one the general solution of (8.3) is

$$
\begin{aligned}
s_{xy} &= \frac{A}{\sqrt{|\alpha_s|}} \begin{matrix}\sinh \\ \sin\end{matrix} \sqrt{|\alpha_s|}\,\tau + S_{xy} \begin{matrix}\cosh \\ \cos\end{matrix} \sqrt{|\alpha_s|}\,\tau, \\
\tfrac{1}{2}\alpha_s &\equiv \alpha_1 + \alpha_3 + \alpha_4 + 3\alpha_1\alpha_3 + \alpha_1\alpha_4 + \alpha_3\alpha_4 + \tfrac{1}{2}\alpha_4^2, \\
A &\equiv 1 + (\alpha_1 + \tfrac{1}{2}\alpha_4)S_{xx} + (1 + \alpha_1 + \tfrac{1}{2}\alpha_4)S_{yy} + \alpha_1 S_{zz}, \\
\frac{s_{zz} - S_{zz}}{2\alpha_3} &= \frac{s_{yy} - S_{yy}}{2\alpha_3 + \alpha_4} = \frac{s_{xx} - S_{xx}}{2 + 2\alpha_3 + \alpha_4} = \frac{s_{xx} - s_{yy} - (S_{xx} - S_{yy})}{2}, \\
&= \int_0^\tau s_{xy}(\xi)\,d\xi = \frac{2A}{|\alpha_s|} \begin{matrix}\sinh^2 \\ \sin^2\end{matrix} \tfrac{1}{2}\sqrt{|\alpha_s|}\,\tau + \frac{S_{xy}}{\sqrt{|\alpha_s|}} \begin{matrix}\sinh \\ \sin\end{matrix} \sqrt{|\alpha_s|}\,\tau,
\end{aligned} \tag{8.6}
$$

where the upper alternatives refer to the case $\alpha_s > 0$, the lower to $\alpha_s < 0$; if $\alpha_s = 0$ these same formulae still hold provided we replace $(8.6)_1$ and $(8.6)_8$ by

$$
\begin{aligned}
s_{xy} - S_{xy} &= A\tau, \\
\int_0^\tau s_{xy}(\xi)\,d\xi &= \tfrac{1}{2}A\tau^2 + S_{xy}\,\tau,
\end{aligned} \tag{8.7}
$$

respectively.

Henceforth we consider only the case of an initially unstressed block. Then $A = 1$, and we have

$$(8.8) \qquad s_{xy} = \begin{cases} \dfrac{1}{\sqrt{|\alpha_s|}} \begin{matrix}\sinh \\ \sin\end{matrix} \sqrt{|\alpha_s|}\,\tau, & \alpha_s \neq 0, \\ \tau \quad , & \alpha_s = 0, \end{cases}$$

for the shear stress on the shear planes. Thus if $\alpha_s > 0$ the body stiffens indefinitely in shear, the shear stress being ultimately exponential. If, on the contrary, $\alpha_s < 0$, the body softens until the shear stress increases to its maximum value $1/\sqrt{|\alpha_s|}$. While according to (8.6) the shear stress will decrease for greater angles of shear, we take this fact as indication that the body will collapse or yield at or before this strain. Thus we may call α_s the *shear stiffness* of the body of grade one and refer to the body itself as *soft, neutral*, or *hard* in shear according as $\alpha_s \lesseqgtr 0$. For a soft body we may call the maximum shear stress, *viz.* $1/\sqrt{|\alpha_s|}$, its *shear strength* s_s, and the corresponding angle

$$(8.9) \qquad \theta_s = \text{Arctan}\,\frac{\pi}{2\sqrt{|\alpha_s|}}$$

its *ultimate shear angle*. Henceforth without further mention we limit all discussion of soft bodies to the case when the ultimate shear angle is not exceeded.

Figure 8.1 shows the hyperboloid $\alpha_s = 0$ in the space whose co-ordinates are $\alpha_1, \alpha_3, \alpha_3 + \frac{1}{2}\alpha_4$. Points inside the hyperboloid represent soft bodies; outside, hard bodies.

Next we consider the normal forces acting upon the shear planes and upon the planes $y =$ const., these latter being of all the planes normal to the shear planes the only ones which are preserved in the deformation. The normal forces s_{yy} and s_{zz} are furnished by $(8.6)_4$ and $(8.6)_5$. From the fact that the last expression in (8.6) is positive for $\tau \neq 0$ (recall that $S_{xy} = 0$ and $A = 1$) follow dynamic interpretations for the coefficients α_3 and $\alpha_3 + \frac{1}{2}\alpha_4$.

First, the sign of s_{zz} is the same as the sign of α_3. If we fail to supply the necessary tension s_{zz} to a specimen in shear, we may expect that it will draw together or spread out in a direction perpendicular to the shear planes according as $\alpha_3 > 0$ or $\alpha_3 < 0$. Thus we may call α_3 the *shear elusiveness*. For a given body, s_{zz} has the same sign for all values of the shear angle θ and is a monotone function of $|\theta|$.

Second, the sign of s_{yy} is the same as the sign of $\alpha_3 + \frac{1}{2}\alpha_4$. If we fail to supply the necessary tension s_{yy} to the planes being sheared, we may expect that these planes will draw together or spread apart from one another according as $\alpha_3 + \frac{1}{2}\alpha_4 > 0$ or $\alpha_3 + \frac{1}{2}\alpha_4 < 0$. Thus we may call $\alpha_3 + \frac{1}{2}\alpha_4$ the *shear tenseness*. For a given body, s_{yy} has the same sign for all values of the shear angle θ and is a monotone function of $|\theta|$.

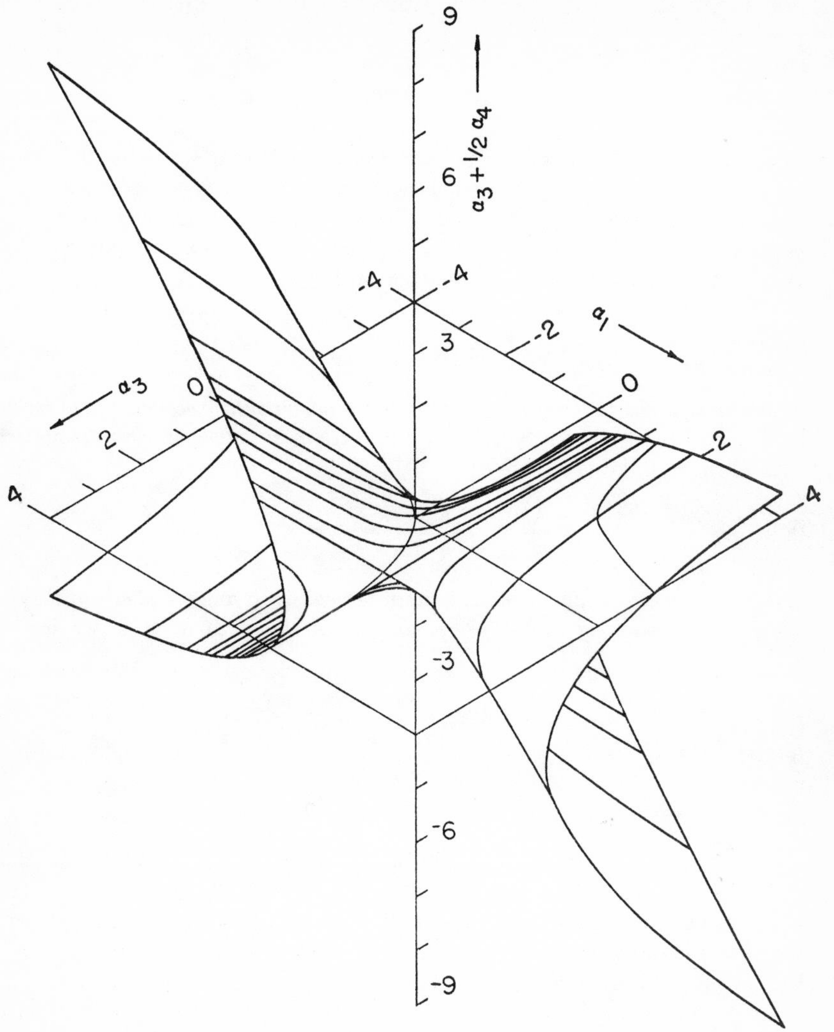

FIGURE 8.1

The hyperboloid $\alpha_s = 0$. Points inside the hyperboloid represent soft bodies; outside, hard bodies.

From (8.6) we have as $\tau \to 0$

$$(8.10)\qquad \frac{s_{zz}}{\alpha_3} = \frac{s_{yy}}{\alpha_3 + \frac{1}{2}\alpha_4} = \tau^2 + O(\tau^4), \\ = s_{xy}^2 + O(\tau^4):$$

For small shears, *the normal forces are proportional to the square*[1] *of the shearing stress and their magnitudes are independent of* α_s, *being determined entirely by* α_3 *and* $\alpha_3 + \frac{1}{2}\alpha_4$, *respectively*. For large shears we must distinguish between hard, neutral, and soft bodies. If $\alpha_s < 0$, $|s_{zz}|$ and $|s_{yy}|$ increase steadily to finite upper limits, obtained at the ultimate shear angle, when

$$(8.11)\qquad \frac{s_{zz}}{\alpha_3} = \frac{s_{yy}}{\alpha_3 + \frac{1}{2}\alpha_4} = \frac{2}{|\alpha_s|} = 2s_s^2:$$

for a soft body, the ratios of normal force to the square of the shearing stress increase from α_3 *and* $\alpha_3 + \frac{1}{2}\alpha_4$ *for small shears to twice those values at the ultimate shear angle.* If $\alpha_s = 0$, however, we have

$$(8.12)\qquad \frac{s_{zz}}{\alpha_3} = \frac{s_{yy}}{\alpha_3 + \frac{1}{2}\alpha_4} = \tau^2 = s_{xy}^2,$$

so that for a neutral body the ratios between normal forces and the square of the shear stress remain precisely α_3 *and* $\alpha_3 + \frac{1}{2}\alpha_4$, *for all shears.* If $\alpha_s > 0$, we have as $\tau \to \infty$

$$(8.13)\qquad \frac{s_{zz}}{\alpha_3} = \frac{s_{yy}}{\alpha_3 + \frac{1}{2}\alpha_4} \sim \frac{1}{\alpha_s} \exp(\sqrt{\alpha_s}\,\tau), \\ \sim \frac{2}{\sqrt{\alpha_s}} s_{xy}:$$

For hard bodies, the initial proportionality between normal stress and the square of the shear stress, independent of α_s, *is converted gradually with increasing shear into proportionality to the shear stress itself, in the ratio* $2/\sqrt{\alpha_s}$. Thus, in particular, the harder is the body the less normal stress relative to shear stress, other things being equal, will be required for large shears.

We turn now to the normal and tangential forces n and s acting upon the slanted faces of the block. These forces are easily calculated from $(8.5)_2$ and $(8.5)_5$. To begin with, from $(8.5)_2$ and $(8.6)_7$ we observe that *for a given angle of shear, s is a functional of s_{xy}. Hence s, like s_{xy}, is a function of α_s and τ only*: the shear stiffness α_s determines the shearing stress on *all* faces of a sheared block, independently of the shear elusiveness and the shear tenseness, which determine

[1] Recall that the components s_{ij} are dimensionless. To interpret these results in terms of the usual stress t_{ij}, multiply (8.10) by $4\mu^2$, obtaining $2\mu t_{zz}/t_{xy}^2 = \alpha_3 + O(\tau^4)$, *etc.*

the normal forces on the shear planes and on the planes z = const. When $\alpha_s \neq 0$ we get

$$
\begin{aligned}
s &= \frac{\dfrac{4\tau}{|\alpha_s|}\dfrac{\sinh^2}{\sin^2}\tfrac{1}{2}\sqrt{|\alpha_s|}\,\tau + \dfrac{1-\tau^2}{\sqrt{|\alpha_s|}}\dfrac{\sinh}{\sin}\sqrt{|\alpha_s|}\,\tau}{1+\tau}, \\
&= \frac{\dfrac{2\tau}{\alpha_s}\left[\sqrt{1+\alpha_s s_{xy}^2} - 1\right] + (1-\tau^2)s_{xy}}{1+\tau^2}, \qquad (8.14) \\
&= \left[1 - \tau^2 + \frac{2\tau}{\sqrt{|\alpha_s|}}\frac{\tanh}{\tan}\tfrac{1}{2}\sqrt{|\alpha_s|}\,\tau\right]\frac{s_{xy}}{1+\tau^2}, \\
&= \frac{s_{xy}}{1+\tau^2} + O(\tau^4) \text{ as } \tau \to 0;
\end{aligned}
$$

while if $\alpha_s = 0$ we get

$$
s = \frac{1}{2}\sin 2\theta = \frac{s_{xy}}{1+s_{xy}^2}, \qquad (8.15)
$$

just as for a body of grade zero. For small shear, of course, $s \approx s_{xy}$; however, $(8.14)_4$ shows that $|s| < |s_{xy}|$ for small shears, and we may ask if s can decrease to zero and change sign. For neutral bodies, (8.15) shows that in fact s decreases steadily to zero. When $\alpha_s \neq 0$, $(8.14)_3$ gives as necessary and sufficient for $s = 0$ when $\tau \neq 0$ the condition

$$
\frac{2}{\sqrt{|\alpha_s|}}\frac{\tanh}{\tan}\tfrac{1}{2}\sqrt{|\alpha_s|}\,\tau = \tau - \frac{1}{\tau}. \qquad (8.16)
$$

For hard bodies there is exactly one root $\bar{\tau}$, and it lies in the range

$$
1 < \bar{\tau} < \frac{1+\sqrt{1+\alpha_s}}{\sqrt{\alpha_s}}. \qquad (8.17)
$$

From $(8.14)_3$ it is plain that

$$
s \sim -s_{xy} \quad \text{as} \quad \tau \to \infty. \qquad (8.18)
$$

For soft bodies the left-hand side of (8.16) exceeds τ for $\tau > 0$ and hence can never equal the right side. Summarizing and slightly augmenting the foregoing analysis, we conclude that *in all bodies of grade one, the magnitude of the shear stress s on the slanted faces falls away from the magnitude of the shear stress s_{xy} on the shearing planes; for soft bodies, it remains of the same sign as s_{xy}, reaching the value*

$$
s = \frac{\pi(4-\pi) - 4\alpha_s}{\pi^2 - 4\alpha_s} = \frac{1 + \pi(1-\frac{1}{4}\pi)s_s^2}{1+\frac{1}{4}\pi^2 s_s^2} \qquad (8.19)
$$

at the ultimate shear angle; for neutral bodies, the magnitude of s decreases steadily to 0 *as* $\tau \to \infty$; *for hard bodies, the magnitude of s decreases until a certain angle* $\tilde{\theta}$, *always greater than* $\frac{1}{4}\pi$ *and limited to the range* (8.17), *is attained; at this angle, s changes sign, and for very large angles of shear s becomes equal and opposite to* s_{xy}.

In Figure 8.2 appears the curve $s = 0$, showing the value of the angle $\tilde{\theta}$ as a function of α_s.

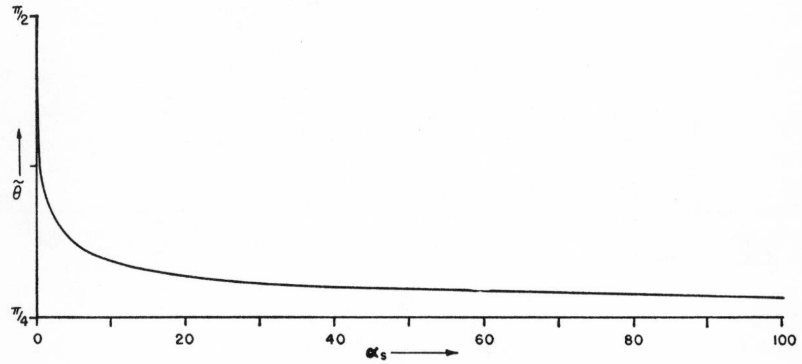

FIGURE 8.2

The angle $\tilde{\theta}$ at which the shear stress s on the slanted faces of a hard body of shear stiffness α_s changes sign.

For the normal force n on the slanted faces we get from $(8.5)_5$ when $\alpha_s \neq 0$

$$n = \frac{-\dfrac{2\tau}{\sqrt{|\alpha_s|}}\begin{smallmatrix}\sinh\\ \sin\end{smallmatrix}\sqrt{|\alpha_s|}\,\tau + \dfrac{4}{|\alpha_s|}[1 + (\alpha_3 + \frac{1}{2}\alpha_4)(1 + \tau^2)]\begin{smallmatrix}\sinh^2\\ \sin^2\end{smallmatrix}\frac{1}{2}\sqrt{|\alpha_s|}\,\tau}{1 + \tau^2},$$

$$(8.20) \qquad = \frac{-2\tau s_{xy} + \dfrac{2}{\alpha_s}[1 + (\alpha_3 + \frac{1}{2}\alpha_4)(1 + \tau^2)][\sqrt{1 + \alpha_s s_{xy}^2} - 1]}{1 + \tau^2},$$

$$= \left\{-\tau + \frac{1}{\sqrt{|\alpha_s|}}\left[1 + (\alpha_3 + \tfrac{1}{2}\alpha_4)(1 + \tau^2)\begin{smallmatrix}\tanh\\ \tan\end{smallmatrix}\tfrac{1}{2}\sqrt{|\alpha_s|}\,\tau\right]\right\}\frac{2s_{xy}}{1 + \tau^2},$$

$$= (\alpha_3 + \tfrac{1}{2}\alpha_4 - 1)\tau^2 + \tfrac{5}{6}\alpha_s(\alpha_3 + \tfrac{1}{2}\alpha_4)\tau^4 + O(\tau^6) \text{ as } \tau \to 0,$$

$$= (\alpha_3 + \tfrac{1}{2}\alpha_4 - 1)s_{xy}^2 + O(\tau^4);$$

while if $\alpha_s = 0$

$$(8.21) \qquad n = -\sin^2\theta + (\alpha_3 + \tfrac{1}{2}\alpha_4)\tan^2\theta.$$

From $(8.20)_4$, (8.21), and $(8.12)_2$ we conclude that as $\tau \to 0$

$$s_{yy} - n = \tau^2 + O(\tau^4) \tag{8.22}$$
$$= s_{xy}^2 + O(\tau^4).$$

This relation, being independent of the values of the α's, must hold for all bodies of grades zero and one. Since it connects three measurable quantities and no empirical constants,[2] it may serve as the basis of an experimental test for the theory. From $(8.20)_4$ and (8.12) follows also *that for small shears in a body such that* $\alpha_3 + \frac{1}{2}\alpha_4 \neq 1$, *n is a pressure or a tension according as*

$$\alpha_3 + \tfrac{1}{2}\alpha_4 \lessgtr 1. \tag{8.23}$$

Thus the magnitude of the shear tenseness, when it is not 1, is the determining factor. *When* $\alpha_3 + \frac{1}{2}\alpha_4 = 1$, *however, at small shears n is a tension in hard or neutral bodies but a pressure in soft bodies.*

To see if n can change sign, we must solve the equation $n = 0$, which by $(8.20)_3$ is equivalent to

$$\frac{1}{\sqrt{|\alpha_s|}} \begin{matrix}\tanh \\ \tan\end{matrix} \tfrac{1}{2}\sqrt{|\alpha_s|}\,\tau = \frac{\tau}{1 + (\alpha_3 + \frac{1}{2}\alpha_4)(1 + \tau^2)} \tag{8.24}$$

in the case $\alpha_s \neq 0$. Analysis of the functions on the two sides of this equation shows easily that for soft bodies there is at most one positive root in the principal branch of the tangent if $|\alpha_3 + \frac{1}{2}\alpha_4| < 1$, no such root if $|\alpha_3 + \frac{1}{2}\alpha_4| \geqq 1$. To see whether such a root exists and, if so, whether it occurs before the ultimate shear angle, it suffices to calculate the value of n at that angle and compare its sign with that given by (8.23). In fact we have

$$n_s = \frac{2}{|\alpha_s|}(\alpha_3 + \tfrac{1}{2}\alpha_4) - \frac{\pi - 2}{|\alpha_s| + \frac{1}{4}\pi^2}; \tag{8.25}$$

this is a non-zero pressure, zero, or a non-zero tension according as

$$\alpha_3 + \frac{1}{2}\alpha_4 \lesseqqgtr \frac{1}{2}\frac{\pi - 2}{1 + \dfrac{\pi^2}{4|\alpha_s|}} < 1. \tag{8.26}$$

By the remark just foregoing and (8.23) we conclude that *for soft bodies, n is always a pressure if*

$$\alpha_3 + \frac{1}{2}\alpha_4 \leqq \frac{1}{2}\frac{\pi - 2}{1 + \dfrac{\pi^2}{4|\alpha_s|}}; \tag{8.27}$$

[2] Except of course the ordinary shear modulus μ, since in terms of the usual stress t_{ij} it reads $2\mu(t_{yy} - t_n) = t_{xy}^2 + O(\tau^4)$.

always a tension if

$$\alpha_3 + \tfrac{1}{2}\alpha_4 \geqq 1; \tag{8.28}$$

while if

$$\frac{1}{2}\frac{\pi - 2}{1 + \dfrac{\pi^2}{4|\alpha_s|}} < \alpha_3 + \frac{1}{2}\alpha_4 < 1, \tag{8.29}$$

n changes from pressure to tension, passing through $n = 0$ at the angle satisfying (8.24); *in all cases,* (8.25) *gives the value of n at the ultimate shear angle.*

For a neutral body (8.21) yields $n = 0$ when

$$\cos^2 \theta = \alpha_3 + \tfrac{1}{2}\alpha_4. \tag{8.30}$$

An angle θ other than 0 or $\tfrac{1}{2}\pi$ satisfying this condition exists if and only if $0 < \alpha_3 + \tfrac{1}{2}\alpha_4 < 1$.

For a hard body we obtain from $(8.20)_3$

$$n \sim \frac{2(\alpha_3 + \frac{1}{2}\alpha_4)}{\sqrt{\alpha_s}} s_{xy} \sim s_{yy} \tag{8.31}$$

as $\tau \to \infty$, provided only $\alpha_3 + \tfrac{1}{2}\alpha_4 \neq 0$. If $\alpha_3 + \tfrac{1}{2}\alpha_4 = 0$, we get instead

$$n\tau \sim -2s_{xy}. \tag{8.32}$$

Thus for very large shears n is a pressure or tension according as $\alpha_3 + \tfrac{1}{2}\alpha_4 \leqq 0$ or $\alpha_3 + \tfrac{1}{2}\alpha_4 > 0$. Moreover, (8.31) and (8.32) show that *for all hard bodies, in very large shear the normal forces on the shear planes and on the slanted faces become equal.*

Analysis of the case $\alpha_s \geqq 0$ is not entirely trivial. If $0 < \alpha_3 + \tfrac{1}{2}\alpha_4 < 1$, the equation (8.24) possesses a single real non-zero root $\hat{\tau} = \tan \hat{\theta}$ such that

$$\operatorname{Arccos} \sqrt{\alpha_3 + \tfrac{1}{2}\alpha_4} \leqq \hat{\theta} < \tfrac{1}{2}\pi, \tag{8.33}$$

and for a fixed value of $\alpha_3 + \tfrac{1}{2}\alpha_4$ this root $\hat{\theta}$ is a monotone increasing function of α_s. By (8.21), the lower bound in (8.33) is achieved in the case of the neutral body, $\alpha_s = 0$. If $\alpha_3 + \tfrac{1}{2}\alpha_4 = 1$, there is a single real non-zero root if $\alpha_s > 6$, no such root if $\alpha_s \leqq 6$. The case $\alpha_3 + \tfrac{1}{2}\alpha_4 > 1$ is more elaborate: There may be two, one, or no non-zero real roots. In fact, let $\hat{\alpha}_s$ be the single positive root of the system

$$\frac{1}{\sqrt{\hat{\alpha}_s}} \tanh \tfrac{1}{2} \sqrt{\hat{\alpha}_s}\, \tau = \frac{\tau}{1 + k(1 + \tau^2)},$$

$$\tau^2 = \frac{\alpha_s - 2k(k+2) - \sqrt{20k^2 + 16k^3 + \alpha_s^2 - 4\alpha_s k(k+2)}}{2k^2}, \tag{8.34}$$

$$k \equiv \alpha_3 + \tfrac{1}{2}\alpha_4 > 1,$$

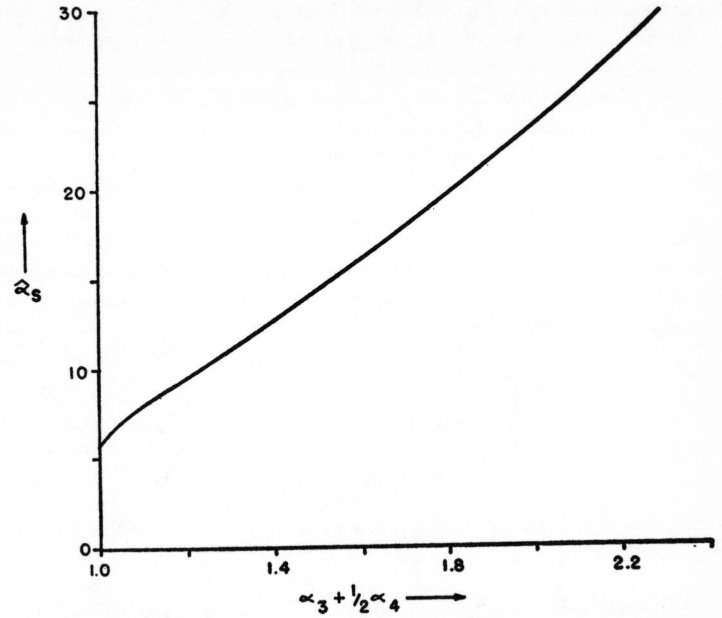

FIGURE 8.3

$\hat{\alpha}_s$, the value of α_s for which the normal tension n on the slanted faces in a body of given shear tenseness experiences a double root.

regarded as an equation for $\hat{\alpha}_s$ as a function of $\alpha_3 + \frac{1}{2}\alpha_4$. Then there are two, one, or no zeros of n according as $\alpha_s \gtreqless \hat{\alpha}_s$. A graph of $\hat{\alpha}_s$, which satisfies the inequalities

$$2k[\sqrt{k^2 - 1} + k + 2] \leqq \hat{\alpha}_s < 4k(1 + k), \tag{8.35}$$

so that $\hat{\alpha}_s \lesssim 4k(1 + k)$ as $k \to \infty$, is shown in Figure 8.3. When $\alpha_s > \hat{\alpha}_s$, at least one of the two roots satisfies

$$\hat{\tau} < \sqrt{\frac{1 + k}{k}}, \tag{8.36}$$

while as $\alpha_s \to \infty$ we have for the two roots $\hat{\tau}_1$ and $\hat{\tau}_2$ the asymptotic forms

$$\begin{aligned} 2\bar{\tau}_1 &\lesssim \sqrt{\alpha_s} - \sqrt{\alpha_s - 4k(k + 1)}, \\ 2\bar{\tau}_2 &\lesssim \sqrt{\alpha_s} + \sqrt{\alpha_s - 4k(k + 1)}; \end{aligned} \tag{8.37}$$

also $\bar{\tau}_1 \searrow 0$, $\bar{\tau}_2 \nearrow \infty$, both being monotone functions of α_s.

Comparison of these results and further ones of a like kind with those in the paragraph preceding and with (8.23) shows that *for hard or neutral bodies, n is always a pressure if* $\alpha_3 + \frac{1}{2}\alpha_4 \leqq 0$; *when* $0 < \alpha_3 + \frac{1}{2}\alpha_4 < 1$, *n changes from pressure to tension at the angle given by the single root* (8.24), *this angle being restricted to the range* (8.33); *when* $\alpha_3 + \frac{1}{2}\alpha_4 = 1$, *n remains always a tension if* $\alpha_s \geqq 6$ *but changes from pressure to tension if* $\alpha_s < 6$; *when* $\alpha_3 + \frac{1}{2}\alpha_4 > 1$, *n remains always a tension if* $\alpha_s < \hat{\alpha}_s$, *where* α_s *is determined by* (8.34) *and saiisfies* (8.35); *if* $\alpha_3 + \frac{1}{2}\alpha_4 > 1$ *and* $\alpha_s = \hat{\alpha}_s$, *n remains a tension except at the single root of* (8.24), *where it vanishes, having previously passed through a maximum and being thereafter to in-*

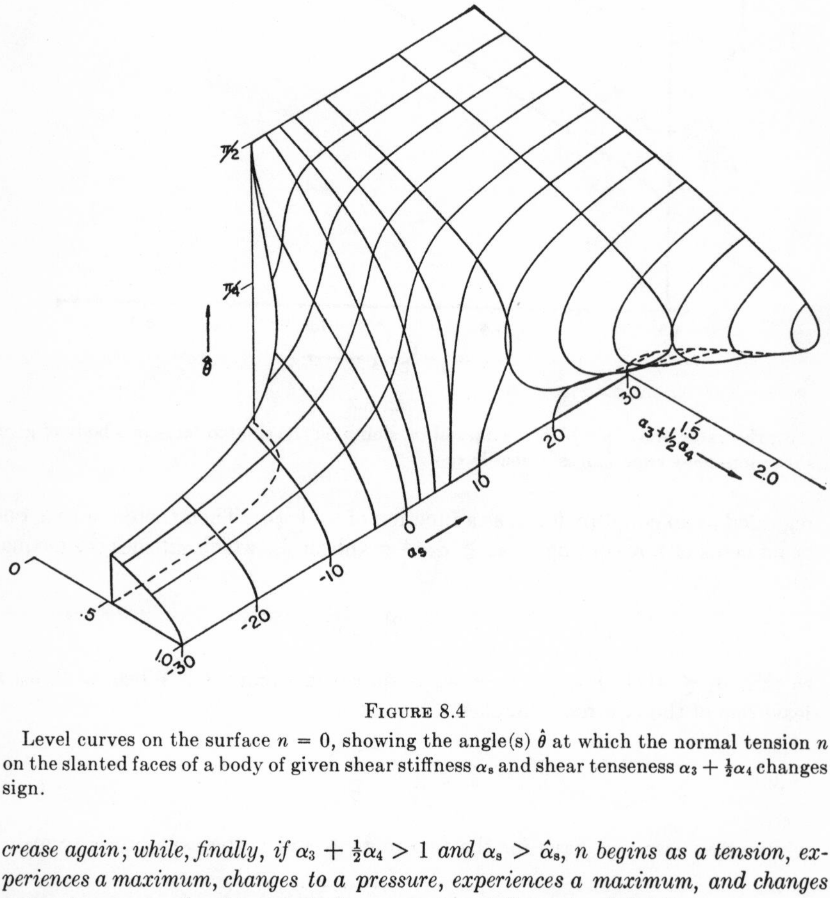

FIGURE 8.4

Level curves on the surface $n = 0$, showing the angle(s) $\hat{\theta}$ at which the normal tension n on the slanted faces of a body of given shear stiffness α_s and shear tenseness $\alpha_3 + \frac{1}{2}\alpha_4$ changes sign.

crease again; while, finally, if $\alpha_3 + \frac{1}{2}\alpha_4 > 1$ *and* $\alpha_s > \hat{\alpha}_s$, *n begins as a tension, experiences a maximum, changes to a pressure, experiences a maximum, and changes to tension again, the changes of sign occurring at the roots of* (8.24).

In Figure 8.4 appears the surface $n = 0$, showing the value(s) of the angle $\hat{\theta}$ as a function of α_s and $\alpha_3 + \frac{1}{2}\alpha_4$.

Our results show that for a body of grade one measurement of s_{zz} and s_{yy} at one angle of shear of any magnitude combined with measurement of s_{xy} at one moderately large angle of shear will serve to determine α_3, $\alpha_3 + \frac{1}{2}\alpha_4$, and α_s, respectively. Hence follows the value of α_1:

$$(8.38) \quad \alpha_1 = \frac{\alpha_s + 2\alpha_3(1 + 3\alpha_3) - 2(1 + \alpha_3)(2\alpha_3 + \alpha_4) - (2\alpha_3 + \alpha_4)^2}{2[1 + \alpha_3 + (2\alpha_3 + \alpha_4)]}.$$

Measurements of these same quantities at other shear angles and measurements of such other quantities as n and s can then test the experimental self-consistency of the theory for simple shear in initially unstressed materials.

On the basis of the foregoing theorems we see that there are 42 different types of response which bodies of grade one may exhibit in shear, determined by the values of the parameters α_1, α_3, α_4. This classification exhausts all compatible combinations of the following possibilities:

1. The body is soft, neutral, or hard. (These may be replaced, if we prefer, by the following mutually exclusive possibilities: s_{xy} has a theoretical maximum, s_{xy} is monotone and s is positive, s_{xy} is monotone and s changes sign.)
2. s_{zz} is positive, identically zero, or negative.
3. s_{yy} is positive, identically zero, or negative.
4. n experiences 0, 1, 2 coincident, or 2 distinct roots.

The stress system in a typical example of each of these 42 types is drawn accurately and to a common scale in Figure 8.5. The abscissa is θ, the angle of shear, allowed to vary from 0 to $\frac{1}{2}\pi$. The ticks on the ordinate scale indicate units.[3] Types 3, 7, 10, 15, 19, 23, 27, 31, 35 differ qualitatively from their immediate predecessors only in that for them n changes sign. In types 37, 39, and 41 n experiences a double root; in types 38, 40, and 42 n experiences two changes of sign.

The first twelve types are soft bodies. For all cases drawn, $\alpha_s = -1$. Thus all twelve have shear stresses s_{xy} and s, the classical objects of measurement, in common, and in all cases $\theta_s = \text{Arctan}\,\frac{1}{2}\pi$, $s_s = 1$. A small part of the theoretical curve for s_{xy} past the ultimate shear angle is shown dashed. A glance at these remarkable curves shows how much nearer to experience they are than might have been expected from the bare formulae (8.6). When the shear angle θ is taken as independent variable, as it is here, the at first thought rather disburbing sinusoidal nature of the shear curve becomes imperceptible. Instead, the shear curve is very nearly a straight line through the entire range $0 \leqq \theta < \theta_s$, while at $\theta = \theta_s$ it suddenly turns down! Thus, as far as shear stress is concerned, the soft bodies exhibit very nearly the classical linear behavior right up to yield in shear. We must add two qualifications: first, the tangent line at $\theta = 0$, which is the prediction of classical elasticity, is not so good an approximation to the hypo-elastic result as would be a line of slightly lesser slope; second, the range of approximate linearity is adjustable through the value of $|\alpha_s|$, in the cases

---

[3] *I.e.*, units of s_{ij}. In ordinary measures, each tick therefore denotes the end of an interval of length 2μ.

Type 1
$(\alpha_1, \alpha_3, \alpha_4) = (-\frac{1}{2}, 0, 0)$

Type 2
$(\alpha_1, \alpha_3, \alpha_4) = (-2, 0, 3)$

Type 3
$(\alpha_1, \alpha_3, \alpha_4) = (-1, 0, 1)$

Type 4
$(\alpha_1, \alpha_3, \alpha_4) = (-\frac{1}{4}, 0, -\frac{1}{2})$

Type 5
$(\alpha_1, \alpha_3, \alpha_4) = (\frac{1}{4}, 1, -2)$

Type 6
$(\alpha_1, \alpha_3, \alpha_4) = (\frac{4}{7}, 3, -3)$

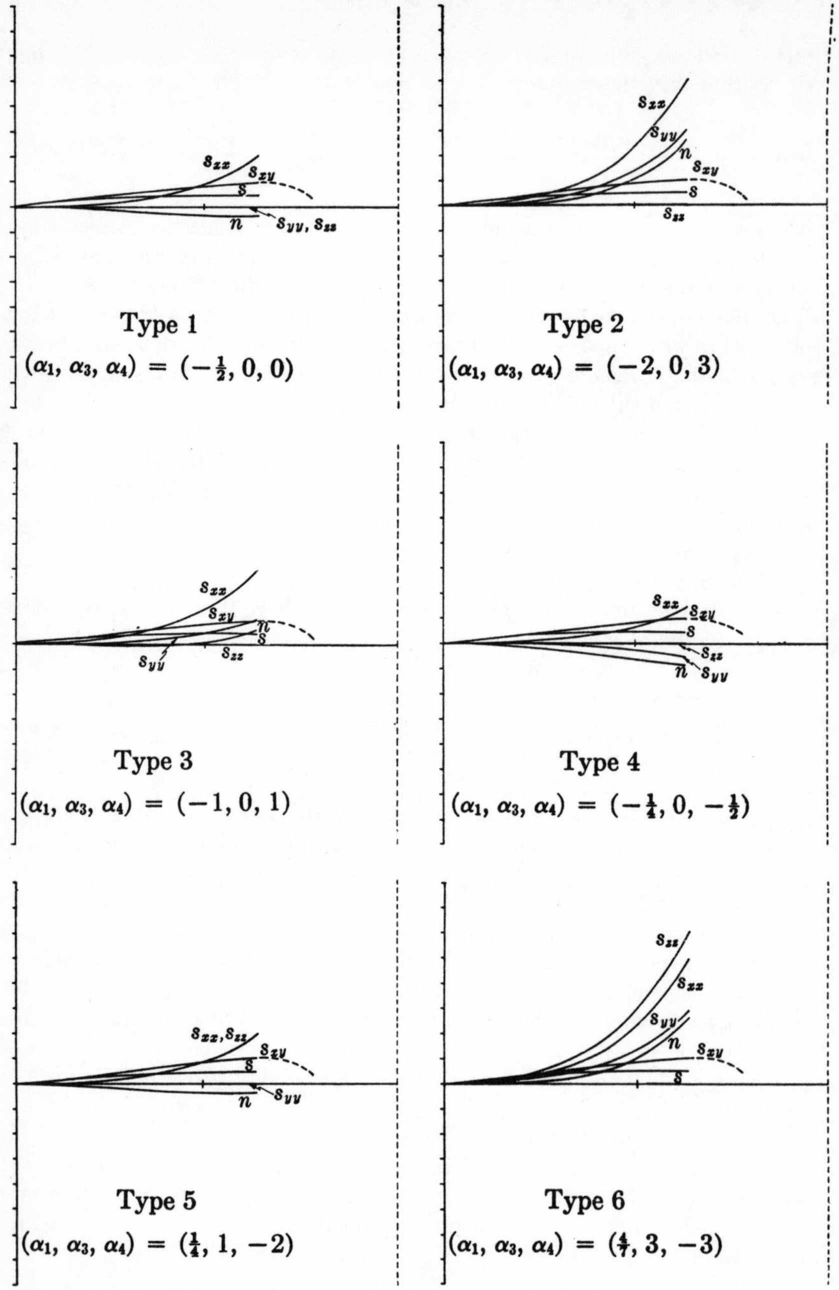

FIGURE 8.5, Types 1–6

The stress systems in typical soft bodies subject to simple shearing. (In all cases, $\alpha_s = -1$, so all the curves for s_{xy} and s are alike.)

Type 7
$(\alpha_1, \alpha_3, \alpha_4) = (0, 1, -1)$

Type 8
$(\alpha_1, \alpha_3, \alpha_4) = (0, \frac{1}{4}, -1)$

Type 9
$(\alpha_1, \alpha_3, \alpha_4) = (-2, -\frac{1}{2}, 1)$

Type 10
$(\alpha_1, \alpha_3, \alpha_4) = (-\frac{20}{7}, -\frac{1}{2}, 4)$

Type 11
$(\alpha_1, \alpha_3, \alpha_4) = (-\frac{6}{5}, -\frac{1}{4}, 1)$

Type 12
$(\alpha_1, \alpha_3, \alpha_4) = (0, -1, 1)$

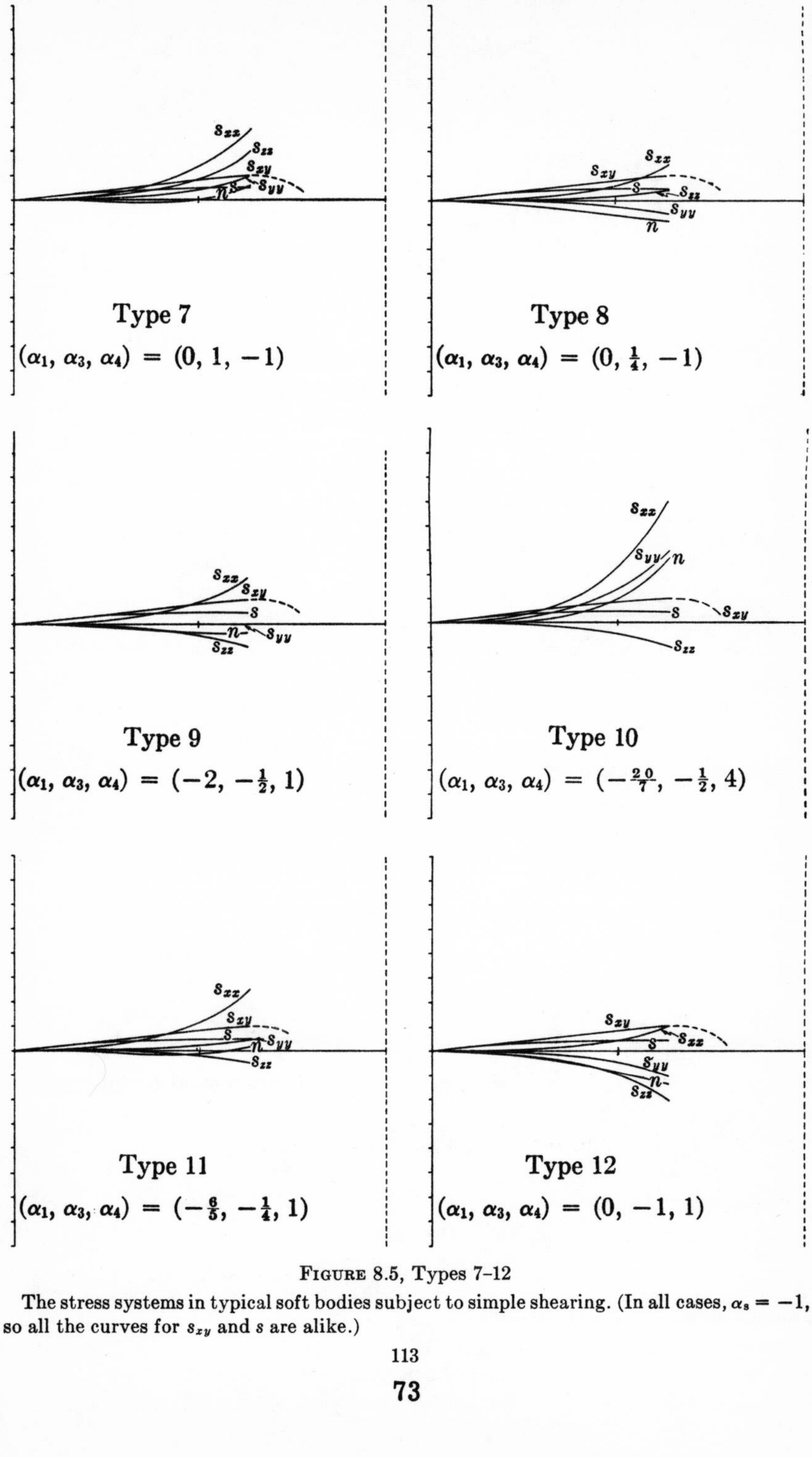

FIGURE 8.5, Types 7–12

The stress systems in typical soft bodies subject to simple shearing. (In all cases, $\alpha_s = -1$, so all the curves for s_{xy} and s are alike.)

Type 13
$(\alpha_1, \alpha_3, \alpha_4) = (0, 0, 0)$

Type 14
$(\alpha_1, \alpha_3, \alpha_4) = (-\frac{15}{8}, 0, 3)$

Type 15
$(\alpha_1, \alpha_3, \alpha_4) = (-\frac{3}{4}, 0, 1)$

Type 16
$(\alpha_1, \alpha_3, \alpha_4) = (\frac{3}{4}, 0, -\frac{1}{2})$

Type 17
$(\alpha_1, \alpha_3, \alpha_4) = (\frac{1}{2}, 1, -2)$

Type 18
$(\alpha_1, \alpha_3, \alpha_4) = (\frac{1}{12}, 2, -1)$

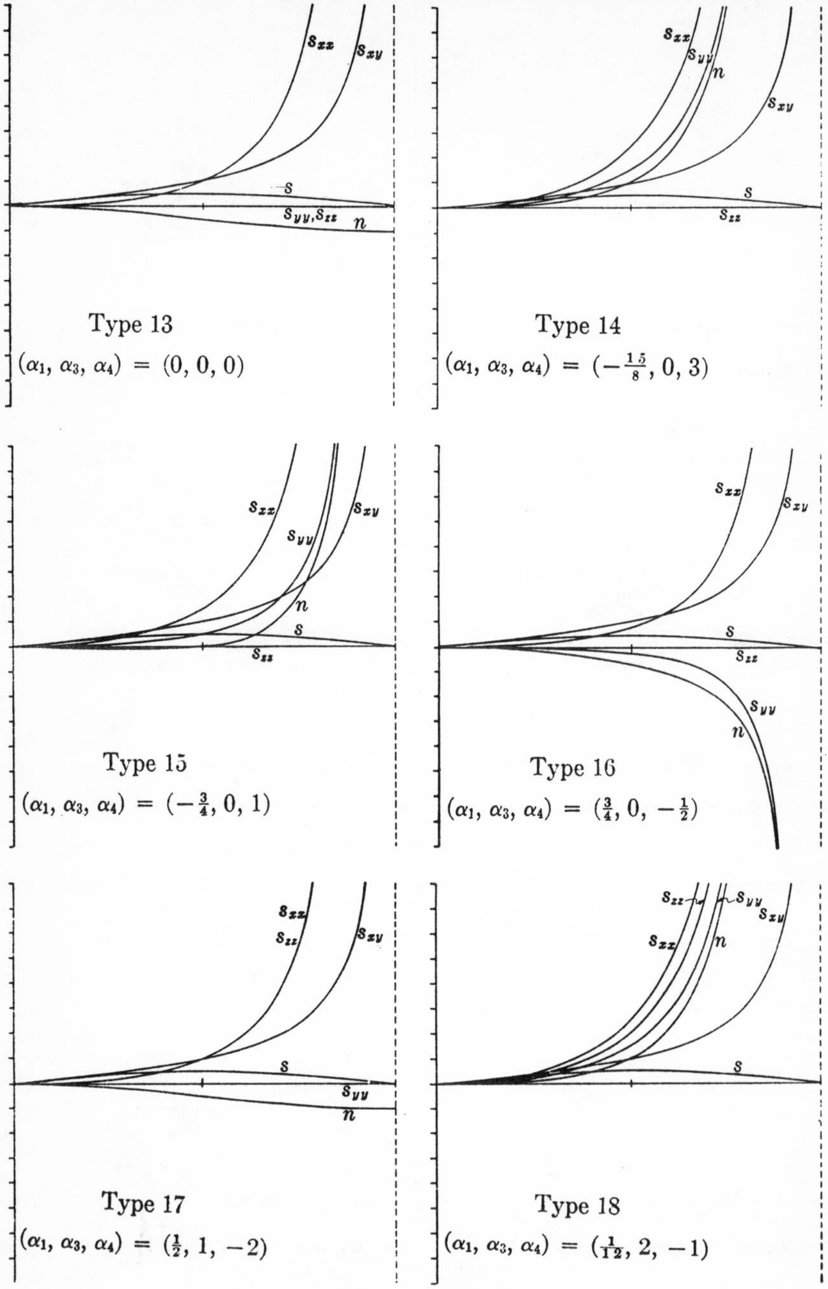

FIGURE 8.5, Types 13–18

The stress systems in typical neutral bodies subject to simple shearing. (Since $\alpha_s = 0$, all the curves for s_{xy} and s are alike.)

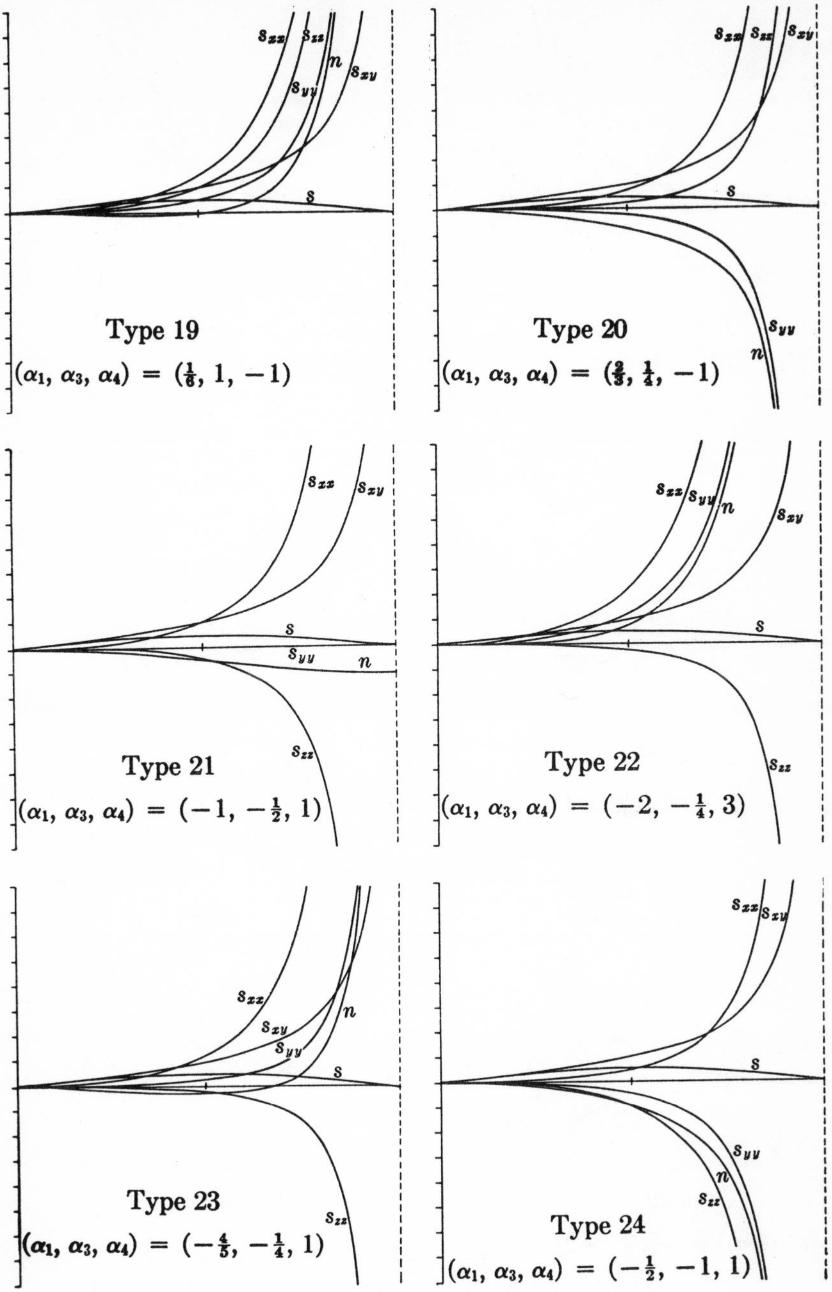

FIGURE 8.5, Types 19–24

The stress systems in typical neutral bodies subject to simple shearing. (Since $\alpha_5 = 0$, all the curves for s_{xy} and s are alike.)

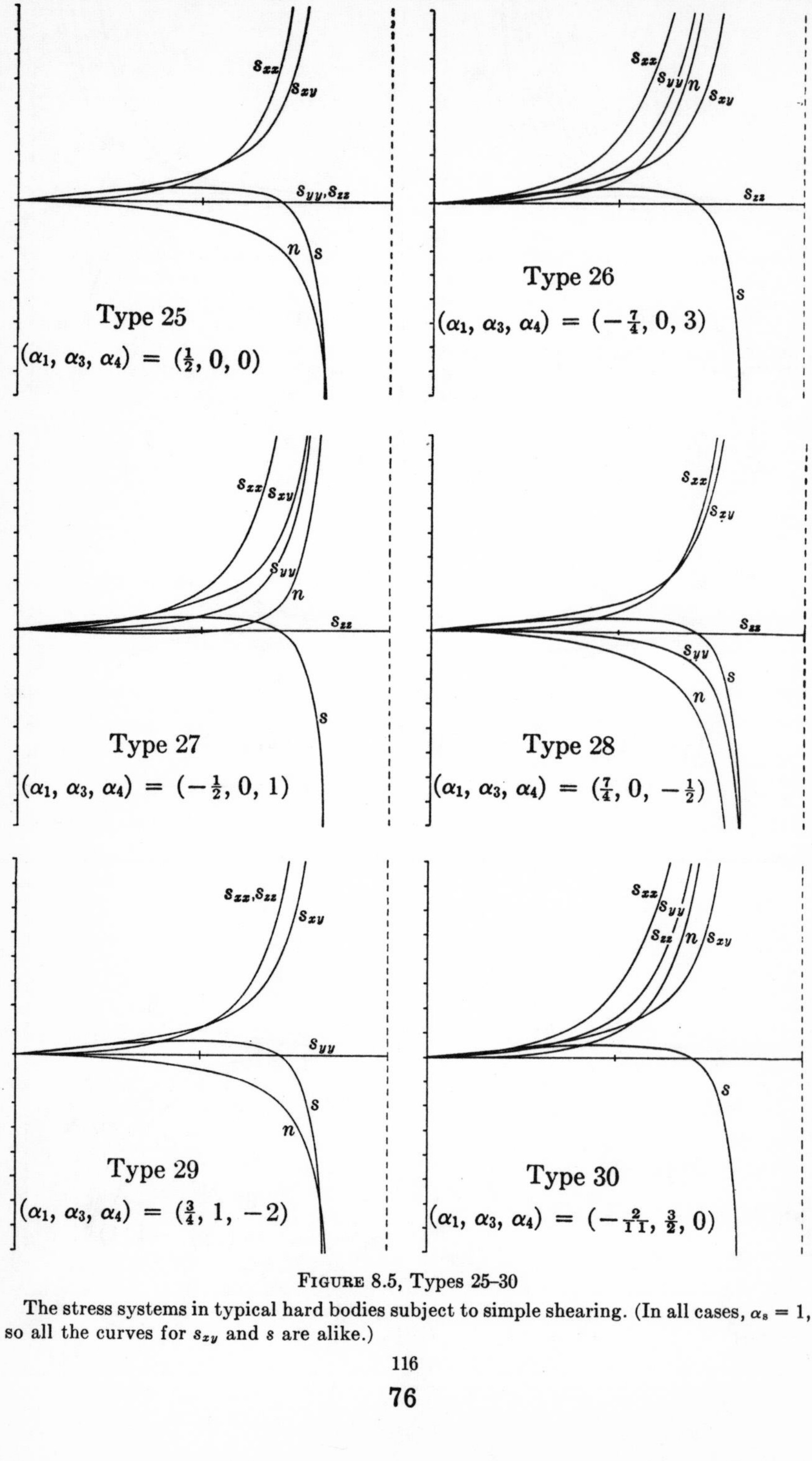

FIGURE 8.5, Types 25–30

The stress systems in typical hard bodies subject to simple shearing. (In all cases, $\alpha_s = 1$, so all the curves for s_{xy} and s are alike.)

Type 31
$(\alpha_1, \alpha_3, \alpha_4) = (\frac{1}{3}, 1, -1)$

Type 32
$(\alpha_1, \alpha_3, \alpha_4) = (\frac{4}{3}, \frac{1}{4}, -1)$

Type 33
$(\alpha_1, \alpha_3, \alpha_4) = (0, -\frac{1}{2}, 1)$

Type 34
$(\alpha_1, \alpha_3, \alpha_4) = (-\frac{32}{15}, -\frac{1}{4}, \frac{7}{2})$

Type 35
$(\alpha_1, \alpha_3, \alpha_4) = (-\frac{2}{5}, -\frac{1}{4}, 1)$

Type 36
$(\alpha_1, \alpha_3, \alpha_4) = (-\frac{4}{3}, -\frac{3}{4}, \frac{1}{2})$

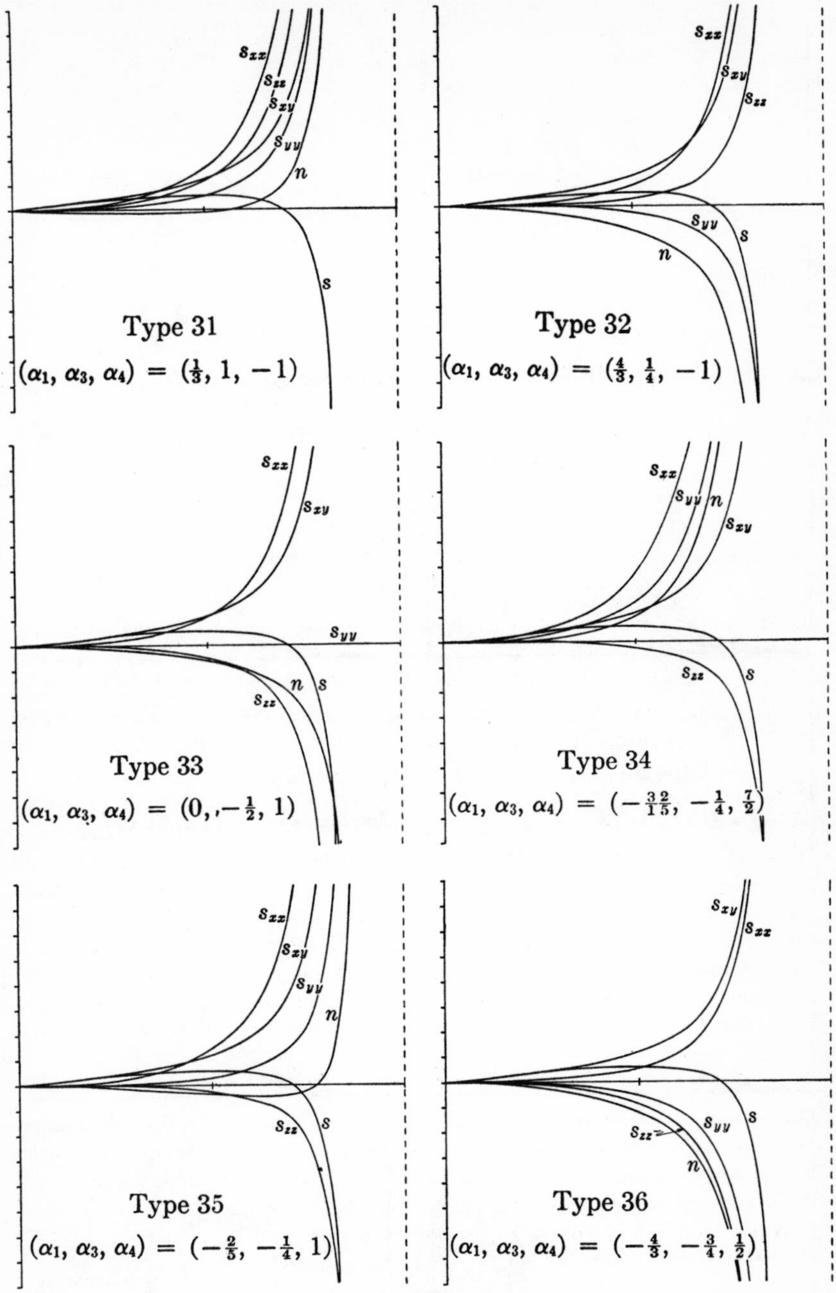

FIGURE 8.5, Types 31–36

The stress systems in typical hard bodies subject to simple shearing. (In all cases, $\alpha_s = 1$, so all the curves for s_{xy} and s are alike.)

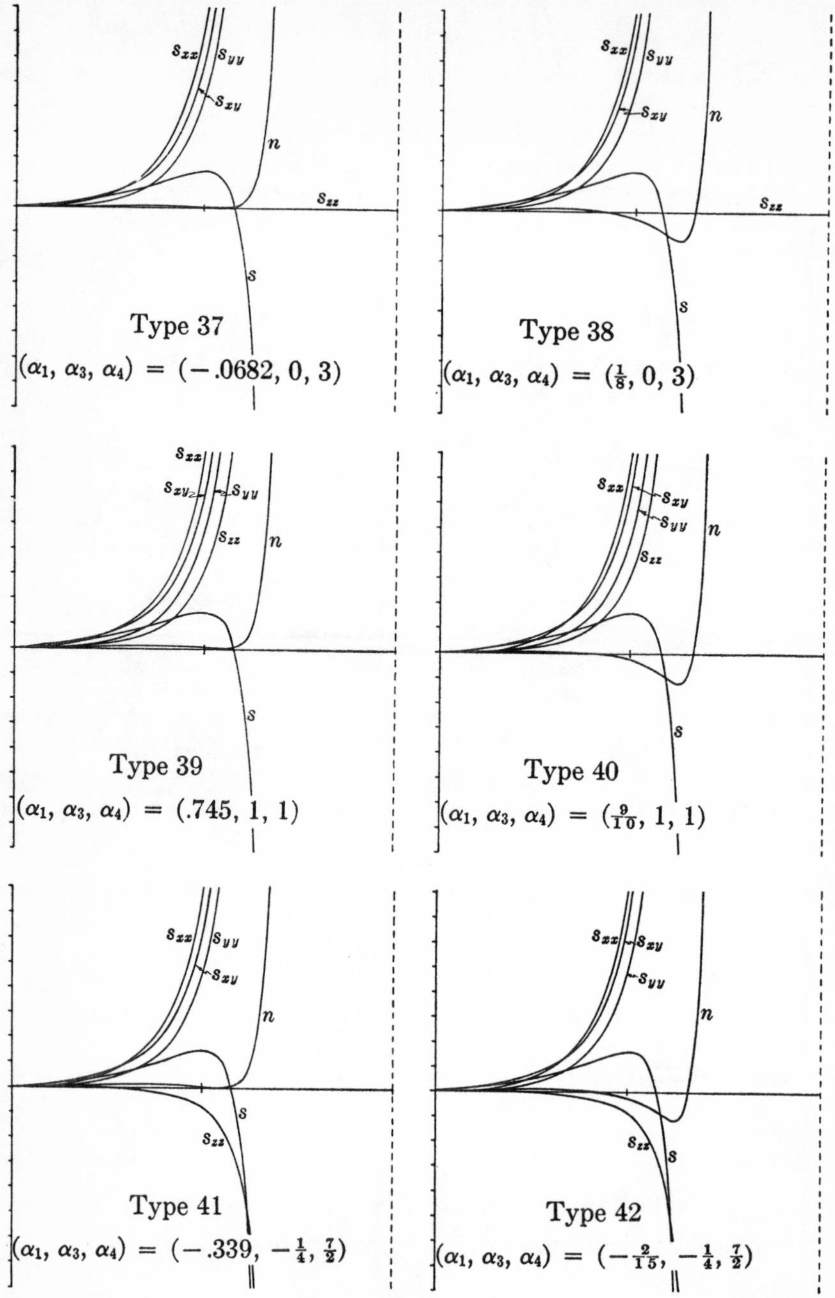

FIGURE 8.5, Types 37–42

The stress systems in typical hard bodies subject to simple shearing. (In these cases n experiences a minimum. In all examples drawn, $\alpha_3 + \frac{1}{2}\alpha_4 = \frac{3}{2}$, so that $\frac{1}{2}\hat{\alpha}_s = 7.227$. For the three cases shown at the left, $\alpha_s = \hat{\alpha}_s$; for the three shown at the right, $\alpha_s = 8$.)

drawn here chosen small enough ($| \alpha_s | = 1$) to make this range strikingly large, greater than 45° of shear.

The twelve different cases of soft bodies show the great variety of non-linear normal stresses which are compatible with a single, virtually classical linear shear stress. An experimenter guided in his expectation by the classical theory might fail to distinguish these different possibilities and might observe only the linearly increasing shear stress and sudden yield.

Types 13–24 are neutral bodies, the body of grade zero being Type 13. The curves of the shear stresses s_{xy} and s, of course, are the same for all neutral bodies but different from one another. The shear s_{xy} on the shear planes is virtually linear for the first 45° of shear, after which the body stiffens markedly. The shear stress s on the slanted faces rather quickly falls away from s_{xy}. The possible behaviors of the normal stresses are again extremely various.

Types 25–36 are hard bodies. As far as these twelve types are concerned, the distinction between neutral and hard bodies when θ instead of τ is used as argument is rather one of quantity than of quality, except in respect to s, which now changes sign and becomes negatively infinite in all cases. The hard bodies stiffen somewhat sooner than the neutral ones. In the cases illustrated, $\alpha_s = 1$, and hence the curves of s_{xy} and s are common to all. For about the first 30° of shear these two curves are virtually identical and virtually linear.

Types 37–42 are those in which the normal tension n on the slanted faces experiences two roots, whether coincident or distinct. In all cases drawn, $\alpha_3 + \frac{1}{2}\alpha_4 = \frac{3}{2}$, so that the curves of s_{xx} and s_{yy} are common to all six. The values of $\frac{1}{2}\alpha_s$ are $\frac{1}{2}\hat{\alpha}_s = 7.227$ for cases 37, 39, 41; 8 for cases 38, 40, and 42. Hence the curves of s_{xy} and s for the former three differ but little from those for the latter. There are two possibilities for n, three for t_{zz}. As was proved above, the physically rather unexpected behavior of n in these six types cannot occur except for very hard bodies in which $\alpha_s > 6$. The rapid stiffening in shear which must accompany so great a value of α_s is hardly more to be expected than the minimum of n, so that it is not likely that these last six types correspond to any physical material.

9. Simple shear of incompressible bodies. To obtain the equations for an incompressible body we may set $\mathfrak{g}_3 = \mathfrak{g}_7 = 0$ and replace $\mathbf{s}$ by $\mathbf{s} - p\mathbf{1}$. To do this in (8.3) for a body of grade one is equivalent to making the same substitution in the solutions (8.6). From $(8.6)_4$ it follows that $s_{zz} - p = S_{zz} - P$; since p is arbitrary, we may take $p = s_{zz}$. For an initially unstressed block, the remaining equations (8.6) then become

$$s_{xy} = \frac{1}{\sqrt{|\alpha_s|}} \frac{\sinh}{\sin} \sqrt{|\alpha_s|}\,\tau,$$

$$\frac{1}{2}\alpha_s \equiv \alpha_1 + \alpha_4 + \alpha_1\alpha_4 + \frac{1}{2}\alpha_4^2, \tag{9.1}$$

$$\frac{s_{yy} - s_{zz}}{\alpha_4} = \frac{s_{xx} - s_{zz}}{2 + \alpha_4} = \frac{s_{xx} - s_{yy}}{2} = \frac{2}{|\alpha_s|} \frac{\sinh^2}{\sin^2} \tfrac{1}{2}\sqrt{|\alpha_s|}\,\tau$$

if $\alpha_8 \neq 0$, while if $\alpha_8 = 0$

$$s_{xy} = \tau, \qquad \frac{s_{yy} - s_{zz}}{\alpha_4} = \cdots = \tfrac{1}{2}\tau^2. \tag{9.2}$$

It is now possible to assign to any one of the normal stresses s_{xx}, s_{yy}, s_{zz}, n an arbitrary value; the rest are then determined. For example, we may take $s_{zz} = 0$.

Results much like those for shear of compressible bodies but simpler in detail may be worked out. We do not pause to obtain them. It is interesting to note that (8.22) remains valid for incompressible bodies, expressing in fact a truly universal property of bodies of grades zero and one.

10. Simple extension of compressible bodies. Elsewhere[1] I have analyzed the special case of the linear velocity field (6.1) in which

$$\mathbf{a} = \mathbf{d} = k \begin{Vmatrix} -\sigma & 0 & 0 \\ 0 & -\sigma & 0 \\ 0 & 0 & 1 \end{Vmatrix}, \qquad \mathbf{b} = 0, \tag{10.1}$$

$$k = k(t) = \frac{k_0}{1 + k_0 t}, \qquad \sigma = \sigma(t) = \sigma_0 \frac{1 + k_0 t}{1 - k_0 \sigma_0 t}.$$

Like the motions treated in §§7–9, this one also is devoid of acceleration, so that its theory in hypo-elasticity falls within the case of §6. For the stress field the form

$$\mathbf{s} = \begin{Vmatrix} -Q & 0 & 0 \\ 0 & -Q & 0 \\ 0 & 0 & T \end{Vmatrix} \tag{10.2}$$

will be general enough for our purpose, since in order to produce the motion (10.1) a stress system initially satisfying (10.2) must continue ever to do so. Then

$$\begin{aligned} I &= T - 2Q, \qquad II = Q(Q - 2T), \qquad III = Q^2 T, \\ M &= k(T + 2\sigma Q), \qquad N = k(T^2 - 2\sigma Q^2), \end{aligned} \tag{10.3}$$

and the constitutive equations (2.3) reduce to

[1] In the note cited in footnote 1 of §1.

$$\frac{1}{k}\frac{dT}{dt} = (1 + 2\sigma)T + (1 - 2\sigma)(g_0 + g_2 T + g_5 T^2)$$
$$+ g_1 + g_4 T + g_8 T^2 + (T + 2\sigma Q)(g_3 + g_6 T + g_9 T^2)$$
$$+ (T^2 - 2\sigma Q^2)(g_7 + g_{10} T + g_{11} T^2) \equiv f(T, \sigma, Q),$$

(10.4)

$$\frac{1}{k}\frac{dQ}{dt} = -Q - (1 - 2\sigma)(g_0 - g_2 Q + g_5 Q^2)$$
$$+ \sigma(g_1 - g_4 Q + g_8 Q^2) - (T + 2\sigma Q)(g_3 - g_6 Q + g_9 Q^2)$$
$$- (T^2 - 2\sigma Q^2)(g_7 - g_{10} Q + g_{11} Q^2).$$

Now in order for a solution of this system to satisfy the dynamical equations also it is necessary and sufficient that $k(t)$ and $\sigma(t)$ be given by $(10.1)_5$ and $(10.1)_7$. If we choose to overlook this fact (*i.e.* to neglect the effect of the inertia of the material), we may leave k and σ arbitrary and put $Q = 0$ for all t. Then $II = III = 0$, so that the g_Γ become functions of T only, and $(10.4)_2$ yields

$$\sigma = \frac{g_0 + g_3 T + g_7 T^2}{2g_0 + g_1} \equiv \hat{\sigma}(T), \tag{10.5}$$

while, since $k = \overline{\log z}^{\bullet}$, from $(10.4)_1$ follows

$$\log \frac{z}{Z} = \int_{T_0}^{T} \frac{d\xi}{f(\xi, \hat{\sigma}(\xi), 0)}, \tag{10.6}$$

where $\hat{\sigma}(T)$ is defined by (10.5) and $f(T, \sigma, Q)$ is defined by $(10.4)_1$. According to this quasi-static treatment, then, the extension is a definite function of the tensile stress T, which in turn, however it may be applied in time, determines the lateral contraction ratio through the relation (10.5): $\sigma(t) = \hat{\sigma}(T(t))$. For example, for a body of grade zero or one (10.5) yields

$$\hat{\sigma}(T) = \frac{\nu + (1 - 2\nu)(\alpha_0 + \alpha_3)T}{1 + (1 - 2\nu)(2\alpha_0 + \alpha_1)T} \tag{10.7}$$

where ν is the usual Poisson modulus. For a body of grade zero this result reduces to the classical $\hat{\sigma}(T) = \nu$. For a body of grade one (10.7) implies that the contraction ratio σ for very large tensile or compressive stress has the value $(\alpha_0 + \alpha_3)/(2\alpha_0 + \alpha_1)$, independently of its value ν for small stresses.

Attractive as are the foregoing products of the quasi-static approach, they cannot be correct.[2] For in order that the motion assumed be dynamically possible it is not only sufficient but also necessary that $(10.1)_5$ and $(10.1)_7$ hold; then (10.5) assumes the form $\hat{\sigma}(T) = \sigma(t)$, yielding a determinate tension $T = T_1(t)$.

[2] The error in this class of results was first noted by ERICKSEN, *Math. rev.* **15**, 178 (1954).

But (10.6) also yields a determinate tension $T = T_2(t)$, and there is no reason to expect that these two determinations will agree. In fact, we may write (10.6) and the time derivative of (10.5) in the respective forms,

$$\begin{aligned} \frac{dT}{d\tau} &= \frac{1}{1+\tau}\left[\frac{1+2\sigma_0+\sigma_0\tau}{1-\sigma_0\tau}T + \frac{1-2\sigma_0-3\sigma_0\tau}{1-\sigma_0\tau}A(T)+B(T)\right], \\ \frac{dT}{d\tau} &= \frac{\sigma_0(1+\sigma_0)C(T)}{(1-\sigma_0\tau)^2 D(T)}, \end{aligned}$$

$$\tag{10.8} \begin{aligned} \tau &\equiv k_0 t, \qquad A(T) \equiv g_0 + g_2 T + g_5 T^2, \\ B(T) &\equiv g_1 + (g_3+g_4)T + (g_6+g_7+g_8)T^2 + (g_9+g_{10})T^3 + g_{11}T^4, \\ C(T) &\equiv (2g_0+g_1)^2, \\ D(T) &\equiv (2g_0+g_1)(g_3+g_3'T+2g_7T+g_7'T^2) \\ &\quad - (2g_0'+g_1')(g_3T+g_7T^2) + g_1g_0' - g_0g_1', \end{aligned}$$

where a prime indicates differentiation with respect to T. In order that these two formulae for $dT/d\tau$ be alike it is necessary and sufficient that

$$\tag{10.9} \begin{aligned} D\{(1+2\sigma_0)T + (1-2\sigma_0)A + B\} &= C\sigma_0(1+\sigma_0), \\ \sigma_0 D\{T - 3A - B - (1+2\sigma_0)T - (1-2\sigma_0)A - B\} &= C\sigma_0(1+\sigma_0), \\ \sigma_0 D\{T - 3A - B\} &= 0. \end{aligned}$$

The solution $D \equiv 0$, $C \equiv 0$ is excluded by the requirement (4.1) for consistency with the classical linear theory in first approximation. Hence $(10.9)_3$ yields $T = 3A + B$. Then $(10.9)_2$ and $(10.9)_1$ become inconsistent unless $\sigma_0 = -1$, the hydrostatic case, treated in §7. Thus we have shown that *in the isotropic hypo-elastic body biaxial extension can never be produced by uniaxial stress.*

This fact does not contradict the consistency of the hypo-elastic theory with classical elasticity theory when the stress is small. Indeed, if at $t = 0$ we put $Q = 0$, $T = 0$ in $(10.4)_2$ we get

$$\tag{10.10} \sigma_0 = \frac{1}{2 + \dfrac{g_1(0,0,0)}{g_0(0,0,0)}} = \frac{1}{2+\dfrac{2\mu}{\lambda}} = \nu$$

as necessary and sufficient that $dQ/dt = 0$ when $t = 0$. For arbitrary σ_0 the hypo-elastic theory yields solutions, and in general both Q and T will rise at about the same rates; if we choose $\sigma_0 = \nu$, however, Q rises much more slowly at first. That a cross-stress Q is necessary to produce simple extention, the exact solutions in other parts of non-linear continuum mechanics might well have led us to expect. If this cross-stress is wanting, we may expect that the body when pulled or pressed will tend to bulge or thin, as is the case in experience but not in the classical linear theory of elasticity.

The quasi-static solutions according to a somewhat less general theory have been discussed in my earlier work.[3] In a preliminary note[4] I have obtained the rigorous solution for bodies of grade zero, and I have shown how the quasi-static solution in this case becomes completely wrong as soon as the strain is large enough to require abandoning the classical linear theory. In the remainder of this section I shall therefore limit attention to the rigorous solutions.

The dimensionless variable $\tau \equiv k_0 t$ may be taken as a measure of the *extension*, since in fact $\tau = (z/Z) - 1$, where Z is the initial co-ordinate of the particle which at time t occupies the place z. In a motion of stretching with contraction ($k_0 > 0$, $\sigma_0 > 0$) the maximum extension is $\tau = \tau_m = 1/\sigma_0$, corresponding to volume zero. We consider here only the case $\sigma_0 = \nu$. Recall that the singularities of linear motions are determined by their initial velocity gradients (§6). In the present example, we must therefore expect yield or collapse at or before the extensional strain $1/\nu$, where ν is the ordinary Poisson modulus of the linear theory of elasticity. That this is so follows from the degeneracy of the motion itself at $\tau = 1/\nu$.

This *limit of extension*, at which (change in length)/(initial length) $= 1/\nu$, should not be confused with tensile strength. It is appropriate only to the special class of extensile motions considered; in order to produce these special accelerationless motions, increasingly large stresses must be applied. If in a test we try to produce such a motion, we must expect failure before, perhaps long before, the strain reaches this very large value $1/\nu$. In this respect the limit of extension is like the ultimate hydrostatic tension or pressure (§7), but different from the shear strength (§8). It is not a limitation of the theory I am proposing, but rather the result of my inability to solve its equations in a more realistic case, that only accelerationless motions are included in the present study of extension. Nevertheless this study retains its value in that the solutions given are *exact*, so that it is at least reasonable to try to test them by experiment.

If we put $\sigma_0 = \nu$ and $\omega = \log(1 + \tau)$, the system (10.4) assumes the form:

(10.11)
$$\frac{dT}{d\omega} = (\sigma A_{IJ} + B_{IJ})T^I Q^J,$$
$$\frac{dQ}{d\omega} = (\sigma C_{IJ} + D_{IJ})T^I Q^J,$$
$$\sigma = \frac{\nu}{(1 + \nu)e^{-\omega} - \nu},$$

[3] See §58 of the *Mechanical foundations* as rewritten in the additions.

[4] The second work cited in footnote 1 of §1.

where the dimensionless coefficients A, B, C, D are material constants. For bodies of grades zero, one, and two, these coefficients are expressed in terms of the defining constants (4.4) through

$$
\begin{aligned}
&\tfrac{1}{2}A_{00} = -\frac{\nu}{1-2\nu}, && B_{00} = \frac{1-\nu}{1-2\nu}, \\
&C_{00} = \frac{1}{1-2\nu}, && D_{00} = -\frac{\nu}{1-2\nu}, \\
&\tfrac{1}{2}A_{10} = 1 - \alpha_1 - \alpha_2, && B_{10} = 1 + \alpha_0 + \alpha_1 + \alpha_2 + \alpha_3 + \alpha_4, \\
&C_{10} = 2\alpha_0 + \alpha_1, && D_{10} = -\alpha_0 - \alpha_3, \\
&\tfrac{1}{2}A_{01} = 2\alpha_0 + \alpha_3, && B_{01} = -2\alpha_0 - 2\alpha_1, \\
&C_{01} = -4\alpha_0 - 2\alpha_1 - 2\alpha_2 - 2\alpha_3 - \alpha_4, && D_{01} = -1 + 2\alpha_0 + \alpha_2, \\
&\tfrac{1}{2}A_{20} = -\beta_0 - \beta_2 - \beta_5, && B_{20} = \beta_0 + \beta_1 + \beta_2 + \beta_3 + \beta_4 + \beta_5 + \beta_6 + \beta_7 + \beta_8, \\
&C_{20} = 2\beta_0 + \beta_1, && D_{20} = -\beta_0 - \beta_3 - \beta_7, \\
&\tfrac{1}{2}A_{11} = 4\beta_0 + 2\beta_0' + 2\beta_2 + \beta_3 + \beta_6, && B_{11} = -4\beta_0 - 2\beta_0' - 4\beta_1 - 2\beta_1' - 2\beta_2 - 2\beta_3 - 2\beta_4, \\
&C_{11} = -8\beta_0 - 4\beta_0' - 4\beta_1 - 2\beta_1' - 2\beta_2 - 2\beta_3 - \beta_4, && D_{11} = 4\beta_0 + 2\beta_0' + \beta_2 + 2\beta_3 + \beta_6, \\
&\tfrac{1}{2}A_{02} = -4\beta_0 - \beta_0' - 2\beta_3 - \beta_7, && B_{02} = 4\beta_0 + \beta_0' + 4\beta_1 + \beta_1', \\
&C_{02} = 8\beta_0 + 2\beta_0' + 4\beta_1 + \beta_1' + 4\beta_2 + 4\beta_3 + 2\beta_4 + 2\beta_5 + 2\beta_6 + 2\beta_7 + \beta_8, && D_{02} = -4\beta_0 - \beta_0' - 2\beta_2 - \beta_5.
\end{aligned}
\tag{10.12}
$$

These coefficients are not mere arbitrary constants. The 4 for which the sum of the suffices is 0 are all determined by ν. The 8 whose suffices add up to one are restricted by the 3 conditions

$$
\begin{aligned}
A_{01} - B_{01} - 2C_{10} + 2D_{10} &= 0, \\
\tfrac{1}{2}A_{01} - \tfrac{1}{2}A_{10} + D_{10} - D_{01} &= 0, \\
B_{10} - B_{01} + C_{01} - C_{10} + D_{01} - D_{10} &= 0.
\end{aligned}
\tag{10.13}
$$

The 12 whose suffices add up to 2 are restricted by 1 linear relation. Thus the hypo-elastic theory of extension, while far more general than the elastic theory, does not result in mere arbitrariness but predicts a definite class of stress-strain relations.

For the case of a body of grade one, it can be shown that for each choice of the coefficients A, B, C, D it is possible either to integrate (10.11) by quadratures or to reduce it to a single linear differential equation. This is rather a matter of analysis than mechanics and will not be presented here,[5] where we shall rest content with the general solution for the body of grade zero, which has been given and discussed in my preliminary work on this subject.

11. The kinematics and dynamics of torsion of a circular cylinder. A class of motions representing torsion of a circular cylinder is given in cylindrical co-ordinates r, θ, z by the contravariant velocity field

$$v^r = r\mathfrak{R}(t), \qquad v^\theta = z\mathfrak{A}(t), \qquad v^z = z\mathfrak{Z}(t), \tag{11.1}$$

where $\mathfrak{A} \not\equiv 0$. For the physical components of $\mathbf{d}$ we have

$$\mathbf{d} = \left\| \begin{matrix} \mathfrak{R} & 0 & 0 \\ \cdot & \mathfrak{R} & \frac{1}{2}r\mathfrak{A} \\ \cdot & \cdot & \mathfrak{Z} \end{matrix} \right\|. \tag{11.2}$$

Hence $\delta = 2\mathfrak{R} + \mathfrak{Z}$, so that the motion is isochoric if and only if $2\mathfrak{R} + \mathfrak{Z} = 0$, while more generally

$$\rho = \rho_0\mathfrak{S}(t), \qquad \mathfrak{S}(t) \equiv \exp\left[-\int (2\mathfrak{R} + \mathfrak{Z})\, dt\right]. \tag{11.3}$$

The acceleration is given by

$$\dot{v}^r = r[\dot{\mathfrak{R}} + \mathfrak{R}^2 - z^2\mathfrak{A}^2], \qquad \dot{v}^\theta \equiv z[\dot{\mathfrak{A}} + \mathfrak{A}(2\mathfrak{R} + \mathfrak{Z})], \qquad \dot{v}^z = z[\dot{\mathfrak{Z}} + \mathfrak{Z}^2]. \tag{11.4}$$

The physical components $\widetilde{ij}$ of $\tilde{\mathbf{s}}$ are easily obtained by (5.1):

$$\begin{aligned} \| \widetilde{ij} \| &= \mathsf{D}\, \| \widehat{ij} \| + (2\mathfrak{R} + \mathfrak{Z})\, \| \widehat{ij} \| \\ &\quad - \left\| \begin{matrix} 2\mathfrak{R} & 2\mathfrak{R} & \mathfrak{R} + \mathfrak{Z} \\ \cdot & 2\mathfrak{R} & \mathfrak{R} + \mathfrak{Z} \\ \cdot & \cdot & 2\mathfrak{Z} \end{matrix} \right\| \cdot \widehat{ij} - \left\| \begin{matrix} 0 & r\mathfrak{A}\widehat{rz} & 0 \\ \cdot & 2r\mathfrak{A}\widehat{\theta z} & r\mathfrak{A}\widehat{zz} \\ \cdot & \cdot & 0 \end{matrix} \right\|, \end{aligned} \tag{11.5}$$

where the quantities $\widehat{ij}$ are the physical components of $\mathbf{s}$ and where

$$\mathsf{D} \equiv \partial_t + z\mathfrak{A}\partial_\theta + z\mathfrak{Z}\partial_z + r\mathfrak{R}\partial_r. \tag{11.6}$$

[5] See a forthcoming work, "The solution of linear differential equations by quadratures," by B. BERNSTEIN & C. TRUESDELL.

Later we shall wish to use the general solution of $\mathsf{D}u = 0$ in the case $\partial_\theta = 0$, namely

$$u = f(re^{-\int \mathfrak{R} dt}, ze^{-\int \mathfrak{Z} dt}). \tag{11.7}$$

If we try to fit to the motion (11.1) a stress system in which

$$\partial_\theta \widehat{ij} = 0, \qquad \widehat{rz} = 0, \tag{11.8}$$

the dynamical equations (2.7) in the case when $f^i = 0$ become

$$\begin{aligned} 2\mu[\partial_r \widehat{rr} + (\widehat{rr} - \widehat{\theta\theta})/r] &= \rho_0 \mathfrak{S} r[\dot{\mathfrak{R}} + \mathfrak{R}^2 - z^2\mathfrak{A}^2], \\ 2\mu[\partial_r \widehat{r\theta} + \partial_z \widehat{\theta z} + 2\widehat{r\theta}/r] &= \rho_0 \mathfrak{S} rz[\dot{\mathfrak{A}} + \mathfrak{A}(2\mathfrak{R} + \mathfrak{Z})], \\ 2\mu[\partial_z \widehat{zz}] &= \rho_0 \mathfrak{S} z[\dot{\mathfrak{Z}} + \mathfrak{Z}^2]. \end{aligned} \tag{11.9}$$

Since all the German letters stand for functions of time only, they may be regarded as constants in the integration, which yields the general solution

$$\begin{aligned} \widehat{\theta z} &= -\partial_r(r^2 \textstyle\int \widehat{r\theta}\, dz)/r^2 + \frac{1}{2}\bar{\rho}\, rz^2 \mathfrak{S}[\dot{\mathfrak{A}} + \mathfrak{A}(2\mathfrak{R} + \mathfrak{Z})] + A, \\ \widehat{\theta\theta} &= \partial_r(r\widehat{rr}) + \bar{\rho}\, r^2\, \mathfrak{S}[z^2\, \mathfrak{A}^2 - \dot{\mathfrak{R}} - \mathfrak{R}^2], \\ \widehat{zz} &= \tfrac{1}{2}\bar{\rho}\, z^2\, \mathfrak{S}[\dot{\mathfrak{Z}} + \mathfrak{Z}^2] + B, \ \bar{\rho} \equiv \rho_0/2\mu \end{aligned} \tag{11.10}$$

where $\widehat{r\theta}$ and $\widehat{rr}$ are arbitrary functions of r, x, t and where A and B are arbitrary functions of r, t. The terms containing $\bar{\rho}$ arise from the inertia of the material.

This general solution will be useful in the attempt to treat torsional motions in any field of the mechanics of continua.

12. Remarks on torsion of compressible hypo-elastic bodies of grade one. In order that $\widehat{rz} = 0$ in the motion (11.1) subject to the stress-system (11.6) and the restrictions (4.3), from (2.3) it is plain that we must have

$$\alpha_4\, \mathfrak{A}\widehat{r\theta} = 0. \tag{12.1}$$

Since $\mathfrak{A} \not\equiv 0$, we must have either $\alpha_4 = 0$ or $\widehat{r\theta} = 0$. From (2.3) follows an equation for $\widehat{r\theta}$:

$$\mathsf{D}\widehat{r\theta} = \widehat{r\theta}[(2\alpha_2 + \alpha_4)\mathfrak{R} + (-1 + \alpha_2)\mathfrak{Z}], \tag{12.2}$$

where the operator D is defined by (11.6) with $\partial_\theta = 0$. From (11.7) it is easy to see that the general solution of this equation is

$$\widehat{r\theta} = e^{\int \mathfrak{E} dt} f(ze^{-\int \mathfrak{Z} dt}, re^{-\int \mathfrak{R} dt}), \tag{12.3}$$

where

$$\mathfrak{E}(t) \equiv (2\alpha_2 + \alpha_4)\mathfrak{R} + (-1 + \alpha_2)\mathfrak{Z}. \tag{12.4}$$

Hence if $\mathfrak{R} \not\equiv 0$ the only solutions satisfying the boundary condition $\widehat{r\theta} = 0$ when $r = a$, a being the radius of the cylinder, is $\widehat{r\theta} \equiv 0$. Thus we have shown that $\widehat{r\theta} \equiv 0$, except possibly in the case $\alpha_4 = \mathfrak{R} \equiv 0$. It is possible that there are certain solutions in which $\mathfrak{R} \equiv 0$, $\widehat{r\theta} \not\equiv 0$, but we shall not pursue them here. Henceforth we put $\widehat{r\theta} \equiv 0$.

From (2.3) we see that the remaining constitutive equations are

$$
\begin{aligned}
\mathsf{D}\widehat{\theta z} &= \tfrac{1}{2}r\mathfrak{A}[1 + \alpha_1 \widehat{rr} + (\alpha_1 + \tfrac{1}{2}\alpha_4)\widehat{\theta\theta} + (2 + \alpha_1 + \tfrac{1}{2}\alpha_4)\widehat{zz}] \\
&\quad + \widehat{\theta z}[(-1 + 2\alpha_2 + \tfrac{1}{2}\alpha_4)\mathfrak{R} + (\alpha_2 + \tfrac{1}{2}\alpha_4)\mathfrak{Z}], \\
\mathsf{D}\widehat{rr} &= \frac{\nu}{1 - 2\nu}(2\mathfrak{R} + \mathfrak{Z}) + \mathfrak{R} \\
&\quad + \widehat{rr}[(-1 + \alpha_0 + \alpha_2)\mathfrak{Z} + (2\alpha_0 + \alpha_1 + 2\alpha_2 + \alpha_3 + \alpha_4)\mathfrak{R}] \\
&\quad + \widehat{\theta\theta}[(2\alpha_0 + \alpha_1 + \alpha_3)\mathfrak{R} + \alpha_0 \mathfrak{Z}] \\
&\quad + \widehat{zz}[(2\alpha_0 + \alpha_1)\mathfrak{R} + (\alpha_0 + \alpha_3)\mathfrak{Z}] \\
&\quad + \widehat{\theta z}[\alpha_3\, r\mathfrak{A}], \qquad (12.5) \\
\mathsf{D}\widehat{\theta\theta} &= \frac{\nu}{1 - 2\nu}(2\mathfrak{R} + \mathfrak{Z}) + \mathfrak{R} \\
&\quad + \widehat{\theta\theta}[(2\alpha_0 + \alpha_1 + 2\alpha_2 + \alpha_3 + \alpha_4)\mathfrak{R} + (1 + \alpha_0 + \alpha_2)\mathfrak{Z}] \\
&\quad + \widehat{zz}[(2\alpha_0 + \alpha_1)\mathfrak{R} + (\alpha_0 + \alpha_3)\mathfrak{Z}] \\
&\quad + \widehat{rr}[(2\alpha_0 + \alpha_1 + \alpha_3)\mathfrak{R} + \alpha_0 \mathfrak{Z}] \\
&\quad + \widehat{\theta z}[(2 + \alpha_3)r\mathfrak{A}], \\
\mathsf{D}\widehat{zz} &= \frac{\nu}{1 - 2\nu}(2\mathfrak{R} + \mathfrak{Z}) + \mathfrak{Z} \\
&\quad + \widehat{zz}[(-2 + 2\alpha_0 + 2\alpha_2)\mathfrak{R} + (1 + \alpha_0 + \alpha_1 + \alpha_2 + \alpha_3 + \alpha_4)\mathfrak{Z}] \\
&\quad + \widehat{rr}[(2\alpha_0 + \alpha_3)\mathfrak{R} + (\alpha_0 + \alpha_1)\mathfrak{Z}] \\
&\quad + \widehat{\theta\theta}[(2\alpha_0 + \alpha_3)\mathfrak{R} + (\alpha_0 + \alpha_1)\mathfrak{Z}] \\
&\quad + \widehat{\theta z}[(\alpha_3 + \tfrac{1}{2}\alpha_4)r\mathfrak{A}].
\end{aligned}
$$

I have obtained solutions of these equations but only for special values of the α's; there is no appropriate solution when their values are assigned arbitrarily. Here I reproduce only the proof that for the case of a compressible body of grade zero no such solution exists. For a body of grade zero, the integral of $(12.5)_2$ is

$$
\widehat{rr} = e^{-\int \mathfrak{Z}\,dt}\left[F(ze^{-\int \mathfrak{Z}\,dt}, re^{-\int \mathfrak{R}\,dt}) + \int \mathfrak{C} e^{\int \mathfrak{Z}\,dt}\,dt\right], \qquad (12.6)
$$

where

$$\mathfrak{C}(t) \equiv \frac{\nu}{1-2\nu}(2\mathfrak{R} + \mathfrak{Z}) + \mathfrak{R}. \tag{12.7}$$

The condition $\widehat{rr} = 0$ when $r = a$ cannot be satisfied unless $\mathfrak{R} = \mathfrak{Z} = 0$ and $\widehat{rr} \equiv 0$. From $(11.10)_1$ we get $\widehat{\theta z} = \frac{1}{2}\bar{\rho}\, rz^2\, \dot{\mathfrak{A}} + A$. But $(12.5)_3$ becomes $\partial_t \widehat{\theta\theta} = 2r\mathfrak{A}\,\widehat{\theta z}$, whence by $(11.10)_2$ we get

$$2\bar{\rho}\, r^2 z^2\, \mathfrak{A}\dot{\mathfrak{A}} = 2r\mathfrak{A}[\tfrac{1}{2}\bar{\rho}\, rz^2\, \dot{\mathfrak{A}} + A], \tag{12.8}$$

impossible unless $\dot{\mathfrak{A}} = 0$, $A = 0$, a case quickly seen to imply a state of rest. Thus we cannot find a simple solution of the type proposed for the problem of torsion of a circular cylinder of compressible material.

13. Torsion of an incompressible hypo-elastic body of grade zero. Disappointed but by no means discouraged by the failure in the last section, we turn now to the incompressible case, where the extra freedom resulting from the constraint of incompressibility gives better chances of a lucky guess at an appropriate solution.

The constitutive equations for the shearing stresses are unaltered; hence we take $\widehat{r\theta} \equiv 0$ again, and the basic solution (11.10) reduces to the form

$$\begin{aligned} \widehat{\theta z} &= \tfrac{1}{2}r[\bar{\rho}z^2\, \dot{\mathfrak{A}} + A], \\ \widehat{\theta\theta} &= \partial_r(r\widehat{rr}) + \bar{\rho}r^2[z^2\, \mathfrak{A}^2 - \dot{\mathfrak{R}} - \mathfrak{R}^2], \\ \widehat{zz} &= \bar{\rho}z^2[-\dot{\mathfrak{R}} + 2\mathfrak{R}^2] + B. \end{aligned} \tag{13.1}$$

By (2.5) we get in place of (12.5)

$$\mathsf{D}\widehat{\theta z} = \tfrac{1}{2}r\mathfrak{A}[1 + 2(\widehat{zz} + p)]. \tag{12.5$'_1$}$$

Henceforth consider only the case when $\mathfrak{R} = 0$.

There are still three constitutive equations to solve. By using (2.5) to modify (12.5), we see that in the present case these reduce to

$$\partial_t(\widehat{rr} + p) = 0, \qquad \partial_t(\widehat{zz} + p) = 0, \qquad \partial_t(\widehat{\theta\theta} + p) = 2r\mathfrak{A}\widehat{\theta z}. \tag{13.4}$$

From the first two and $(13.1)_3$ we get

$$\widehat{rr} = \widehat{zz} + f(r, z) = B(r, t) + f(r, z). \tag{13.5}$$

In order to satisfy the condition $\widehat{rr} = 0$ when $r = a$, this result must reduce to

$$\widehat{rr} = \widehat{zz} = B(r, t), \qquad B(a, t) = 0. \tag{13.6}$$

We can now eliminate $\widehat{\theta\theta}$ between $(13.4)_3$ and $(13.1)_2$, making use of (13.6) and $(13.1)_1$. The result is

(13.7) $$\partial_r \partial_t B - r\mathfrak{A}A = -\rho z^2 r\mathfrak{A}\dot{\mathfrak{A}}.$$

Since the left-hand side is independent of z, each side must vanish separately. The vanishing of the right-hand side yields

(13.8) $$\mathfrak{A} = \text{const.}$$

By $(13.4)_2$ and $(12.5)_1'$ follows

$$\partial_t^2 \widehat{\theta z} = 0, \quad \text{or} \quad \tfrac{1}{2}rA(r, t) = A_0(r) + A_1(r)t.$$

For an initially unstressed material this is equivalent to the solution $A = \mathfrak{A}t$ from the classical theory of elasticity. Equating to zero the left-hand side of (13.7) yields $B = \frac{1}{4}(r^2 - a^2)\mathfrak{A}^2 t^2$, where the constants of integration have been chosen so as to render the radial stress initially zero throughout and always zero on the boundary $r = a$. Hence by (13.1) and (13.6) follows

(13.10) $$\begin{aligned} \widehat{\theta z} &= \mathfrak{A}t \\ \widehat{\theta\theta} &= \tfrac{1}{4}(3r^2 - a^2)\mathfrak{A}^2 t^2 + \bar{\rho} r^2 z^2 \mathfrak{A}^2, \\ \widehat{rr} &= \widehat{zz} = B = \tfrac{1}{4}(r^2 - a^2)\mathfrak{A}^2 t^2. \end{aligned}$$

The class of solutions obtained is not general enough to represent the torsion of a cylinder initially without hoop stress, since.

(13.12) $$\widehat{\theta\theta} = \bar{\rho} r^2 z^2 \mathfrak{A}^2 \qquad \text{when } t = 0,\ 0 \leqq r \leqq a.$$

Thus the initial hoop stress is small (in a precise and obvious sense) near the axis and near the plane of no twist. If the inertia of the material is relatively small[1] the initial hoop stress is small throughout the cylinder.Our equation (13.8) results from consideration of the inertia of the material. Had we chosen to neglect inertia, $\mathfrak{A}$ would be an arbitrarily assignable function of t, and (13.7) with right-hand side zero would yield the corresponding B."

Thus in the torsion problem as in the theory of extension, a quasi-static "approximation" in the equations would have permitted a gross over-determination of the solution.

14. Concluding remarks. This paper presents the beginnings of a new theory of the large deformation of materials which are perfectly elastic in small strain. Confined to simple problems in torsion and homogeneous stress, the present

[1] In a well defined sense which is obvious from (13.10) and (13.12). Note that this statement is of a type entirely different from those current regarding inertial effects. We do not, as is usual, drop small inertial terms in a differential equation and then hope that the resulting error is small. Rather, we note *precisely* the effect of inertia on the *solution* to a particular problem.

study is obviously far less than a patient unfolding of the potentials of this new theory. The rapid flow of fundamental research on continuum mechanics coming into print almost daily makes it better to publish what I have done now so that others need not waste their labor on the same ground. The only reason that I do not label this paper "Part I" is that extensive commitments make unlikely the effort which Part II would require until after a lapse of years, in which the face of continuum mechanics may be changed and these simple thoughts quite overridden. Thus, incomplete as are the foregoing notes, I venture now to make certain comments.

While at first sight the results might suggest that the hypo-elastic theory rests upon stress-strain relations, that is not the case. Such relations as (7.6) or (8.4), for example, can result only from definite assumptions regarding the *motion*. If a body of grade zero is compressed or expanded in such a way that the particles suffer non-zero accelerations, the pressure cannot satisfy (7.6); if in shearing a body of grade zero we move the shear planes at non-uniform speed the shear stress cannot satisfy (8.4). A relation between stress and strain is thus the *outcome*, not the assumption, of our theory, and the form of this relation depends on the manner in which the stress is applied in time.

However, the time enters the various results in a dimensionless product $k_0 t$, where k_0 is an *arbitrary* constant of dimension T^{-1}. Indeed, our constitutive equations (1.6) contain no modulus of the dimension of time, and thus such a conclusion must be perfectly general.[1] While in each case the relation between stress and strain will depend on the *manner* in which the motion takes place in time, it cannot depend on the *speed*. In particular, to expect that in a motion which is slow enough it will be permissible to neglect the inertia of the material can hardly lead to anything else than serious error. In the case of shear, for example, the correctness of our results as solutions of the basic equations has nothing to do with the speed at which the motion occurs: at any uniform speed, however large or small, they are solutions, and at any non-uniform speed they are not. As we have seen, neglecting the inertia of the material allows gross over-determination of the problem. Whether the true solution or another more or less in accord with it is chanced upon in the exercise of this illicit license depends only on "physical intuition" or other psychological factors.

At the risk of boring mathematicians and engineers equally but for the opposite reason, I recall that every mathematician knows that it is possible for a small term in a differential equation to have a large effect on the solutions, while engineers or specialists in perturbation processes are inclined to regard the mathematicians' examples as "pathological" and to rely on personal taste to give them confidence that the terms which they choose to neglect are harmless. Inertia is a case in point. There is a school of plasticity which neglects the

---

[1] Since this statement was written, Dr. NOLL has proved a theorem substantiating it. See §14 of his paper cited in §2 above.

inertia of the material, often without even mentioning it, and in dynamic elasticity it is customary to neglect the non-linear part of the inertia. Now in §13 we have seen an example of the danger in such neglect. *However small are the inertial terms in the differential equations there studied, they alone yield the definitive condition to be satisfied.* If they are neglected, an infinite number of solutions becomes possible. The correct one is included, but so also are infinitely many incorrect ones.[2] In the single exact solution, there is a term depending on the inertia. This term in many applications will be small and can justly be neglected. The result of neglecting this term in the *solution* is in general entirely different from the result of neglecting the inertial terms in the *differential equations*.

A remarkable product of our study has been the discovery of phenomena indicative of yield or rupture. I say "discovery," since our theory is put intentionally in terms of analytic differential equations: its postulates are entirely free from statements regarding yield or rupture or any sort of discontinuity, so that such phenomena, if they are to appear at all, must be predicted in the course of solution of particular problems. The results are of two types. In some cases, indefinitely increasing stress is required to produce a certain finite strain; this outcome I regard as indicating that a somewhat lesser stress must rupture the body and thus deprive the theory of its continued validity. In other cases, as a given stress is approached the strain increases indefinitely; this I regard as yield. In still others, increased stress theoretically reduces the strain; this is more difficult to interpret, but certainly the theory cannot continue to describe actual materials past the maximum of the strain. Tentatively I regard this last effect as a prediction that if rupture does not occur at a lower strain, then the material must yield in a sense distinct from that described above: the material suffers a structural change resulting in a different mechanical response and the consequent need for a different theory at greater strains.

It is not the least in importance to recall that our theory really embodies no new ideas of mechanical behavior beyond those of classical linear elasticity. Rather, it simply extends the classical view of elastic response by formulating it in terms of rates. That these ideas in some cases predict yield without assuming a yield condition indicates their strength and potential relevance.

Finally, some of the unexplored possibilities of this theory should be mentioned. First, there is the more liberal field for initial stresses, a field which was noted but not investigated. In particular, it is possible that there are solutions showing stresses which cannot be relaxed without destroying the continuity of the body, thus leading to a continuous model for phenomena usually treated by the theory of dislocations. Second, this paper contains no study of the effect of reversing a deformation and no attempt to fit together one solution for loading and another for unloading. Third, energy relations and the thermodynamics of this theory remain untouched.

---

[2] This situation recalls the problem of stress in the classical theory, where neglect of the conditions of compatibility gave rise to various "approximate" theories about half a century ago.

Reprinted from JOURNAL OF RATIONAL MECHANICS AND ANALYSIS
Vol. 4, No. 6, November, 1955
Printed in U.S.A.

Correction to C. Truesdell's "Hypo-elasticity"

Professor A. E. GREEN and Dr. K. ZOLLER have kindly pointed out errors in the calculation of the examples given in §8 and §13 of "Hypo-elasticity," this *Journal* **4,** 83–133 (1955).

$(8.2)_1$ should read $\tau \equiv 2kt$. In (8.3), in the first matrix on the right replace $-s_{xy}$ by s_{yy}, and multiply each of the g's by $\frac{1}{2}$. The result of this correction is to insert factors of $\frac{1}{2}$ at many places in §8 and §9. Since the main conclusions are unaltered, we list here only the more important of these numerical corrections. Multiply α_1, α_3, and α_4 by $\frac{1}{2}$ in every equation. The numerical constant in A as defined by $(8.6)_1$ is $\frac{1}{2}$, not 1. In addition to the foregoing corrections, the right-hand sides of the following equations should be multiplied by $\frac{1}{2}$: $(8.5)_3$, $(8.5)_4$, $(8.5)_7$, $(8.5)_8$, (8.8), $(8.14)_1$, $(8.15)_1$, $(8.20)_1$, (8.21), $(8.22)_1$. All figures purporting to show an angular scale θ show in fact the scale Arctan ($\frac{1}{2}$ tan θ). In Figure 8.5, the vertical scale should be cut down by $\frac{1}{2}$. The shear strength (p. 102) should be cut down by $\frac{1}{2}$. P. 102, ll. 2 and 13, read $A = \frac{1}{2}$.

The following are the correct forms of certain equations:

$$(8.4)\qquad \begin{aligned} s_{yy} - S_{yy} = 0, \qquad s_{xy} - S_{xy} &= (\tfrac{1}{2} + S_{yy})\tau, \\ s_{xx} - S_{xx} &= (\tfrac{1}{2} + S_{yy})\tau^2 + 2S_{xy}\tau, \end{aligned}$$

$$(8.14)_2\qquad = \frac{\dfrac{\tau}{\alpha_s}\left[\sqrt{1 + 4\alpha_s s_{xy}^2} - 1\right] + (1 - \tau^2)s_{xy}}{1 + \tau^2},$$

$$(8.15)_2\qquad = \frac{s_{xy}}{1 + 4s_{xy}^2},$$

$$(8.20)_4\qquad = [\tfrac{1}{4}(\alpha_3 + \tfrac{1}{2}\alpha_4) - \tfrac{1}{2}]\tau^2 + (\tfrac{1}{2} - \tfrac{1}{8}\alpha_s)\tau^4 + O(\tau^6)$$

$$(8.20)_5\qquad = [\alpha_3 + \tfrac{1}{2}\alpha_4 - 2]s_{xy}^2 + O(\tau^4),$$

$$(8.22)\qquad \begin{aligned} s_{yy} - n &= \tfrac{1}{2}\tau^2 + O(\tau^4), \\ &= 2s_{xy}^2 + O(\tau^4). \end{aligned}$$

The denominator of $(8.14)_1$ is $1 + \tau^2$. The radical in $(8.20)_2$ is $\sqrt{1 + 4\alpha_s s_{xy}^2}$. Verbal changes to conform to these numerical changes are required in some of the statements.

In the present reprint, the further corrections originally published in this note have been incorporated in the text of the article.

No. 7

HYPO-ELASTIC SHEAR

C. Truesdell

Journal of Applied Physics, Volume 27, pp. 441-447 (1956).

The first part of this note reproduces a lecture given to the Society of Rheology. Part II shows by working out a special solution for a very special hypo-elastic material of grade 2 that hypo-elasticity may include a description of continuous transition from "elastic" to "plastic" behavior, according to one possible interpretation of these vague physical terms. There are, of course, other such theories, one of them being mentioned in the footnote indicated by "††". The hypo-elastic theory presented here differs from them not only in being based on properly invariant equations but also in predicting a relation between the "yield strain" and the "yield stress," as those terms are defined here, and for the special problem considered. Figure 2(e) illustrates the case regarded as appropriate.

As to be expected, normal-stress effects must occur, but they are negligibly small if K, the dimensionless yield stress, is small. Indeed, as $K \rightarrow 0$, Eqs. (28) give the following asymptotic forms for the stresses at yield:

$$s_{xy} \sim K/\sqrt{2}\ , \quad s_{yy} \sim -K^2,$$

while from (33) and (34) we have for the shear angle at yield

$$\theta_0 \sim \theta_s \sim 2\sqrt{2}\ K \log \frac{1}{\sqrt{2}\,K}.$$

The existence of a definite yield strain follows as a consequence of an effect usually associated with finite strain, namely, the necessity for using an invariant stress rate rather than simply the time derivative of the stress. An intuitive reason for needing to use an invariant rate even for small strains according to a rate theory lies in the fact that the linearized rotation is proportional to the amount of shear in a small shear. The "incremental" theories of plasticity neglect this fact and related ones. In the present example, the term $\frac{1}{2}(s_{yy} - s_{xx})$ in $(19)_1$ is the difference between an invariant rate and the time derivative. It is the presence of this term that couples the equations and gives rise to the whole phenomenon discussed.

The foregoing remarks are generally misunderstood in circles where plasticity theories are cultivated. There, students of hypo-elasticity are sometimes represented as claiming that yield occurs as a result of large strain, contrary to experimental evidence that "plastic flow" occurs at very small strain. No such claim is made in the paper reprinted here or in any other publication on hypo-elasticity.

Reprinted from JOURNAL OF APPLIED PHYSICS, Vol. 27, No. 5, 441–447, May, 1956

Hypo-Elastic Shear

C. TRUESDELL
Graduate Institute for Mathematics and Mechanics, Indiana University, Bloomington, Indiana
(Received February 1, 1956)

Part I reproduces the lecture given at the meeting of the Society of Rheology and furnishes a nonmathematical introduction to the theory of hypo-elasticity. Hypo-elasticity is a smooth, simple theory of elastic response based on time rates. For small strains it agrees with the classical linear theory of elasticity. To determine stress-strain relations for large deformation is a mathematical problem, the answer to which varies from one special case to another. Simple shear is taken as an example. Here it turns out that hypo-elastic materials may soften or stiffen in shear, depending on the value of a dimensionless constant which has no effect when the strain is small. For bodies which soften, a theoretical prediction of "hypo-elastic yield" is obtained.

Part II concerns a new special type of hypo-elastic body in some ways more general, in other ways more special than that considered in Part I. According to this theory, yield of the von Mises type appears to follow if the stress intensity is sufficiently great. The equations of this theory are solved for the case of simple shear. It is shown that if von Mises yield occurs, hypo-elastic yield must occur at a lesser stress. For large values of a certain parameter, von Mises yield is imaginary and only hypo-elastic yield occurs. For moderate values of the parameter, hypo-elastic yield appears as primary yield, with von Mises yield as secondary yield at infinite strain. For small values of the parameter, hypo-elastic yield and von Mises yield are indistinguishable, and the stress-strain curve is similar to the idealized forms assumed at the outset in the conventional Prandtl-Reuss theory.

PART I. INTRODUCTION TO HYPO-ELASTICITY

RHEOLOGISTS are accustomed to represent different types of material response by schematic diagrams and the corresponding one-dimensional mathematical models. A typical viscoelastic model, the Maxwellian body, is one in which stress σ and strain e are related by

$$\frac{ds}{dt}=\frac{de}{dt}-\frac{s}{\tau}, \tag{1}$$

where $s\equiv\sigma/(2\mu)$, μ being the elastic rigidity, and τ is the time of relaxation. If we take $\tau=\infty$, the resulting limit case is

$$ds/dt=de/dt, \tag{2}$$

and this is said to correspond to the perfectly elastic body, since

$$s=e+C. \tag{3}$$

Specialists in mechanics are accustomed to a different approach to elasticity. Since the classical linear theory starts from the assumption

$$\text{small stress}=f\text{ (small strain from an unstressed state)}, \tag{4}$$

a natural generalization appears to be

$$\text{stress}=f\text{ (finite strain)}. \tag{5}$$

The resulting theory is now a century old and has been the subject of much research, especially some notable investigations in the last decade.

Stimulated by some earlier attempts by Jaumann (1911) and Murnaghan (1944–1949), in a work written in 1949 and published in 1952 I suggested that the basic idea (4) of the classical linear theory could be regarded as a first approximation to an idea for large strains quite different from (5). This idea was

$$\text{stress increment}=f\text{ (strain increment)}, \tag{6}$$

or, in more precise terms,

$$\text{rate of stress}=f\text{ (rate of deformation)}. \tag{7}$$

The purpose was to get a concept of elastic behavior expressed entirely in terms of rates, yet without any effects of viscosity, relaxation, etc. Looking back to the one-dimensional language of rheology, we find (2) as the counterpart of (7), while (3) with $C=0$ is the counterpart of (5). In one dimension, the difference is only that the new theory allows the initial state to be arbitrarily stressed, while the old theory insists that the unstrained state is also unstressed. In fact the difference is greater, since the three-dimensional equations allow us to connect the phenomena of extension, shear, hydrostatic pressure, and others, and some interesting special solutions were found.

However, Dr. Ericksen pointed out to me that my equations were not right, since I had taken "rate of stress" to mean just the rate of change of stress as apparent to an observer moving with the material. This would mean that in a bar rotating rigidly, the stress tensor would remain constant. For a physical theory, such a conclusion is impossible, because in fact in a rigid motion the whole stress configuration should remain rigidly attached to the body, and to secure this convection of stress the individual components must change appropriately. Dr. Ericksen's remarks reminded me of something I had read earlier, and on checking back I found that the problem had been understood and its correct solution obtained, in somewhat different ways, by Cauchy (1829)[1] and by Zaremba (1903).[2] In 1953, I formulated what seemed an adequate modern view of the question and showed that, according to this view, the "rate of stress" should be the tensor* $D_T\mathbf{s}$ which is related to the dimensionless stress $\mathbf{s}$ by

$$D_T\mathbf{s} \equiv D\mathbf{s} - [\mathbf{s}\cdot\operatorname{grad}\mathbf{v} + (\mathbf{s}\cdot\operatorname{grad}\mathbf{v})_c] + \mathbf{s}\operatorname{div}\mathbf{v} \qquad (8)$$

[(Truesdell,[3] Sec. 55, bis), also (Truesdell,[4] Sec. 1)]. Since then, other views[5–8] have been put forward,† leading to somewhat different expressions for $D_T\mathbf{s}$. However, for the particular theory presented here, which of these forms of $D_T\mathbf{s}$ is used makes no difference. The resulting differential equations are the same.

Our objective is to get *a rate theory of purely elastic behavior*. From the foregoing, then, the constitutive equations of such a theory will be of the form

$$D_T\mathbf{s} = \mathbf{f}(\mathbf{d},\mathbf{s}), \qquad (9)$$

where $\mathbf{d}$ is the rate of deformation tensor. From dimensional considerations it can be shown [Truesdell,[9] Sec. 56; Truesdell,[4] Sec. 1; Noll,[5] Sec. 14] that if no relaxation effects are included, then

1. $\mathbf{f}$ is linear in $\mathbf{d}$.

Such bodies‡ I call hypo-elastic.§ Here we add two further requirements:

2. $\mathbf{f}$ is linear in $\mathbf{s}$.
3. The material is isotropic.

The body described by the equations is then called *hypo-elastic of grade one.*‖ The resulting differential equations (derived in Truesdell[10]), are

$$D_T\mathbf{s} = \left(\frac{\lambda}{2\mu} - 3\tilde{\omega}\alpha_0\right)\vartheta\mathbf{1} + (1 - 3\tilde{\omega}\alpha_1)\mathbf{d}$$
$$- 3\alpha_2\vartheta\mathbf{s} + \alpha_3(\mathbf{s}:\mathbf{d})\mathbf{1} + \tfrac{1}{2}\alpha_4(\mathbf{sd}+\mathbf{ds}), \qquad (10)$$

where λ, μ are the Lamé constants of the classical linear theory, $2\mu\tilde{\omega}$ is the mean pressure, ϑ is the rate of expansion, and α_0, α_1, α_2, α_3, α_4 are dimensionless material constants.

This theory is one of pure elasticity, since every modulus of the body is a multiple of its shear modulus. Under the assumptions usual in deriving the classical linear theory of elasticity, (10) reduces to the classical stress-strain relations (Truesdell,[10] Sec. 3). Thus every result obtained from the classical linear theory follows also from hypo-elasticity, for small strains from an unstressed state. However, for large deformations the theory is truly dynamical. To solve its equations, we must find the *motion* actually experienced by the specimen under test. The basic relations connect only *rates*. True, in any given problem there will be a relation between stress and strain, but that relation is not known in advance. It may well vary, depending on the manner in which the specimen is loaded. In each problem, part of the task of the theorist consists in solving mathematically the equations of rates in order to find the stress-strain relations. There is no general way of doing this.

Consider the case of simple shear. This is a situation usually treated as one dimensional in the rheological literature, but the hypo-elastic equations (10) do not reduce to (2). In fact, recent experiments bear out the prediction of theory that one-dimensional deformation cannot in general be produced by a one-dimensional system of stresses. Nothing of interest could come of (2) in the present case, but as we shall see, the prediction of the theory of hypo-elasticity is entirely different.

To solve the equations for simple shear, we have to find the motion as well as the stresses. For different rates of shearing, the answers will be different. For lack of mathematics, we can solve only the simplest case,

[1] A. Cauchy, *Oeuvres* (2), (1829), Vol. 4, p. 342.

[2] S. Zaremba, Bull. intern. acad. sci. Cracovie 594, 614 (1903). Also, Mém. Sci. Math., No. 82 (1937), see Chap. I, Sec. 2.

* Because of the limitations of available type, $D\mathbf{s}$ and $D_T\mathbf{s}$, respectively, replace the usual symbols $\mathbf{s}$ with a tilde and $\mathbf{s}$ with a dot.

[3] C. Truesdell, J. Rational Mech. Anal. **2**, 593 (1953).

[4] C. Truesdell, Comm. Pure Appl. Math. N. Y. U. **8**, 123 (1955).

[5] W. Noll, J. Rational Mech. Anal. **4**, 3 (1955).

[6] B. Cotter and R. S. Rivlin, Quart. Appl. Math. **13**, 177 (1955).

[7] T. Y. Thomas, Proc. Natl. Acad. Sci. **41**, 716 (1955).

[8] T. Y. Thomas, Proc. Natl. Acad. Sci. **41**, 762 (1955).

† Since a question of priority has been raised, I take this occasion to remark that in proposing (8) I attributed priority to Cauchy and Zaremba. Expressions similar to (8) have occurred in the literature of plasticity theory [H. Fromm, Ing.-Arch. **4**, 432 (1933), part VB6, and H. Hencky, Research **2**, 437 (1949)]. In my opinion, the considerations in Fromm's paper are not clear, and those in Hencky's are largely incorrect. The first satisfactory general treatment of invariant time derivatives is that of Oldroyd [J. G. Oldroyd, Proc. Roy. Soc. (London) **A200**, 532 (1950)]. So far as I know, the equations of the theory of hypo-elasticity first appeared in Truesdell.[3] See also the second paragraph of Part II of this article.

‡ The more general bodies satisfying (9) without the restriction 1 are called *hygrosteric* by Noll,[5] who obtains and analyses solutions in several important special cases.

§ The terminology is as follows: *hypo-elastic* for the bodies defined here, *elastic* for bodies defined by (5), *hyper-elastic* for the special case of (5) when there is a strain energy. This terminology is supported by the inclusion diagram hypo-e.$\supset$e.$\supset$hyper-e., the first inclusion having been proved by Noll[5] [Sec. 14b] and the second being obvious.

‖ Other grades are defined and studied in Truesdell.[4,10] The definition of the body of grade zero is not invariant with respect to admissible choices of $D_T\mathbf{s}$. A special body of grade 2 is studied in Part II of the present paper.

[9] C. Truesdell, J. Rational Mech. Anal. **1**, 125 (1952).

that of *uniform rate of shearing:*

$$\mathbf{v}=2ky\mathbf{i}, \tag{11}$$

i being a unit vector in the x-direction and k the constant rate of shearing, If we put

$$\tau\equiv 2kt, \tag{12}$$

in τ we have a convenient dimensionless measure of the finite amount of shear at time t. Naturally, the magnitude of the rate k can have no effect on the relation between shear stress s_{xy} and shear strain τ, since our theory does not involve a time of relaxation. All results necessarily will involve the time only in the dimensionless product $2kt$.

Since the acceleration is zero, the equations of motion are satisfied if the stresses are uniform in space but varying arbitrarily in time. The time variation is then obtained by solving (10) as a system of six differential equations in six unknowns. The solution is straightforward (see Truesdell,[10] Sec. 8 as corrected). If we put

$$\alpha_s\equiv\alpha_1+\alpha_3+\alpha_4+\tfrac{3}{2}\alpha_1\alpha_3+\tfrac{1}{2}\alpha_3\alpha_4+\tfrac{1}{2}\alpha_3\alpha_4+\tfrac{1}{4}\alpha_4^2, \tag{13}$$

we get

$$s_{xy}=\begin{cases}\dfrac{1}{2(\alpha_s)^{\frac{1}{2}}}\sinh(\alpha_s)^{\frac{1}{2}}\tau & \text{if } \alpha_s\geqq 0,\\[2ex] \dfrac{1}{2(-\alpha_s)^{\frac{1}{2}}}\sin(-\alpha_s)^{\frac{1}{2}}\tau & \text{if } \alpha_s\leqq 0,\end{cases} \tag{14}$$

assuming the specimen is initially unstressed. This is the relation between shear stress and shear strain. As expected, for small shears we get $s_{xy}\approx\frac{1}{2}\tau$, just as in the classical linear theory, and in this approximation the value of α_s is irrelevant. For large shears, the result is entirely different.

Consider first the case $\alpha_s>0$. The curve of s_{xy} against τ always lies above its tangent at $\tau=0$ and goes on turning upward as τ increases. Thus if $\alpha_s>0$ the body stiffens steadily in shear. Such a body may be called *hard.*

If $\alpha_s=0$, we get $s_{xy}=\frac{1}{2}\tau$. For this case the relation between shear stress and shear strain is just the same as in the linear theory, with τ as the measure of finite shear. Such a body may be called *neutral.*

Now consider $\alpha_s<0$. The curve of s_{xy} against τ lies below its tangent at $\tau=0$, so that the shear stress always produces a greater shear than the linear theory would predict. The body steadily gives way and may be called *soft.* But this is not all. At the value of τ given by

$$\tau=\frac{\frac{1}{2}\pi}{(-\alpha_s)^{\frac{1}{2}}}, \tag{15}$$

the curve of s_{xy} flattens and turns down. Since in an experiment stress cannot decrease with increasing strain, this result might at first seem to discredit the theory. Upon reflection, however, we recall that a standard theoretical approach to elastic buckling i to calculate the smallest load at which increased loa theoretically decreases the strain. Not only is bucklin not to be expected in shear, but also here we hav just the opposite situation. The theory asserts that th load cannot increase, no matter what happens. That is of itself hypo-elasticity gives us for soft bodies a maximum shear stress, and we must expect that th theory fails to describe actual materials at or befor this stress is reached. In a smooth theory making n assumption whatever regarding yield or rupture, w have obtained *an upper bound for the yield stress.*

A sine curve for stress against strain may seem difficult to accept, but that our result is a sine curv follows only from our choice of τ as a measure of shear If we take the actual angle of shear, $\theta=\arctan\tau$, as a measure, the curve is no longer a sine curve.¶ In fact the curve of shear stress against shear angle is strikingl like a straight line for most of its length, suddenl turning down and flattening out just before the maxi mum is reached. That is, our result looks very muc like the measured curves of stress against strain tha are usually taken as justifying a yield condition. Th difference is that in hypo-elasticity, unlike the theorie of plasticity, yield is not assumed as a postulate bu rather is *predicted.* The maximum of s_{xy} is called th *shear strength,* s_s, and the angle θ_s at which it occurs i called the *ultimate shear angle:*

$$\theta_s=\arctan\frac{\pi}{2(-\alpha_s)^{\frac{1}{2}}},\quad s_s=\frac{\frac{1}{2}}{(-\alpha_s)^{\frac{1}{2}}}. \tag{16}$$

Simple accelerationless shear cannot be produced b shearing forces alone. The normal stresses on the shea planes and on the planes of shearing are given by

$$\frac{s_{yy}}{\alpha_3+\frac{1}{2}\alpha_4}=\frac{s_{zz}}{\alpha_3}=\begin{cases}\dfrac{1}{\alpha_s}\sinh^2\tfrac{1}{2}(\alpha_s)^{\frac{1}{2}}\tau & \text{if } \alpha_s\geqq 0,\\[2ex] \dfrac{1}{-\alpha_s}\sin^2\tfrac{1}{2}(-\alpha_s)^{\frac{1}{2}}\tau & \text{if } \alpha_s\leqq 0.\end{cases} \tag{17}$$

Thus independently of whether the body is soft neutral, or hard, the signs and amounts of these norma stresses are governed by the independent parameter $\alpha_3+\frac{1}{2}\alpha_4$ and α_3. We may call the latter the *shear elusiveness,* the former the *shear tenseness* of the body. Thes names are motivated by the fact if we fail to supply th necessary tension s_{zz} to a specimen in shear, it wil tend to draw together or spread apart within the plane being sheared according as $\alpha_3>0$ or $\alpha_3<0$, while if w fail to supply s_{yy}, the shearing planes themselves wil spread apart or draw together according as $\alpha_3+\frac{1}{2}\alpha_4>0$ or $\alpha_3+\frac{1}{2}\alpha_4<0$. Behavior such as this is predicted by th

¶ Also it lies slightly above, rather than below, its tangent a zero strain.

lassical theory of finite elastic strain [Truesdell,[9] Sec. 42F], but not in such freedom: According to the heory of finite strain, it is not possible to specify a body such that s_{yy} and s_{zz} stand in arbitrary constant ratio but are not zero.

In hypo-elasticity so far only the problems of shear, extension, hydrostatic pressure, and torsion have been solved. Each of these except the last leads to results of striking interest. Comparison of theory with experiment must wait until a reasonable number of theoretical cases are fully understood. In conclusion it is necessary to repeat a warning issued earlier: In hypo-elasticity, the stress-strain relations are not independent of the load path. For example, the results concerning shear just presented were derived subject to the assumption that the shearing is executed without acceleration. The truly dynamical theory of hypo-elasticity gives us no reason to expect these answers to hold for accelerated shearing, and in fact they can be proved not to hold more generally except for small shears.

PART II. HYPO-ELASTIC YIELD AND *M*-YIELD IN SHEAR**

In Part I we have seen that a simple case of hypo-elasticity indicates yield or rupture by a theoretical maximum of shear stress as shear strain increases. This theoretical phenomenon we shall call *hypo-elastic yield*. According to the view of yield held by advocates of the common theories of plasticity, a certain invariant of stress or strain reaches and maintains a preassigned value. The most trusted criterion, due to Maxwell and v. Mises, refers to the invariant S:

$$S\equiv\mathbf{s}:\mathbf{s}. \tag{18}$$

The theoretical phenomenon $S=K^2$ we shall call *M-yield*.

T. Y. Thomas[11] has observed that certain special cases of hypo-elasticity appear to imply continuous increase of stress intensity up to M-yield. He has determined the class of hypo-elastic materials which besides satisfying certain other assumptions are such that when once S reaches the value K^2, then S if analytic remains constant. A. E. Green[12] has made a similar observation; confining attention to incompressible materials, he has studied simple shear and has concluded that M-yield occurs only at infinite strain. Superficially, this work resembles long prior studies by Prager,[13–15] who for loading in the elastic and plastic regimes alike proposed certain uniform equations in rates. In fact, such resemblance is as shallow as that between hypo-elasticity and the old rate theory of Jaumann. Prager's equations, like Jaumann's, contain the usual undefined time rates of plasticity theory, standing presumably either for the local time derivative or for the material derivative. Thus, apparently, Prager's theory is intended for small deformations. While Prager's work must be regarded as a notable contribution toward a uniform theory of elastic and plastic phenomena, the viewpoint in works on hypo-elasticity is that *finite deformations are of the essence of the problem*.††

Our purpose here is to investigate hypo-elastic yield and M-yield in simple shear for compressible bodies satisfying the equations advocated by Thomas. These equations are identical in form with the equations of the Prandtl-Reuss theory of plasticity but for two all-important differences:

1. The yield constant K^2 of the Prandtl-Reuss equations is replaced by S. That is, M-yield is *not* assumed, and the rate of stress is a *nonlinear* function of $\mathbf{s}$.
2. The rate of stress is modified by nonlinear convective terms in such a way that the theory is dynamically possible for large strains. (The time flux used by Thomas is not $D_T\mathbf{s}$ but rather $D\mathbf{s}-\mathbf{s}\cdot\mathbf{w}-\mathbf{w}\cdot\mathbf{s}$, where $\mathbf{w}$ is the vorticity tensor; this is the form due to Zaremba. As in the Prandtl-Reuss equations, Thomas considers the stress deviator rather than the entire stress, but for the present problem this makes no difference.)

For the problem of simple shear, the differential equations are

$$\left.\begin{aligned} s_{xy}'&=\tfrac{1}{2}\left(s_{yy}-s_{xx}+1-\frac{2s_{xy}^2}{K^2}\right),\\ s_{xx}'&=s_{xy}\left(1-\frac{s_{xx}}{K^2}\right),\\ s_{yy}'&=-s_{xy}\left(1+\frac{s_{yy}}{K^2}\right),\\ s_{zz}'&=-s_{xy}\frac{s_{zz}}{K^2},\end{aligned}\right\} \tag{19}$$

[10] C. Truesdell, J. Rational Mech. Anal. 4, 83 (1955); corrections, *ibid.* 4, 983 (1955).

** Acknowledgment: The drawings were made by an assistant working under Office of Naval Research contract.

[11] T. Y. Thomas, Proc. Natl. Acad. Sci. 41, 720 (1955).

[12] A. E. Green, Proc. Roy. Soc. (London) (to be published).

[13] W. Prager, Proc. 5th Int. Congr. Applied Mech., Cambridge, Massachusetts 234 (1938).

[14] W. Prager, Rev. fac. sci. univ. Istanbul (A) 5, 215 (1941).

[15] W. Prager, Duke Math. J. 9, 228 (1942).

†† It appears necessary to make this distinction entirely plain. For definiteness, consider Prager's treatment of simple shear [reference 14, Sec. 2]. Since Prager's basic equations do not contain the convective terms in the stress rate, the stress-strain relations emerging from his theory in the case of shear [reference 14, Eq. (5)] are not the same as our result (32); to get Prager's formula from ours, linearize $(32)_1$ with respect to K and ϕ, then in $(31)_3$ linearize the left side entirely but the right side only partially. Thus, from the point of view of the present theory, Prager's theory emerges by neglecting some nonlinear terms while retaining others of about the same magnitude.

Second, Prager's theory, being partially linearized, fails to predict what I have called hypo-elastic yield in shear, and Prager does not give any hint of the magnitude of the shears for which his theory is intended. Moreover, in his treatment of shear Prager does not mention the accompanying normal stress s_{yy}, typical of theories of large strain. We note that according to the theory

where the prime denotes $d/d\tau$, τ being the measure of finite strain given by (12). The special case $K=\infty$ represents a particular soft body of grade one, the value of α_s being -1. From (19) we derive

$$S'=s_{xy}\left(1-\frac{S}{K^2}\right), \tag{20}$$

whence it follows that $S'=0$ when $S=K^2$ and moreover, for sufficiently smooth solutions, $d^nS/d\tau^n=0$ when $S=K^2$. This is Thomas's result, specialized to the present case. Our problem is to find whether or not there are in fact real solutions of (19) such that $S=K^2$. We restrict attention to the case of an initially unstressed specimen.

Put

$$u\equiv s_{xx}-s_{yy},\quad v\equiv s_{xx}+s_{yy}. \tag{21}$$

Then from (19) follows

$$u'=s_{xy}\left(2-\frac{u}{K^2}\right),\quad v'=-s_{xy}\frac{v}{K^2}. \tag{22}$$

Since $s_{zz}=0$ and $v=0$ when $\tau=0$, from $(19)_4$ and $(22)_2$ we get

$$s_{zz}=0,\quad v=0,\quad s_{yy}=-s_{xx},\quad u=2s_{xx}=-2s_{yy}. \tag{23}$$

Hence

$$S=2(s_{xy}{}^2+s_{yy}{}^2). \tag{24}$$

Moreover, $(19)_1$ and $(22)_1$ become

$$s_{xy}'=\tfrac{1}{2}+s_{yy}-\frac{s_{xy}{}^2}{K^2},\quad s_{yy}'=-s_{xy}\left(1+\frac{s_{yy}}{K^2}\right). \tag{25}$$

The solution of the problem is reduced to the integration of this system.

By inspection of $(25)_2$ we see that $s_{yy}<0$, at least for sufficiently small strain. That is, the shearing planes must be pressed together. From $(25)_1$ it follows that s_{xy} is a convex function of τ, experiencing a single maximum. Not only is the shear stress always less than that predicted by the classical theory of elasticity, but also *hypo-elastic yield always occurs at a smaller strain than does M-yield* (if M-yield occurs at all). Thus the equations proposed by Thomas do not offer the possibility of a steady increase of shear up to M-yield.

The foregoing result follows directly from (25), as stated, but it is worthwhile to complete the integration. We readily preceive the intermediate integral

$$s_{xy}{}^2=-s_{yy}\left[1+(\tfrac{1}{2}+K^2)\frac{s_{yy}}{K^2}\right]. \tag{26}$$

explained below the normal stress, which for small shears is of course of the order of the square of the angle of shear, also rises rapidly to a yield value. According to (28), the yield value for s_{yy} is of the order K^2 as $K/\sqrt{2}$, the yield value of s_{xy}, approaches 0. Thus neglect of s_{yy} is justified, according to the present theory, only for very small K.

The purpose of this footnote is not to compare the physical relevance of Prager's theory and the theory of hypo-elasticity, but only to make it clear that they are different theories.

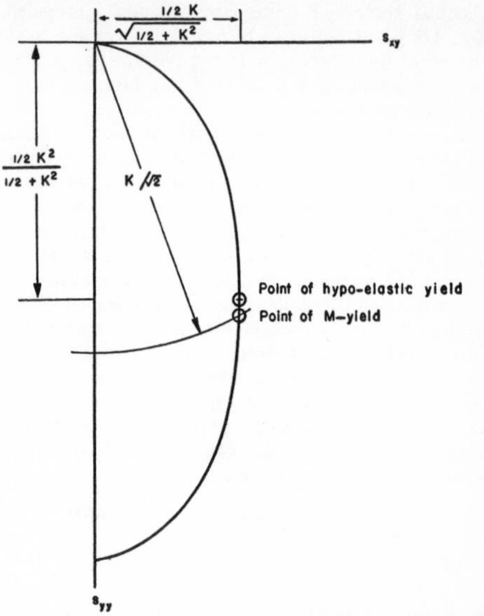

FIG. 1. Shear stress as a function of normal stress in simple shear. (The figure is drawn for the case $K=\frac{1}{2}$.)

This proves that $s_{yy}<0$ for all strains. Moreover, s_{xy} and s_{yy} are such as to lie on a semiellipse with center at $s_{xy}=0$, $s_{yy}=-\frac{1}{2}K^2/(\frac{1}{2}+K^2)$ and with semiaxes of lengths $\frac{1}{2}K/(\frac{1}{2}+K^2)^{\frac{1}{2}}$ and $\frac{1}{2}K^2/(\frac{1}{2}+K^2)$ (see Fig. 1). By (24), the locus $S=K^2$ is a circle with center at $s_{xy}=s_{yy}=0$ and radius $K/\sqrt{2}$. M-yield occurs at the values of s_{xy} and s_{yy} corresponding to intersection of the circle and the semiellipse. Since for all K the radius of the circle exceeds the distance from the origin to the nearer vertex of the semiellipse, we have fresh proof that M-yield cannot occur until after hypo-elastic yield. Moreover, there is or is not a real point of intersection according as $K^2\leqq\frac{1}{2}$ or $K^2>\frac{1}{2}$. That is, *a necessary condition for M-yield is* $K^2\leqq\frac{1}{2}$. To show that the condition is sufficient, we should have to prove that there is a real strain τ corresponding to the point of M-yield. A glance at Fig. 1 shows that for small values of K the shear stress at M-yield and the shear stress at hypo-elastic yield are so nearly the same as to be indistinguishable. In the following we shall give a formal proof of this fact.

For an algebraic proof of the condition $K^2\leqq\frac{1}{2}$, use (26) to put (24) into the form

$$S=-2s_{yy}\left(1+\frac{s_{yy}}{2K^2}\right); \tag{27}$$

hence at M-yield we have

$$s_{yy}=-K^2,\quad s_{xy}=K(\tfrac{1}{2}-K^2)^{\frac{1}{2}}\leqq\tfrac{1}{4}, \tag{28}$$

the maximum yield value of s_{xy} being achieved for $K=\frac{1}{2}$. At hypo-elastic yield, on the other hand, we have

$$s_{yy}=-\frac{\frac{1}{2}K^2}{\frac{1}{2}+K^2}>-\tfrac{1}{2},\quad s_{xy}=s_s=\frac{\frac{1}{2}K}{(\frac{1}{2}+K^2)^{\frac{1}{2}}}<\tfrac{1}{2},\quad (29)$$

where the bounds correspond to $K=\infty$. *Thus an effect of the terms involving K in* (19) *is to decrease the hypo-elastic shear strength.*

Finally, we observe from (25) and (28) that *at a point of M-yield, the derivatives of s_{xy} and s_{yy} vanish.* If the phenomenon of M-yield occurs, then, it entails the maintenance of *all* stresses at constant values. When $K^2<\frac{1}{2}$ we have from (28) and (29)

$$\frac{s_s}{\text{shear stress at } M\text{-yield}}=\frac{\frac{1}{2}}{(\frac{1}{4}-K^4)^{\frac{1}{2}}}.\quad (30)$$

Now K is the stress intensity at M-yield, measured in units of twice the elastic shear modulus. Experiments purporting to determine the yield stress in physical materials claimed to obey the criterion of Maxwell and v. Mises give a result much less, in fact orders of magnitude less, than the elastic shear modulus. Hence in any attempt to apply our theory to such materials, the dimensionless constant K will doubtless be taken very small. As $K\to 0$, the right-hand side of (30) approaches 1. Thus, *for small K, the shear stress at hypo-elastic yield is substantially the same as the shear stress at M-yield.* For very small K, then, the shear stress as a function of shear strain will rise quickly to a value approximately $K/\sqrt{2}$, overshoot to a slightly larger value, and then level off again.

What remains is to complete the integration so as to get stress-strain relations and to determine the strains at which the two types of yield occur. For a measure of finite strain, select ϕ as given by

$$\tan\tfrac{1}{2}\phi\equiv\begin{cases}\left(\dfrac{K^2+\frac{1}{2}}{K^2-\frac{1}{2}}\right)^{\frac{1}{2}}\tan\left[\dfrac{(K^2-1)^{\frac{1}{2}}}{2K}\tau\right] & \text{if } K^2>\frac{1}{2},\\ \tau/\sqrt{2} & \text{if } K^2=\frac{1}{2},\\ \left(\dfrac{\frac{1}{2}+K^2}{\frac{1}{2}-K^2}\right)^{\frac{1}{2}}\tanh\left[\dfrac{(\frac{1}{2}-K^2)^{\frac{1}{2}}}{2K}\tau\right] & \text{if } K^2<\frac{1}{2}.\end{cases}\quad (31)$$

Then the solution of (25) corresponding to zero initial values is

$$s_{xy}=\frac{\frac{1}{2}K}{(K^2+\frac{1}{2})^{\frac{1}{2}}}\sin\phi,\quad s_{yy}=-\frac{K^2}{K^2+\frac{1}{2}}\sin^2\tfrac{1}{2}\phi.\quad (32)$$

Hypo-elastic yield occurs at $\phi=\frac{1}{2}\pi$; in other words (16) is replaced by

$$\theta_s=\begin{cases}\arctan\left[\dfrac{2K}{(K^2-1)^{\frac{1}{2}}}\arctan\left(\dfrac{K^2-\frac{1}{2}}{K^2+\frac{1}{2}}\right)^{\frac{1}{2}}\right] & \text{if } K^2>\frac{1}{2},\\ \arctan\sqrt{2} & \text{if } K^2=\frac{1}{2},\\ \arctan\left[\dfrac{K}{(\frac{1}{2}-K^2)^{\frac{1}{2}}}\log\dfrac{\frac{1}{2}+(\frac{1}{4}-K^2)^{\frac{1}{2}}}{K^2}\right] & \text{if } K^2<\frac{1}{2}.\end{cases}\quad (33)$$

If $K^2>\frac{1}{2}$, s_{xy} becomes imaginary before M-yield occurs. If $K^2\leqq\frac{1}{2}$, M-yield occurs, *but only asymptotically as the strain becomes infinite.* The value θ_0 of the angle of shear at which the M-yield value of the shear stress is first reached is given by

$$\theta_0=\arctan\left[\frac{K}{(\frac{1}{2}-K^2)^{\frac{1}{2}}}\log\frac{1}{2K^2}\right].\quad (34)$$

From $(33)_3$ follows

$$\theta_s/\theta_0\to 1\quad\text{as}\quad K\to 0.\quad (35)$$

Thus *the shear at which the stress* first *reaches its value for M-yield and the shear at which hypo-elastic yield occur are very nearly the same when K is small.*

The assumption common among the researchers in plasticity is that up to M-yield a body obeys the equations of linear elasticity. In the present problem, the corresponding stress-strain curve would be a straight line of slope $\frac{1}{2}$ joined to the horizontal straight line $s_{xy}=K/\sqrt{2}$. We have seen that the horizontal line for yield emerges from the present theory by demonstration as approximate when K is small. Not so for the slanted line. If we let θ_l be the angle of shear for which the line $s_{xy}=\frac{1}{2}\tau$ intersects the yield line $s_{xy}=K/\sqrt{2}$, by (34) we get

$$\theta_0/\theta_l\to\infty\quad\text{as}\quad K\to 0.\quad (36)$$

It follows that according to the present theory *the softening which occurs prior to yield cannot be neglected,* even in approximation, when K is small. If we are to approximate the stress-strain curve prior to yield by a straight line, its tangent at the origin is not sufficient, but rather its chord might be used. As $K\to 0$, the slope of this chord approaches zero.

Figure 2 presents the curves of stress against angle of shear for several values of K. From these it appears that for very small K a mathematical consequence of Eqs. (19) is a response in shear very like that often postulated in works on plasticity. For moderate and large K, however, there is no such similarity, but instead occurs a phenomenon of hypo-elastic yield much like that discussed in Part I. In fact the curve following from the present theory for $K=\frac{1}{2}$ is rather more similar to Bauschinger's experimental curve for extension reproduced in Sec. 77 of Love's *Elasticity* than are the idealized straight lines used in plasticity theory. There is slight softening, followed by gradual primary

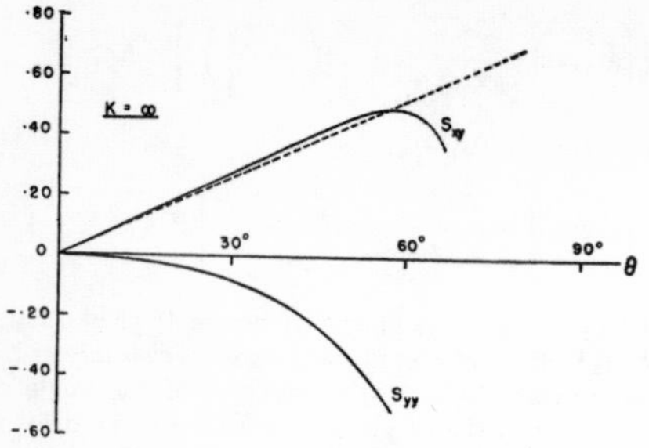

(a) $K=\infty$. The case discussed in Part I. Purely hypo-elastic yield.

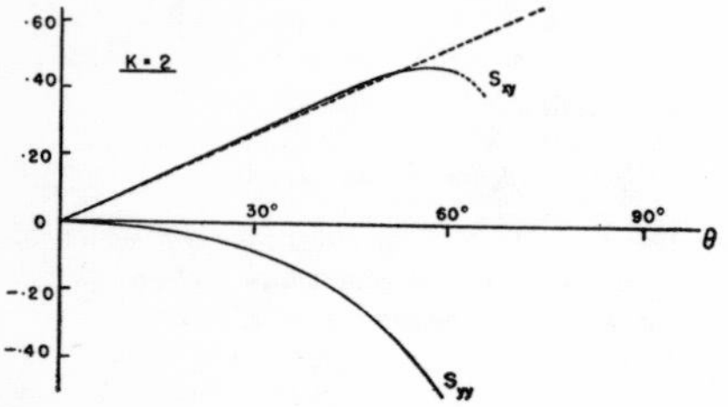

(b) $K=2$. Purely hypo-elastic yield.

FIG. 2. Shear stress and normal stress as functions of the angle of shear. In all cases the dashed line, which is the tangent to the curve of shear stress at the origin, gives the shear stress according to linear elasticity.

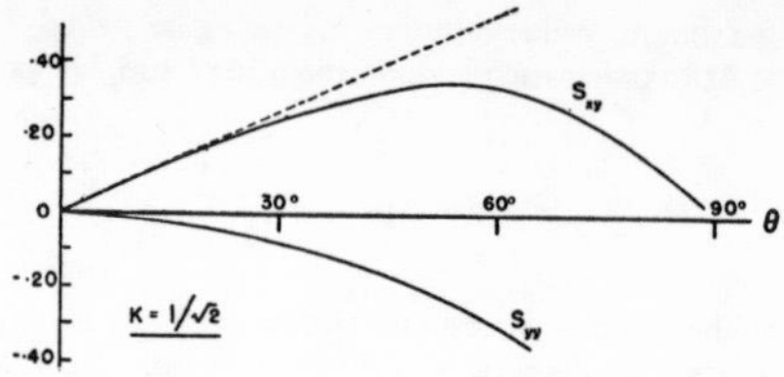

(c) $K=1/\sqrt{2}$. The smallest K for which M-yield occurs.

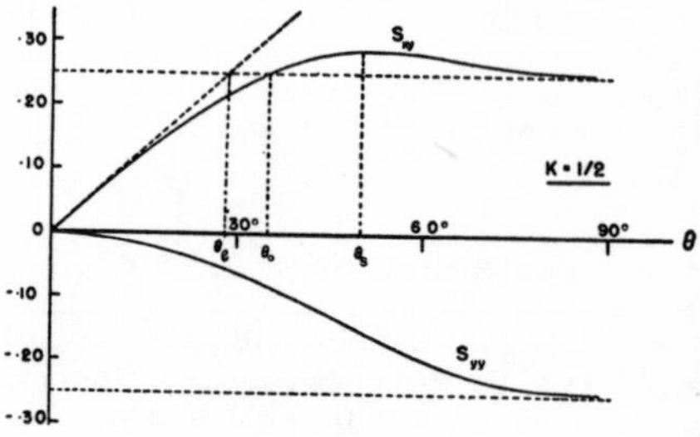

(d) $K=\frac{1}{2}$. Hypo-elastic yield followed by M-yield.

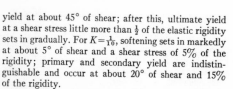

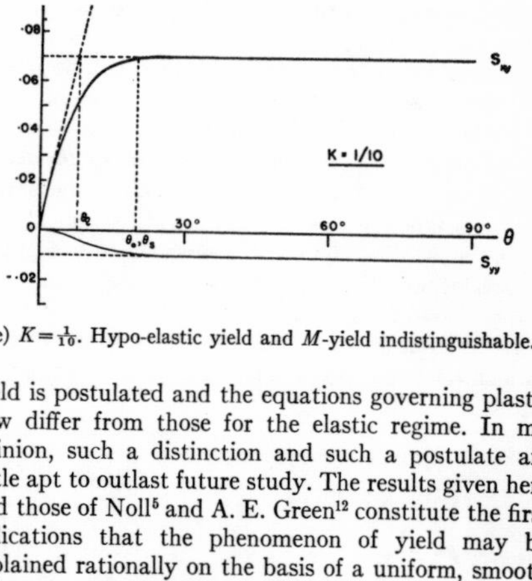

(e) $K=\frac{1}{10}$. Hypo-elastic yield and M-yield indistinguishable.

yield at about 45° of shear; after this, ultimate yield at a shear stress little more than $\frac{1}{2}$ of the elastic rigidity sets in gradually. For $K=\frac{1}{10}$, softening sets in markedly at about 5° of shear and a shear stress of 5% of the rigidity; primary and secondary yield are indistinguishable and occur at about 20° of shear and 15% of the rigidity.

In the current theories of plasticity, usually limited (if only tacitly) to problems of very small deformations, yield is postulated and the equations governing plastic flow differ from those for the elastic regime. In my opinion, such a distinction and such a postulate are little apt to outlast future study. The results given here and those of Noll[5] and A. E. Green[12] constitute the first indications that the phenomenon of yield may be explained rationally on the basis of a uniform, smooth mechanical theory, meaningful alike for small strain and large.

No. 8

THE MAIN UNSOLVED PROBLEM OF THE THEORY OF FINITE ELASTIC STRAIN

C. Truesdell

(Das ungelöste Hauptproblem der endlichen Elastizitätstheorie), Zeitschrift für angewandte Mathematik und Mechanik, Volume 36, pp. 97-103 (1956).

The text here printed is a translation of a lecture to the German Society for Applied Mathematics and Mechanics, delivered on June 1, 1955. The " main unsolved problem" is that of determining what restrictions should be placed on the stored-energy function of a hyperelastic material in order to ensure that physically reasonable resuhs follow. For isotropic materials according to the linearized theory, such restrictions are provided by the inequalities $\mu > 0$, $3\lambda + 2\mu > 0$.

This lecture presents the subject as it appeared half way through the recent thorough searching of the foundations of the classical theory of finite elastic strain. The problem has not yet been solved, but now much more is known about it than was in 1955. Other papers bearing on it are reprinted as Nos. 3, 9, and 11 in this volume and Nos. 7, 14, and 15 in PNE. For a survey of everything presently known concerning it, see Sections 51-52, 87 of NFTM.

THE MAIN OPEN PROBLEM IN THE FINITE THEORY OF ELASTICITY

C. Truesdell in Bloomington[1]

(Translation, by the author, of "Das ungelöste Hauptproblem der endlichen Elastizitätstheorie," Zeitschrift für angewandte Mathematik und Mechanik, Volume 36, pp. 97-103, (1956)).

The remarkable progress of the last few years in the finite theory of elasticity is due to the avoidance of special assumptions. The solutions, whether exact or numerical, are valid for arbitrary strain energy function Σ. In the usual, linear theory, Σ is a quadratic form, but even here it cannot be completely arbitrary, but must be positive-definite. For the finite theory, three years ago the author raised the analogous question of what restriction should be placed upon Σ, and at that time he suggested certain inequalities, which he conjectured to be necessary but not sufficient. This report summarizes later investigations of this question.

1. Position of the Finite Theory

The finite theory of elasticity is no novelty in mechanics. KIRCHHOFF and KELVIN laid down its principles, and in 1894 JOSEF FINGER gave it the formulation that remains today the most convenient in most cases. When, at the beginning of this century, HADAMARD and HILBERT treated the foundations of elasticity in their lectures, naturally they presented, not the linear, but non-linear theory. Nevertheless, during the succeeding decades the general theory of elasticity was virtually forgotten, so that the recent reawakening of interest has required almost a rediscovery of the subject.

There are several reasons. First, from lack of appropriate notations the formal apparatus of the theory looked frightful. Second, in the last century it was only the leading theorists of mechanics who fully mastered the mechanical principles of the theory, so that even otherwise excellent treatises, e.g., those of LOVE and TODHUNTER and PEARSON, give a most fragmentary and hence confusing if not actually confused presentation of the finite theory. The beautiful work of FINGER remained unnoticed until 195 Third, the creators showed little interest in the details, the worked-out numerical examples, which, according to the British tradition, seem to be the main thing in the applied mathematics of our century. Doubts have even been expressed as to whether there exist physical materials that can experience finite but still purely elastic deformations — in other words, whether the ideal elastic material is merely a mathematical curiosity.

Ten years ago, a new period in mechanics began. Generality is sought once more. In several countries various scientists already possessing the armament of pure mathematics have turned their attention to the most difficult problems of the mechanics of continua. In elasticity theory it is mainly tensor analysis that has simplified everything. Through tensorial notations the problems are neither changed nor solved, yet through them we get a prospect that changes the most elaborate into the simplest for eye and mind. We may see a parallel to the introduction of organized calculus into mass-point mechanics in the seventeenth century; nothing really new was added, but in consequence classical mechanics became a science for everyman. So it is for finite elasticity theory since today the wide knowledge of relativity or modern geometry has put simple tensor calculus in the hands of everyone.

At the same time, some very significant special solutions were discovered. Of course these correspond only to special deformations, but in other respects they are as general as possible, retaining their validity for the most general form of the theory. For an **incompressible** material there is a remarkable and penetrating simplification scarcely to be conjectured from the infinitesimal theory. Rubber is nearly incompressible; for a century it resisted every effort to subsume its mechanical behaviour under a theory of elasticity. That was a stain upon the theory, since rubber offers the most immediate example of a physically elastic material. Toward qualitative explanation of the mechanical action of rubber, several profound theories of the physical or chemical kind were meanwhile announced, and elasticity theory had been dismissed as being unsuited. Finally, however, the new, general solutions according to the finite theory have been compared with new, fit, and exact experiments, leading to complete and astonishingly exact agreement. Moreover, these experiments have shown insufficient the various special assumptions, differing from each other but always derived by their proponents from compelling physical reasons, which lie at the bottom of the superabundant and tedious literature on elastic stability. The behavior of rubber in large deformations has been explained from purely mechanical basic laws, giving rise to development in the last few years of a new branch of engineering, the engineering theory of rubber. It is a triumph of mechanical principles and of generality.

Naturally we cannot expect that every physical material which behaves elastically in infinitesimal deformations will remain purely elastic in large deformations. That in certain, even if relatively few, physical materials purely elastic finite deformations are possible, at least in fair approximation, suffices to make for the finite theory of elasticity a place of honor at the table of the classical field theories.

2. Formal Presentation of the Theory(cf., e.g.,[1]).

Let us turn now to the formal theory. Let the desired tranformation of the material point X^α into the place x^i be

$$x^i = x^i(X^\alpha) \qquad (1).$$

According to GREEN, elastic deformations are reversible, and there exists a **strain-energy function** Σ, which represents the density of stored energy per unit mass. It is assumed that this density of energy depends only on the deformation gradients $x^i{}_{,\alpha} \equiv \partial x^i/\partial X^\alpha$. The usual stress components $t^i{}_j$, referred to the deformed state, are obtained from the fundamental theorems of KIRCHHOFF and FINGER, respectively:

$$t^i{}_j = III^{\frac{1}{2}} x^i{}_{,\alpha} \frac{\partial \Sigma}{\partial x^j{}_{,\alpha}} \qquad (2a),$$

$$t^i{}_j = 2\, III^{\frac{1}{2}} \left[\left(II \frac{\partial \Sigma}{\partial II} + III \frac{\partial \Sigma}{\partial III}\right) \delta^i{}_j + \frac{\partial \Sigma}{\partial I}(c^{-1})^i{}_j - III \frac{\partial \Sigma}{\partial II} c^i{}_j\right] \qquad (2b),$$

where the second form is appropriate to isotropic materials, and where the notations are as follows:

$c_{ij} \equiv G_{\alpha\beta}\, X,^\alpha{}_i\, X,^\beta{}_j$ (CAUCHY'S deformation tensor)

$G_{\alpha\beta}$ = metric tensor in material co-ordinates

$(c^{-1})^i{}_j$ = tensor reciprocal to $c^i{}_j$, that is $c^i{}_j(c^{-1})^j{}_k = \delta^i{}_k$,

I, II, III = principal invariants of the tensor $(c^{-1})^i{}_j$.

For an incompressible body, III = 1, and $t^i{}_j$ in (2b) is determined only to within an arbitrary hydrostatic pressure $-\delta^i{}_j$. Let

$$C_{\alpha\beta} \equiv g_{ij}\, x^i{}_{,\alpha}\, x^j{}_{,\beta}$$

be GREEN's deformation tensor. In (2a) Σ is to be regarded in the general case as an arbitrary function of the six quantities $C_{\alpha\beta}$:

$$\Sigma = \Sigma(C_{\alpha\beta}) \quad (3a).$$

In the case of an isotropic material, however,

$$\Sigma = \Sigma(I,\ II,\ III) \quad (3b).$$

CAUCHY's field equations are

$$t^{ij}{}_{,j} + f^i = \rho\, \ddot{x}^i \quad (4),$$

where f^i is the density of external mass forces, ρ is the mass density, and $\ddot{x}^i$ is the acceleration. The stress formula (2) is to be substituted into these field equations in order to yield the general differential equations of the theory.

The linear theory results as a special case if one assumes the function Σ to be quadratic and neglects certain terms.

In the finite theory, to every particular choice of the form of the function Σ correspond particular values of the stresses t^i_j for any given deformation. If we please, we may say that every choice of the function Σ defines a particular elastic body.

I have already mentioned that we now possess some particular solutions which are as general as possible. I. e., these solutions[2] are valid for **arbitrary** Σ. The new period in the development of the theory is characterized by the avoidance of all restricting assumptions in regard to Σ. Only in this way has a satisfactory theory for rubber been found. In the simpler cases of deformation this generality occasions no trouble in the solution; rather, the derivation of the new general solutions is simpler than that of so called approximations according to particular theories or perturbation processes. Through comparison of these general results with experimental values, numerical tables for Σ as a function of its two arguments, I and II, have been obtained for various kinds of rubber. In more complicated cases one takes refuge in numerical calculations; here, however, a good numerical table for the values of the function Σ (I, II) offers an obvious advantage over a conjectural and in any case inexact formula. The generality of the strain-energy function is the key to the remarkable recent progress.

3. The Main Problem

I have said that the function Σ ($C_{\alpha\beta}$), or Σ (I, II, III), or Σ(I, II), is "arbitrary" Of course I did not mean "fully arbitrary." Even in the linear theory, where Σ is a quadratic form, everybody knows that this form cannot be fully arbitrary, since it must be positive-definite. And why?

1. A deformation from an unstressed state must use up mechanical work and cannot give it out (compatibility with the second law of thermostatics).

2. If Σ is positive-definite, the usual boundary-value problems have an unique solution (KIRCHHOFF's uniqueness theorem), and this solution is stable in the sense of energy (minimal property of the elastic energy).

In the finite theory, neither of these avenues of though leads to usable, comprehensible restriction of the function Σ. Certainly the second law of thermostatics remains valid, but in its strict formulation it refers properly to an instantaneous rate of change, not to the total energy. In the linear theory the displacements are always very small and hence may be regarded as proportional to time rates in a fictitious process. In the finite theory the energy added is not a differential form. Up to the present, thermostatics has had no success in the non-linear theory. The second avenue, likewise, has been fruitless, since there is no uniqueness theorem in the general theory of elasticity. However, at the end of the lecture I will return to this second avenue.

Here lies the main problem: **What is the class of functions Σ that may serve as stored-energy densities for perfectly elastic materials?**

4. Hadamard's Theorem [3][3].

The first, it seems, to have hinted at this problem, was the great HADAMARD. In the course of his brilliant researches on wave propagation he set the problem of deciding whether the speed of a possible acceleration wave invading a quiet region of the material be real. He defined a deformation as **stable** if the second variation of the corresponding total energy is positive in the class of first and second displacement variations that vanish on the boundary. He then showed that in a stable deformation all wave velocities are real.

HADAMARD's analysis looks rather complicated. Dr. ERICKSEN has kindly turned over to me a version of it which is shortened by a better choice of deformation variables and simplified by use of tensorial methods. For stability in HADAMARD's sense it turns out to be necessary — and perhaps also sufficient — that

$$\frac{\partial^2 \Sigma}{\partial x^i_{,\alpha} \partial x^i_{,\beta}} \xi^i \xi^j \nu_\alpha \nu_\beta \geqq 0 \qquad (5),$$

where ξ^i and ν_α are arbitrary vectors. This condition is also necessary and sufficient that for an **arbitrary** direction of propagation all roots of the equation for the wave velocities be real. This result concerns the most general compressible elastic materials. Restriction of the function Σ was not the real aim of HADAMARD's investigation, which sought rather to cast light upon general properties of waves. It would be too much to demand that the form of Σ be such as to render (5) valid in **every** deformation. Rather, (5) is a test condition for a Σ and a deformation together: If a certain deformation of a certain elastic material satisfies (5), then waves can propagate in any direction.

The connection of HADAMARD's theorem with our main problem lies in the idea that according to a good theory, acceleration waves ought to be possible. However, that **every** surface element be able to carry **three** waves is perhaps too much to ask. In any case, the connection between wave propagation and stability is certainly interesting. Naturally, a good non-linear theory of elasticity ought to include the phenomenon of buckling and hence of instability under suitable conditions. At a place where the elastic equilibrium is not stable, suppose that, coming from a neighboring region where stability holds, an acceleration wave arrives. What happens? Here we have another difficult, unsolved problem. Perhaps this wave suddenly splits, degenerates, or amplifies: perhaps it becomes at this instant a shock wave or a displacement wave. If this is the case, then we have here a mechanism for the buckling phenomenon, since we may safely assume that weak waves of the acceleration or higher derivatives are always present as a sort of noise.

In other words, HADAMARD's inequality (5) seems to be too restrictive to be laid down as a general requirement for Σ. Nevertheless, if we apply it to the linear theory for isotropic bodies, it yields only $\mu \geqq 0$, $\lambda + 2\mu \geqq 0$; as is known, these inequalities are necessary and sufficient that all waves be real, but they do not suffice to render Σ positive-definite. Hence the HADAMARD condition is in this application too weak.

5. The Considerations of Truesdell ([1], pp. 181-182).

In 1952 I pointed out the main problem and made a small step toward its solution. I appealed to the principle that, in the loading of a body, Σ must grow. While I was unable to formulate a satisfactory definition of a loading process, I remarked that in an incompressible material where two of the principal extensions δ_i have the same sign, it is certainly a case of loading if one of them is increased. That is, if

$$\delta_1 > 0, \ \delta_2 > 0, \ d\delta_1 > 0, \ d\delta_2 = 0 \qquad (6)$$

then we should find that

$$d\Sigma > 0.$$

As a necessary condition I derived the following inequality:

$$\frac{\partial \Sigma}{\partial I} + (1+\delta_i)^2 \frac{\partial \Sigma}{\partial II} > 0, \quad i = 1, 2, \dots \qquad (7)$$

for all values of δ_i.

In the linear theory (7) reduces to the usual condition that the shear modulus be positive. The experimental values of the function Σ for various rubbers satisfy the stronger conditions

$$\frac{\partial \Sigma}{\partial I} > 0, \qquad \frac{\partial \Sigma}{\partial II} > 0 \qquad (8)$$

While the condition (5), involved in HADAMARD's analysis, concerns the second derivatives of the function Σ, my inequalities (7) restrict only the first derivatives.

6. The theorem of Baker & Ericksen [6]

As is known, in an isotropic elastic body the principal directions of stress and strain are identical. By FINGER's theorem (2b), a particular principal extension δ_i is set into correspondence with a particular principal stress t_i. We say that t_1 is the principal stress in the direction of the principal extension δ_1, etc. BAKER & ERICKSEN noticed and used this fact in such a way as to restrict the function Σ. They laid down the mechanical principle that the greatest stress shall always be in the direction of the greatest extension, that is

$$t_i > t_j \qquad \text{if} \qquad \delta_i > \delta_j \tag{9}$$

To clothe this principle in formulae, they derived a new theorem in the algebra of isotropic functions. After a short calculation, they found that their principle (9) is fully equivalent to my conditions (7), if the δ_i are distinct; if, however, $\delta_2 = \delta_3$, then ">" must be replaced by "$\geqq$" when i = 1.

This beautiful theorem of BAKER & ERICKSEN holds also for compressible materials.

7. Ericksen's Theorem [7]

Before the investigation just sketched, ERICKSEN attacked the problem by the aid of wave-transmission properties. He noticed that for an isotropic incompressible material the speeds had not yet been calculated. All waves in such a material are transverse. ERICKSEN derived a relatively simple formula for the speeds of acceleration waves and waves of higher order. For the speeds of arbitrarily oriented waves ERICKSEN's formula, like HADAMARD's, involves second as well as first derivatives of Σ, but in the special case of a wave surface that is normal to the principal direction in which δ_1 is the principal extension, for the speeds of propagation c he found

$$\frac{\rho c^2}{2(1+\delta_1)^2} = \left\{ \begin{array}{l} \dfrac{\partial \Sigma}{\partial I} + \dfrac{\partial \Sigma}{\partial II}(1+\delta_2)^2 \\ \dfrac{\partial \Sigma}{\partial I} + \dfrac{\partial \Sigma}{\partial II}(1+\delta_3)^2 \end{array} \right. \tag{10}$$

Hence my conditions (7) are also necessary and sufficient for the reality of all such waves.

8. The Latest Investigation of ERICKSEN & TOUPIN [8].

On my trip to Berlin I stopped briefly in Washington so as to learn the latest progress of Mr. ERICKSEN & Mr. R. TOUPIN. They are probing anew the condition (5) of HADAMARD. For the case of an isotropic material, they succeeded in putting it into a form from which definite and important consequences may be derived. First, if the directions of wave normal, wave jump, and a principal direction of strain coincide, then HADAMARD's inequality (5) reduces to

$$\frac{\partial t_1}{\partial \delta_1} \geqq 0 \tag{11}$$

This inequality asserts that the principal stress in this common direction shall not decrease as the principal extension increases. In the usual linear theory this means $\lambda + 2\mu \geqq 0$. Second, if the wave normal falls upon a principal direction of strain, but the jump points along a different principal direction, then HADAMARD's inequality (5) becomes identical with my condition (7). Hence we may conclude as follows regarding HADAMARD's inequality:

1. For the usual, linear theory, it is too weak.
2. For mechanical reasons, for a non-linear theory, it seems to be too strong.
3. It contains as special cases the two mechanical conditions (7) and (11).

Mr. ERICKSEN has remarked that HADAMARD's inequality (5) is also sufficient to secure the uniqueness of the displacement boundary-value problem for an infinitesimal deformation superimposed upon a given finite deformation.

9. Criticism.

The foregoing theorems are quite beautiful, but they all show a trait of incompleteness. I have no doubt of the correctness of my conditions (7), but I think they will turn out to be merely necessary, not sufficient for a satisfactory theory. In the derivations, moreover, there is a certain lack of generality. Apart from the requirement of HADAMARD, which is too strong, the arguments and condition themselves are suited only to isotropic bodies and are not easily adapted to the general case. Isotropy is not a principle of mechanics; rather, it is only a purely mathematical simplification which, luckily, is often justified in good approximation in particular physical applications. A method of proof that rests essentially upon isotropy fills want of principle by mathematical artifice. Thus it is in our main problem, since we have so far been able to make no conjecture toward conditions fit for the general case of anisotropy.

10. Uniqueness and Stability.

At the beginning we mentioned a second line of thought in the infinitesimal theory, namely, the requirement of uniqueness. For unique solution of boundary-value problems it is sufficient that Σ be positive-definite. Can we construct from the requirement of uniqueness a characterization of admissible strain-energy functions? I doubt it. From particular examples we know already that non-uniqueness of solution results if certain indefinite forms for Σ are allowed. For in certain plane problems, described by the bihaumonic equation, uniqueness holds always, whatever the sign of Σ. The question of a necessary and sufficient condition for uniqueness of solution remains thus an open question in the linear theory. If we are to get in the general theory information about the functional form of the strain-energy function through uniqueness, we shall have to begin with this unsolved problem of the infinitesimal theory.

In the linear theory every solution is unique and also stable. A main aim of the finite theory is the lifting of this all-inclusive uniqueness and stability. So as to calculate critical loads, the smallest proper number allowing failure of uniqueness is sought. However, if we impose no restriction at all upon the function Σ, such proper numbers generally have no meaning, since even for infinitesimal deformations uniqueness may fail when Σ is not restricted in any way.

Finally I come to a problem with which I might well have begun. In the years of this century, when the general theory of elasticity was sinking into oblivion, a number of special theories of stability were constructed, theories supported by special non-linear assumptions for elasticity. This or that term for that or this reason, was truncated or left off. For elastic behavior itself we know from the more recent general investigations that such so-called "approximations" are will-o'-the-wisps. Let us then look for the true stability theory and calculate critical loads from the general theory of elasticity. In principle, we are not yet in a condition to do so. We may only put in other words what was explained above; The correct theory of elastic stability must wait for the correct restricting conditions on the stored-energy function.

FOOTNOTES

[1] Lecture held at the Berlin meeting of the Gesellschaft für angewandte Mathematik und Mechanik, June 1, 1955. The work was supported by a contract between the U. S. Office of Naval Research and Indiana University. It is a pleasant duty for the author to thank Dr. ERICKSEN for his kind criticism of this report.

[2] In a certain sense, ERICKSEN [2] has derived and explained the totality of these solutions.

[3] I recognize this opportunity to call attention also to the investigations of stability and the wave properties of elastic materials we owe to the profound DUHEM [4]. The general considerations of HADAMARD and DUHEM probably deserve a new exposition, shortened by modern notations.

[4] His proof and his result have been questioned by SIGNORINI and TOLOTTI [5], but I can find nothing wrong with them. It seems to me that Mr. TOLOTTI has neglected HADAMARD's requirement of stability.

[5] Part of TOLOTTI's investigation [5] might have been turned toward this end.

REFERENCES

[1] C. TRUESDELL, **The mechanical foundations of elasticity and fluid dynamics**, J. Rational Mech. Anal. 1, 125-300 (1952); Corrections and additions, ibid, 2, 593-616 (1953). See especially Chapter IVA. See also C. TRUESDELL, **A program of physical research in classical mechanics**, Z. angew. Math. Phys. 3, 79-95 (1952).

[2] J. L. ERICKSEN, **Deformations possible in every isotropic, incompressible, perfectly elastic body**, Z. angew. Math. Phys. 5, 466-489 (1954).

[3] J. HADAMARD, **Leçons sur la Propagation des Ondes et les Équations de l' Hydrodynamique**, Paris, 1903.

[4] P. DUHEM, **Recherches sur l'élasticité**, Troisième Partie, Ann. École Normale (3) 22, 143-271 (1905); **Quatrième Partie**, ibid. 23, 169-223 (1906). The four parts appeared also as a volume, Paris, 1906.

[5] C. TOLOTTI, **Deformazioni elastische finite: onde ordinarie di discontinuità e caso** tipico di solidi elastici isotropi, Rend. Sem. Mat. Univ. Rome (5) 4, 34-59 (1943).

[6] M. BAKER & J. L. ERICKSEN, **Inequalities restricting the form of the stress-deformation relations for isotropic elastic solids and Reiner-Rivlin fluids**, J. Wash. Acad. Sci. 44, 33-35 (1954).

[7] J. L. ERICKSEN, **On the propagation of waves in isotropic incompressible perfectly elastic materials**, J. Rational Mech. Anal. 2, 329-337 (1953).

[8] J. L. ERICKSEN & R. A. TOUPIN, Can. J. Math., being printed.

No. 9

IMPLICATIONS OF HADAMARD'S CONDITION FOR ELASTIC STABILITY WITH RESPECT TO UNIQUENESS THEOREMS

J. L. Ericksen & R. A. Toupin

Canadian Journal of Mathematics, Volume 8, pp. 432-436 (1956).

While the French and Italian literature has regularly mentioned Hadamard's magnificent work on finite elasticity in 1899-1900, writers in other languages almost uniformly ignored it until MF appeared in 1952, and the paper here reprinted is the first to go beyond it in any respect. (For modern proofs of HADAMARD's theorems, see Sections 71 and 89 of NFTM.) In Section 3 it is shown very simply that if a deformation is stable in a sense slightly stronger than HADAMARD's ("≧" is replaced by ">"), the problem of determining a superimposed infinitesimal displacement with prescribed boundary values has at most one solution, while the corresponding stress boundary-value problem, in general, has not.

Both results have since been strengthened. Hadamard himself indicated that in a stable deformation, the equations of equilibrium must be, in more recent nomenclature, elliptic for that deformation. The corresponding linearized equations for a superimposed deformation are then almost strongly elliptic; if, again, we assume they are in fact strongly elliptic, a general theorem asserts not only uniqueness but also existence of solution of the displacement boundary-value problem, under suitable conditions of regularity. While Theorem 2 is proved by a single counter-example from the linearized theory, the whole question of necessary and sufficient conditions for uniqueness of solution to various boundary-value problems in that theory has since been settled. A summary, with references, is given in footnote[3] on p. 2 of the paper by C. TRUESDELL & R. TOUPIN, **Static grounds for inequalities in finite elastic strain**, Archive for Rational Mechanics and Analysis, Volume 12, pp. 1-33 (1963).

IMPLICATIONS OF HADAMARD'S CONDITIONS FOR ELASTIC STABILITY WITH RESPECT TO UNIQUENESS THEOREMS

J. L. ERICKSEN AND R. A. TOUPIN

Introduction. The purpose of this paper is to discuss implications of Hadamard's condition for elastic stability **(2**, §269**)** with respect to uniqueness of solutions of boundary value problems in the theory of small deformations superimposed on large. We show that a slightly refined form of his condition implies a uniqueness theorem for displacement boundary value problems. We construct a counter-example showing that his condition does not imply uniqueness of solutions for one type of stress boundary value problem. Hadamard **(2**, Ch. VI**)** showed that his condition implies the reality of all possible velocities of propagation of acceleration waves. To our knowledge, this is the only other known consequence of his condition.

Truesdell **(8)** has focused attention on the question of what conditions should be imposed on the strain energy to exclude physically unacceptable behavior. We are indebted to him for discussing this problem with us, thereby stimulating our interest in the topics considered here, and for his constructive criticisms of our work.

It is sufficient for our purposes to require that all vector fields considered be of class C^2 at all points of the undeformed body, which points constitute a regular region of space $\mathfrak{R}$, as defined in **(3)**.

1. Elasticity theory. The theory of elasticity with which we are concerned is based on the existence of a strain energy per unit of undeformed volume Σ, which is a function of displacement gradients $U^\alpha{}_{,\beta}$. Here U^α are the components of the displacement vector referred to a material[1] coordinate system and the comma denotes covariant differentiation with respect to these coordinates. We assume Σ is of class C^3 for all $U^\alpha{}_{,\beta}$, that there are no constraints on the deformation, and that inertial and body forces vanish. The basic equations may then be written

$$(1) \qquad (\partial \Sigma / \partial U^\alpha{}_{,\beta})_{,\beta} = 0,$$

as was shown by Kirchhoff **(4)**.

To obtain the equations of the theory of small deformations superimposed on (possibly) large deformations, one writes $U^\alpha = V^\alpha + W^\alpha$, linearizes Eq. (1) with respect to the W^α, and assumes that the displacement V^α satisfies (1).

Received September 13, 1955.

[1]The adjective "Lagrangian" is used more frequently. For reasons pointed out in **(7**, §14**)**, "material" is preferable.

We thus have

$$(2)\qquad \begin{cases} \partial\Sigma/\partial U^\alpha{}_{,\beta} = \partial\Sigma/\partial V^\alpha{}_{,\beta} + W^\gamma{}_{,\delta}\partial^2\Sigma/\partial V^\alpha{}_{,\beta}\partial V^\gamma{}_{,\delta}, \\ (\partial\Sigma/\partial V^\alpha{}_{,\beta})_{,\beta} = 0, \\ (W^\gamma{}_{,\delta}\partial^2\Sigma/\partial V^\alpha{}_{,\beta}\partial V^\gamma{}_{,\delta})_{,\beta} = 0. \end{cases}$$

Alternative formulations are given in **(1)** and **(6**, §55**)**. Here V^α is regarded as known, whereas W^α is to be determined by the linear equations (2) and appropriate boundary conditions. A displacement boundary value problem is set by specifying W^α on the bounding surface $\mathfrak{S}$ of $\mathfrak{R}$. To show that two displacement vectors satisfying these same conditions are identical, it suffices, because of linearity, to show that any W^α which satisfies (2) and vanishes on $\mathfrak{S}$ must vanish in $\mathfrak{R}$. For equations (1), one type of stress boundary value problem is set by specifying $N_\beta\partial\Sigma/\partial U^\alpha{}_{,\beta}$ on $\mathfrak{S}$, N_α being a unit vector normal to $\mathfrak{S}$. In the above linearized theory, this leads to a problem in which the quantities

$$(3)\qquad T_\alpha \equiv N_\beta W^\gamma{}_{,\delta}\partial^2\Sigma/\partial V^\alpha{}_{,\beta}\partial V^\gamma{}_{,\delta}$$

are specified on $\mathfrak{S}$.

If one sets $V^\alpha{}_{,\beta} = 0$ in (2), W^α becomes a small deformation about the state of zero deformation. It is customary to assume that $\partial\Sigma/\partial V^\alpha{}_{,\beta} = 0$ when $V^\alpha{}_{,\beta} = 0$. We make no use of this assumption. If one places certain restrictions on $\partial^2\Sigma/\partial V^\alpha{}_{,\beta}\,\partial V^\gamma{}_{,\delta}$ evaluated at $V^\alpha{}_{,\beta} = 0$, one obtains the usual equations of the classical linear theory of elasticity. For example, for isotropic materials, one takes

$$(4)\qquad \partial^2\Sigma/\partial V^\alpha{}_{,\beta}\partial V^\gamma{}_{,\delta}|_{V^\rho{}_{,\sigma}=0} = \lambda\delta^\beta_\alpha\delta^\delta_\gamma + \mu(\delta^\beta_\gamma\delta^\delta_\alpha + G^{\beta\delta}G_{\alpha\gamma})$$

where λ and μ are the Lamé constants and $G_{\alpha\beta}$ is the metric tensor. The boundary data (3), which become

$$(5)\qquad T_\alpha \equiv \lambda W^\beta{}_{,\beta}N_\alpha + \mu(W_{\alpha,\beta} + W_{\beta,\alpha})\,N^\beta$$

when (4) holds, is the data ordinarily prescribed in stress boundary value problems in the linear theory. The Kirchhoff uniqueness proof, valid when $(3\lambda + 2\mu)\,\mu > 0$, establishes that $T_\alpha = 0$ on $\mathfrak{S}$ implies that $W_{\alpha,\beta} + W_{\beta,\alpha} = 0$ in $\mathfrak{R}$. In other words, the boundary data (5) determines the displacement field W^α to within an infinitesimal rigid motion. It seems reasonable to expect that this uniqueness theorem will hold for the small deformation when $V^\alpha{}_{,\beta} \neq 0$ if suitable restrictions are placed on Σ and V^α. What constitutes a set of "suitable restrictions" on Σ is, according to Truesdell **(8)**, the main open problem in the theory of finite elastic deformations. We shall show that the desired uniqueness does not follow from Hadamard's stability condition.

2. Elastic stability. Hadamard **(2**, §269**)** calls a deformation stable whenever the second variation in total strain energy is non-negative for all variations in U^α which vanish on $\mathfrak{S}$. Formally, stability means that

(6) $$\Phi \equiv \delta^2 \int_{\mathfrak{R}} \Sigma dV \geqslant 0$$

whenever $\delta U^\alpha = \delta^2 U^\alpha = 0$ on $\mathfrak{S}$, dV being the volume element. We have $\Phi = \Phi_1 + \Phi_2$, where

(7) $$\Phi_1 = \int_{\mathfrak{R}} \delta^2 U^\alpha{}_{,\beta} \partial \Sigma / \partial U^\alpha{}_{,\beta} dV,$$
$$\Phi_2 = \int_{\mathfrak{R}} \delta U^\alpha{}_{,\beta} \delta U^\gamma{}_{,\delta} \partial^2 \Sigma / \partial U^\alpha{}_{,\beta} \partial U^\gamma{}_{,\delta} dV.$$

From (1), (6) and (7),

$$\Phi_1 = \int_{\mathfrak{R}} (\delta^2 U^\alpha \partial \Sigma / \partial U^\alpha{}_{,\beta})_{,\beta} dV = \oint_{\mathfrak{S}} \delta^2 U^\alpha \partial \Sigma / \partial U^\alpha{}_{,\beta} dS_\beta = 0$$

where dS_β is the vector element of area. Similarly, from (6) and (7),

(8) $$\Phi_2 = - \int_{\mathfrak{R}} \delta U^\alpha (\delta U^\gamma{}_{,\delta} \partial^2 \Sigma / \partial U^\alpha{}_{,\beta} \partial U^\gamma{}_{,\delta})_{,\beta} dV.$$

Thus (6) can be replaced by

$$\Phi_2 \geqslant 0 \text{ wherever } \delta U^\alpha = 0 \text{ on } \mathfrak{S},$$

Φ_2 being given by (7) or (8). An analysis made by Kelvin **(5)** suggests that it is desirable to distinguish neutral or labile stability, for which $\Phi_2 = 0$ for some $\delta U^\alpha \not\equiv 0$, from ordinary stability, for which $\Phi_2 = 0$ implies $\delta U^\alpha \equiv 0$, and we find it essential for our purposes to make this distinction. Henceforth, "stability" means ordinary stability, neutral stability being excluded. There was no reason for Hadamard to make this distinction since the results which he obtained are insensitive to it.

3. Uniqueness. We begin by proving a uniqueness theorem for displacement boundary value problems.

THEOREM 1. *In the theory of small deformations superimposed on large, if the large deformation is stable, the displacement boundary value problem for the small deformation has at most one solution.*

Proof. Let W^α be any solution of (2) such that $W^\alpha = 0$ on $\mathfrak{S}$. Multiplying the last of equations (2) by W^α, summing on α, and integrating the result over $\mathfrak{R}$, we obtain

$$\int_{\mathfrak{R}} W^\alpha (W^\gamma{}_{,\delta} \partial^2 \Sigma / \partial V^\alpha{}_{,\beta} \partial V^\gamma{}_{,\delta})_{,\beta} dV = 0.$$

From this and (8), we see that Φ_2, evaluated for $U^\alpha = V^\alpha$ and $\delta U^\alpha = W^\alpha$, vanishes. If V^α is stable, $\Phi_2 = 0$ implies $W^\alpha \equiv 0$. Thus, if a solution exists for a given displacement boundary value problem, it is unique.

We now proceed to determine necessary and sufficient conditions for the stability of the state of zero deformation of isotropic materials. In this case (4) holds and we obtain from (7) with $U^\alpha{}_{,\beta} = 0$,

$$\Phi_2 = \int_{\mathfrak{R}} [\lambda(\delta U^\alpha{}_{,\alpha})^2 + \mu(\delta U^\alpha{}_{,\beta}\delta U^\beta{}_{,\alpha} + \delta U^{\alpha,\beta}\delta U_{\alpha,\beta})]dV.$$

Using the fact that $\delta U^\alpha = 0$ on $\mathfrak{S}$, we have

$$0 = \int_{\mathfrak{S}} [\delta U^\alpha \delta U^\beta{}_{,\beta} - \delta U^\beta \delta U^\alpha{}_{,\beta}]dS_\alpha = \int_{\mathfrak{R}} [\delta U^\alpha \delta U^\beta{}_{,\beta} - \delta U^\beta \delta U^\alpha{}_{,\beta}]_{,\alpha} dV$$

$$= \oint_{\mathfrak{R}} [(\delta U^\alpha{}_{,\alpha})^2 - \delta U^\beta{}_{,\alpha}\delta U^\alpha{}_{,\beta}]dV.$$

Also,

$$\delta U^{\alpha,\beta}\delta U_{\alpha,\beta} = \delta U^\alpha{}_{,\beta}\delta U^\beta{}_{,\alpha} + 2\omega^{\alpha\beta}\omega_{\alpha\beta},$$

where $2\omega_{\alpha,\beta} = U_{\alpha,\beta} - U_{\beta,\alpha}$. Using these relations, we obtain

$$\Phi_2 = (\lambda + 2\mu)\int_{\mathfrak{R}} (\delta U^\alpha{}_{,\alpha})^2 dV + 2\mu \int_{\mathfrak{R}} \omega^{\alpha\beta}\omega_{\alpha\beta} dV, \tag{9}$$

a result due to Kelvin (**5**). Since each integral is non-negative, we have stability, or at least neutral stability, of zero deformation, so long as $\lambda + 2\mu \geqslant 0$ and $\mu \geqslant 0$. A slightly sharper result is easily obtained.

LEMMA. *For stability of the state of zero deformation of an isotropic elastic material, it is necessary and sufficient that* $\lambda + 2\mu > 0$ *and* $\mu > 0$.

Proof of sufficiency. If $\lambda + 2\mu > 0$ and $\mu > 0$, it is clear from (9) that $\Phi_2 \geqslant 0$, the equality holding if and only if $\delta U^\alpha{}_{,\alpha} = \omega^\alpha{}_\beta = 0$. These conditions imply that $\delta U_\alpha = \phi_{,\alpha}$, where ϕ is harmonic. Since $\phi_{,\alpha} = 0$ on $\mathfrak{S}$ and ϕ is harmonic in $\mathfrak{R}$, $\phi_{,\alpha} \equiv 0$. Hence $\Phi_2 > 0$, unless $\delta U^\alpha \equiv 0$.

Proof of necessity. To show that $\Phi_2 > 0$ implies $\lambda + 2\mu > 0$, it suffices to construct functions δU^α such that $\delta U^\alpha = 0$ on $\mathfrak{S}$, $\omega^\alpha{}_\beta \equiv 0$ in $\mathfrak{R}$, $\delta U^\alpha{}_{,\alpha} \not\equiv 0$, as is clear from (9). One can take $\delta U_\alpha = \psi_{,\alpha}$, where ψ is any function, not a constant, whose gradient vanishes on $\mathfrak{S}$. For example if, $\mathfrak{C} \subset \mathfrak{R}$ is a sphere of radius $r_0 > 0$, we may take $\psi = 0$ in $\mathfrak{R} - \mathfrak{C}$, $\psi = (r - r_0)^4$ in $\mathfrak{C}$, where r denotes the distance measured from the center of $\mathfrak{C}$. Similarly, to show that $\Phi_2 > 0$ implies $\mu > 0$, one need only construct δU^α with $\delta U^\alpha = 0$ on $\mathfrak{S}$, $\delta U^\alpha{}_{,\alpha} \equiv 0$, $\delta U^\alpha \not\equiv 0$, and use (9). Such variations are easily constructed.

THEOREM 2. *For the stress boundary value problem* (3), *stability of the deformation* V^α *does not imply that the displacements* W^α *will be determined to within an infinitesimal rigid motion.*

Proof. It suffices to establish that uniqueness does not follow from stability in the special case when $V^\alpha{}_{,\beta} = 0$ and (4) holds. By the lemma, we have stability if $3\lambda + 2\mu = 0$, $\mu > 0$. It follows, using (4), that (2) is satisfied by any W^α such that $W^\alpha{}_{,\beta} = a\,\delta^\alpha{}_\beta$, where a is an arbitrary constant. For any such displacement, (5), with $3\lambda + 2\mu = 0$, gives $T_\alpha = 0$ for arbitrary N_α. If $a \neq 0$, the displacement considered above is not an infinitesimal rigid motion, whence the theorem follows.

This theorem indicates that the definition of stability used here leads to results in disagreement with the intuitive notion, expounded by many writers in stability, that such non-uniqueness should be associated with instability. This might be regarded as an indication that it would be desirable to introduce further criteria to enable one to refine further the classification of types of stability used here.

THEOREM 3. *Neutral stability of the deformation V^α does not imply uniqueness of solutions to displacement boundary value problems in the theory of small deformations superimposed on large.*

Proof. Again it suffices to establish the theorem in the special case when (4) holds with $\lambda + 2\mu = 0$, $\mu > 0$. From (9) and the lemma, we then have neutral stability, but not stability. From the proof of the lemma, we can construct functions $W^\alpha = \psi^{,\alpha}$ such that $W^\alpha = 0$ on $\mathfrak{S}$, $W^\alpha \not\equiv 0$ in $\mathfrak{R}$. It follows easily, using (4), that when $\lambda + 2\mu = 0$, any such displacement satisfies (2). Since $W^\alpha \equiv 0$ is another solution satisfying the same boundary conditions, we do not have uniqueness.

Theorems 1 and 3 illustrate the importance of distinguishing between ordinary and neutral stability. As is pointed out by Whittaker (**9**, pp. 145–148), the case $\lambda + 2\mu = 0$, $\mu > 0$ is of some historical interest, having been considered as an aether theory.

REFERENCES

1. A. E. Green, R. S. Rivlin, and R. T. Shield, *General theory of small elastic deformations superposed on finite elastic deformations*, Proc. Roy. Soc. London (A), *211* (1951), 128–154.

2. J. Hadamard, *Leçons sur la propagation des ondes et les équations de l'hydrodynamique* (Paris, 1903).

3. O. D. Kellogg, *Foundations of Potential Theory* (New York, 1929).

4. G. Kirchhoff, *Ueber die Gleichungen des Gleichgewichts eines elastischen Körpers bei nicht unendlich kleinen Verschiebungen seiner Theile*, Akad. Wiss. Wien Sitz., *9* (1852), 762–773.

5. W. Thomson (Lord Kelvin), *On the reflexion and refraction of light*, Phil. Mag., *26* (1888), 414–425.

6. C. Truesdell, *The mechanical foundations of elasticity and fluid dynamics*, J. Rational Mech. Anal., *1* (1952), 125–300.

7. C. Truesdell, *The Kinematics of Vorticity* (Bloomington, 1954).

8. C. Truesdell, *Das ungelöste Hauptproblem der endlichen Elastizitätstheorie*, to appear in Z.a.M.M.

9. E. Whittaker, *A History of the Theories of Aether and Electricity* (New York, 1951).

Applied Mathematics Branch,
Naval Research Laboratory, Washington, D.C.

No. 10

THE ELASTIC DIELECTRIC

R. A. Toupin

Journal of Rational Mechanics and Analysis, Volume 5, pp. 849-916 (1956).

While notable success was gained in the nineteenth century by the theories of linearized elasticity and linear viscosity, the outcome of similar approaches to more entwined physical situations was not so happy. Between 1850 and 1950 anything was superimposed on everything, under the title of "approximation", until finally it was seen, at least by some, that nothing really comes out. The paper here reprinted is the first to treat simultaneous electrification and change of shape as physical phenomena worthy of thorough, thoughtful, and exact analysis. The first nine sections carefully gather and formalize the appropriate general concepts and principles, stripped clear of "approximations". Section 7 serves as a molecular motivation which may or may not be helpful, depending on the reader's background and inclinations. If some of the remaining explanation may seem surprising in view of the level of competence in mechanics presumed in other works in this volume, it may be remarked that this paper was written so as to be understandable also by physicists.

The constitutive assumptions of TOUPIN's theory are stated as Eqs. (9.2), (10.9), and (10.10). The final constitutive equations are (10.33) and (10.34), subject to the requirement of material indifference, which leads to the condition (10.36) on the skew part of the stress tensor.

In Section 11 the theory is specialized to isotropic materials, with the result that the stored-energy function may be regarded as a function of the six scalar invariants listed in Eq. (11.9). Eqs. (11.16) and (11.17) give more explicit forms for the constitutive equations.

Section 12 solves the problem of simple shear of an isotropic dielectric subject to homogeneous polarization in the plane of shear. As well as modifying the Poynting effect, the presence of polarization gives rise to an effect of electrostriction. The solution for general homogeneous strain in a homogeneously polarized material is then obtained and interpreted for an ellipsoidal specimen. By comparing this solution with measured values, for a sufficient range of parameters, the form of the stored-energy function could be determined from experiment.

After obtaining a reduced form for the stored-energy function of a material of arbitrary symmetry, the paper closes with a discussion of various linearized theories.

There are other ways of regarding both the general theory of electromagnetism in material media and the defining hypotheses of the present theory. For the former, see CFT, Chapter F. For the latter, and in particular for derivation from a "Lagrangean" variational principle, see a later paper by TOUPIN, **Stress tensors in elastic dielectrics**, Archive for Rational Mechanics and Analysis, Volume 5, pp. 440-452 (1960). Presentation of the fully dynamical theory suggested in Section 17 of the present paper is made the occasion for developing a new and simpler approach to the whole subject in TOUPIN's **A dynamical theory of the elastic dielectric**, Journal of Engineering Science, Volume 1, pp. 101-126 (1963).

Despite more recent researches, the paper here reprinted has lost none of its value. The frankness and depth of questioning, the completeness and precision of self-contained development, and the simple clarity of writing make it not only a classic of mechanics but also, even today, a work that can be given to a beginner with the counsel: read this, and not only will you see what modern continuum mechanics is about, but also you will learn how to work in it yourself.

The Elastic Dielectric

RICHARD A. TOUPIN

Communicated by C. TRUESDELL

CONTENTS

1. Introduction

Elastic dielectrics are an important and interesting class of solid materials. The photoelastic and piezoelectric effects are but two of the physical phenomena associated with elastic dielectrics which have found applications in engineering and in the laboratory. F. E. NEUMANN was the first to treat systematically the photoelastic effect in isotropic materials [1, 2].[1] POCKELS [3] extended NEUMANN's theory of the photoelastic effect to the case of crystalline media. What might be called the classical linear theory of piezoelectricity is generally attributed to VOIGT [4].[2]

The theories of NEUMANN, POCKELS, and VOIGT are restricted to the case of infinitesimal motions (strains and rotations). Also, certain limitations must be placed on the magnitude of the electric field to insure a consistent scheme of approximation. In the case of NEUMANN's photoelastic theory, some attempt has been made to treat large deformations [2, pp. 192–194]. The results which we obtain here are not inconsistent with the basic hypotheses of this extended Neumann theory of the photoelastic effect in *isotropic* materials. Although we have not made a detailed and specific study of the photoelastic effect in this paper, some of our results may be useful in the analysis of the photoelasticity of crystals. There have been attempts also to generalize VOIGT's linear piezoelectric relations to account for finite strain and higher order electrical effects [6]. Our results differ strikingly from the results of others, particularly for the class of elastic dielectrics whose degree of symmetry does not prohibit the piezoelectric effect. For example, if the general theory of elastic dielectrics developed here is specialized to a "polynomial approximation," we find that a "first order" theory results which is consistent with VOIGT's classical linear theory of the piezoelectric effect. However, if higher order "photoelastic" terms involving products of a displacement gradient and the electric field or polarization are retained in a consistent manner, the stress tensor does *not* reduce to a polynomial in the symmetric part of the displacement gradients only. The symmetric part of the displacement gradients is the customary measure of infinitesimal strain. It has been a common element of endeavors to generalize VOIGT's linear theory to assume that the stress tensor is a polynomial in the electric field (or polarization) and the elements of the infinitesimal strain measure. It can be demonstrated that this assumption violates the invariance of the stored energy to rigid rotations *even to the neglect of terms of first degree in the displacement gradients.*

The theory of stress and the mechanical equilibrium of dielectric media

---

[1] The historical development of theory and experiment on the photoelastic effect is traced in [2].

[2] VOIGT's work on the piezoelectric effect was originally reported in a series of papers dating from 1890. An excellent bibliography of this subject is given by CADY [5].

presents new problems not encountered in elasticity theory. The material contained in MAXWELL's original treatise cannot be considered definitive. This is according to his own admission [7, Vol. I, §111, p. 166]. LARMOR [8] considered some of the questions pertinent to the mechanics of continuous media which were raised by MAXWELL's theory of electricity and magnetism. New insight was gained with the advent of LORENTZ's particle model of continuous dielectric media [9], but the problem is yet unsettled. BORN's theory of polarizable lattices of particles [10] has done much to clarify the conceptual arrangement and the nature of the forces which determine the electromechanical behavior of crystalline dielectrics. The greatest progress has been made in the study of these particle models. However, the role played by the local field and a theory of stress in dielectrics based on the methods of continuum mechanics and MAXWELL's continuum theory of electricity and magnetism has received too little attention. To illustrate some of the novel questions which arise, we may cite the following: If the electric field and polarization are not parallel to each other, the Maxwell stress tensor in a dielectric medium is not symmetric. Hence, if the medium is to be in static equilibrium there must be an additional stress system whose antisymmetric part is equal and opposite to the antisymmetric part of the Maxwell stress tensor. For our immediate purposes, we may loosely refer to this additional stress system as the "elastic" or "local" stress tensor. Now the Maxwell tensor has the same form in all dielectric materials, whether they be elastic solids, fluids, or other forms of continuous media. The local stress is to be compared with the stress tensor of elasticity theory. There it is assumed that the stress is determined by the deformation and local thermodynamic state of the elastic medium through constitutive relations (stress-strain-temperature relations) whose form varies from one material to another. Is this the part of the stress then to which VOIGT refers in his theory of the piezoelectric effect? Of course, the Maxwell tensor is always quadratic in the electric field and polarization (the antisymmetric part is just $E^iP^j - P^iE^j$) and so is a quantity neglected within the context of the linear theory of piezoelectricity. But we must reckon with such problems in a general theory of the stress in dielectrics. That is, we must entertain the need for constitutive relations which yield an asymmetric stress tensor. It has been claimed elsewhere [11] that such constitutive relations can never be obtained from an energy principle.[3] In §10 of this paper we present an energy principle from which we obtain constitutive relations for an asymmetric local stress tensor. Furthermore, its antisymmetric part has just the required value.

As we have indicated above, there are many new problems not encountered in elasticity theory which must be considered when the combined effects of electrical and elastic properties of dielectrics are considered. For this reason,

[3] The proof is based on a formula relating the stress to derivatives of an energy function which is valid only in an approximation which neglects the antisymmetric part of the stress tensor.

we have reviewed in some detail the essential preliminary topics of kinematics of continuous media, the theory of stress, and the Maxwell-Faraday electrostatics. The material in these sections is conventional for the most part. Some relatively new and interesting material is introduced in the section on Euclidean tensors. The notion of two-point tensor fields and the application of these tensors in the kinematics of continuous media may be of interest even to those not interested in dielectrics. To illustrate the general theory, we have dealt at some length with the isotropic dielectric. Solutions for the homogeneous deformation of an isotropic dielectric ellipsoid and of an infinite slab placed in a uniform external electric field are given as illustrations of the qualitative features of the behavior of elastic dielectrics predicted by the theory. Finally, the theory has been specialized by assuming a special form for the stored energy function. We have done this so that a comparison with the existing approximate theories of the stress and field relations in dielectrics could be made. As far as possible we shall adhere to the notation and shall make free use of the formalism and results of continuum mechanics as presented in the comprehensive review article by C. TRUESDELL [12].

2. Static Equilibrium States of a Continuous Medium

Each point of a continuous medium may be assigned certain physical properties such as position, temperature, density, crystallographic directions, chemical constitution, polarization, stress, *etc.* What constitutes an independent set of such variables will depend on the nature of the substance and on the range of physical phenomena encompassed by the particular theory under consideration. The *local state* of a point in the medium is known if, at the point, the values of an independent set of state variables are specified. A function of the independent variables will be called a *state function.* If the local state of *every* point in the medium is known, we shall say that the *global state* of the medium is known. The distinction which has been made between the concepts of local state and global state will be found useful. For example, consider the gravitational self field of a continuous medium. Let the density of mass ρ be chosen as one of the independent state variables. Then the gravitational potential φ satisfies the Poisson equation $\nabla^2\varphi = -G\rho$. Hence, the potential is not a state function; however, its value at any point may be determined if the global state of the medium is specified.[4] It is, in a broad sense, a functional on the global state of the medium. The environment of a continuous medium consists of the alterable external influences to which we may subject the medium. We shall assume that the medium responds to changes in its environment and that when these changes have ceased the local state of each point in the medium assumes essentially unique equilibrium values commensurate with the static environment.

For the purpose of this work we shall define an elastic dielectric as a continuous medium whose local state is determined by the local deformation of the medium relative to some natural state and by the electric polarization density. It is clear that we are ignoring many interesting physical phenomena by this limited choice of independent state variables. For example, temperature effects will not be considered. Variables which provide a quantitative measure of the deformation and polarization will be defined and their properties will be discussed at the appropriate time. The environment of the elastic dielectric will be a prescribed set of mechanical surface tractions and an externally applied electric field. Hence, we set ourselves the problem: Can a determinate theory based on the principles of mechanics and electrostatics be established which will fix the global state of an elastic dielectric as defined here if the mechanical surface tractions and external electric field are prescribed data?

---

[4] Certain continuity and boundary conditions must also be supplied in order that the Poisson equation admit a unique solution.

3. Coordinate Systems and Two-Point Tensor Fields in Euclidean Space

The motion of a continuous medium is conveniently described in terms of two coordinate systems which simultaneously span Euclidean space [12, 13]. The two coordinate systems are introduced in a description of the motion in the following way. A reference configuration of the material particles P of the medium is prescribed by giving the coordinate values $X^A(P)$ of the positions of the particles in one freely chosen coordinate system. If the medium is deformed or displaced rigidly, the material particles move to new positions which may be specified by giving their coordinate values $x^i(P)$ in a second freely chosen coordinate system. For example, the reference configuration of a rectangular block of material may be conveniently described in a rectangular Cartesian coordinate system. If the block is deformed into a spherical cap, it may prove convenient to describe this deformed configuration in a spherical polar coordinate system. Some workers in elasticity theory prefer the use of the so-called convected coordinate systems. Here, the choice of the second coordinate system is made in such a way that the coordinate values of the position of a given particle are the same in the reference and deformed configurations. Thus, each motion or deformed configuration implies a new choice of the second coordinate system. We mention this only as an example since we do not restrict ourselves to this convention. New problems arise in the mathematical formalism of continuum mechanics because of this use of two simultaneous coordinate systems. For this reason we shall review and extend some of the fundamental notions of the tensor analysis.

Since the space is Euclidean, it can be spanned by a rectangular Cartesian net Z^α. The metric tensor in this coordinate system is just the Kronecker delta, $\delta_{\alpha\beta}$. Let V_1^α be the rectangular Cartesian components of a vector at the point Z_1^α. The vector $\mathbf{V}_1$ can be translated by parallel displacement to a second point Z_2^α. The law of parallel displacement is particularly simple in Euclidean space if the coordinate system is rectangular Cartesian. For in this case, the components V_2^α of the displaced vector are numerically equal to the given components V_1^α. Let $V_1^{\alpha\beta\cdots}$ be the components of a tensor of arbitrary rank defined at the point Z_1^α. The components $V_2^{\alpha\beta\cdots}$ of the parallel displaced tensor at an arbitrary point Z_2^α are then given by

$$V_2^{\alpha\beta\cdots} = \delta_\gamma^\alpha \delta_\lambda^\beta \cdots V_1^{\gamma\lambda\cdots}. \tag{3.1}$$

The simplicity of this formula, indeed, its triviality, we owe to the choice of coordinate systems in which we have expressed the components of $\mathbf{V}_1$ and $\mathbf{V}_2$. We wish to obtain the formula analogous to (3.1) for the case when the coordinate system is not rectangular Cartesian. In fact, we wish to allow that the components of $\mathbf{V}_1$ and $\mathbf{V}_2$ might be referred to two different curvilinear coordinate systems. This is done easily and the results are quite useful. Let two coordinate transformations be defined on the Z^α,

$$X^A = X^A(Z^\alpha), \qquad Z^\alpha = Z_1^\alpha(X^A); \qquad x^i = x^i(Z^\alpha), \qquad Z^\alpha = Z_2^\alpha(x^i). \tag{3.2}$$

The metric tensor in these two coordinate systems has components given by

$$g_{AB} = \delta_{\alpha\beta} \frac{\partial Z_1^\alpha}{\partial X^A} \frac{\partial Z_1^\beta}{\partial X^B}, \qquad g_{ij} = \delta_{\alpha\beta} \frac{\partial Z_2^\alpha}{\partial x^i} \frac{\partial Z_2^\beta}{\partial x^j}. \tag{3.3}$$

Now define the parallel displacement two-point tensor field $g_i^A(\mathbf{X}, \mathbf{x})$ by

$$g_i^A(\mathbf{X}, \mathbf{x}) \equiv \delta_\beta^\alpha \frac{\partial X^A}{\partial Z^\alpha} \frac{\partial Z_2^\beta}{\partial x^i}. \tag{3.4}$$

Note that g_i^A is not an ordinary tensor field. In order to fix the values of its components two points must be specified. That is, *the* g_i^A *are functions of six independent variables.* Ordinary single-point tensor fields are ordered sets of functions of only *three* independent variables—namely, the coordinates of a single point in the region of space where the tensor field is defined.[5] Simple examples of the displacement tensor are obtained when both coordinate transformations (3.2) reduce to the identity transformation or when both transformations (3.2) yield new coordinate systems which are again rectangular Cartesian. In the first instance, the displacement tensor is just δ_β^α, while in the second instance, the displacement tensor is an orthogonal matrix which would carry the two sets of transformed coordinate axes into parallel sets. In a more general situation when either or both of the coordinate systems are curvilinear, the components of the displacement tensor will be non-constant functions of the six variables, X^A and x^i. If we are given the components of the displacement tensor in one set of coordinate systems (X^A, x^i), the values of the components in a second set (X^{*A}, x^{*i}), where $X^{*A} = X^{*A}(X)$, $x^{*i} = x^{*i}(x)$ are independent coordinate transformations on the two argument points, the new values of the components of the displacement tensor are given by

$$g^{*A}_{\ \ i} = g_j^B \frac{\partial X^{*A}}{\partial X^B} \frac{\partial x^j}{\partial x^{*i}}. \tag{3.5}$$

The formula which generalizes (3.1) and is invariant to the choice of coordinate systems in which we wish to express the tensor $V_1^{AB\cdots}$ or its translated counterpart $V_2^{ij\cdots}$ is

$$V_2^{ij\cdots} = g_A^i g_B^j \cdots V_1^{AB\cdots}. \tag{3.6}$$

That is, for fixed x^i, the $V_2^{ij\cdots}$ are the components in the coordinate system x^i of the tensor obtained from $V_1^{AB\cdots}$ by parallel displacement of this tensor from

[5] We restrict our attention to three-dimensional Euclidean space. Many of our statements are trivially generalized to flat spaces of arbitrary dimension.

the point X^A to the point x^i. A useful application of the displacement tensor is illustrated by the following example. Let $f^i(\mathbf{x})$ be the components of the force per unit of volume on a continuous medium. The *resultant* or *total* force on the medium is an important quantity in Newtonian mechanics. If the components f^i of the force density are given in a curvilinear coordinate system, the integrals $\int f^i\,dV$ taken over the body are *not* the components of the resultant force. In fact, the three integrals so obtained do not transform as the components of a vector under general coordinate transformations. Only if the components f^i refer to the rectangular Cartesian components[6] of the force density will these integrals yield the components of the resultant force. In order to calculate the resultant force in a manner which is invariant to the choice of coordinate system, we must translate the force on each infinitesimal region of the body to a fixed common point by parallel displacement. The resultant force can then be obtained by summing or integrating *at that fixed point*. That is,

$$F^A(\mathbf{X}) = \int g^A_{\ i}(\mathbf{X}, \mathbf{x}) f^i(\mathbf{x})\,dV \tag{3.7}$$

are the components of the resultant force as they appear at the point $\mathbf{X}$. The point $\mathbf{X}$ may be chosen freely. Note that the components F^A are the components of the resultant force $\mathbf{F}$, not in the coordinate system in which the f^i were given, but in the coordinate system X^A. The form of integral expressions of non-scalar tensor quantities such as resultant force, resultant moment, resultant angular momentum, *etc.*, which is invariant to choice of coordinate system will have the structure indicated by this example. Unless the factor $g^A_{\ i}$ is included in the integrand, such integrals of non-scalar quantities in curvilinear coordinate systems have no particular transformation properties or physical significance.

Let $T^{AB\cdots ij}_{CD\cdots kl}(\mathbf{X}, \mathbf{x})$ be the components of a two-point tensor field of arbitrary rank. Corresponding to (3.5) we have the general transformation law,

$$T^{*AB\cdots ij}_{\ \ CD\cdots kl} = (x/x^*)^w (X/X^*)^W T^{EF\cdots mn}_{GH\cdots pq} \frac{\partial X^{*A}}{\partial X^E} \frac{\partial X^{*B}}{\partial X^F} \frac{\partial X^G}{\partial X^{*C}} \cdots \frac{\partial x^{*i}}{\partial x^n} \frac{\partial x^q}{\partial x^{*l}}, \tag{3.8}$$

for a two-point relative tensor of weight w with respect to $\mathbf{x}$ transformations and weight W with respect to $\mathbf{X}$ transformations. (x/x^*) and (X/X^*) denote the Jacobians of the coordinate transformations. An *absolute* two-point tensor field is a relative two-point tensor field with both weights zero.[7]

---

[6] More precisely, the components f^i may be any set obtained from a rectangular Cartesian set by an affine transformation.

[7] Michal [14] emphasized the use of two-point tensor fields in the kinematics of continuous media. Ericksen & Doyle [15] further developed the formalism and applications. Truesdell suggested the apt notation $g^A_{\ i}$ for the displacement tensor and suggests calling it the "shifter." The tensor formalism which we use here is a natural extension of Truesdell's [12]. Many of the formulæ of the kinematics and mechanics of continuous media which have previously defied efforts to place them in coordinate invariant form can now be so written with the help of two-point tensor fields, in particular, with the aid of the displacement tensor or shifter.

We shall denote *partial covariant derivatives* with respect to either type of index by a comma followed by the appropriate index. The partial covariant derivative of a two-point tensor field is defined as follows:

$$T^{A\cdots}_{i\cdots,C} = \frac{\partial T^{A\cdots}_{i\cdots}}{\partial X^C} + T^{D\cdots}_{i\cdots}\Gamma^A_{DC} + \cdots$$
$$T^{A\cdots}_{i\cdots,j} = \frac{\partial T^{A\cdots}_{i\cdots}}{\partial x^k} - T^A_k\Gamma^k_{ij} + \cdots . \tag{3.9}$$

That is, the partial covariant derivative is defined as for single-point tensor fields if we regard the upper case (lower case) indices as mere labels when differentiating covariantly with respect to a lower case (upper case) index. A further word of caution—the two-point tensor field is a function of six independent variables; therefore, the partial derivative indicated in the formulæ (3.9) means a partial derivative holding the remaining *five* independent variables fixed. The Christoffel symbols Γ^C_{AB} and Γ^i_{jk} are given by

$$\Gamma^C_{AB} = \frac{\partial^2 Z^\alpha_1}{\partial X^A\, \partial X^B}\frac{\partial X^C}{\partial Z^\alpha}, \qquad \Gamma^k_{ij} = \frac{\partial^2 Z^\alpha_2}{\partial x^i\, \partial x^j}\frac{\partial x^k}{\partial Z^\alpha}. \tag{3.10}$$

As a special case of (3.9) we have

$$g^A_{i,j} = \frac{\partial g^A_i}{\partial x^j} - g^A_k\Gamma^k_{ij} . \tag{3.11}$$

From the definitions of the parallel displacement tensor and the Christoffel symbols we have

$$\frac{\partial g^A_i}{\partial x^j} = \frac{\partial X^A}{\partial Z^\alpha}\frac{\partial^2 Z^\alpha_2}{\partial x^i\, \partial x^j} = g^A_k\Gamma^k_{ij} . \tag{3.12}$$

Substituting (3.12) into (3.11) it follows that the partial covariant derivative of the displacement tensor vanishes,

$$g^A_{i,j} = 0. \tag{3.13}$$

By similar argument we can show that $g^A_{i,B} = 0$ and as usual that

$$g_{AB,C} = 0, \qquad g_{ij,k} = 0. \tag{3.14}$$

One may readily verify that

$$g_{AB} = g_{ij}g^i_Ag^j_B . \tag{3.15}$$

The identification of the particles P of a continuous medium with their coordinates $X^A(P)$ in a reference configuration and a second identification of the particles with their coordinates $x^i(P)$ in a deformed configuration leads to the existence of a one-to-one mapping of the points $X^A \in V_0$ onto the points $x^i \in V$,

$$x^i = x^i(X^A), \qquad X^A = X^A(x^i), \tag{3.16}$$

where V_0 is the region of space occupied by the body in the reference configuration and V is the region of space occupied by the body in the deformed configuration. We shall assume for our purposes here that the mapping (3.16) is differentiable as many times as may be desired. In the mechanics of continuous media we are concerned with two-point tensor fields $T^{A\cdots}_{i\cdots}(\mathbf{X}, \mathbf{x})$ which are defined for values of the arguments X^A and x^i which range over the regions V_0 and V respectively. However, we wish to consider the case when the argument points X^A and x^i are not independent but are functionally related by the mapping (3.16). Under these circumstances, we shall define the *total covariant derivative* of a two-point tensor field which we denote by the semicolon followed by the appropriate index,

$$\begin{aligned} T^{A\cdots}_{i\cdots;B} &\equiv T^{A\cdots}_{i\cdots,B} + T^{A\cdots}_{i\cdots,j}x^j{}_{;B} \\ T^{A\cdots}_{i\cdots;j} &\equiv T^{A\cdots}_{i\cdots,j} + T^{A\cdots}_{i\cdots,B}X^B{}_{;j} \end{aligned} \tag{3.17}$$

where we have set $x^i{}_{;A} \equiv \partial x^i/\partial X^A$, $X^A{}_{;i} \equiv \partial X^A/\partial x^i$. It follows from (3.17) and the relations $x^i{}_{;A}X^A{}_{;j} = \delta^i{}_j$, $x^i{}_{;A}X^B{}_{;i} = \delta^B_A$, that

$$\begin{aligned} T^A_{i;B} &= T^A_{i;j}x^j{}_{;B} \\ T^A_{i;j} &= T^A_{i;B}X^B{}_{;j} . \end{aligned} \tag{3.18}$$

It should be noted that if the argument points of a two-point tensor field are not functionally independent but are related by a mapping, then either of the ordinary covariant derivatives (3.9) is ambiguous; but the total covariant derivative is not.

4. Measures of Deformation and Rotation

Let C_0 denote the reference configuration of the material particles of a continuous medium and let C denote any other configuration. Let (3.16) be the mapping which relates the coordinates of the particles in the configurations C_0 and C.

Consider now the two points X^A and $X^A + dX^A$ of the medium in the configuration C_0. The same two particles in the configuration C will have coordinates x^i and $x^i + dx^i$, and since we refer to the same two particles, their respective coordinates will be related by the mapping (3.16). In particular, we have

$$dx^i = dX^A \, x^i{}_{;A} \, . \tag{4.1}$$

The square of the distance between the two particles in the configuration C_0 is given by

$$dS^2 = g_{AB} \, dX^A \, dX^B = c_{ij} \, dx^i \, dx^j, \tag{4.2}$$

where

$$c_{ij} = g_{AB} X^A{}_{;i} X^B{}_{;j} \, . \tag{4.3}$$

The square of the distance between the particles in the configuration C is given by

$$ds^2 = g_{ij} \, dx^i \, dx^j = C_{AB} \, dX^A \, dX^B \tag{4.4}$$

with

$$C_{AB} = g_{ij} x^i{}_{;A} x^j{}_{;B} \, . \tag{4.5}$$

Now consider the sphere at X^A swept out by the vectors dX^A which satisfy the condition $k^2 = G_{AB} \, dX^A \, dX^B$. The set of points on this sphere is carried by the mapping (3.16) into the quadric surface $k^2 = c_{ij} \, dx^i \, dx^j$ at the point x^i. From the non-singular character of the mapping and the positive definiteness of g_{AB}, it follows that c_{ij} is a positive definite matrix; hence, the quadric at x^i is an ellipsoid. Similarly, the points which satisfy the condition $l^2 = g_{ij} \, dx^i \, dx^j$ and which constitute a sphere at x^i are carried by the inverse mapping into the ellipsoid $l^2 = C_{AB} \, dX^A \, dX^B$ at the point X^A. The two ellipsoids that we have introduced above are called the *spatial* and *material strain ellipsoids*. Let n_Γ^i ($\Gamma = 1, 2, 3$) be an orthogonal triplet of unit vectors at the point x^i,

$$g_{ij} n_\Gamma^i n_\Delta^j = \delta_{\Gamma\Delta} \, ,$$

and N_Γ^A a similar triplet at the point X^A,

$$g_{AB} N_\Gamma^A N_\Delta^B = \delta_{\Gamma\Delta} \, .$$

We can always orient these orthonormal triplets so that they satisfy the equations

$$c_{ij}n_\Gamma^i = c_\Gamma n_{\Gamma j}\ , \qquad C_{AB}N_\Gamma^A = C_\Gamma N_{\Gamma B}\ , \tag{4.6}$$

where the c_Γ and C_Γ are the eigenvalues of the matrices c_j^i and C_B^A and satisfy the cubic characteristic equations

$$\det \|c^i{}_j - c_\Gamma \delta^i{}_j\| = 0, \qquad \det \|C^A{}_B - C_\Gamma \delta^A{}_B\| = 0. \tag{4.7}$$

If c_Γ , n_Γ^i is a solution of $(4.6)_1$, $(4.7)_1$, it can be shown that C_Γ and N_Γ^A given by

$$\begin{aligned} C_\Gamma &= c_\Gamma^{-1} \\ N_\Gamma^A &= X^A{}_{,k}n_\Gamma^k/\sqrt{c_\Gamma} \end{aligned} \tag{4.8}$$

constitute a solution of $(4.6)_2$, $(4.7)_2$. If the eigenvalues $c_\Gamma(C_\Gamma)$ are distinct, then the orthonormal triplets $\pm n_\Gamma^i(\pm N_\Gamma^A)$ which satisfy (4.6) are uniquely determined. In this case the eigenvalues c_Γ and C_Γ may be ordered $c_1 > c_2 > c_3$, $C_1 < C_2 < C_3$ and (4.8) constitutes a unique pairing of the eigenvalues and eigenvectors of **c** and **C**. The sign of a normalized eigenvector always remains arbitrary; however, in (4.8) we have made a choice of sign for the square root of c_Γ which fixes the signs of the N_Γ^A in terms of the signs of the n_Γ^k . We shall adhere to this convention in what follows. Now consider the vector $L_\Gamma^A = L_\Gamma N_\Gamma^A$ of length $L_\Gamma > 0$ and parallel to an eigenvector of C_{AB} . It is carried by the mapping into the vector $L_\Gamma^i = (L_\Gamma + \Delta L_\Gamma)x^i{}_{,A}N^A$ of length $(L_\Gamma + \Delta L_\Gamma) > 0$. The vector L^A is carried by the mapping in the sense that a curve of points $X^A(t)$, passing through the point X^A and whose tangent $\dot{X}^A(t)$ at that point is parallel to N^A, is carried by the mapping into a curve $x^i(t)$, passing through the point x^i and whose tangent $\dot{x}^i(t)$ at x^i is locally parallel to n_Γ^i . The ratio of lengths, $L_\Gamma/(L_\Gamma + \Delta L_\Gamma)$ coincides with the ratio of lengths of tangents, $\sqrt{G_{AB}\dot{X}^A\dot{X}^B}/\sqrt{g_{ij}\dot{x}^i\dot{x}^j}$. From $(4.8)_2$ it follows easily that $(L_\Gamma + \Delta L_\Gamma)/L_\Gamma = \sqrt{C_\Gamma}$. Similarly, the vector $l_\Gamma^i = (l_\Gamma + \Delta l_\Gamma)n_\Gamma^i$ is carried by the inverse mapping into the vector $l_\Gamma^A = l_\Gamma N_\Gamma^A$ where $(l_\Gamma + \Delta l_\Gamma)/l_\Gamma = 1/\sqrt{C_\Gamma}$. Hence, by $(4.8)_1$, the ratios $\Delta L_\Gamma/L_\Gamma$ and $\Delta l_\Gamma/l_\Gamma$ have a common value, say δ_Γ . These are the *principal extensions*. The quantities $(1 + \delta_\Gamma)$ are called *principal extension ratios*. The tensors c_{ij} and C_{AB} are called the *Cauchy-Green deformation tensors* and their eigenvectors n_Γ^i and N_Γ^A determine the *principal spatial* and *material axes of strain*.

Let X^A and x^i be the coordinates of the same material particle in the configurations C_0 and C and let the principal extensions for this particle be distinct. Translate the orthonormal triplet n_Γ^i by parallel displacement from the point x^i to the point X^A. We can then write

$$N_\Gamma^A = R^A{}_B n_\Gamma^B\ , \qquad n_\Gamma^B = g^B{}_i n_\Gamma^i\ , \tag{4.9}$$

whereby a unique rotation matrix $R^A{}_B$, $g_{AB}R^A{}_C R^A{}_C R^B{}_D = g_{CD}$, is determined. The matrix $R^A{}_B$ has a single real vector invariant which we denote by k^A, $R^A{}_B k^B = k^A$, $k^A k_A = 1$, and a single independent scalar invariant, say R_A^A . The rotation of the orthogonal triplet n_Γ^A into the orthogonal triplet N_Γ^A is the result of a rotation through an angle θ about an axis parallel to k^A. The cosine of θ is fixed by the relation $R_A^A = 1 + 2 \cos \theta$. We may take the scalar function, $W = \frac{1}{4}(3 - R_A^A)$, $0 \leqq W \leqq 1$, and the vector invariant k^A as a measure of the local rotation of the configuration C with respect to the configuration C_0. If $W \ll 1$, the local rotation is said to be small. It should be noted that at a point where $W = 0$, k^A is undefined.

If

$$W_{;A} = 0, \qquad k^A{}_{;B} = 0, \qquad C_{AB;C} = 0, \tag{4.10}$$

the deformation is *homogeneous*. If

$$W = 0, \qquad \mathbf{C} \text{ arbitrary} \tag{4.11}$$

we have a *pure deformation*, which is a special case of

$$W = \text{constant}, \qquad k^A{}_{;B} = 0, \qquad \mathbf{C} \text{ arbitrary} \tag{4.12}$$

which differs from a pure deformation by a gross rigid motion of the configuration C with respect to the configuration C_0.

The components of the orthonormal triplets N_Γ^A and n_Γ^i satisfy the relations,

$$\sum_\Gamma N_\Gamma^A N_\Gamma^B = g^{AB}, \qquad \sum_\Gamma n_\Gamma^i n_\Gamma^j = g^{ij}. \tag{4.13}$$

And the following relations hold between the components of the tensors C^{AB}, c^{ij}, their eigenvalues C_Γ, c_Γ, and the N_Γ^A, n_Γ^i:

$$c^{ij} = \sum_\Gamma c_\Gamma n_\Gamma^i n_\Gamma^j, \qquad C^{AB} = \sum_\Gamma C_\Gamma N_\Gamma^A N_\Gamma^B. \tag{4.14}$$

We also have the more general relations

$$(c^n)^{ij} = \sum_\Gamma c_\Gamma^n n_\Gamma^i n_\Gamma^j, \qquad (C^n)^{AB} = \sum_\Gamma C_\Gamma^n N_\Gamma^A N_\Gamma^B, \tag{4.15}$$

where n may be a fractional exponent. Using (4.8–9) and (4.13–15), one can readily verify the important relations,

$$(C^n)^{AB} = R^A{}_C R^B{}_D g^C{}_i g^D{}_j (c^{-n})^{ij}, \tag{4.16}$$

$$(c^n)_{ij} = R^A{}_C R^B{}_D g^C{}_i g^D{}_j (C^{-n})_{AB}, \tag{4.17}$$

$$x^i{}_{,A} = (c^{-\frac{1}{2}})^i{}_j g^j{}_B R_A{}^B = (C^{\frac{1}{2}})^B{}_A g^i{}_C R_B{}^C, \tag{4.18}$$

$$X^A{}_{,i} = (C^{-\frac{1}{2}})^A{}_C g^B{}_i R^C{}_B = (c^{\frac{1}{2}})^j{}_i g^B{}_j R^A{}_B. \tag{4.19}$$

Consider the vector dX^A at the point X^A. It is carried by the mapping into the vector $dx^i = x^i{}_{;A}\, dX^A$. Using (4.18), the vector dx^i can be written in the form $dx^i = (c^{-\frac{1}{2}})^i{}_j g^j{}_B R_A{}^B\, dX^A$. This latter form of dx^i can be read as follows: The vector dX^A is first rotated rigidly into the vector $dX^{*B} = R_A{}^B\, dX^A$, then translated by parallel displacement to the point x^i which gives us the components $dx^{*i} = g^i{}_B\, dX^{*B}$ of the vector at that point. Finally, the vector dx^{*i} is stretched into the vector $dx^i = (c^{-\frac{1}{2}})^i{}_j \, dx^{*j}$. Hence, (4.18) constitutes a local decomposition of the motion of a continuous medium into a rotation followed by a displacement and a final "stretching."[8]

The tensors $c^i{}_j$, $C^A{}_B$ and $R^A{}_B$ measure the finite relative deformation and rotation of two configurations of a continuous medium in the way we have described. In order to summarize the description of the motion in terms of these tensors we may state: The mapping $x^i = x^i(X^A)$ carries a sphere of points in the neighborhood of a given point X^A in the configuration C_0 into an ellipsoid of points in the neighborhood of x^i in the configuration C. Conversely, a sphere of points in the neighborhood of x^i in the configuration C is carried into an ellipsoid of points in the neighborhood of X^A by the inverse mapping. The principal axes of the ellipsoids are eigenvectors of the symmetric tensors c^{ij} and C_{AB}. If the eigenvalues of c^{ij} and C_{AB} are distinct, there is a unique set of three mutually orthogonal directions at X^A which are carried by the mapping into three corresponding mutually orthogonal directions at x^i. These directions are the three uniquely determined eigenvectors of C_{AB} and of c_{ij}, respectively. The principal extension ratios $(1 + \delta_\Gamma)$ are related to the eigenvalues of c_{ij} and C_{AB} by $(1 + \delta_\Gamma) = \sqrt{C_\Gamma} = 1/\sqrt{c_\Gamma}$. The rotation tensor $R^A{}_B$ rotates the translated orthogonal triplet of eigenvectors of c_{ij} into coincidence with the orthogonal triplet of eigenvectors of C_{AB}.

In order to reduce the general theory of the elastic dielectric to a linear approximation which can be compared with the classical linear theory of VOIGT and others, we shall have to show how the tensor measures, **c**, **C**, and **R**, of *finite* strain and rotation are related to the corresponding measures of *infinitesimal* strain and rotation. Let R^A and r^i be the position vectors of the material particle P in the configurations C_0 and C. The components of the position vectors in the arbitrary coordinate systems X^A and x^i are related to the rectangular Cartesian coordinates Z_1^α of P in C_0 and Z_2^α of P in C by the formulæ,

$$R^A = Z_1^\alpha \frac{\partial X^A}{\partial Z^\alpha}, \qquad r^i = Z_2^\alpha \frac{\partial x^i}{\partial Z^\alpha}, \tag{4.20}$$

where $X^A(Z)$ and $x^i(Z)$ are the coordinate transformations (3.2). The total covariant derivatives of the position vectors reduce to

$$R^A{}_{;B} = \delta^A{}_B, \qquad r^i{}_{;j} = \delta^i{}_j. \tag{4.21}$$

The displacement vector of the particle X^A is defined by

$$U^A \equiv g^A{}_i r^i - R^A. \tag{4.22}$$

From (3.13), (3.18), and (4.21), it follows that

$$x^i{}_{,A} = g^i{}_B(U^B{}_{;A} + \delta^B{}_A) \tag{4.23}$$

[8] Note that if and only if dX^A is an eigenvector of C_{AB} will this final stretching not involve a further rotation of the vector dx^{*i}.

$$X^A{}_{;i} = g^A{}_j(\delta^j{}_i - u^j{}_{;i}) \tag{4.24}$$

where $U^A{}_{;B}$ and $u^i{}_{;j} \equiv U^A{}_{;j}g^i{}_A$ are called *displacement gradients.* Note that these are distinct tensors and, in general, we do *not* have $u^i{}_{;j} = g^i{}_A g^B{}_j U^A{}_{;B}$. Eliminating $x^i{}_{;A}$ and $X^A{}_{;i}$ from (4.23–24) we get

$$U^B{}_{;A} = g^B{}_i g^i{}_C(U^C{}_{;A} + \delta^C{}_A)u^i{}_{;i} . \tag{4.25}$$

It follows from (4.25) that if the physical components [21] of either set of displacement gradients are small, then the physical components of the other set are correspondingly small. To first order terms in the displacement gradients, (4.25) reduces to

$$U_{B;A} \cong g^i{}_B g^j{}_A u_{i;j} . \tag{4.26}$$

Substituting (4.23) and (4.24) into the defining relations, (4.3) and (4.5), of the Cauchy-Green deformation tensors, we obtain expressions for these tensors in terms of the displacement gradients,

$$C_{AB} = g_{AB} + (U_{A;B} + U_{B;A}) + g_{CD}U^C{}_{;A}U^D{}_{;B} , \tag{4.27}$$

$$c_{ij} = g_{ij} - (u_{i;j} + u_{j;i}) + g_{kl}u^k{}_{;i}u^l{}_{;j} . \tag{4.28}$$

Eliminating $x^i{}_{;A}$ from (4.18) and (4.23), we get

$$R_A{}^B = g^B{}_j g^C{}_i (c^{\frac{1}{2}})^{ij}(U_{C;A} + g_{CA}). \tag{4.29}$$

Retaining only first and zero order terms in the displacement gradients, we obtain the following approximate relations from (4.27–29):

$$C_{AB} - g_{AB} \cong (U_{A;B} + U_{B;A}) = 2\tilde{E}_{AB} , \tag{4.30}$$

$$g_{ij} - c_{ij} \cong (u_{i;j} + u_{j;i}) = 2\tilde{e}_{ij} , \tag{4.31}$$

$$g_{ij} - (c^{\frac{1}{2}})_{ij} \cong \tilde{e}_{ij} , \tag{4.32}$$

$$R_{AB} - G_{AB} \cong \tfrac{1}{2}(U_{B;A} - U_{A;B}) = \Omega_{BA} \tag{4.33}$$

$$\Omega_{AB} \cong \tfrac{1}{2}g^i{}_A g^j{}_B(u_{j;i} - u_{i;j}) = g^i{}_A g^j{}_B \omega_{ij} , \tag{4.34}$$

where we have introduced the notation $\tilde{E}_{AB}$ and $\Omega_{AB}(\tilde{e}_{ij}$ and $\omega_{ij})$ for the symmetric and antisymmetric parts of the displacement gradients $U_{A;B}(u_{i;j})$. The symmetric and antisymmetric parts of the displacement gradients are the tensors used to measure infinitesimal strain and rotation in the classical linear theory of elasticity and in VOIGT's theory of the elastic dielectric. The approximate relations (4.30–34) exhibit clearly the relations between these tensor measures of infinitesimal strain and rotation and the tensor measures of finite strain and rotation. In addition, it is seen that no distinction need be made between the displacement gradients $U_{A;B}$ and $u_{i;j}$ in any description of the deformation of a continuous medium which discards all nonlinear terms in either set of displacement gradients.

5. Static Mechanical Equilibrium of Continuous Media

Let the dielectric medium occupy a regular region V with boundary B. We assume that the medium is in static equilibrium with a set of mechanical surface tractions T^i and an external electric field E_0^i. If a particle in the medium is polarized there will be an interaction of the particle with the external field. This interaction gives rise to an extrinsic body force density f^i and an extrinsic body moment density m^{ij} which act on the particle. The magnitude and direction of this force and moment will depend on the degree of polarization as well as the strength and direction of the external electric field. We defer giving explicit forms for the force and moment until later.

The surface tractions and external field exert a resultant force F^A_{ext} on the dielectric. The components of this resultant force are given by the integrals

$$F^A_{\text{ext}} = \int_V g^A{}_i f^i \, dV + \int_B g^A{}_i T^i \, dS. \tag{5.1}$$

The particles of the medium also exert forces on each other. For example, the cohesive forces which bind the medium into an elastic solid are of this interparticle type. Also, if the medium is polarized, the electric self field of this polarized matter interacts with a given polarized particle of the medium. These interparticle forces are sometimes classified according to their "range" of interaction. Thus we hear of "short-range" and of "long-range" interactions. As we shall see later, there is some advantage to introducing these concepts in a continuum theory as well as in the theory of particle interactions where they usually occur. Whatever way the forces of mutual interactions of the particles of the dielectric may be classified, we shall make the *stress hypothesis.* Thus we assume the following: Let v be an arbitrary regular region of space. This region may be either entirely or partially contained in V, or its intersection with V may be zero. The forces of interparticle interaction between particles contained in v and the particles in $V - v$ are *equipollent* to a system of *stress vectors* distributed over the surface of the region v. Let b denote the surface of v. The stress vector field is a function only of position on the surface b and on the direction of the normal to b.[9] Let t^i denote the field of stress vectors. We have then $t^i = t^i(x^i, n^i)$ where n_i are the components of the *unit outward normal* to the surface b at the point x^i. Thus, the stress vector field is not an ordinary vector field whose components are functions only of position. The resultant force exerted by the particles in the region $V - v$ on the particles in the region v is given by

[9] Thus we exclude phenomenon such as surface tension. To include such effects, we would have to assume that the stress vector might also depend on local properties of the surface other than the direction of its normal, *e.g.*, its curvature.

$$F^A_{\text{int}} = \int_b g^A{}_i t^i(\mathbf{x}, \mathbf{n})\, dS. \tag{5.2}$$

The total force on the particles contained in the region v is the sum of the resultant extrinsic force and the resultant interparticle or intrinsic force (5.2). This total force on the arbitrary region v has the form,

$$F^A = \int_b g^A{}_i t^i\, dS + \int_{v\cap B} g^A{}_i T^i\, dS + \int_{v\cap V} g^A{}_i f^i\, dV, \tag{5.3}$$

where $v \cap B$ denotes the set of points common to the region v and the boundary of the dielectric. If the medium is in static mechanical equilibrium, *this total force vanishes for an arbitrarily chosen region v*. Applying this condition of equilibrium to a tetrahedron with a vertex which is not a point of B and passing to the limit of vanishing dimensions of the tetrahedron, we can demonstrate the existence of a *stress tensor* field $t^{ij}(x)$ such that

$$t^i(\mathbf{x}, \mathbf{n}) = t^{ij}(\mathbf{x})n_j\,. \tag{5.4}$$

Thus, the stress vector is the contracted product of an ordinary tensor field of second rank and the unit normal $\mathbf{n}$. The proof of this standard result depends on the assumption that the stress vector is bounded and continuous throughout space (except at the surface B) and that the extrinsic body force is everywhere bounded. We may also apply the condition of vanishing total force to a pill-box region which contains points of the surface B. On taking the appropriate order of limits as the dimensions of the pill-box approach zero, we obtain the important boundary condition,

$$[t^{ij}]n_j + T^i = 0. \tag{5.5}$$

In (5.5), $[t^{ij}] \equiv t^{+ij} - t^{-ij}$, where t^{+ij} and t^{-ij} are the limiting values of the stress tensor as the surface B is approached from the exterior and interior of the dielectric respectively.[10]

[10] There are alternative methods of formulating the stress hypothesis and its consequences. For example, in elasticity theory, many authors prefer to identify what we have called "surface tractions" with $t^{+ij}n_j$. The boundary condition corresponding to (5.5) then reads $[t^{ij}]n_j = 0$, and $t^{+ij}n_j$ is regarded as prescribed data. With the arrangement of definitions we have used, the stress tensor in ordinary elastic media vanishes outside the medium; hence, $t^{+ij}n_j$ would be zero in (5.5). If the medium is polarized, however, this is no longer true. What we have done here is to make the stress hypothesis only for the forces of interaction of a limited part of the overall mechanical system—that is, for the forces of interaction between the particles of the dielectric itself. Thus we have treated the extrinsic and intrinsic force systems quite differently. The action of outside agencies (the environment) is to be described by a body force and surface traction—the interaction of the particles of the dielectric itself by a system of stress vectors. The two methods of description of force systems are not entirely equivalent. The use of ex-

The resultant moment exerted on the dielectric by the surface tractions and external electric field is given by

$$M^{AB}_{\text{ext}} = \int_V g^A{}_i g^B{}_j m^{ij} \, dV + \int_B g^A{}_i g^B{}_j (r^i T^j - r^j T^i) \, dS + \int_V g^A{}_i g^B{}_j (r^i f^j - r^j f^i) \, dV, \tag{5.6}$$

where the r^i are the components of the position vectors to the points of application of the forces.

The interparticle interaction gives rise to a resultant moment on the region v which is given by

$$M^{AB}_{\text{int}} = \int_b g^A{}_i g^B{}_j (r^i t^j - r^j t^i) \, dS. \tag{5.7}$$

The total moment on the region v is given by

$$M^{AB} = \int_{v \cap B} g^A{}_i g^B{}_j (r^i T^j - r^j T^i) \, dS + \int_{v \cap V} g^A{}_i g^B{}_j (r^i f^j - r^j f^i) \, dV + \int_{v \cap V} g^A{}_i g^B{}_j m^{ij} \, dV + \int_b g^A{}_i g^B{}_j (r^i t^j - r^j t^i) \, dS. \tag{5.8}$$

If the medium is in static mechanical equilibrium this total moment on an arbitrary region v must vanish. From these integral forms of the conditions of equilibrium it follows that if the stress tensor is continuously differentiable except perhaps at points of the boundary of the dielectric then at equilibrium we have

---

trinsic body forces and surface tractions in continuum mechanics arises from a desire to focus attention on a limited part of the physical universe. For example, the effect of the earth's gravitational field on the mechanical behavior of continuous media on or near the earth's surface is usually accounted for by a body force type of description. The self gravitational field of the material and the counter effect of the body upon the earth is neglected in many applications. However, for bodies of large size such as the earth itself, this cannot be done and a classification of the forces of interparticle interaction into a "body force" and a "stress tensor" is not particularly appealing or profitable. It may still be desirable in a theory of the mechanics of the planet Earth, to introduce the gravitational force of the sun and other planets as an extrinsic body force. In a universal or cosmological theory, a unified treatment of the entire system of forces by means of a stress hypothesis would probably be a more fundamental formulation of the basic equations of continuum mechanics. However, unless we set ourselves the problem of the mechanics of a completely self contained mechanical system, the device of describing the environment of a limited system which is in interaction with outside agencies by means of a body force and surface traction seems particularly useful. It allows us to simplify the problem by not having to give a detailed account of the mechanics of the external agencies and of the counter effect of the system under consideration upon its environment.

$$\begin{aligned} t^{ij}{}_{,i} + f^j &= 0 \qquad x \,\varepsilon\, V - B \\ t^{ij}{}_{,i} &= 0 \qquad x \,\varepsilon\, E - V - B \end{aligned} \tag{5.9}$$

$$\begin{aligned} t^{ji} - t^{ij} + m^{ij} &= 0 \qquad x \,\varepsilon\, V - B \\ t^{ji} - t^{ij} &= 0 \qquad x \,\varepsilon\, E - V - B \end{aligned} \tag{5.10}$$

where E denotes all of Euclidean space. If we formally define f^i and m^{ij} to have the value zero outside the dielectric we avoid the need for writing $(5.9)_2$ and $(5.10)_2$.

CAUCHY's equations of force balance (5.9) and the COSSERATS' moment equations (5.10) constitute the local conditions of static mechanical equilibrium of a continuous medium. If the extrinsic body moment vanishes, as it usually does in pure elasticity theory, (5.10) reduces to the usual rule that the stress tensor be symmetric. In a theory of the elastic dielectric, greater care and attention must be given to the moment equations (5.10) than is necessary in elasticity theory.

6. The Maxwell-Faraday Theory of the Electric Field in Dielectrics

According to the Maxwell-Faraday electrostatic theory of dielectrics, the electric field is determined by the two conditions,

$$\int_C E_{\mathsf{M}}^i \, dx_i = 0, \tag{6.1}$$

$$\int_S D^i n_i \, dS = Q, \tag{6.2}$$

and a constitutive relation between the components of the *displacement vector* D^i and the Maxwell-Faraday electric field E_{M}^i. The form of this constitutive relation between $\mathbf{D}$ and $\mathbf{E}_{\mathsf{M}}$ may depend on any of the variables which describe the local state of the medium. In a vacuum, the constitutive relation reduces to $D^i = e_0 E_{\mathsf{M}}^i$ where e_0 is a dimensional constant. The surface S in (6.2) is the boundary of an arbitrary regular region R, and Q is the total *free charge* contained in R. By (6.1), the line integral of the electric field around an arbitrary space curve C vanishes. For our purposes here, a sufficiently general form for the total charge Q will be

$$Q = \int_R \sigma \, dV + \sum_k \int_{B_k \cap R} \omega \, dS \tag{6.3}$$

where σ is the volume density of free charge and ω is the surface density of free charge defined over a set of closed surfaces B_k. These surfaces are normally the surfaces of electrical conductors. The electric field and displacement vanish inside a conductor. Let the constitutive relation between $\mathbf{D}$ and $\mathbf{E}_{\mathsf{M}}$ be written in the form

$$D^i - e_0 E_{\mathsf{M}}^i = P^i(E_{\mathsf{M}}^i). \tag{6.4}$$

We shall call P^i the polarization density. The polarization density vanishes in vacuum and in electrical conductors. The local state of a dielectric medium may be characterized in part by the value of the polarization density. That is, we may choose the polarization density as one of the independent variables of state for an elastic dielectric. Let V again denote the region of space occupied by the dielectric and let B denote the boundary of V. Let P^i be zero everywhere except in V. Let V_k denote the regions enclosed by the charge bearing surfaces B_k and let V_0 denote the remainder of space. We assume that the electric field and displacement are continuously differentiable functions of position in each of the regions, V, V_k, and V_0. It then follows from the law (6.1) that in each of these regions we may represent the electric field as the gradient of a scalar field,

$$E_{\mathsf{M}}^{i} = -\varphi_{,}{}^{i}. \tag{6.5}$$

We also assume that the electric field suffers at most a finite discontinuity at the surfaces B and B_k. We can then use (6.1) to prove that the jump $[\varphi]$ in the scalar field φ is at most a constant over each of these surfaces. Since E_{M} determines only the gradient of φ, we may thus assume without loss in generality that φ is continuous throughout space. The scalar field so defined is called the *electrostatic potential*. From (6.2) it follows that in each of the regions V, V_k, and V_0 we have

$$e_0\varphi_{,}{}^{i}{}_{i} = -\sigma + P^{i}{}_{,i}\,. \tag{6.6}$$

It also follows from (6.2) that at the boundary of the dielectric where the polarization is discontinuous the discontinuity in the normal derivative of the electrostatic potential is given by

$$e_0 n^{i}[\varphi_{,i}] = n^{i}[P_i], \tag{6.7}$$

where n^i is the unit normal to the surface of the dielectric. At the surface of a conductor we have

$$e_0 n^{i}[\varphi_{,i}] = \omega. \tag{6.8}$$

If one now adds the boundary condition that φ vanish at infinity the Poisson equation (6.6) and the boundary conditions (6.7) and (6.8) determine the electrostatic potential uniquely throughout space. The solution can be put in the form

$$\begin{aligned} e_0\varphi(X) = \int \sigma(1/r)\,dV + \sum_k \int_{B_k} \omega(1/r)\,dS \\ - \int_V P^{i}{}_{,i}(1/r)\,dV + \int_B P^{i}n_i(1/r)\,dS \end{aligned} \tag{6.9}$$

where $r = \sqrt{(r^i - g^i{}_A R^A)(r_i - g^B{}_i R_B)}$ and $(r^i - g^i{}_A R^A)$ are the components of the position vector of the point of integration x^i relative to the point X^A at which the potential is evaluated. Let us put $\varphi = \varphi_0 + \varphi_{\mathsf{MS}}$ where $e_0\varphi_{\mathsf{MS}}$ is the sum of the last two integrals on the right-hand side of (6.9) and $e_0\varphi_0$ is the sum of the two remaining integrals. The *extrinsic field* $\mathbf{E}_0$ will be given by the negative gradient of φ_0. The negative gradient of φ_{MS} will be called the *Maxwell self electric field* of the dielectric and will be denoted by $\mathbf{E}_{\mathsf{MS}}$. The potential of the self field is seen to be equivalent to the potential of a volume distribution of free charge $(-P^{i}{}_{,i})$ plus a surface distribution of free charge $(P^{i}n_i)$ over the boundary of the dielectric. These are called the *Poisson-Kelvin equivalent charge distributions* of a polarized dielectric. If the electrostatic potential is calculated from (6.9) for a point where the free charge or equivalent charge distributions do not vanish, the integrand of one or more of the integrals will be infinite at the point owing to the factor $(1/r)$. In such a case, the value of the integral is defined by a limit process. A detailed discussion of the convergence of improper integrals of this general type can be found in [16]. Omitting details, we outline here the definition of such improper integrals. If $F(\mathbf{x})$ is singular at the single point $x_0^i \varepsilon V$, then the integral of F over the region V is defined by

$$\int_V F\,dV \equiv \lim_{d\to 0} \int_{V-v} F\,dV \tag{6.10}$$

where v is a regular region containing the point $\mathbf{x}_0$ and whose maximum chord is d. If the limit exists and is independent of the shape of the region v, the integral is said to converge or to exist and its value is defined as the limit of the sequence on the right-hand side of (6.10).

Accordingly, each of the integrals in (6.9) can be shown to converge for every point X^A. If the point X^A lies outside the dielectric we may differentiate the integral expressions for φ_{MS} under the integral sign to obtain

$$e_0 E^A_{\mathsf{MS}} = \int_V P^i{}_{,i}(1/r)_,{}^A\,dV - \int_B P^i n_i(1/r)_,{}^A\,dS. \tag{6.11}$$

We now make the observation that $(1/r)_,{}^A = -(1/r)_,{}^i g^A{}_i$—a result which may be readily verified by direct calculation of the two different derivatives of the expression which defines the function $r(X^A, x^i)$. If this substitution be made for the factor $(1/r)_,{}^A$ in (6.11), and if Green's theorem be used to transform the resulting surface integral into a volume integral, certain terms will cancel and the final result can be put in the form,

$$e_0 E^A_{\mathsf{MS}} = \int_V g^A{}_i P^i (1/r)_{,i}{}^i\,dV = -\int_V P^i(1/r)_{,i}{}^A\,dV. \tag{6.12}$$

Thus, the self field at a point outside the dielectric is given by a generalized "Coulomb's law." It is for this reason that $\mathbf{P}$ is called a polarization density. We cannot use (6.12) to calculate the electric self field at a point inside the dielectric. This is so because the integral expressions for the potential of the self field inside the dielectric have singular integrands and the order of integration and the subsequent differentiation of the potential cannot be interchanged. That is, if we made the formal attempt to evaluate the self field inside the dielectric using (6.12), the integrals would not converge. This does not constitute a flaw in the Maxwell theory. The potential (6.9) which converges everywhere must *first* be obtained, then its gradient may be computed without ambiguity. Within the context of Maxwell-Faraday electrostatic theory, the issue of convergence of (6.12) for points inside a dielectric medium is not relevant. It does give rise to the so-called *Kelvin cavity definitions* of the electrostatic field within a polarized dielectric. A region of definite shape may be excluded from the region of integration in (6.12). Taking the limit as the maximum chord of these differently shaped excluded regions tends to zero, one obtains values of the electric self field which can be varied continuously between certain finite limits. Without further hypotheses of a physical nature, no one of these cavity fields suggests itself as having superior physical significance in the electrostatic theory of dielectrics. As we have seen, the two Maxwell-Faraday laws of electrostatics (6.1) and (6.2) are sufficient to determine a unique self field inside and outside a dielectric which is polarized a given amount. For example, if a sphere of dielectric material is homogeneously polarized to an amount P^i, the Maxwell self field is a constant field inside the dielectric and has a value given by $E^i_{MS} = -(4\pi/3e_0)P^i$. In the next section we take up certain modifications and extensions of the continuum theory of the electrostatics of dielectrics which were discovered by LORENTZ. The self field of a polarized dielectric will be our major concern.

7. The Lorentz Theory of the Electric Field in Dielectrics

Lorentz has calculated the electrostatic field of an array of point dipoles arranged on a uniform space lattice [9, pp. 305–308]. If the distance between neighboring particles is small compared to the overall dimensions of the lattice, a correspondence may be set up between the electric field of the set of particles and the electric field of a polarized continuum. Of course, since the electric field of an array of point dipoles varies rapidly in the neighborhood of each particle and contains a singularity at the position of each particle, a correspondence between the field of a set of particles and the smooth, differentiable Maxwell field must involve some degree of approximation or some averaging process. We shall review the Lorentz theory here and use his result to motivate an independent hypothesis concerning the electric self field of a continuous elastic dielectric medium. The Lorentz theory of the self field will be presented in a manner which illustrates the physical point of view which we wish to carry over into the continuum theory and which places our hypothesis concerning the electric self field in elastic dielectrics in the most favorable light of known results on particle models of dielectric media.

Let $\underset{\alpha}{r}^i$ denote the components of the position vector to the αth lattice site of a uniform lattice. Let h_Γ^i $(\Gamma = 1, 2, 3)$ be three vectors whose directions coincide with the crystal axes and whose lengths are proportional to the lattice spacing. We can choose the constant of proportionality so that the parallelepiped formed by the h_Γ^i will have unit volume, *i.e.*, $\sqrt{g}\det h_\Gamma^i = 1$. The lattice vectors can be expressed in terms of the h_Γ^i as follows:

$$\underset{\alpha}{r}^i = \epsilon(\underset{\alpha}{n}_1 h_1^i + \underset{\alpha}{n}_2 h_2^i + \underset{\alpha}{n}_3 h_3^i) = \epsilon \sum_\Gamma \underset{\alpha}{n}_\Gamma h_\Gamma^i \tag{7.1}$$

where the $\underset{\alpha}{n}_\Gamma$ are integers which pick out the lattice vector $\underset{\alpha}{r}^i$. Let $v_a = \epsilon^3$ denote the volume of the unit cell of the lattice. We shall consider here the case of a uniformly polarized lattice with a single particle in each cell. Each lattice site is occupied by a point dipole $\underset{\alpha}{p}^i$ and by uniform polarization we mean that $\underset{\alpha}{p}^i$ is independent of the index α. Let p^i denote the common value of the $\underset{\alpha}{p}^i$. Let $\underset{\alpha}{r} = \sqrt{(g^A{}_i \underset{\alpha}{r}^i - R^A)(g^i{}_A \underset{\alpha}{r}_i - R_A)}$ denote the distance between the lattice site $\underset{\alpha}{r}^i$ and the point whose position vector is $\mathbf{R}$. If $\mathbf{R}$ does not coincide with a lattice site, the electrostatic field of the array of dipoles has a value at X^A which is given by the sum,

$$e_0 E_S^A(\mathbf{X}) = \sum_\alpha \underset{\alpha}{p^i}(1/r)_{,B}{}^A g^B{}_i$$
$$= \sum_\alpha \underset{\alpha}{p^i} \left\{ \frac{3(\underset{\alpha}{r^i} g_i{}^A - R^A)(\underset{\alpha}{r_k} g^k{}_B - R_B) g^B{}_i}{\underset{\alpha}{r^5}} - \frac{g^A{}_i}{\underset{\alpha}{r^3}} \right\}. \tag{7.2}$$

If the point X^A coincides with a lattice site, the field is given by the sum (7.2) with the infinite term omitted. If such be the case, we will indicate the modified summation by placing a prime on the summation sign. Now let v be an arbitrarily small but finite regular region which contains the lattice point $\underset{0}{r^i}$ and let $V - v$ be a regular region which contains the lattice points not in v. Divide the sum (7.2) into two partial sums, $E_S^A|_v$ and $E_S^A|_{V-v}$, where the former is the sum over all $\underset{\alpha}{r^i} \varepsilon\, v$ and the latter over all $\underset{\alpha}{r^i} \varepsilon\, V - v$. Let $r = \sqrt{(g^A{}_i r^i - R^A)(g^k{}_A r_k - R_A)}$ be the distance from the lattice site $\underset{0}{r^i}$ to an arbitrary point r^i in the region $V - v$. The function $(1/r)$ is analytic throughout $V - v$, and the function $(1/r)_{,i}{}^i g^A{}_i$ is Riemann integrable over this same region. From the definition of the Riemann integral we have

$$-\int_{V-v} P^i(1/r)_{,i}{}^A \, dV \equiv - \lim_{\Delta V_n \to 0} \sum_n P^i(1/r)_{,i}{}^A \Big|_{r=r_n} \Delta V_n \tag{7.3}$$

where r_n is any point which lies in the three-dimensional interval ΔV_n . P_i is a constant vector whose value we will assign in a moment. The limit is independent of the manner in which the region $V - v$ is subdivided into intervals ΔV_n and independent of the manner in which one chooses the points r_n within the intervals. Hence, we may choose the intervals ΔV_n so that they are the cells of a regular lattice whose corner points are given by (7.1). At the boundary of the region, the intervals may consist of partial lattice cells. We may choose the points r_n so that they coincide with the lattice points (7.1). Let us now identify P^i as the ratio, $p^i/v_a = p^i/\epsilon^3$. Let the limit $\Delta V_n \to 0$ be identified as the limit $\epsilon^3 \to 0$. In this way we see that the integral (7.3) is the limiting value of the sum $E_S^A|_{V-v}$ as the dimensions of the lattice cell approach zero and the dipole moment of each particle approaches zero in a manner which maintains the ratio p^i/ϵ^3 finite and equal to P^i. Now if the lattice has cubic or higher symmetry, the primed sum $E_S^A|_v$, representing the field at $\underset{0}{r^i}$ of the dipoles within any *sphere* with center at $\underset{0}{r^i}$, vanishes for every finite value of ϵ. Hence, the limit of this sum as $\epsilon \to 0$ exists and has the value zero. Thus, if the dimensions of the unit cell and the dipole moment on each lattice site are allowed to approach zero, maintaining the ratio $p^i/v_a = P^i$, then the self field of a lattice having cubic symmetry when evaluated at a lattice site is given by

$$e_0 E_S^A = -\int_{V-v} P^i (1/r)_{,i}{}^A \, dV \tag{7.4}$$

where the region v is a sphere whose center is at the lattice site and P^i is the constant density of dipole moment.

The volume integral (7.4) may be transformed into the sum of two surface integrals, one over the boundary of the sphere v and one over the boundary of the dielectric. Since $P^i{}_{,i} = 0$, we have

$$e_0 E_S^A = -\int_b P^i n_i (1/r)_{,}{}^A \, dS + \int_B P^i n_i (1/r)_{,}{}^A \, dS = (4\pi/3) P^A + e_0 E_{MS}^A , \tag{7.5}$$

where we have evaluated the first surface integral explicitly and have identified the last integral as the Maxwell self electric field at an *interior* point of a uniformly polarized continuous medium with polarization density P^i. If the lattice has symmetry lower than cubic, then in general a different value of the excess of E_S^i over the corresponding Maxwell-Faraday field E_{MS}^i is obtained. Whatever the lattice symmetry may be, we shall write E_S^i in the form

$$E_L^i = E_L^i + E_{MS}^i \tag{7.6}$$

where E_L is called the *Lorentz local field.* If a cubic lattice is deformed homogeneously and the deformed lattice has lower symmetry than cubic, then the local field will have a value which differs from $(4\pi/3e_0)P^i$. Hence, *the local field is a function of the lattice deformation.* The deformation of a lattice may be described quantitatively in the following way. The three linearly independent vectors h_Γ^i which we now let represent the crystal axes of the deformed lattice are the result of rotating and elongating the vectors H_Γ^A which define the crystal axes of the undeformed lattice. If one puts $h_\Gamma^i = S^i{}_A H_\Gamma^A$, then $S^i{}_A$ is determined uniquely in terms of the h_Γ^i and H_Γ^A . It is assumed, of course, that neither det h_Γ^i nor det H_Γ^A is zero. If we introduce the set of three vectors B_A^Γ which are reciprocal to the H_Γ^A , *i.e.*,

$$B_A^\Gamma = \tfrac{1}{2}\sqrt{g}\, \epsilon^{\Gamma\Delta\Upsilon} \epsilon_{ABC} H_\Delta^B H_\Upsilon^C , \qquad B_A^\Gamma H_\Delta^A = \delta_\Delta^\Gamma , \qquad \sum_\Gamma B_A^\Gamma H_\Gamma^B = \delta^B{}_A ,$$

then

$$S^i{}_A = \sum_\Gamma h_\Gamma^i B_A^\Gamma . \tag{7.7}$$

The nine parameters $S^i{}_A$ afford a quantitative measure of the deformation of the lattice cell. If more than one particle occupies each cell of the lattice, further parameters may be introduced to describe changes in the internal configuration of the particles in a given cell. If the lattice deformation is not homogeneous, then $S^i{}_A$ will vary from cell to cell and we must label the parameters $S^i{}_A$ by the cell index α. If there are N cells in the specimen, a general inhomogeneous deformation of the specimen is described by the $9N$ parameters $\underset{\alpha}{S}{}^{i}{}_{A}$. Recall that in the section on kinematics of *continuous* media, it was shown that the vector dX^A at X^A is carried by the mapping $x^i(X^A)$, which describes the relative configurations of the particles of a continuous medium, into the vector $dx^i = x^i{}_{;A}\, dX^A$ at the point x^i. If this be compared with $h^i_\Gamma = S^i{}_A H^A_\Gamma$, we see that the continuum analogues of the $\underset{\alpha}{S}{}^{i}{}_{A}$ are the displacement gradients $x^i{}_{;A}(X^A)$. The displacement gradients are continuous functions of the material coordinates X^A which replace the discrete index α of the $\underset{\alpha}{S}{}^{i}{}_{A}$. In the lattice theory, the local field at a lattice point $\underset{\alpha}{r}{}^{i}$ depends on the $\underset{\alpha}{S}{}^{i}{}_{A}$ and $\underset{\alpha}{p}{}^{i}$ for the cells in the immediate neighborhood of the point $\underset{\alpha}{r}{}^{i}$. In the continuum theory, we shall set down as a primitive assumption that

$$E^i_{\mathrm{S}} = E^i_{\mathrm{MS}} + E^i_{\mathrm{L}}(x^i{}_{;A}\, , P^i). \tag{7.8}$$

That is, *the electrostatic self field of a polarized and deformed continuous elastic dielectric is the sum of the Maxwell electrostatic self field and a local field which is a state function of the displacement gradients and polarization density.* We assume that the relation (7.8) holds not only in dielectrics having a crystal structure but also in elastic dielectrics such as rubber or plastic.

8. The Equations of Intramolecular Force Balance

It may be said that in adding the polarization vector to the list of independent state variables of an elastic medium we have ascribed an internal structure to the continuum "particle." That is, independent of the values of the displacement gradients which provide a quantitative description of the relative configuration of the particles in the neighborhood of a given one, the magnitude and direction of the polarization vector at a point describes the internal structure of the continuum particle. The forces which maintain this internal configuration must be a static equilibrium system of forces as well as the system of forces which maintain the relative positions of neighboring particles at stationary values. For our purposes here, it proves convenient to refer to a dumbbell model of a single "particle" in an elastic dielectric. According to this model, a polarized particle consists of two equal electric charges of opposite sign separated along a line parallel to the polarization vector. If this particle is in static mechanical equilibrium, the forces which act on either charge must have a zero resultant. The electrical force which acts on a charge q placed in an electrostatic field $\mathbf{E}$ is just $q\mathbf{E}$. The electrostatic field which acts on the charge in an elastic dielectric has three distinct components—they are (1) the Maxwell electric self field $\mathbf{E}_{\mathsf{MS}}$, (2) the Lorentz local field $\mathbf{E}_{\mathsf{L}}$, (3) the external or extrinsic field $\mathbf{E}_0$. In addition to the resultant electrostatic force due to these three components of the electrostatic field, other forces act on either charge of the polarized particle. These are the molecular forces which are made up of the Coulomb attraction between the charges of the particle, dynamical forces and other non-classical or quantum forces. Let $q\mathbf{F}$ denote the resultant of all these molecular forces. Then at static equilibrium we must have

$$q(F^i + E^i_{\mathsf{L}} + E^i_{\mathsf{MS}} + E^i_0) = 0 \tag{8.1}$$

which is just the Newtonian law of force balance applied to either charge of the polarized particle. We shall set $F^i + E_{\mathsf{L}} = \bar{E}^i_{\mathsf{L}}$ and call the sum of these two terms the *effective local field*. We shall assume that *the effective local field in an elastic dielectric is a state function of the displacement gradients and polarization density*. Thus we have

$$\bar{E}^i_{\mathsf{L}}(x^i_{;A}, P^i) + E^i_0 + E^i_{\mathsf{MS}} = 0. \tag{8.2}$$

We call (8.2) *the equation of intramolecular force balance*. The total Maxwell field is just $\mathbf{E}_{\mathsf{M}} = \mathbf{E}_{\mathsf{MS}} + \mathbf{E}_0$; so that we can write (8.2) in the form[11]

$$\bar{E}^i_{\mathsf{L}}(x^i_{;A}, P^i) + E^i_{\mathsf{M}} = 0. \tag{8.3}$$

[11] Equation (8.3) could be written in the form $D^i = e_0 E^i_{\mathsf{M}} + P^i = D^i(x^i_{;A}, E_{\mathsf{M}})$ which is formally identical to a constitutive relation between the displacement vector, the Maxwell electric field, and the displacement gradients. A constitutive relation of this type is always assumed to exist in Maxwell-Faraday electrostatic theory. We have arrived at a relation of this type using notions of mechanical equilibrium. The two points of view are quite different, however. Equation (8.3) is a condition of static equilibrium, not a constitutive relation. Its form would change if we passed to the dynamical case. As we shall see in §10, the *equilibrium condition* (8.2) results quite naturally from a principle of virtual work.

9. The Form of the Stress Tensor, Extrinsic Body Force and Extrinsic Body Moment in an Elastic Dielectric

In elasticity theory it is assumed that the stress tensor is a state function of the displacement gradients. That is, the displacement gradients are the only state variables and a constitutive relation between the components of the stress tensor and the displacement gradients which is characteristic of the particular elastic material is assumed to exist. To assume a constitutive relation between the stress and displacement gradients implies the physical notion that the stress tensor at a point in the material is determined solely in terms of the local state of the medium. The state of the medium at distant points may be altered without changing the values of the stress tensor components at a given point. The existence of a constitutive relation between stress and local deformation also implies the physical notion of "short-range" forces. Thus, in pure elasticity theory it may be said that the elastic response of the medium is due solely to "short-range" forces. This assumption is in need of modification for the elastic dielectric. Here, in addition to the "short-range" elastic forces which are determined by the local state of the medium, the polarized dielectric interacts with the self field. We have made the stress hypothesis and have assumed that this interaction together with the "short-range" interaction will be described by a system of stress. Now it is known from Maxwell's work that the resultant electrostatic force on a region containing polarized matter is given by $\int_v g^A_{\ i} t^{ij}_{\mathsf{MS}} n_j \, dS$ where t^{ij}_{MS} is the Maxwell stress tensor given by

$$t^{ij}_{\mathsf{MS}} = e_0 E^i_{\mathsf{MS}} E^j_{\mathsf{MS}} + E^i_{\mathsf{MS}} P^j - \tfrac{1}{2} e_0 E^2_{\mathsf{MS}} g^{ij}. \tag{9.1}$$

It is clear that the Maxwell stress tensor is not a state function if the displacement gradients and polarization density are the independent state variables. It has the same form in all materials. For a given global state of polarization, we can determine the value of the Maxwell stress using the laws of Maxwell-Faraday electrostatics.

We shall assume that the stress tensor in a polarized elastic dielectric has the form

$$t^{ij} = t^{ij}_{\mathsf{L}}(x^i_{\ ;A}, P^i) + t^{ij}_{\mathsf{MS}} \tag{9.2}$$

where t^{ij}_{L} is a state function called the local stress. Note that the Maxwell stress tensor does not vanish at points outside the dielectric. The resultant electrostatic force on any region which lies entirely outside the dielectric is zero. The local stress will be assigned the value zero outside the dielectric.

The interaction of the polarized dielectric with the extrinsic field E^i_0 is given by the following expressions for the extrinsic body force and extrinsic body moment:

$$f^i = E^i_{0,j} P^j, \tag{9.3}$$

$$m^{ij} = P^i E^j_0 - P^j E^i_0 . \tag{9.4}$$

Since $e_0 E^i_{\mathsf{MS},i} = -P^i_{\ ,i}$, it follows that $t^{ij}_{\mathsf{MS},j} = E^i_{\mathsf{MS},j} P^j$ at every point of continuity of $\mathbf{E}_{\mathsf{MS}}$ and $\mathbf{P}$. However, at the boundary of the dielectric where $\mathbf{P}$ is discontinuous so also is the self field. From the boundary condition $[e_0 E^i_{\mathsf{MS}} + P^i]n_i = 0$, we deduce that the discontinuity in the stress vector of the Maxwell tensor at the boundary of the dielectric is given by

$$[t^{ij}_{\mathsf{MS}}]n_j = (\tfrac{1}{2}e_0)(P^i n_j)^2 n^i. \tag{9.5}$$

Summarizing these results and substituting the special forms for the stress tensor, body force, and body moment into the force and moment equations (5.9) and (5.10) we get the following system of equations:

$$t^{ij}_{\mathsf{L},j} + t^{ij}_{\mathsf{MS},j} + E^i_{0,j}P^j = 0 \tag{9.6}$$

$$t^{ji}_{\mathsf{L}} - t^{ij}_{\mathsf{L}} + t^{ji}_{\mathsf{MS}} - t^{ij}_{\mathsf{MS}} + E^j_0 P^i - E^i_0 P^j = 0 \tag{9.7}$$

$$\overline{E}^i_{\mathsf{L}} + E^i_0 + E^i_{\mathsf{MS}} = 0 \tag{9.8}$$

which may also be written in the form

$$t^{ij}_{\mathsf{L}} + E^i_{\mathsf{M},j}P^j = 0, \tag{9.9}$$

$$t^{ji}_{\mathsf{L}} - t^{ij}_{\mathsf{L}} + E^j_{\mathsf{M}}P^i - E^i_{\mathsf{M}}P^j = 0 \tag{9.10}$$

$$\overline{E}^i_{\mathsf{L}} + E^i_{\mathsf{M}} = 0. \tag{9.11}$$

Substituting (9.5) into the boundary condition (5.5), we obtain

$$-t^{-ij}_{\mathsf{L}}n_j + (\tfrac{1}{2}e_0)(P^j n_j)^2 n^i + T^i = 0. \tag{9.12}$$

Recall that t^{-ij}_{L} denotes the limiting values of the local stress as the boundary of the dielectric is approached from the interior.

In order to complete the summary of equations and boundary conditions which will determine the behavior of elastic dielectrics we list the following results from Maxwell-Faraday electrostatic theory:

$$e_0 \varphi_{\mathsf{MS},}{}^i{}_i = P^i{}_{,i}\,, \tag{9.13}$$

$$e_0 n^i[\varphi_{\mathsf{MS},i}] = n^i[P_i]. \tag{9.14}$$

Finally, in addition to the above equations and equations (9.9–12), two sets of constitutive relations characteristic of the material must be given. These are

$$t^{ij}_{\mathsf{L}} = t^{ij}_{\mathsf{L}}(x^i{}_{;A}\,, P^i) \tag{9.15}$$

and

$$\overline{E}^i_{\mathsf{L}} = \overline{E}^i_{\mathsf{L}}(x^i{}_{;A}\,, P^i). \tag{9.16}$$

The form of these constitutive relations for the local stress and the effective local field is restricted by certain symmetry properties of the material. Further restrictions are also imposed by the manner in which the dependent variables must transform as the deformed and polarized body is rotated rigidly in space. We take up these questions regarding the form of the constitutive relations in greater detail later.

10. A Principle of Virtual Work for the Elastic Dielectric

In elasticity theory there are two methods which have been used to arrive at stress-strain relations [12, p. 173]. The method used by CAUCHY was to assume that the components of the stress tensor were functions of strain. GREEN's method assumes the existence of a stored energy function which is a function of strain. An energy or work principle is then used to establish formulæ for the components of the stress tensor in terms of certain combinations of the partial derivatives of the stored energy with respect to the variables used to measure the strain. The stress-strain relations obtained by these two different procedures are not always identical. By CAUCHY's method, we obtain stress-strain relations which contain those obtained by GREEN's method as a special case. To this point, we have not used the mechanical concept of work nor have we made any use of the concept of stored energy in formulating the equations of an elastic dielectric summarized at the end of the preceding section. By assuming that the local stress and effective local field were functions of displacement gradients and polarization we have followed a procedure analogous to CAUCHY's method in elasticity theory. In this section, we wish to present a natural generalization of GREEN's method which yields equations and boundary conditions equivalent to those already proposed. As a generalization of the result in elasticity theory, we shall show that the constitutive relations for the local stress and effective local field will follow from a single stored energy function which is characteristic of the material.

The *natural state* of an elastic dielectric is the equilibrium state which the material assumes in the absence of applied surface tractions and an external electric field. Let the material particles of the elastic dielectric be identified by their coordinates X^A in this natural state configuration. As before, let x^i denote the coordinates of the particles in the deformed and polarized equilibrium configuration when surface tractions T^i and an electric field $E^i_\circ$ are applied. If X^A and x^i are the coordinates of the same material particle in the natural and deformed configurations, then

$$x^i = x^i(X^A). \tag{10.1}$$

As X^A ranges over the region V_0 occupied by the body in its natural state, the correspondence (10.1) constitutes a continuous mapping of the region V_0 onto the region V occupied by the body in its deformed and polarized state. Let B_0 and B denote the boundary of the dielectric in the natural and deformed states respectively. The *total mass* of the dielectric body is given by

$$M = \int_V \rho \, dV \tag{10.2}$$

where ρ is the mass density in the deformed state. Let J denote the absolute scalar given by

$$J = +\sqrt{\frac{\det g_{ij}}{\det g_{AB}}}\,|\det x^i{}_{;A}| = \det g^A{}_i x^i{}_{;A}\,. \tag{10.3}$$

The law of conservation of mass may be stated in the form

$$\rho_0(X^A) = J\rho(x^i(X^A)), \tag{10.4}$$

where ρ_0 is the density of mass in the natural state. If the body is homogeneous in the natural state, ρ_0 is a constant independent of X^A. We have found it convenient to introduce the polarization per unit of mass as an independent variable of state instead of the polarization per unit of volume. Let π^i denote the polarization per unit of mass. We have then

$$P^i = \rho\pi^i. \tag{10.5}$$

If the polarization per unit of mass is defined for each point in the deformed and polarized body, we have a vector field $\pi^i(\mathbf{x})$ defined on the region V. There is a corresponding vector field defined on the region V_0 by the following process: Let the vector $\pi^i(\mathbf{x})$ at the point $\mathbf{x}$ be translated by parallel displacement to the point $\mathbf{X}$ which is the position in the natural state of the material particle now at $\mathbf{x}$. Thus we have

$$\pi^A(\mathbf{X}) = g^A{}_i(\mathbf{X}, \mathbf{x})\pi^i(\mathbf{x}); \tag{10.6}$$

whereby a vector field $\pi^A(\mathbf{X})$ is defined over the region V_0 occupied by the body in its natural state. Conversely, if we are given the field π^A we may generate the field π^i by the inverse process,

$$\pi^i = g^i{}_A\pi^A. \tag{10.7}$$

Since the mapping (10.1) has been defined only over the limited regions of space that are occupied by the natural and deformed states of the dielectric medium, the correspondence between tensor fields defined by the process just described can only be extended over these same two limited portions of space. We could regard all of space as being filled with a continuous material medium. A correspondence between material particles would then give us a mapping like (10.1) between every pair of positions in space. Suppose, however, that a portion of space is devoid of material matter. What physical significance could then be attached to a mapping of such a region upon another? A question of this nature arises in our work here in connection with the electrostatic potential of the self electric field of the polarized dielectric. We have met the problem in the following way which appears to be logically sound and physically correct. Let us formally extend the mapping (10.1) throughout all space in an arbitrary fashion. We require only that it join smoothly with the mapping of V onto

V_0 to which we have ascribed physical significance and that it have as many derivatives as we shall need for convenience. A correspondence between tensor fields can now be set up throughout space with formulæ analogous to (10.6) and (10.7). In particular, if $\varphi(\mathbf{x})$ is the electrostatic potential of the self electric field of the polarized and deformed dielectric, it has a value at every point $\mathbf{x}$ and we can define the function $\varphi(\mathbf{X})$ for every point $\mathbf{X}$ by setting

$$\varphi(\mathbf{X}) = \varphi(\mathbf{x}(\mathbf{X})). \tag{10.8}$$

Let Σ denote the *stored energy function of deformation and polarization*. That is, the stored energy Σ is a state function and we have

$$\Sigma = \Sigma(x^i{}_{;A}, \pi^i). \tag{10.9}$$

The principle of virtual work for the elastic dielectric is as follows:

$$\delta\left[-\int_V \rho\Sigma(x^i{}_{;A}, \pi^i)\, dV + \tfrac{1}{2}e_0 \int_E \varphi^{;i}\varphi_{;i}\, dV + \int_V \varphi_{;}{}^{i}P_i\, dV\right] + \int_B T_i\delta' x^i\, dS + \int_V f_i\delta' x^i\, dV + \int_V \rho E_{0i}\delta''\pi^i\, dV = 0. \tag{10.10}$$

The last three integrals in this variational expression represent, respectively, the work done by the applied surface tractions if the boundary of the dielectric is displaced from equilibrium by a small amount $\delta' x^i$, the work done by the body force if any point in the dielectric is displaced from its equilibrium position, and the work done by the external field in changing the polarization a small amount from its equilibrium value. The sum of these three virtual work terms is set equal to the variation in potential energy of the elastic dielectric. This potential energy is written as the sum of three parts which are enclosed in the large brackets in (10.10). The first of these terms represents the variation in the stored energy of deformation and polarization. This term is quite analogous to the stored elastic energy of elasticity theory. The second term is the variation in the potential energy of the self electric field. The third term in the bracket represents an interaction energy between the self field and a polarized particle of the dielectric.

The independent variations of the field variables are now listed:

$$x^i(\mathbf{X}) \to x^i(\mathbf{X}) + \delta' x^i(\mathbf{X}) \tag{10.11}$$

$$\pi^A(\mathbf{X}) \to \pi^A(\mathbf{X}) + \delta''\pi^A(\mathbf{X}) \tag{10.12}$$

$$\varphi(\mathbf{X}) \to \varphi(\mathbf{X}) + \delta'''\varphi(\mathbf{X}). \tag{10.13}$$

The total variation δ of the terms in large brackets in (10.10) means the resultant first order change in the value of these integrals under the replacements

(10.11–13). Note that the total covariant derivative of the electrostatic potential is used in (10.10). Thus we have $\varphi_{;i} = \varphi_{;A} X^A{}_{;i}$. Some useful preliminary results are now listed:

$$\delta(x^i{}_{;A}) = (\delta' x^i)_{;A} \tag{10.14}$$

$$\delta(X^A{}_{;i}) = -X^A{}_{;j} X^B{}_{;i} (\delta' x^j)_{;B} \tag{10.15}$$

$$\delta J = J X^A{}_{;i} (\delta' x^i)_{;A} \tag{10.16}$$

$$\begin{aligned} \delta(\varphi_{;i}) &= (\delta''' \varphi)_{;A} X^A{}_{;i} + \varphi_{;A} \delta'(X^A{}_{;i}) \\ &= (\delta''' \varphi)_{;i} - \varphi_{;j} (\delta' x^j)_{;i} \, . \end{aligned} \tag{10.17}$$

We shall also use the Euler-C. Neumann identities [12, p. 140],

$$(X^A{}_{;i} J)_{;A} = 0, \qquad (J^{-1} x^i{}_{;A})_{;i} = 0. \tag{10.18}$$

Since the boundary of the region V is subject to variation, it is convenient to transform all the integrals in (10.10) into integrals over the undeformed body V_0 or over the region $E - V_0$ outside the undeformed body. These transformed integrals will then have fixed limits and we may commute the operations of integration and variation. If this be done we find that (10.10) can be put in the form

$$\begin{aligned} &\int_{B_0} \left\{ \left[-\rho_0 \frac{\partial \Sigma}{\partial x^i{}_{;A}} + J(\overset{+}{t}_{\mathrm{MS}\,i}{}^j - \overset{-}{t}_{\mathrm{MS}\,i}{}^j) X^A{}_{;j} + T_i N^A \left(\frac{dS}{dS_0} \right) \right] \delta' x^i \right. \\ &\qquad \left. + \left[e_0 (\overset{+}{E}_{\mathrm{MS}}{}^i - \overset{-}{E}_{\mathrm{MS}}{}^i - e_0^{-1} P^i) X^A{}_{;i} \right] J \, \delta''' \varphi \right\} N_A \, dS_0 \\ &\quad + \int_{V_0} \left\{ \rho_0 \left[-\frac{\partial \Sigma}{\partial \pi^j} + E_{\mathrm{MS}\,j} + E_{0j} \right] g^j{}_A \delta'' \pi^A \right. \\ &\quad + \left[\left(\rho_0 \frac{\partial \Sigma}{\partial x^i{}_{;A}} \right)_{;A} + J t_{\mathrm{MS}\,i}{}^j{}_{;j} + J f_i \right] \delta' x^i \\ &\quad \left. + J[-e_0 \nabla^2 \varphi + \nabla \cdot P] \delta''' \varphi \, dV_0 \right\} \\ &\quad + \int_{E - V_0} \{ e_0 \nabla^2 \varphi \delta''' \varphi + t_{\mathrm{MS}\,i}{}^j{}_{;j} \delta' x^i \} J \, dV_0 = 0. \end{aligned} \tag{10.19}$$

In writing the above result we have grouped certain of the terms using the definition of the Maxwell stress tensor t_{MS}^{ij} . We have also set $\mathbf{E}_{\mathrm{MS}} = -\nabla\varphi$. The quantities N^A are the components of the outward unit normal to the surface of the undeformed dielectric. The ratio of the magnitudes of the surface elements (dS/dS_0) is given by

$$dS/dS_0 = J \sqrt{(C^{-1})^{AB} N_A N_B} = J / \sqrt{(c^{-1})^{ij} n_i n_j} \, . \tag{10.20}$$

We thus obtain the following field equations which must be satisfied at every point inside the dielectric:

$$J^{-1}\left(\rho_0 \frac{\partial \Sigma}{\partial x^i{}_{;A}}\right)_{;A} + t_{\mathrm{MS}\,i}{}^{i}{}_{;i} + E_{0i;j}P^j = 0 \tag{10.21}$$

$$-\frac{\partial \Sigma}{\partial \pi^i} + E_{\mathrm{MS}\,i} + E_{0i} = 0 \tag{10.22}$$

$$-e_0\nabla^2\varphi + \boldsymbol{\nabla}\cdot\mathbf{P} = 0. \tag{10.23}$$

At every point outside the dielectric we must have

$$\nabla^2\varphi = 0 \tag{10.24}$$

$$t^{ij}_{\mathrm{MS};j} = 0. \tag{10.25}$$

Equation (10.24) follows from the principle of virtual work by the requirement that the variation of the electrostatic potential of the self field at a point outside the dielectric will give no first order change in the left-hand side of (10.1). Equation (10.25) follows from the same principle applied to a variation of the mapping $x^i(X)$ as extended to points outside the dielectric. But this extended mapping was assigned no physical significance; therefore, it is a happy circumstance that the field equation (10.25) is satisfied identically if the field equation (10.24) is satisfied.

In addition to the above set of field equations we obtain the boundary conditions which we now list.

$$-\rho \frac{\partial \Sigma}{\partial x^i{}_{;A}} N_A - (\bar{t}_{\mathrm{MS}\,i}{}^{j} - \overset{+}{t}_{\mathrm{MS}\,i}{}^{j})X^A{}_{;j}N_A + T_i\sqrt{(C^{-1})^{AB}N_AN_B} = 0, \tag{10.26}$$

$$[e_0(\overset{+}{E}_{\mathrm{MS}}{}^{i} - \bar{E}_{\mathrm{MS}}{}^{i}) - P^i]X^A{}_{;i}N_A = 0. \tag{10.27}$$

In addition we have the continuity of the electrostatic potential which was assumed in the variational principle. The field equations (10.21–24) and the boundary conditions (10.26–27) are the *material form of the equilibrium conditions for an elastic dielectric.* Using the identities (10.18) and the relation $n_i = JN_AX^A{}_{;i}$ between the components of the unit normals to the deformed and undeformed dielectric, the corresponding *spatial* form of the equilibrium conditions can be obtained from the material form. It is as follows:

$$\left(\rho \frac{\partial \Sigma}{\partial x^i{}_{;A}} x^j{}_{;A}\right)_{;j} + t_{\mathrm{MS}\,i}{}^{j}{}_{;j} + E_{0i;}{}^{j}P_j = 0 \tag{10.28}$$

$$-\frac{\partial \Sigma}{\partial \pi_i} + E^i_{\mathrm{MS}} + E^i_0 = 0 \tag{10.29}$$

$$-e_0\nabla^2\varphi + \nabla\cdot\mathbf{P} = 0 \tag{10.30}$$

$$-\rho \frac{\partial \Sigma}{\partial x^i{}_{;A}} x^j{}_{;A} n_j + [t_{\mathsf{MS}i}{}^j] n_j + T_i = 0 \tag{10.31}$$

$$(e_0[E^i_{\mathsf{MS}}] - P^i) n_i = 0. \tag{10.32}$$

We need only to identify the local stress and effective local field as the expressions,

$$t_{\mathsf{L}i}{}^j = \rho \frac{\partial \Sigma}{\partial x^i{}_{;A}} x^j{}_{;A} \tag{10.33}$$

$$\overline{E}^i_{\mathsf{L}} = -\frac{\partial \Sigma}{\partial \pi_i} \tag{10.34}$$

in order to make the above set of equilibrium equations identical in form to the set of field equations and boundary conditions summarized at the end of the previous section. We do not obtain the moment equation (9.7) as a direct consequence of the principle of virtual work. We can, however, show that *the moment equation is satisfied identically if the stored energy function is invariant under a rigid rotation of the deformed and polarized dielectric.* The proof of this statement is based on the following well known result on invariant functions of several vectors.

Let $F(V^i_1, V^i_2, \cdots, V^i_n)$ be a function of the components V^i_Γ ($\Gamma = 1, 2, \cdots, n$) which is invariant under the substitutions

$$V^i_\Gamma \rightarrow S^i{}_j V^j_\Gamma$$

where $S^i{}_j$ is an arbitrary rotation; that is, $g_{ij} S^i{}_k S^j{}_l = g_{kl}$ and $\det S^i{}_j = 1$. An infinitesimal rotation has the form $S^i{}_j = \delta^i{}_j + \epsilon^i{}_j$ where ϵ_{ij} is an arbitrary antisymmetric tensor. Since

$$F(V^i_1, \cdots V^i_n) = F(S^i{}_j V^j_1, \cdots S^i{}_j V^j_n) = F(\overline{V}^i_1, \cdots \overline{V}^i_n)$$

we have as necessary conditions

$$dF = \frac{\partial F}{\partial \overline{V}^i} \frac{\partial \overline{V}^i}{\partial S^k{}_l} dS^k{}_l = 0.$$

Hence, for differentials $S^k{}_l$ about the values $S^k{}_l = \delta^k{}_l$ (the identity transformation) the above condition reads

$$\frac{\partial F}{\partial V^i} V^j \epsilon^i{}_j = 0$$

where ϵ_{ij} is an arbitrary antisymmetric tensor. This condition implies that the coefficients of ϵ_{ij} in this expression are the components of a *symmetric* tensor. We use the notation $T^{[ij\cdots k]}$ to denote the antisymmetric part of a tensor.

For example, $T^{[ij]} = \frac{1}{2}(T^{ij} - T^{ji})$. A necessary and sufficient condition that a tensor of second rank be symmetric is that $T^{[ij]} = 0$. Thus we have the necessary conditions

$$\sum_{\Gamma} \frac{\partial F}{\partial V_{\Gamma[i}} V_{\Gamma}^{j]} = 0 \tag{10.35}$$

if F is a function of n vectors V_{Γ}^{i} which is invariant to a rigid rotation of the vectors. It can also be shown that the conditions (10.35) are sufficient to insure the invariance of F under *finite* rotations.[12]

If the deformed and polarized state of the elastic dielectric is rotated rigidly in space, the displacement gradients and polarization vector change to new values given by

$$x^{i}{}_{;A} \to S^{i}{}_{j} x^{j}{}_{;A}$$

$$\pi^{i} \to S^{i}{}_{j} \pi_{j}.$$

Hence, if we assume that the stored energy function of deformation and polarization is invariant under a rigid rotation of the deformed and polarized state it follows from the above theorem that

$$\frac{\partial \Sigma}{\partial x^{[i}{}_{;A}} x_{j];A} + \frac{\partial \Sigma}{\pi^{[i}} \pi_{j]} = 0.$$

Multiplying this equation by ρ and using (10.33–34), it may be put in the form

$$t_{\mathrm{L}}^{[ij]} - \bar{E}_{\mathrm{L}}^{[i} P^{j]} = 0. \tag{10.36}$$

This equation implies the physical notion that the moment exerted on a particle of the dielectric by the system of local stresses is just the moment exerted by the effective local field $\mathbf{E}_{\mathrm{L}}$ acting on the polarized particle. We should comment that (10.36) is identically statisfied whether we are in an equilibrium state or not. It depends only on the assumption that the stored energy function is invariant to rigid rotations. If the result (10.36) is combined with the equilibrium condition (10.29) we find that the moment equation (9.7) is satisfied identically. That is, the equilibrium condition which we have called *intramolecular force balance*, together with the invariance of the stored energy function to rigid rotations, insures that the moment equation will be satisfied. This is to be compared with the corresponding result in elasticity theory where invariance of the stored elastic energy to rigid rotations is sufficient to insure the *symmetry* of the stress tensor in that theory. As is sometimes done in elasticity theory, we could impose the moment equation (symmetry of the stress tensor

[12] The results stated in this theorem are well known consequences of the Lie theory of compact groups.

in the case of elasticity theory) as a side condition. The invariance of the stored energy function to rigid rotations would then follow as a necessary consequence of this side condition instead of by mere assumption. In a theory based on the laws of mechanics, this latter arrangement is probably the preferred order of stating the hypotheses.

We have demonstrated that the variational principle (10.10) yields field equations and boundary conditions in complete agreement with the equilibrium conditions of an elastic dielectric. The main additional result obtained by assuming the existence of a stored energy function of deformation and polarization and the validity of the principle of virtual work lies in the restrictions which are imposed on the constitutive relations for the local stress and effective local field. If the energy principle is used, we see that a single scalar function of the variables of state is sufficient to characterize the mechanical and electrostatic properties of an elastic dielectric completely. Without the energy principle, the same formal set of equations and boundary conditions can be arrived at but the constitutive relations for the local stress and effective local field must be given separately in order to characterize the properties of the material. It is clear that the energy principle leads to constitutive equations for the stress and effective local field which are much less general than they are in the absence of a stored energy function. As in elasticity theory, it is probable that for many elastic dielectrics the restrictions imposed on the constitutive relations by using (10.33) and (10.34) instead of the "Cauchy" forms (9.15) and (9.16) are desirable and are actually borne out by experiment.

11. The Homogeneous Isotropic Elastic Dielectric

There are many important examples of elastic dielectrics which are homogeneous and isotropic. For a study of the effects of large deformations, rubber is the first material which comes to mind. Early experiments on the photoelastic effect were concerned with isotropic media such as glass. Today, the numerous varieties of transparent plastics, which may be regarded as isotropic in their natural state, are widely used in the study of the photoelastic effect. The piezoelectric effect cannot occur, however, in isotropic media.

As we have seen, the properties of a particular elastic dielectric are determined by specifying the form of a single scalar function of the state variables if we adopt the energy principle set forth in §10. Hence, if an elastic dielectric is isotropic or has any other type of material symmetry, this fact must make itself known through the form of the stored energy function of deformation and polarization. It is now our purpose to determine the most general functional form of the energy function which is consistent with the assumption that a particular elastic dielectric is homogeneous and isotropic.

The natural state of a homogeneous isotropic elastic dielectric is a state of zero polarization. The surface tractions and extrinsic electric field vanish. There are no intrinsic directions defined in the material. Without loss in generality we may assume that the stored energy has the value zero in the natural state. We assume that *the stored energy in the deformed and polarized state is a single valued function of the following quantities and following quantities only*:

$$\Sigma = \Sigma(x^i{}_{;A}\,,\pi^i,\,g_{ij}\,,g^i{}_A). \tag{11.1}$$

For emphasis, this may be compared with the case when an intrinsic direction exists in the undeformed and unpolarized dielectric. The intrinsic direction may be characterized by a vector H^A. In this case, the stored energy function could also depend on the components of the vector $\mathbf{H}$. By excluding material descriptors or tensors of this type from the list (11.1), we have given substance to the physical notion of material isotropy. The homogeneity of the material is given quantitative expression by the device of omitting the position vector components R^A from the list (11.1).

Two distinct types of invariance requirements will be made on the stored energy function. These are, *coordinate invariance* and *invariance to rigid rotations*. In many treatments of this and similar problems which arise in the formulation of constitutive relations for continuous media, little or no attempt is made to distinguish clearly between these separate demands. Here, in this work, all of the kinematical and mechanical theory has been developed and presented in a form which is invariant to an arbitrary simultaneous choice of two coordinate systems—one for the description of the natural state configuration, one for the description of the deformed and polarized state. The transformation law of each of the tensor variables listed in (11.1) is properly indicated by the type and placement of the indices. *Coordinate invariance* requires only that Σ be an absolute scalar function of the list of tensor variables. For example, a term proportional to $g^A{}_i x^i{}_{;A}$ could occur in the stored energy function if coordinate invariance were all that was demanded. That a term of this form cannot occur in the expression for the stored energy function which is also invariant to rigid rotations of the deformed and polarized material will soon be made apparent. In §10, it was shown that the moment equation will not be satisfied unless Σ is invariant to rigid rotations. The transformation law of the variables listed in (11.1) under a rigid rotation of the deformed and polarized body is given by

$$\begin{aligned} x^i{}_{;A} &\to x^j{}_{;A} S^i_j \\ \pi^i &\to \pi^j S^i{}_j \\ g_{ij} &\to g_{ij} \\ g^i{}_A &\to g^i{}_A \end{aligned} \tag{11.2}$$

where $S^i{}_j$ is a rotation tensor and satisfies the equations, $g_{ij} S^i{}_k S^j{}_l = g_{kl}$, $\det S^i{}_j = +1$. Note that the choice of the two coordinate systems is fixed so that the components of the metric and shifter are not altered by this operation. If the natural state of the medium is rotated holding the deformed and polarized state fixed, the transformation law for the variables is

$$\begin{aligned} x^i{}_{;A} &\to x^i{}_{;B} S^B{}_A \\ \pi^i &\to \pi^i \\ g_{ij} &\to g_{ij} \\ g^i{}_A &\to g^i{}_A \end{aligned} \tag{11.3}$$

where $S^A{}_B$ is a rotation tensor satisfying the equations $g_{AB} S^A{}_C S^B{}_D - g_{CD} = 0$, $\det S^A{}_B = +1$. Physically, the two transformations (11.2) and (11.3) represent equivalent operations—namely, a *relative* rotation of the deformed and polarized state and the natural state of the dielectric. If the stored energy function is made insensitive to either type of transformation, it will automatically be insensitive to the other.

We now make use of a theorem on invariant functions of several vectors first given by Cauchy [17]. If $F(V_1^i, V_2^i, \cdots, V_n^i)$ is a single valued function of the components of n vectors which is invariant to a rigid rotation of the system of vectors, F must reduce to a function of their lengths and scalar products, $I_{\Gamma\Delta} = g_{ij} V_\Gamma^i V_\Delta^j$, and the determinants of their components taken three at a time, $D_{\Gamma\Delta\Upsilon} = \epsilon_{ijk} V_\Gamma^i V_\Delta^j V_\Upsilon^k$.

Let us now impose the condition that Σ be invariant under the substitutions (11.2). By CAUCHY's theorem, Σ must reduce to a function of the following variables:

$$
\begin{aligned}
C_{AB} &= g_{ij}x^i{}_{;A}x^j{}_{;B} \,, \\
\Pi_A &= g_{ij}x^i{}_{;A}\pi^j, \\
\pi^2 &= g_{ij}\pi^i\pi^j, \\
J &= \tfrac{1}{6}(\det g^A{}_i)\epsilon_{ijk}\epsilon^{ABC}x^i{}_{;A}x^j{}_{;B}x^k{}_{;C} \,, \\
D^A &= \tfrac{1}{2}(\det g^A{}_i)\epsilon_{ijk}\epsilon^{ABC}x^i{}_{;B}x^j{}_{;C}\pi^k, \\
& g_{AB} \,, \, g^i{}_A \,.
\end{aligned}
\tag{11.4}
$$

That is, if the stored energy function is to be invariant to rigid rotations, the original list of variables in (11.1) can occur only in the combinations listed in (11.4). We can now show, however, that the list (11.4) is somewhat redundant. Since $\det C^A{}_B = J^2$ and for real motions J is always positive, we can eliminate J from the list (11.4) since it is determined by the variables C_{AB} and g_{AB}. Also, if we use the fact that $D^A = JX^A{}_{;i}\pi^i$, it is not difficult to show that $C_{AB}\,D^B = J\Pi_A$, or $D^A = J(C^{-1})^A{}_B\Pi^B$. Since we have already shown that J is expressible in terms of the $C^A{}_B$, we can now eliminate the variables D^A from the list (11.4). In this manner we reduce Σ to a function of the variables now indicated:

$$\Sigma = \Sigma(C_{AB}\,, \Pi_A\,, \pi^2, g_{ij}\,, g^i{}_A). \tag{11.5}$$

The next step is to require coordinate invariance under independent transformations of either set of coordinate systems. With the exception of $g^i{}_A$ and g_{ij} all of the quantities in (11.5) are absolute scalars under coordinate transformations of the x^i. The only absolute scalars which can be formed from the metric and the shifter are the components g_{AB} of the metric in the X^A coordinate system. A well known result which we now use is that a coordinate transformation of the X^A can be made which simultaneously reduces the symmetric tensor C_{AB} and the metric tensor g_{AB} to diagonal form. Let C_1, C_2, and C_3 be the diagonal entries of the matrix C_{AB} in this special coordinate system and let Π_1, Π_2, and Π_3 be the corresponding components of the vector $\mathbf{\Pi}$.[13] The metric has unit entries along the diagonal. Thus, in this special coordinate system, the stored energy function is expressible as a function of the C_Γ and Π_A and we have

$$\Sigma = \Sigma(C_1\,, C_2\,, C_3\,, \Pi_1\,, \Pi_2\,, \Pi_3\,, \pi^2). \tag{11.6}$$

[13] If the eigenvalues of $\mathbf{C}$ are unique, they can be ordered in such a way that $C_1 > C_2 > C_3$. The coordinate transformation which diagonalizes $\mathbf{C}$ and produces this ordering is unique up to a reversal in the direction of any one of the coordinate axes.

Now under the coordinate transformation from this special coordinate system to one which is obtained by a simple reversal of one of the coordinate directions, the C_Γ are unaltered, π^2 is invariant, but one of the components of the vector $\mathbf{\Pi}$ suffers a change in sign. Since Σ is a single valued function of its arguments and invariant to arbitrary coordinate transformations, it must involve the components of the vector $\mathbf{\Pi}$ only by even powers. By this line of reasoning we see that Σ must reduce to a function of the arguments indicated below:

$$\Sigma = \Sigma(C_1\,, C_2\,, C_3\,, (\Pi_1)^2, (\Pi_2)^2, (\Pi_3)^2, \pi^2). \tag{11.7}$$

It can then be shown that each of the arguments in (11.7) is a *single valued* function of the six independent scalar invariants given by

$$\begin{aligned} I_1 &= \delta^A{}_B C^B{}_A = \text{trace } \mathbf{C} \\ I_2 &= (\tfrac{1}{2}!)\delta^{AB}_{CD} C^C{}_A C^D{}_B = \text{sum of the principal minors of } \mathbf{C} \\ I_3 &= (1/3!)\delta^{ABC}_{DEF} C^D{}_A C^E{}_B C^F{}_C = \det C^A{}_B \\ I_4 &= \Pi_A \Pi^A = \Pi^2 \\ I_5 &= C^A{}_B \Pi^B \Pi_A = \mathbf{\Pi}\cdot\mathbf{C}\cdot\mathbf{\Pi} \\ I_6 &= \pi^2. \end{aligned} \tag{11.8}$$

The scalar invariants $I_1\,, \cdots, I_6$ can all be written as functions of the strain measure $(c^{-1})^i{}_j$:

$$\begin{aligned} I_1 &= \text{tr } \mathbf{c}^{-1} \\ I_2 &= \text{sum of the principal minors of } \mathbf{c}^{-1} \\ I_3 &= \det \mathbf{c}^{-1} \\ I_4 &= \boldsymbol{\pi}\cdot\mathbf{c}^{-1}\cdot\boldsymbol{\pi} \\ I_5 &= \boldsymbol{\pi}\cdot\mathbf{c}^{-2}\cdot\boldsymbol{\pi} \\ I_6 &= \pi^2. \end{aligned} \tag{11.9}$$

This set is entirely equivalent to the set (11.8). Still other choices of the independent variables can be made. For example, in making approximations it is sometimes convenient to take the set obtained from (11.9) by replacing the strain measure $\mathbf{c}^{-1}$ by the strain measure $(\mathbf{c}^{-1} - \mathbf{1})$.

We have proven that a *single valued* stored energy function for an elastic dielectric is reducible to a *single valued* function of the scalar invariants (11.8) or (11.9). The classical theory of invariant functions of vectors and tensors [18] is concerned primarily with the reduction of tensor invariant *polynomial* functions of the components of a set of tensors to *polynomial* functions in a minimal set of basic tensor invariants which are the elements of the so-called *integrity basis*. We may state the general problem treated there as follows: Let $F^{AB\cdots}$ be the components of a tensor **F** of given rank. It is supposed that the components of **F** are polynomial functions of the components of a set of dependent variables which we shall denote by $H_1^{AB\cdots}$, $H_2^{AB\cdots}$, *etc.* This leads to a set of relations having the form

$$F^{AB\cdots} = F^{AB\cdots}(H_1^{AB\cdots}, H_2^{AB\cdots}, \cdots) \tag{11.10}$$

where the right-hand side denotes a polynomial in the variables listed. Let $T^A{}_B$ denote the elements of a "transformation matrix," **T**. Under the transformation **T**, the dependent variables $F^{AB\cdots}$ and each of the independent variables are transformed according to a definite law of transformation. For our purposes here, we may assume that this law of transformation is

$$\begin{aligned} F^{AB\cdots} &\to T^A{}_C T^B{}_D \cdots F^{CD\cdots} \\ H_\Gamma^{AB\cdots} &\to T^A{}_C T^B{}_D \cdots H_\Gamma^{CD\cdots}. \end{aligned} \tag{11.11}$$

That is, the law of transformation is the linear homogeneous law of transformation for tensors. The notation of (11.10) and (11.11) may be conveniently shortened by the use of the more abstract symbolic notation $\mathbf{F} = \mathbf{F}(\mathbf{H}_1, \mathbf{H}_2, \cdots)$, $\mathbf{F} \to \mathbf{TF}$, $\mathbf{H}_\Gamma \to \mathbf{TH}_\Gamma$. If **F** is an *invariant* tensor function of the $\mathbf{H}_\Gamma$ under the transformation **T**, then

$$\mathbf{TF} = \mathbf{F}(\mathbf{TH}_1, \mathbf{TH}_2, \cdots). \tag{11.12}$$

More generally, a *set* of elements $\mathbf{T}_\Gamma$ which form a group $\mathcal{G}$ under the multiplication law $T^A_{\Gamma B} T^B_{\Delta C} = T^A_{\Upsilon C}$, are defined and the functional relation (11.12) is required to be satisfied for each element of the group. The group may be finite or continuous. For example, $\mathbf{T}_\Gamma$ may be defined as an arbitrary element of the orthogonal group or T_Γ may be an arbitrary element of a finite subgroup of the orthogonal group. The tensor **F** is then said to be an invariant tensor function of the tensors $\mathbf{H}_\Gamma$ under the group of transformations $\mathcal{G}$. A fundamental theorem of the classical invariant theory states that an arbitrary tensor invariant *polynomial* function of a set of tensors $\mathbf{H}_\Gamma$ under any finite or compact group $\mathcal{G}$, is reducible to a *polynomial* in a *finite* set of basic tensor invariants $\mathbf{I}_1, \mathbf{I}_2, \cdots, \mathbf{I}_h$. If the set $\{\mathbf{I}\}$ is minimal, the set constitutes an *integrity basis* [18, p. 274]. The elements of an integrity basis may not be functionally independent. Polynomial relations called syzygies more often exist than not between the elements of an integrity basis. Many important special cases of the above stated problem of finding the integrity basis which is relevant to a given dependent tensor **F**, a given set of variable tensors $\mathbf{H}_\Gamma$ and a given group $\mathcal{G}$ have been considered by the workers in this field of mathematics. It is sometimes difficult to translate these known results, particularly those results found in the older literature on invariant theory, into the language we have chosen to state the problem here. However, a little patience is well rewarded and answers to many difficult problems can be found. For example, suppose that the $F^{AB\cdots}$ are constant functions and G is the orthogonal group, then (11.12) reduces to

$$T^A{}_C T^B{}_D \cdots F^{CD} = F^{AB},$$

where $T^A{}_B$ is an arbitrary solution of the equations $g_{AB}T^A{}_C T^B{}_D - g_{CD} = 0$. Then it is known [18, p. 144] that the elements g^{AB} of the metric tensor constitute an integrity basis. That is, an arbitrary constant, invariant tensor of the orthogonal group is expressible as a linear combination of outer products of g^{AB} with coefficients which transform as scalars under the group $\mathcal{G}$. An immediate corollary of this theorem is that there exists no constant invariant tensor of the orthogonal group which is of odd rank. If **F** is an invariant constant tensor, its rank is even and **F** has the general form

$$F^{A_1A_2\cdots A_{2n}} = C_{pq\cdots rs}\, g^{A_pA_q} \cdots g^{A_rA_s}, \tag{11.13}$$

where $(p, q, \cdots, r, s)$ is a permutation of the numbers $(1, 2, \cdots, 2n)$ and the $C_{pq\cdots rs}$ are scalars. We shall use the result (11.13) in §13 of this paper where we consider polynomial approximations to the stored energy function. We conclude this digression on classical invariant theory by pointing out that the integrity basis for scalar invariant functions of a single symmetric tensor, a single vector under the orthogonal group, the metric tensor g_{ij}, and its inverse g^{ij} under the full linear group (arbitrary coordinate transformations) is a known result of classical invariant theory [19, p. 61]. But this is just the problem which confronts us in the reduction of the stored energy function of an elastic dielectric after reaching the point (11.5) if we demand that Σ be a *polynomial* in the variables listed in (11.5) and we wish to preserve the polynomial character of Σ. The scalar invariants (11.7) and (11.9) also constitute an *integrity basis* for the same variables under the full linear group. That is, *if we assume that the stored energy function is a polynomial function of the components* $(c^{-1})_{ij}$, π^i, g_{ij}, g^{ij}, *it is expressible as a polynomial in the basic invariants* $I_1, I_2, \cdots, I_6$. Since the set of basic invariants $I_1, I_2, \cdots, I_6$ are functionally independent, there are no syzygies.

Let us assume that, for some range of values of the invariants I_Γ, Σ is a differentiable function of the I_Γ. Then, from (10.33) and (10.34) we have

$$t_{\text{L}i}{}^{i} = \rho \sum_\Gamma \frac{\partial \Sigma}{\partial I_\Gamma} \frac{\partial I_\Gamma}{\partial x^i{}_{;A}}\, x^i{}_{;A} \tag{11.14}$$

$$\overline{E}{}^i_{\text{L}} = -\sum_\Gamma \frac{\partial \Sigma}{\partial I_\Gamma} \frac{\partial I_\Gamma}{\partial \pi_i}. \tag{11.15}$$

Working out the various expressions $(\partial I_\Gamma/\partial x^i{}_{;A})x^i{}_{;A}$ and $\partial I_\Gamma/\partial \pi_i$, and substituting in (11.14) and (11.15) we obtain the following expressions for the local stress and effective local field in an isotropic elastic dielectric:

$$t_{\mathrm{L}i}{}^i = 2\rho\left\{I_3 \frac{\partial \Sigma}{\partial I_3} \delta^i{}_i + \left(\frac{\partial \Sigma}{\partial I_1} + I_1 \frac{\partial \Sigma}{\partial I_2}\right)(c^{-1})^i{}_i - \frac{\partial \Sigma}{\partial I_2}(c^{-2})^i{}_i \right. \tag{11.16}$$

$$\left. + \frac{\partial \Sigma}{\partial I_4}(c^{-1})^i{}_k \pi^k \pi_i + \frac{\partial \Sigma}{\partial I_5}(c^{-2})^i{}_k \pi^k \pi_i + \frac{\partial \Sigma}{\partial I_5}(c^{-1})^i{}_k (c^{-1})_i{}^l \pi_l \pi^k \right\}$$

$$\overline{E}{}^i_{\mathrm{L}} = -2\left\{\frac{\partial \Sigma}{\partial I_4}(c^{-1})^i{}_j + \frac{\partial \Sigma}{\partial I_5}(c^{-2})^i{}_j + \frac{\partial \Sigma}{\partial I_6}\delta^i{}_j\right\}\pi^j. \tag{11.17}$$

The above set of constitutive relations between the local stress, effective local field, strain, and polarization are the general form which they take in isotropic homogeneous materials if we assume the validity of the energy principle. In the next section, we shall determine some simple solutions of the equilibrium equations using the stress-strain-field-polarization relations for isotropic materials. These special solutions reveal many interesting physical phenomena predicted by the general non-linear theory.

12. Some Simple Solutions for an Arbitrary Form of the Stored Energy Function of Isotropic Dielectrics

We shall consider, first, the simple shearing of an infinite slab of homogeneous isotropic elastic dielectric whose deformed and undeformed boundaries are the planes $X^1 = 0, a$. We here choose the X^A and x^i coordinate systems to be one and the same rectangular Cartesian system. By simple shearing of the slab, we mean the deformation indicated by the mapping,

$$x^1 = X^1, \qquad x^2 = X^2 + \beta X^1, \qquad x^3 = X^3 \tag{12.1}$$

where the constant β is a measure of the amount of shear. In addition, let the dielectric be polarized in the amount,

$$\boldsymbol{\pi} = (\pi_1 , \pi_2 , 0) \tag{12.2}$$

where π_1 and π_2 are constants throughout the slab. For the deformation (11.1), the $x^i{}_{;A}$ has the matrix of values

$$||x^i{}_{;A}|| = \begin{Vmatrix} 1 & 0 & 0 \\ \beta & 1 & 0 \\ 0 & 0 & 1 \end{Vmatrix} \tag{12.3}$$

from which it follows that $J = \det |x^i{}_{;A}| = 1$, whence $\rho = \rho_0$. The deformation tensor $(c^{-1})^i{}_j$ has the form

$$||(c^{-1})^i{}_j|| = \begin{Vmatrix} 1 & \beta & 0 \\ \beta & 1+\beta^2 & 0 \\ 0 & 0 & 1 \end{Vmatrix}. \tag{12.4}$$

The Maxwell self field of the polarized slab is equivalent to that of a uniform surface charge density of strength $P \cdot n/e_0 = \pm\rho_0\pi_1/e_0$ on the faces of the slab, the positive sign holding on the face $x^1 = a$, the negative sign holding on the face $x^1 = 0$. The self field is of the form

$$\begin{aligned} \mathbf{E}_{\mathrm{MS}} &= [-\rho_0\,\pi_1/e_0 , 0, 0] && 0 < x < a \\ \mathbf{E}_{\mathrm{MS}} &= [0, 0, 0] && x < 0 \\ & && x > a. \end{aligned} \tag{12.5}$$

Since the deformation, the polarization, *and the Maxwell self field* are homogeneous, the divergence of the local stress and the Maxwell stress vanish separately, $t_{\mathrm{L}}^{ij}{}_{;j} = t_{\mathrm{MS};j}^{ij} = 0$. Hence, the slab will be in equilibrium in the absence of an extrinsic body force. The extrinsic body force will vanish provided the external field $\mathbf{E}_0$ is uniform throughout the slab. The external field $\mathbf{E}_0$ plus the Maxwell field $\mathbf{E}_{MS}$ must be equal and opposite to $-\partial\Sigma/\partial\pi^i$ at each interior point of the slab, so that

$$E_0^i = -E_{MS}^i + \frac{\partial \Sigma}{\partial \pi_i} \tag{12.6}$$

is a condition of equilibrium. Working out the consequences of this requirement, we find

$$E_0^1 = e_0^{-1}\rho_0\pi_1 + 2\left\{(\pi_1 + \beta\pi_2)\frac{\partial\Sigma}{\partial I_4} + [(1+\beta^2)\pi_1 + \beta(2+\beta^2)\pi_2]\frac{\partial\Sigma}{\partial I_5} + \pi_1\frac{\partial\Sigma}{\partial I_6}\right\} \tag{12.7}$$

$$E_0^2 = 2\left\{[\beta\pi_1 + (1+\beta^2)\pi_2]\frac{\partial\Sigma}{\partial I_4} + \beta(2+\beta^2)\pi_1 + [(1+3\beta^2+\beta^4)\pi_2]\frac{\partial\Sigma}{\partial I_5} + \pi_2\frac{\partial\Sigma}{\partial I_6}\right\} \tag{12.8}$$

$$E_0^3 = 0. \tag{12.9}$$

Consider for a moment the expression (12.8) for E_0^2. It is a rather general function of the parameters π_1, π_2, and β,

$$E_0^2 = E_0^2(\pi_1, \pi_2, \beta), \tag{12.10}$$

whose form is not known explicitly until one specifies the stored energy function Σ explicitly. Let us regard the parameters β and π_1 as having specified values and attempt to satisfy the condition $E_0^2 = 0$, by suitable choice of π_2. For given β, there is always the solution obtained by setting $\pi_1 = \pi_2 = 0$. Then, if the derivative $\partial E_0^2/\partial\pi_2$ is non-zero and continuous, we are assured of non-zero solutions $\pi_2 = \pi_2(\pi_1, \beta)$ in some neighborhood of the zero solution. This follows from the theory of implicit functions [20]. Hence, we may contemplate an equilibrium state of a sheared elastic dielectric slab in the presence of an applied field $\mathbf{E}_0$ which is *normal* to the faces of the slab. In general, the polarization of the slab will have a component π_2 perpendicular to the applied field for non-zero values of the shear measure β. This will, of course, give rise to an extrinsic body moment of the form

$$m^{ij} = \begin{Vmatrix} 0 & -\rho_0\pi^2E_0^1 & 0 \\ \rho_0\pi^2E_0^1 & 0 & 0 \\ 0 & 0 & 0 \end{Vmatrix} \tag{12.11}$$

tending to rotate the slab about the x^3 axis.

Consider, next, the boundary condition (10.31), which implies that to maintain the state of deformation and polarization, mechanical surface tractions T^i must be applied to the faces of the slab. They are given by

$$T^i = t_{\mathsf{L}}^{ij} n_j - [t_{\mathsf{MS}}^{ij}] n_j \,. \tag{12.12}$$

We find that

$$[t_{\mathsf{MS}}^{ij}] n_j = \pm(\tfrac{1}{2} e_0^{-1} (P_1)^2, 0, 0), \tag{12.13}$$

the positive sign holding at the surface $x^1 = a$, and the negative sign at the surface $x^1 = 0$. Hence, the Maxwell self field gives rise to a stress system which exerts an *apparent* normal surface traction on the faces of the slab which tends to elongate the slab. A normal surface traction over and above that required to balance the local stress $t_{\mathsf{L}}^{ij} n_j$ must be applied to maintain the prescribed state of deformation and polarization. Using the stress-deformation-polarization relations (11.15) for the local stress, we find that the total surface traction which must be applied to the face of the slab, $x^1 = a$, in order to maintain equilibrium has components given by

$$\begin{aligned} T_1 = 2\rho_0 \Big\{ &\Big(I_3 \frac{\partial \Sigma}{\partial I_3} + \frac{\partial \Sigma}{\partial I_1} + I_1 \frac{\partial \Sigma}{\partial I_2} \Big) - \frac{\partial \Sigma}{\partial I_2} (1 + \beta^2) \\ &+ \Big(\frac{\partial \Sigma}{\partial I_4} + 2 \frac{\partial \Sigma}{\partial I_5} - \tfrac{1}{4} e_0^{-1} \rho_0 \Big) (\pi_1)^2 \\ &+ \beta \Big(\frac{\partial \Sigma}{\partial I_4} + 4 \frac{\partial \Sigma}{\partial I_5} \Big) \pi_1 \pi_2 + \beta^2 \frac{\partial \Sigma}{\partial I_5} [(\pi_1)^2 + (\pi_2)^2] + \beta^3 \frac{\partial \Sigma}{\partial I_5} \pi_1 \pi_2 \Big\} \end{aligned} \tag{12.14}$$

$$\begin{aligned} T_2 = 2\rho_0 \Big\{ &\beta \Big(\frac{\partial \Sigma}{\partial I_1} + I_1 \frac{\partial \Sigma}{\partial I_2} - 2 \frac{\partial \Sigma}{\partial I_2} \Big) - \beta^3 \frac{\partial \Sigma}{\partial I_2} \\ &+ \Big(\frac{\partial \Sigma}{\partial I_4} + 2 \frac{\partial \Sigma}{\partial I_5} \Big) \pi_1 \pi_2 + \beta \Big(\frac{\partial \Sigma}{\partial I_4} + 3 \frac{\partial \Sigma}{\partial I_5} \Big) (\pi_1)^2 \\ &+ \beta \frac{\partial \Sigma}{\partial I_5} (\pi_2)^2 + \beta^2 \Big(\frac{\partial \Sigma}{\partial I_4} + 5 \frac{\partial \Sigma}{\partial I_5} \Big) \pi_1 \pi_2 \\ &+ \beta^3 \frac{\partial \Sigma}{\partial I_5} [(\pi_1)^2 + (\pi_2)^2] + \beta^4 \frac{\partial \Sigma}{\partial I_5} \pi_1 \pi_2 \Big\} \end{aligned} \tag{12.15}$$

$$T_3 = 0. \tag{12.16}$$

At the face $x^1 = 0$, tractions equal in magnitude and opposite in direction to those listed above must be applied.

A number of qualitative features of the theory are apparent upon examination of the above expressions for the surface tractions. Since the theory is equivalent to the theory of finite deformations of homogeneous isotropic perfectly elastic solids if one neglects the dependence of the stored energy function on the invariants I_4, I_5, and I_6, all of the qualitative features of that theory will occur here as possibilities even in the limit of vanishing polarization. If the various scalar coefficients in the expressions for surface traction are thought of as power series expansions about the undeformed and unpolarized state, $\pi_1 = \pi_2 = \beta = 0$, there occurs a term in the normal component of the surface traction of order zero in the polarization components and of second order in the shear measure β. This is the well known *Poynting effect*, whereby to maintain a state of finite simple shear, tangential surface tractions are insufficient. This is a non-linear effect and does not occur in the classical linear theory of elasticity. There also occur terms in the normal component of the surface traction which are of zero order in the shear parameter β and which involve the components of the polarization to at least the second power. We identify the existence of such terms with the well known electrostrictive effect. It is sometimes argued that the *electrostrictive effect* is due solely to the tendency of the Maxwell field to elongate the slab, but it is apparent here that what might be called the local field electrostrictive effect may either support this tendency to elongate or have an overriding influence in the opposite direction tending to shorten the slab. The ambiguity that remains is similar to that which remains at this stage of development of the theory of non-linear elasticity in any discussion of the sign of the Poynting effect. It is possible that arguments based on stability or thermodynamic inequalities may dictate the positive or negative character of the electrostrictive phenomenon, but we do not enter upon these questions here. It is also clear on examination of the terms in T_1 that there is a modification of the electrostrictive effect due to shearing of the slab. If we assume, as is reasonable, that $\pi_2 \sim \beta$, then this deformation-polarization cross effect is of at least second order in the shear parameter, and hence would not occur in a linear theory of the deformation.

As a second example, we consider the homogeneously deformed and polarized ellipsoid.

KELLOGG [16] exhibits the solution of the following problem in potential theory:

$$\nabla^2 U = -\kappa/e_0 \qquad x \in V, \qquad \kappa = \text{constant}, \tag{12.17}$$

$$\nabla^2 U^* = 0 \qquad x \in E - V. \tag{12.18}$$

The region V is the interior of an ellipsoid with semi-axes a_1, a_2, and a_3. The solution is rendered unique by the conditions, (1) $U = U^*$ at the boundary B of the ellipsoid, (2) $U_{,i} = U^*_{,i}$ at B, (3) U^* regular at infinity. We now demonstrate that φ, as determined by

$$\varphi = -U_{,i}P^i/\kappa \qquad x \in V, \qquad P^i = \text{constant}, \tag{12.19}$$

$$\varphi^* = -U^*_{,i}P^i/\kappa \qquad x \in E - V, \tag{12.20}$$

is the potential of a homogeneously polarized ellipsoid. That is, φ is a solution of the potential problem,

$$\nabla^2\varphi = 0 \qquad x \,\varepsilon\, V \tag{12.21}$$

$$\nabla^2\varphi^* = 0 \qquad x \,\varepsilon\, E - V \tag{12.22}$$

$$[e_0\varphi_{,i} - e_0\varphi^*{}_{,i} - P_i]n^i = 0 \qquad x \,\varepsilon\, B. \tag{12.23}$$

It follows from (12.17–18) that φ and φ^* satisfy (12.21–22). From the continuity of the gradient, $U_{,i}$, it follows [16] that the jump $[U_{,ij}] \equiv U_{,ij} - U^*{}_{,ij} = K_i n_j$. The symmetry of $[U_{,ij}]$ in the indices i and j allows one to set $[U_{,ij}] = Kn_i n_j$. We can evaluate K by taking the trace of this latter form and employing the field equations (12.17–18) satisfied by U and U^*. In this manner we deduce that

$$[\varphi_{,i}] \equiv \varphi_{,i} - \varphi^*{}_{,i} = -[U_{,ij}]P^j/\kappa = e_0^{-1}n_i n_j P^j. \tag{12.24}$$

Substituting this result for the jump in $\varphi_{,i}$ into the boundary condition (12.23), we readily verify that it is satisfied by this solution; furthermore, the solution is unique.

The solution for the potential U at interior points of the ellipsoid [16, p. 194] is

$$U = -A_1x^2 - A_2y^2 - A_3z^2 + D \tag{12.25}$$

where the A_Γ and D are positive constants given by

$$A_\Gamma = \tfrac{1}{4}a_1a_2a_3\kappa e_0^1 \int_0^\infty ds/(a_\Gamma^2 + s)\sqrt{\psi(s)}$$

$$D = \tfrac{1}{4}a_1a_2a_3\kappa e_0^{-1} \int_0^\infty ds/\sqrt{\psi(s)} \tag{12.26}$$

$$\psi(s) = (a_1^2 + s)(a_2^2 + s)(a_3^2 + s).$$

In the solution (12.25), the center of the ellipsoid is at the origin. The principal axes of the ellipsoid coincide with the coordinate axes of the rectangular Cartesian frame, (x, y, z). In a general coordinate system, U has the form,

$$U = -A_{ij}(r^i - r_0^i)(r^j - r_0^j) \tag{12.27}$$

where the proper values of the symmetric tensor A_{ij} are the A_Γ of (12.26), and the principal directions of A_{ij} are the principal directions of the ellipsoid. The r^i are the components of the position vector of an interior point of an ellipsoid centered at the point r_0^i. Thus, *the Maxwell self field, $E_{MS}^i = -\varphi_{,}{}^i$, in the interior of a homogeneously polarized ellipsoid, is a homogeneous field whose value is given by*

$$E_{MS}^i = -A^i{}_j P^j. \tag{12.28}$$

This is a known result of electrostatic theory, and is of major importance for obtaining non-trivial inverse solutions for a deformed and polarized elastic dielectric. It is conjectured that the ellipsoid and its various degenerate forms, such as the sphere and the infinite slab, are the only bodies for which a homogeneous polarization field leads to a *homogeneous* self field at interior points.

Consider the homogeneously deformed and polarized ellipsoid whose interior points satisfy the condition $S_{ij}(r^i - r_0^i)(r^j - r_0^j) \leqq 1$. A general homogeneous deformation may be characterized by the condition,

$$x^i{}_{;A;B} = x^i{}_{;A;j} = 0. \tag{12.29}$$

The equilibrium condition (10.29) requires the applied field E_0^i to be uniform throughout the body. Since the applied field is uniform, the extrinsic body force, which is proportional to the gradient of $\mathbf{E}_0$, vanishes. The equilibrium condition (10.22) reduces to $t_i{}^j{}_{;j} = 0$. Since all of the quantities upon which $t_i{}^j$ depends are constant tensor fields in a homogeneously deformed and polarized ellipsoid, the equilibrium condition (10.22) will be satisfied for homogeneous deformations of an elastic dielectric ellipsoid subjected to a uniform applied electric field.

Using the boundary condition (10.32), it can be shown that the non-local part of the stress, $t_{\mathrm{MS}i}{}^j$, *i.e.*, the Maxwell stress, always yields an *apparent* surface traction $[t_{\mathrm{MS}i}{}^j]n_j = \frac{1}{2}e_0^{-1}P_n^2 n_i$, where P_n is the component of polarization normal to the surface. The surface tractions required to maintain the homogeneously deformed and polarized ellipsoidal dielectric body in equilibrium will be

$$T_i = t_{\mathrm{L}i}{}^j n_j - \tfrac{1}{2}e_0^{-1}P_n^2 n_i . \tag{12.30}$$

The local part of the stress, $t_{\mathrm{L}i}{}^j$, will be given by the expression (11.15) with $(c^{-1})_i{}^j$ and π^i restricted to the class of constant tensors. The uniform external field required to maintain equilibrium will be

$$E_0^i = A^i{}_j P^j + \frac{\partial \Sigma}{\partial \pi_i}. \tag{12.31}$$

In principle, the solutions (12.30) and (12.31) for homogeneous deformation and polarization of an ellipsoid would be sufficient to determine the stored energy function $\Sigma(I_\Gamma)$ if sufficient data relating measured values of the $(T_i\,,\, E_0^i)$ to the corresponding values of $((c^{-1})_{ij}\,,\, \pi_i)$ were available.

As an illustration of the solutions (12.30–31), consider the case when the principal directions n_Γ^i of the deformation tensor $\mathbf{c}^{-1}$, and the principal axes of the ellipsoid coincide. Let π^i be in one of these directions, say n_1^i, and let π be its magnitude. For this case, the applied field given by (12.31), is parallel to the polarization and has magnitude E_0 given by

$$E_0 = \left[\rho A_1 + 2\frac{\partial \Sigma}{\partial I_4}(c_1)^{-1} + 2\frac{\partial \Sigma}{\partial I_5}(c_1)^{-2} + 2\frac{\partial \Sigma}{\partial I_6}\right]\pi. \tag{12.32}$$

At the vertices of the ellipsoid, the surface tractions are normal to the surface and have magnitudes $T^{(\Gamma)}$ given by

$$T^{(\Gamma)} = 2\rho\left\{I_3 \frac{\partial \Sigma}{\partial I_3} + \left(\frac{\partial \Sigma}{\partial I_1} + I_1 \frac{\partial \Sigma}{\partial I_2}\right)(c_\Gamma)^{-1} - \frac{\partial \Sigma}{\partial I_2}(c_\Gamma)^{-2}\right\} \qquad \Gamma = 2, 3$$

$$T^{(1)} = 2\rho\left\{I_3 \frac{\partial \Sigma}{\partial I_3} + \left(\frac{\partial \Sigma}{\partial I_1} + I_1 \frac{\partial \Sigma}{\partial I_2}\right)(c_1)^{-1} - \frac{\partial \Sigma}{\partial I_2}(c_1)^{-2}\right. \tag{12.33}$$

$$\left. + \left(\frac{\partial \Sigma}{\partial I_4}(c_1)^{-1} + 2\frac{\partial \Sigma}{\partial I_5}(c_1)^{-2} - \tfrac{1}{4}e_0^{-1}\rho\right)(\pi^2)\right\}.$$

The solution (12.32–33) for this subclass of homogeneous deformations and polarization of an ellipsoid is not sufficient to determine the stored energy function completely. The essential lack of generality in this solution results from the requirement that the polarization be in the direction of a principal axis of the deformation tensor. However, in principle, sufficient information about the form of Σ can be obtained from data relating measured values of the $(T^{(\Gamma)}, E_0)$ to the corresponding values of $(c_\Gamma\ , \pi)$ in this class of solutions to enable one to make quantitative predictions in the general problem of plane strain of an elastic dielectric polarized in a direction normal to the plane of strain.

13. Anisotropic Dielectrics

In many applications of elastic dielectrics, the deformations are extremely small. Voigt's theory of the piezoelectric effect is based on constitutive relations for the stress and electric field which are linear in the displacement gradients and polarization. We wish to show that the linear constitutive relations of this classical theory are contained as a special case of (10.33) and (10.34). However, since the piezoelectric effect can occur only in anisotropic media with exceptional symmetry properties, we shall have to consider first the conditions imposed on the form of the stored energy function by the symmetry of an anisotropic medium.

A fundamental assumption of our energy principle is that the stored energy is a single valued function of the $9 + 3 = 12$ variables $x^i{}_{;A}$ and π^i. In the course of our discussion of isotropic dielectrics, we made the functional character of Σ more explicit by assuming that

$$\Sigma = \Sigma(x^i{}_{;A}, \pi^i, g_{ij}, g^i{}_A). \tag{13.1}$$

That is, the metric tensor and shifter were explicitly listed as variables. This was done so as not to exclude the dependence of Σ on variables such as $\pi_i = g_{ij}\pi^j$ or $\pi_A = g^i{}_A\pi_i$, which represent (measure) the *same* physical quantity. It was stated that, for isotropic materials, the energy function depends *only* on the variables listed in (13.1). This was motivated by the notion of material isotropy of the natural state.

Now in anisotropic dielectrics we shall again single out the natural state as the state of zero polarization.[14] It is the equilibrium state of the dielectric in the absence of applied surface tractions and external field. The local stress and effective local field vanish in the natural state.

The *point symmetry* of a crystalline medium may be fully characterized by a finite subgroup of the orthogonal group. We shall also be interested in anisotropic media which are not crystalline. For example, materials which possess *transverse isotropy* are of some interest in elasticity theory [15, 21, p. 160]. We shall make our discussion of anisotropic media general enough to include the case of *curvilinear anisotropy* [21, p. 164]. An example of a curvilinear anisotropic state of a continuous medium is the case of an elastic medium which is isotropic in some natural state and which has been deformed inhomogeneously. At each point in the deformed medium, the symmetry may be characterized by the group of orthogonal transformations which generate the eight equivalent points of the Cauchy deformation ellipsoid (the quadric of c_{ij}) corresponding to a given point on the ellipsoid. Stated otherwise, it is the subgroup of the orthogonal group which leaves the Cauchy deformation quadric invariant.

Whatever may be the material point symmetry of a particular state of a continuous

---

[14] There are examples of materials possessing a permanent polarization or electric moment. We do not consider these materials here.

medium, we shall assume that the symmetry is fully characterized by some subgroup $\mathcal{G}$ *of the orthogonal group* $\mathcal{O}$.

This subgroup may be finite as in the case of crystalline media, or may be continuous as in the case of transversely isotropic media. In a given coordinate system X^A with metric g_{AB}, each element of the orthogonal group has a matrix representation $T^A{}_B$ which satisfies the equations

$$g_{AB}T^A{}_CT^B{}_D - g_{CD} = 0. \tag{13.2}$$

Under coordinate transformations, the elements of the matrix $T^A{}_B$ transform as the elements of a mixed tensor of rank two. Hence (13.2) is a coordinate invariant definition of an "orthogonal matrix."

An *invariant tensor* of the group $\mathcal{G}$ is any tensor which satisfies each of the equations,

$$T^{A_1}{}_{B_1}T^{A_2}{}_{B_2} \cdots T^{A_n}{}_{B_n}H^{B_1B_2\cdots B_n} = H^{A_1A_2\cdots A_n}, \tag{13.3}$$

for every element T of the group. If $H^{AB\cdots}$ is an invariant tensor of the group which characterizes the point symmetry of the *natural* state of a continuous elastic medium, we shall call $H^{AB\cdots}$ a *material descriptor* or simply a *material tensor*. Note that an arbitrary scalar satisfies (13.3).

If the natural state is *homogeneous*, all the material descriptors are *spatially constant*. A spatially constant tensor is one whose covariant derivative vanishes.

The characteristic group for materials whose natural state is isotropic is the complete orthogonal group. According to a previously mentioned result (11.12), the material descriptors of isotropic materials are tensors of even rank which can be constructed by taking linear combinations of products of the metric tensor. The coefficients in these linear combinations are arbitrary scalar material descriptors. If an isotropic material is also homogeneous, it follows that each of these scalar coefficients must be spatially constant.

If the characteristic group of the material symmetry of the natural state of an elastic dielectric is a *proper* subgroup of the orthogonal group we shall call the dielectric *anisotropic*. If the material descriptors are not all spatially constant, we shall say that the material is *inhomogeneous*. If the material symmetry of the natural state is described by one of the thirty-two finite crystal groups, we shall call the material a *crystalline dielectric*.

An assumption which generalizes (13.1) to the case of anisotropic media and which includes (13.1) as a special case is that the stored energy function depends only on the following list of variables:

$$\Sigma = \Sigma(x^i{}_{;A}, \pi^i, H_\Gamma^{AB\cdots}, g_{ij}, g^i{}_A) \tag{13.4}$$

where the set of tensors $H_\Gamma^{AB\cdots}$ $(\Gamma = 1, 2, \cdots)$ denotes the set of material descriptors. Let us adopt the convention that given the dependence of Σ on the contravariant components f^i of any tensor that the possible dependence of Σ on the covariant or shifted components, $f_i = g_{ij}f^j$, $f^A = g^A{}_if^i$ is to be understood. Using this standard convention, (13.4) may be shortened to

$$\Sigma = \Sigma(x^i{}_{;A}, \pi^i, H_\Gamma^{AB\cdots}). \tag{13.5}$$

We have introduced, so far, three distinct types of transformations on the variables which occur in (13.5). These are: (I) independent *coordinate transformations* of the two coordinate systems which simultaneously span the Euclidean space; (II) the two groups of *rotations*—the first of which corresponds to rigid rotations of the deformed and polarized dielectric, the second of which corresponds to a rigid rotation of the natural state of the dielectric; (III) the subgroup $\mathcal{G}$ of the orthogonal group which describes the material point symmetry of the dielectric. The law of transformation of each of the variables under these three groups of transformations is as follows:

(I) Under coordinate transformations, each of the variables transforms according to the general transformation law for two-point tensor fields given in §3. The index notation and the convention regarding the type and position of the indices are sufficient to identify at a glance the law of transformation of any particular set of variables in (13.5).

(II) A. Under the group of rigid rotations of the deformed and polarized dielectric, the variables transform according to

$$\begin{aligned} x^i{}_{;A} &\to S^i{}_j x^j{}_{;A} \\ \pi^i &\to S^i{}_j \pi^j \\ H_\Gamma^{AB\cdots} &\to H_\Gamma^{AB\cdots}. \end{aligned} \tag{13.6}$$

(II) B. Under the group of rigid rotations of the natural state of the dielectric, the variables transform according to

$$\begin{aligned} x^i{}_{;A} &\to S^B{}_A x^i{}_{;B} \\ \pi^i &\to \pi_i \\ H_\Gamma^{AB\cdots} &\to S^A{}_C S^B{}_D \cdots H_\Gamma^{CD\cdots}. \end{aligned} \tag{13.7}$$

Note that material descriptors are invariant under a rigid rotation of the deformed and polarized state and that the polarization is not. The converse is true for rigid rotations of the natural state.

(III) Under the group $\mathcal{G}$, characteristic of the material symmetry, the variables transform according to

$$\begin{aligned} x^i{}_{;A} &\to x^i{}_{;A} \\ \pi^i &\to \pi^i \\ H_\Gamma^{AB\cdots} &\to T^A{}_C T^B{}_D \cdots H_\Gamma^{CD\cdots} \end{aligned} \tag{13.8}$$

where $\mathbf{T}$ is an arbitrary element of the group $\mathcal{G}$. Note that under this group of transformations, the displacement gradients and the polarization are invariants.[15]

[15] In physical theories, yet another type of transformation of the variables is important. These are the dimensional transformations. TRUESDELL [12] has considered the restrictions placed on the form of some types of constitutive relations by the requirement of dimensional invariance.

A fundamental assumption in this theory of anisotropic elastic dielectrics is that the stored energy function of deformation and polarization is absolutely invariant under each of the three types of transformations (I), (II), *and* (III).

We shall consider the restrictions placed on the form of the energy function by each type of transformation in the order (III), (II), (I). Since we have already assumed that the $H_{\Gamma}^{AB}\ldots$ are material descriptors, no further conditions on the form of Σ follow from (III). That is, each and every variable listed in (13.5) is invariant under (III), hence an arbitrary function of the variables is invariant under (III). Next, consider the transformations (II). Precisely the same argument which carried us from (11.1) to (11.5) in the case of isotropic materials allows us to conclude that if Σ is invariant to rigid rotations of the deformed and polarized state, it is reducible to a function of the variables indicated now:[16]

$$\Sigma = \Sigma(C_{AB}, \Pi_A, H^{AB\cdots}), \tag{13.9}$$

where the C_{AB} are the components of the Cauchy measure of strain $C_{AB} \equiv g_{ij}x^i_{;A}x^j_{;B}$, and the Π_A are given by $\Pi_A \equiv x^i_{;A}\pi_i$. Note that the Π_A are not the shifted components of π_i. We shall refrain from giving the vector Π_A any physical interpretation.

In the case of isotropic materials, we were able at this point to use the invariance of Σ under the coordinate transformations (I) to demonstrate that a single valued stored energy function of an isotropic dielectric must reduce to a function of only six independent variables—namely, the six scalar invariants (11.7–8). A further result which we were able to establish was that the same six scalar invariants constituted an integrity basis. Unfortunately, we are unable to proceed with such generality here in the case of anisotropic media. This is so for a number of reasons. First of all, the number and rank of the material descriptors is not known until the material symmetry is specified. Each type of material symmetry must therefore be considered separately. Depending on the type of material symmetry, the invariant theoretic problem which must be solved may involve considerable labor. For these reasons and others, we have assumed a special form for the energy function which allows us to proceed with the theoretical development without a specification of the material symmetry. The classical linear theory of the piezoelectric effect will be shown to follow from this special form for the energy function if the special constitutive relations for the local stress and effective local field are linearized.

---

[16] We have omitted writing π^2 in the list (13.9) since it is a single valued function of the C_{AB} and Π_A. In discussing the isotropic case, we retained π^2 in the list of variables since we were also interested in the case where Σ was a polynomial in the variables listed. Since π^2 is not a polynomial in the C_{AB} and Π_A, a polynomial in the set C_{AB}, Π_A, π^2 is not reducible in general to a polynomial in the functionally independent set C_{AB} and Π_A. Of course, π^2 can be written as a power series in the remaining variables so that polynomials in the C_{AB} and Π_A can approximate a given analytic function of π^2 as closely as desired. Since we shall later assume that Σ is a polynomial in C_{AB} and Π_A, the effect of eliminating π^2 from the list (13.9) should be understood at this time.

14. A Special Form for the Stored Energy Function—Polynomial Approximations

We have shown that the energy function of an anisotropic (includes isotropic as a special case) dielectric is reducible to the variables listed in (13.9). For purposes of approximation, it is convenient to introduce the tensor measure of strain $E_{AB} = (C_{AB} - g_{AB})$ which vanishes in the natural state. No loss in generality is incurred by writing (13.9) in the form

$$\Sigma = \Sigma(E_{AB}, \Pi_A, H_\Gamma^{AB\cdots}). \tag{14.1}$$

Any single valued absolute scalar function of these variables is a possible energy function for some elastic dielectric. Since each of the variables E_{AB} and Π_A vanishes in the natural state, we have been led to consider the following special form of the function

$$\begin{aligned}\rho_0\Sigma = {} & H_0{}^A\Pi_A + H_1{}^{AB}\Pi_A\Pi_B + H_2{}^{AB}E_{AB} + H_3{}^{ABCD}E_{AB}E_{CD} + H_4{}^{ABC}E_{AB}\Pi_C \\ & + H_5{}^{ABCD}E_{AB}\Pi_C\Pi_D + H_6{}^{ABCDE}E_{AB}E_{CD}\Pi_E \\ & + H_7{}^{ABCDEF}E_{AB}E_{CD}\Pi_E\Pi_F,\end{aligned} \tag{14.2}$$

where the $H_\Gamma^{AB\cdots}$ $(\Gamma = 1, 2, \cdots, 7)$ are independent of the E_{AB} and Π_A. It follows that the $H_\Gamma^{AB\cdots}$ are material descriptors of the rank and type as indicated by the number and position of their indices. The invariance of Σ under each type of transformation (I), (II), and (III) is insured. Since this special form of the stored energy function satisfies all of the invariance requirements *without approximation*, we can regard it in either of two ways: (1) the exact form of the energy function of an elastic dielectric which may or may not be found in nature, or (2) the first few terms in a power series expansion about the natural state of an arbitrary elastic dielectric. As a polynomial in the E_{AB} and Π_A we have included all possible terms of order zero, one, and two in the E_{AB} and all possible terms of order zero, one, and two in the polarization. In the sense of (2), it can only be expected that quantitative predictions based on this form of the energy function will be accurate for sufficiently small values of the strains and for weak fields.[17]

Many of the terms in (14.2) may vanish identically owing to the material symmetry. For example, if the natural state is isotropic, there are no material descriptors of odd rank; hence, no terms of odd degree in the polarization can occur in (14.2) if the dielectric is isotropic. This constitutes a formal reason why

[17] From dimensional considerations which we do not give here, it is possible to establish dimensionless criteria for "small strain and weak fields."

isotropic dielectrics do not exhibit the piezoelectric effect. The tensor coefficients in (14.2) will be assumed to have the same symmetry as the tensor of variables. For example, in the term $H_1^{AB}\Pi_A\Pi_B$, only the symmetric part of the tensor H_1^{AB} contributes to the value of the indicated sum over A and B; therefore, it is assumed that $H_2^{AB} = H_2^{BA}$.

We have established the general formulæ for the local stress and effective local field when the energy principle is adopted. These are

$$t_{\mathsf{L}i}{}^{j} = \rho \frac{\partial \Sigma}{\partial x^i{}_{;A}} x^j{}_{;A} \tag{14.3}$$

$$\bar{E}_{\mathsf{L}}{}^{i} = -\frac{\partial \Sigma}{\partial \pi_i}. \tag{14.4}$$

It is a matter of straightforward calculation now to determine the form of the stress-strain-field-polarization relations of an anisotropic media whose stored energy function is given by (14.2) or whose stored energy function is approximated by this form for sufficiently small strain and polarization. To carry out this calculation, it is convenient to introduce the following preliminary formulæ:

$$x^j{}_{;C}\frac{\partial E_{AB}}{\partial x_{i;C}} = x^i{}_{;B}x^j{}_{;A} + x^i{}_{;A}x^j{}_{;B} \equiv M_{AB}^{ij} ,$$

$$x^j{}_{;B}\frac{\partial \Pi_A}{\partial x_{i;B}} = x^j{}_{;A}\pi^i \equiv N_A^{ij}$$

$$\frac{\partial \Pi_A}{\partial \pi_i} = x^i{}_{;A} .$$

We find that the local stress and effective local field have the form

$$\begin{aligned}\frac{\rho_0}{\rho} t_{\mathsf{L}}^{ij} = {} & H_0{}^A N_A^{ij} + 2H_1{}^{AB}N_A^{ij}\Pi_B + H_2{}^{AB}M_{AB}^{ij} + 2H_3{}^{ABCD}M_{AB}^{ij}E_{CD} \\ & + H_4{}^{ABC}M_{AB}^{ij}\Pi_C + H_4{}^{ABC}E_{AB}N_C^{ij} + H_5{}^{ABCD}M_{AB}^{ij}\Pi_C\Pi_D \\ & + 2H_5{}^{ABCD}E_{AB}\Pi_C N_D^{ij} + 2H_6{}^{ABCDE}E_{AB}M_{CD}^{ij}\Pi_E + H_6{}^{ABCDE}E_{AB}E_{CD}N_E^{ij} \\ & + 2H_7{}^{ABCDEF}E_{AB}\Pi_E\Pi_F M_{CD}^{ij} + 2H_7{}^{ABCDEF}E_{AB}E_{CD}\Pi_E N_F^{ij},\end{aligned} \tag{14.5}$$

$$\begin{aligned}\rho_0\bar{E}_{\mathsf{L}}^{i} = {} & -[H_0{}^A x^i{}_{;A} + 2H_1{}^{AB}x^i{}_{;A}\Pi_B + H_4{}^{ABC}E_{AB}x^i{}_{;C} \\ & + 2H_5{}^{ABCD}E_{AB}\Pi_C x^i{}_{;D} + H_6{}^{ABCDE}E_{AB}E_{CD}x^i{}_{;E} \\ & + 2H_7{}^{ABCDEF}E_{AB}E_{CD}\Pi_E x^i{}_{;F}].\end{aligned} \tag{14.6}$$

It follows from (14.5) that, if the local stress is to vanish in the natural state, we must set $H_2{}^{AB} = 0$. Similarly, it follows from (14.6) that, if the effective local field is to vanish in the natural state, we must set $H_0{}^A = 0$. Since M^{ij}_{AB} is symmetric in i and j, it is a simple matter to write down the antisymmetric part of the local stress. We have

$$\begin{aligned}\frac{\rho_0}{\rho} t_{\mathrm{L}}^{[ij]} = [2H_1{}^{AB}\Pi_B + H_4{}^{BCA}E_{BC} + 2H_5{}^{DBCA}E_{DB}\Pi_C \\ + H_6{}^{EBCDA}E_{EB}E_{CD} + 2H_7{}^{FBCDEA}E_{FB}E_{CD}\Pi_E]N_A^{[ij]}.\end{aligned} \tag{14.7}$$

Multiplying (14.6) by π^j and taking the antisymmetric part of the tensor $(\rho_0/\rho)E_{\mathrm{L}}{}^iP^j$ obtained in this manner, we verify that

$$\frac{\rho_0}{\rho} t_{\mathrm{L}}^{[ij]} = \frac{\rho_0}{\rho} \overline{E}_{\mathrm{L}}^{[i}P^{j]}. \tag{14.8}$$

This result serves to check the general theorem proven in §10, (10.36). That is, since the special form for the energy function (14.2) is invariant to rigid rotations of the deformed and polarized dielectric, we are thereby insured that the moment equation will be satisfied as an algebraic identity if the constitutive relations (14.5) and (14.6) for the local stress and effective local field are adopted.

We next take up the questions of approximate constitutive relations, linearizations, small rotations, approximate invariance of the stored energy function, *etc.* We shall show that by linearizing the forms (14.5) and (14.6) we obtain VOIGT's piezoelectric constitutive relations.

15. Linearizations of the Constitutive Relations of an Elastic Dielectric

To effect a comparison of the constitutive relations (14.5–6) corresponding to the special form of the stored energy function (14.2) with the stress and field relations of Voigt's linear theory we must first write (14.5–6) in terms of the displacement gradients $u_{i;j}$ or $U_{A;B}$ which were defined in §4. As pointed out in §4, the symmetric part of either of these tensors is the customary measure of infinitesimal strain. To first order terms in the components of either set of these displacement gradients we have $u_{i;j} \approx g^A{}_i g^B{}_j U_{A;B}$. That is, according to the convention by which we regard the shifted components of a tensor merely as a different representation of the *same* tensor, no distinction need be made between the two sets of displacement gradients $u_{i;j}$ and $U_{A;B}$; however, if the displacement gradients are not regarded as infinitesimals they are not equivalent tensors.[18] In order to show that Voigt's linear piezoelectric constitutive relations are contained in (14.5–6) as a special case, it is sufficient to linearize these expressions with respect to both the displacement gradients $u_{i;j}$ and the polarization π_i . In order to show that various non-linear generalization of Voigt's linear relations which have been proposed are *not* contained as a special case of (14.5–6), it is sufficient to linearize with respect to the displacement gradients only and to retain all the terms in the polarization. Therefore, for either purpose, we may first examine the approximate form of (14.5–6) obtained by regarding the displacement gradients $u_{i;j}$ (or $U_{A;B}$) as infinitesimals. This linearization process is facilitated by the use of the approximate relations:

$$M^{ij}_{AB} \approx (g^i{}_A g^j{}_B + g^i{}_B g^j{}_A) + (g^i{}_A g^k{}_B + g^i{}_B g^k{}_A) u^j{}_{;k} + (g^i{}_A g^k{}_B + g^j{}_B g^k{}_A) u^i{}_{;k}$$

$$N^{ij}_A \approx g^j{}_A \pi^i + g^k{}_A u^j{}_{;k} \pi^i$$

$$x^i{}_{;A} \approx g^i{}_A + g^k{}_A u^i{}_{;k} \, .$$

Substituting these approximate expressions for M^{ij}_{AB} , N^{ij}_A , and $x^i{}_{;A}$ into (14.5–6) we have obtained the following approximate relations for the stress and field:

---

[18] One often finds non-linear generalizations of Voigt's linear piezoelectric constitutive relations which involve non-linear expressions in *the* displacement gradients. It would seem desirable in such circumstances to have a more explicit definition of what is meant by *the* displacement gradients. The components of these tensors have different transformation laws under rigid rotations of the deformed and natural states. A little thought will reveal that the transformation laws of the $u_{i;j}$ and $U_{A;B}$ are extremely complicated if any non-linear terms in these quantities are retained in a consistent fashion. It is for this reason that we have preferred to use the $x^i{}_{;A}$ as independent variables since their transformation law is considerably simpler than the transformation law of the $u_{i;j}$ or $U_{A;B}$ under rotations of the deformed or undeformed material.

$$\frac{\rho_0}{\rho} t_{\mathsf{L}}^{ij} \approx 2H_1{}^{ik}\pi^i\pi_k + 2H_1{}^{ik}u^l{}_{;k}\pi^i\pi_l + 2H_1{}^{kl}u^i{}_{;k}\pi^i\pi_l + 4H_3{}^{ijkl}\tilde{e}_{kl}$$

$$+ 2H_4{}^{ijk}\pi_k + 2H_4{}^{ijk}u^l{}_{;k}\pi_l + 2H_4{}^{ikl}u^j{}_{;k}\pi_l + 2H_4{}^{jkl}u^i{}_{;k}\pi_l + H_4{}^{kli}\tilde{e}_{kl}\pi^i$$

$$+ 2H_5{}^{ijkl}\pi_k\pi_l + 2H_5{}^{imkl}u^j{}_{;m}\pi_k\pi_l + 2H_5{}^{jmkl}u^i{}_{;m}\pi_k\pi_l + 4H_5{}^{ijkl}u^m{}_{;l}\pi_k\pi_m \qquad (15.1)$$

$$+ 2H_5{}^{klmi}\tilde{e}_{kl}\pi_m\pi^i + 2H_6{}^{klijm}\tilde{e}_{kl}\pi_m + 2H_7{}^{klijmn}\tilde{e}_{kl}\pi_m\pi_n ,$$

$$\rho_0 \overline{E}_{\mathsf{L}}^i \approx -[2H_1{}^{ik}\pi_k + 2H_1{}^{ik}u^l{}_{;k}\pi_l + 2H_1{}^{kl}u^i{}_{;k}\pi_l + H_4{}^{kli}\tilde{e}_{kl} + 2H_5{}^{klmi}\tilde{e}_{kl}\pi_m]. \qquad (15.2)$$

For infinitesimal displacement gradients we also have $(\rho_0/\rho) = 1 + \tilde{e}^k{}_k$; hence, this factor may be cleared from the expression for the stress by multiplying each term on the right which does not already contain a displacement gradient by the factor $(1 - \tilde{e}^k{}_k)$. Note that, even for infinitesimal displacement gradients, the components of the local stress and effective local field do *not* in general reduce to polynomials in the symmetric part of the displacement gradients only, as is sometimes assumed.

If we now completely linearize these constitutive relations by dropping all terms involving squares of the polarization or a product of a polarization component and a displacement gradient, we obtain the linear relations:

$$t_{\mathsf{L}}^{ij} \approx 4H_3{}^{ijkl}\tilde{e}_{kl} + 2H_4{}^{ijk}\pi_k \qquad (15.3)$$

$$\overline{E}_{\mathsf{L}}^i \approx -[2H_1{}^{ik}\pi_k + H_4{}^{kli}\tilde{e}_{kl}]. \qquad (15.4)$$

Now, at *static* equilibrium we have $\overline{\mathbf{E}}_{\mathsf{L}} + \mathbf{E}_{\mathsf{M}} = 0$, (§8, (8.3)), where $\mathbf{E}_{\mathsf{M}}$ is the total Maxwell field at a point inside the dielectric. This is the field which occurs in VOIGT's relations. Also, the total stress t^{ij} which is always symmetric if we neglect the Maxwell stress tensor (a legitimate approximation in this linearized theory since it always involves the field or polarization squared) must be assumed to be the stress tensor referred to in VOIGT's theory, since the concept of a local stress is not introduced. For the linearized theory, this is not an issue since $t^{ij} - t_{\mathsf{L}}^{ij}$ is negligible; hence, we may set $t^{ij} \approx t_{\mathsf{L}}^{ij}$ in (15.3). Thus we have from (15.3) and (15.4) that at *static* equilibrium

$$t^{ij} \approx c^{ijkl}e_{kl} + q^{ijk}P_k \qquad (15.5)$$

$$e_0 E_{\mathsf{M}}^i \approx (\chi^{-1})^{ik}P_k + p^{kli}e_{kl} \qquad (15.6)$$

with $c^{ijkl} = 4H_3{}^{ijkl}$, $q^{ijk} = (2/\rho_0)H_4{}^{ijk}$, $(\chi^{-1})^{ij} = (2e_0/\rho_0{}^2)H_1{}^{ij}$, and $p^{kli} = (e_0/\rho_0)H_4{}^{kli}$.

The linear relations (15.5) and (15.6) are identical in form to the piezoelectric relations proposed by VOIGT. The values of the components of the tensors c^{ijkl}, q^{ijk}, p^{ijk}, and χ^{ij} in certain special coordinate systems are called by some authors, elastic constants, piezoelectric constants, and susceptibility constants. Note that within the context of the theory of elastic dielectrics given here, (15.5–6) cannot be strictly regarded as constitutive relations. In order to obtain these particular formulæ we had to assume that the dielectric was in static equilibrium. That is, to eliminate the effective local field from (15.4) and obtain the relations (15.6) involving the Maxwell field, we used the static equilibrium condition $\overline{\mathbf{E}}_{\mathrm{L}} + \mathbf{E}_{\mathrm{M}} = 0$. It is to be expected that in the dynamic case, the right-hand side of this last equation will not be zero. In elasticity theory when acceleration forces are taken into account, the constitutive relations for the stress in terms of the strain are the same as they are in the static case. Thus, by analogy, we can expect that the constitutive relations (15.3–4) would be unaltered if we were to treat dynamic equilibrium of an elastic dielectric. However, it is not expected that VOIGT's linear relations will follow as a necessary consequence of the linear constitutive relations of this theory except in the special case of static equilibrium which has been considered throughout this paper.

16. The Linear Constitutive Relations for Isotropic Elastic Dielectrics

We have already considered the isotropic elastic dielectric and have obtained the form of the constitutive relations for the stress and effective local field corresponding to an arbitrary isotropic stored energy function (§11, (11.16–17)). It is instructive, however, to follow the formalism developed for anisotropic materials in §13, regarding the isotropic dielectric as a special case. The stress and field relations (15.1) and (15.2) which have been linearized with respect to displacement gradients will be specialized to the isotropic case. The work in this section will serve to illustrative the methods we use to treat materials of arbitrary symmetry. Also, the isotropic form of (15.1–2) can be compared with the work of Helmholtz [22, pp. 140–146].

According to the formalism of §13, if the natural state of an elastic dielectric is isotropic, the material descriptors H_Γ^{AB} are invariant tensors of the orthogonal group. Invariant tensors of the orthogonal group are also called *isotropic tensors*. As pointed out before, it is known that the most general form of an isotropic tensor is a linear combination of outer products of the metric tensor.[19] Given this result, we can now reduce the approximate constitutive relations (15.1) and (15.2) to their most general form in isotropic dielectrics. First, the material descriptors $H_4{}^{ijk}$ and $H_6{}^{ijklm}$ must vanish identically since there are no isotropic tensors of odd rank. The remaining material descriptors can now be written down in their most general form allowed by isotropic symmetry. These are

$$
\begin{aligned}
2H_1{}^{ij} &= a_1 g^{ij} \\
4H_3{}^{ijkl} &= \lambda g^{ij} g^{kl} + \mu (g^{ik} g^{jl} + g^{il} g^{jk}) \\
2H_5{}^{ijkl} &= a_2 g^{ij} g^{kl} + a_3 (g^{ik} g^{jl} + g^{il} g^{jk}) \\
2H_7{}^{ijklmn} &= a_4 g^{ij} g^{kl} g^{mn} + a_5 (g^{ik} g^{jl} + g^{jk} g^{il}) g^{mn} \\
&\quad + a_6 [(g^{im} g^{jn} + g^{jm} g^{in}) g^{kl} + (g^{km} g^{ln} + g^{lm} g^{kn}) g^{ij}] \\
&\quad + a_7 [g^{jk} (g^{im} g^{ln} + g^{in} g^{lm}) + g^{ik} (g^{jm} g^{ln} + g^{jn} g^{lm}) \\
&\quad + g^{jl} (g^{im} g^{kn} + g^{in} g^{km}) + g^{il} (g^{jm} g^{kn} + g^{jn} g^{km})].
\end{aligned} \tag{16.1}
$$

---

[19] There exists an elegant and simple theorem in the theory of group representations (the theorem on characters) which enables one to calculate the number of linearly independent invariant tensors of given rank for finite or compact groups. This application of the theory of group representations was first made by Racah [23] to calculate the number of linearly independent invariant tensors of given rank for the rotation subgroup of the orthogonal group in three dimensions. Invariant tensors of the rotation group are called hemitropic tensors. Bhagavantam and his coworkers [24] have made many applications of this same theorem on characters in the study of invariant tensors of the crystal groups.

Each of the above material tensors has been symmetrized to have the same symmetry as the tensor of variables in (14.2). For example, since H_7^{ijklmn} is the tensor of coefficients of the variable tensor $E_{ij}E_{kl}\Pi_m\Pi_n$, in writing (16.1) we have made H_7^{ijklmn} symmetric in each of the pairs (ij), (kl), and (mn) and also symmetric under an interchange of the pairs (ij) and (kl). This is important since it will in general reduce the number of scalar material descriptors necessary to define the material tensor descriptor completely. For example, there are three linearly independent isotropic tensors of rank four but only two with the symmetry of either H_3^{ijkl} or H_5^{ijkl}. We can determine from (16.1) that nine scalar material descriptors are necessary to determine the special form of the stored energy function (14.2) in the isotropic case. If the dielectric is also homogeneous, these nine descriptors will be spatially constant. It is appropriate to call these scalars *material constants*. Substituting (16.1) into (15.1–2), we obtain

$$\begin{aligned} t_{\mathsf{L}}^{ij} \approx {} & [\lambda\tilde{e}^k{}_k + a_2\pi^2 + 2(a_2 + a_6)\boldsymbol{\pi}\cdot\mathbf{e}\cdot\boldsymbol{\pi} + (a_4 - a_2)\tilde{e}^k{}_k\pi^2]g^{ij} \\ & + [2\mu + 2(a_2 + a_5)\pi^2]\tilde{e}^{ij} + [(a_1 + 2a_3) + (a_2 + 2a_6 - a_1 - 2a_3)\tilde{e}^k{}_k]\pi^i\pi^j \qquad (16.2) \\ & + 2(a_1 + 3a_3 + 2a_7)\tilde{e}^i{}_k\pi^j\pi^k + 4(a_3 + a_7)\tilde{e}^j{}_k\pi^i\pi^k, \end{aligned}$$

$$-\rho_0\overline{E}{}_{\mathsf{L}}^i \approx (a_1 + a_2\tilde{e}^k{}_k)\pi^i + 2(a_1 + a_3)\tilde{e}^i{}_k\pi^k. \qquad (16.3)$$

From (16.2–3), it follows that the antisymmetric part of the local stress is given by

$$t_{\mathsf{L}}^{[ij]} \approx \overline{E}{}_{\mathsf{L}}^{[i}P^{j]} = 2(a_1 + a_3)\tilde{e}^{[i}{}_k\pi^{j]}\pi^k. \qquad (16.4)$$

We may call the stress-strain-field-polarization relations (15.1–2) the quasilinear constitutive relations of an elastic dielectric since, in obtaining these forms, we have linearized with respect to displacement gradients but have retained nonlinear terms in the polarization and terms which are a product of a displacement gradient and a polarization component. Note that the *isotropic* quasilinear local stress *is* a polynomial in the components of the infinitesimal strain measure $\tilde{e}_{ij}$; whereas, the quasilinear local stress of an anisotropic dielectric does not in general reduce to a polynomial in the symmetric part of the displacement gradients only.

The quasilinear constitutive relations for isotropic materials may be further specialized by dropping all the terms which contain a product of a displacement gradient and a component of polarization. This process yields

$$\begin{aligned} t_{\mathsf{L}}^{ij} &\approx \lambda\tilde{e}^k{}_k g^{ij} + 2\mu\tilde{e}^{ij} + a_2\pi^2 g^{ij} + (a_1 + 2a_3)\pi^i\pi^j \\ \rho_0\overline{E}{}_{\mathsf{L}}^i &= -a_1\pi^i. \end{aligned} \qquad (16.5)$$

Then using the equilibrium condition $E_{\mathsf{M}} + \overline{E}_{\mathsf{L}} = 0$, we can write the local stress in this approximation in the form

$$t_{\mathsf{L}}^{ij} \approx \tilde{e}^k{}_k g^{ij} + 2\mu\tilde{e}^{ij} + A_1E_{\mathsf{M}}^2 g^{ij} + A_2E_{\mathsf{M}}^iE_{\mathsf{M}}^j \qquad (16.6)$$

where the A's are material constants. This last formula is identical to the stress-strain-field-relation derived by STRATTON [22, pp. 140–146] from an energy principle attributed to HELMHOLTZ and KORTEWEG.

17. Photoelasticity

The photoelastic effect cannot be properly treated within the context of statics. By its very nature, optics is a dynamical phenomenon. We can, however, give a qualitative sketch of the relations between static electro-elastic theory and the classical theories of the photoelastic effect.

Historically, the theories of the piezoelectric and photoelastic effects were developed using quite different physical principles. An account of the development of the theory of photoelasticity is given by Coker & Filon [2]. It appears that Neumann was the first to formulate a definite theory of the photoelastic effect. If we adopt Maxwell's electromagnetic equations and assume that the photoelastic medium is magnetically isotropic in an arbitrary state of deformation, the propagation of electromagnetic waves through such a medium can then be discussed in terms of the *inductive capacity tensor* $\epsilon^i{}_j$. This tensor is defined by writing the Maxwellian constitutive relation between the electric displacement and Maxwell electric field in the form

$$D^i = \epsilon^i{}_j E^j_{\mathsf{M}} . \tag{17.1}$$

We have shown that such a relation between $\mathbf{D}$ and $\mathbf{E}_{\mathsf{M}}$ exists at static equilibrium of an elastic dielectric as defined here. The tensor $\epsilon^i{}_j$ is a function of the state of deformation and polarization. In a magnetically isotropic medium $\mathbf{B} = \mu\mathbf{H}$ where $\mathbf{B}$ is called the magnetic induction, $\mathbf{H}$ is the magnetic field and μ is the magnetic inductive capacity. The quadric surface defined by the reciprocal of the tensor $\mu\epsilon^{ij}$ is called the *Fresnel ellipsoid*. Let F_{ij} denote the tensor which describes the Fresnel ellipsoid at a point in the deformed dielectric. Neumann's theory of the photoelastic effect in isotropic dielectrics was based on the assumption that the Fresnel tensor F^{ij} was a linear isotropic function of the infinitesimal strain measure $\tilde{e}_{ij}$. That is, he assumed

$$F^{ij} = H_0{}^{ij} + H_1{}^{ijkl}\tilde{e}_{kl} \tag{17.2}$$

where the $\mathbf{H}_\Gamma$ are isotropic material descriptors. The most general form of (17.2) is

$$F^{ij} = a_1 g^{ij} + a_2 g^{ij}\tilde{e}^k{}_k + a_3\tilde{e}^{ij} \tag{17.3}$$

where the a_Γ are scalar material descriptors. If the dielectric is homogeneous, the a_Γ are spatially constant.

According to Coker & Filon, Pockels was the first to recognize that Neumann's photoelastic relations (17.3) should not be applied in the analysis of the photoelastic effect in crystalline media. In effect, Pockels' theory is based on (17.2) also, where the $\mathbf{H}_\Gamma$ are material descriptors of the crystalline medium and not necessarily isotropic tensors.

Both NEUMANN's and POCKELS' theories are restricted to the case of infinitesimal displacement gradients. The quasilinear constitutive relation for the effective local field in isotropic elastic dielectrics (16.3) leads to a Maxwellian constitutive relation (17.1) where $\epsilon^i{}_j$ is a linear isotropic function of the infinitesimal strain measure $\tilde{e}_{ij}$. Hence, if we assume that the medium is magnetically isotropic in any state of deformation, we are led, in this case, to a Fresnel tensor in agreement with NEUMANN's form (17.3). For anisotropic media, we are unable to reproduce POCKELS' generalization of (17.2) since, in general, the effective local field in crystals does not reduce to a polynomial in the infinitesimal strain measure. We are reluctant to consider the topic of photoelasticity beyond these few observations. It is our opinion that the dynamics of elastic dielectrics and the theory of electromagnetic wave propagation through general non-linear media must first be formulated from a unified point of view before the foundations of these approximate theories of NEUMANN and POCKELS will be properly understood.

ACKNOWLEDGMENTS

I am indebted to Dr. J. L. ERICKSEN for many valuable discussions and criticisms on the whole of this work. I express here my gratitude to Professor C. TRUESDELL for his personal encouragement and for his advice on several of the topics treated. The work has also benefited much by the comments of Professor R. S. RIVLIN.

Naval Research Laboratory, Washington, D. C.

REFERENCES

[1] F. E. NEUMANN, *Die Gesetze der Doppelbrechung des Lichts in comprimierten oder ungleichförmig erwärmten unkrystallinischen Körpern*, Abh. Akad. Wissenschaften Berlin, Part II, 1–254 (1841).

[2] E. G. COKER & L. N. G. FILON, *Photoelasticity*, Cambridge Univ. Press, London (1931).

[3] F. POCKELS, *Ueber den Einfluss elastischer Deformationen speciell einseitigen Druckes, auf das optische Verhalten krystallinischer Körper*, Ann. d. Phys., **37**, 144–172 (1889).

[4] W. VOIGT, *Lehrbuch der Kristallphysik*, Teubner, Leipzig, 1st ed. (1910).

[5] W. G. CADY, *Piezoelectricity*, McGraw-Hill, London (1946).

[6] W. P. MASON, *Optical Properties and the Electro-optic and Photoelastic Effects in Crystals Expressed in Tensor Form*, Bell System Tech. J., **29**, 161–188 (1950).

[7] J. C. MAXWELL, *A treatise on Electricity and Magnetism*, two volumes, Oxford, 3rd ed. (1892).

[8] J. LARMOR, *On the theory of electrodynamics as affected by the nature of the mechanical stresses in excited dielectrics*, Proc. Roy. Soc. **52**, 55–66 (1892) = Math. and Phys. Papers **1**, pp. 274–287.

[9] H. A. LORENTZ, *The Theory of Electrons*, Teubner, Leipzig (1906).

[10] M. BORN & K. HUANG, *Dynamical Theory of Crystal Lattices*, Oxford (1954).

[11] W. F. BROWN, *Electric and magnetic forces: A direct calculation I*, Am. J. Phys. **19**, 290–304 (1951).

[12] C. TRUESDELL, *The Mechanical Foundations of Elasticity and Fluid Dynamics*, J. Rational Mech. and Anal. **1**, 125–300 (1952).

[13] F. D. MURNAGHAN, *Finite Deformations of an Elastic Solid*, John Wiley and Sons, New York (1951).

[14] A. D. MICHAL, *Functionals of r-dimensional manifolds admitting continuous groups of point transformations*, Trans. Am. Math. Soc. **29**, 612–646 (1927).

[15] T. C. DOYLE & J. L. ERICKSEN, *Nonlinear Elasticity*, Advances in Applied Mechanics **4** (1956).

[16] O. D. KELLOGG, *Foundations of Potential Theory*, Springer, Berlin (1926).

[17] A. L. CAUCHY, *Mémoire sur les systèmes isotropes de points matériels*, Mem. Acad. Sci. **XXII**, 615 (1850) = Oeuvres (1)2, 351.

[18] H. WEYL, *The Classical Groups*, Princeton University Press (1946).

[19] R. WEITZENBÖCK, *Invariantentheorie*, P. Noordhoff, Groningen (1923).

[20] T. CHAUNDY, *The Differential Calculus*, Clarendon Press, Oxford, Ch. XI, p. 294 (1935).

[21] A. E. H. LOVE, *A Treatise on the Mathematical Theory of Elasticity*, 4th Ed., Cambridge Univ. Press (1927).

[22] J. A. STRATTON, *Electromagnetic Theory*, McGraw-Hill, New York (1941).

[23] G. RACAH, *Determinazione del numero dei tensori isotropi indipendinti di rango n*, Rend. Lincei (6) **17**, 386–389 (1933).

[24] BHAGAVANTAM, S. Proc. Indian Acad. Sci. **16**, 359 (1942).

No. 11

ON THE THERMOSTATICS OF CONTINUOUS MEDIA

B. D. Coleman & W. Noll

Archive for Rational Mechanics and Analysis, Volume 4, pp. 97-128 (1959).

At the end of paper No. 8 it was suggested that restrictions on the form of the stored-energy function should follow from a proper thermodynamic theory of deformation. While GIBBS treated finite elastic deformations in his classic work of 1875, he obtained thermodynamic **inequalities** only for ideal fluids. An ideal fluid is a special elastic material. In the present work, COLEMAN & NOLL construct a generalization of GIBBS' theory of fluids to elastic materials in general.

While most writers on thermodynamics have failed to maintain GIBBS' level of explicitness and clarity, the present paper goes beyond it in giving precise mathematical form to ideas left not fully specified by GIBBS. The usual paraphernalia of thermodynamic concepts that never enter the formal structure (heat, heat reservoir, boiler, condenser, quasi-static process, cycle, reversible, heat engine, etc., etc., etc., etc.) are here in welcome total absence. Instead, the logical and mathematical standards of modern continuum mechanics are applied to an analysis of equilibrium of a deformable material having a caloric equation of state of the form (3.1).

The theory is purely static. The definition of equilibrium is a broad generalization of the classic principle of minimum energy. The definition of the free energy to be minimized is stated by Eq. (6.1). Given a Piola-Kirchhoff stress tensor and a temperature, the specific entropy and the deformation gradient are to be so adjusted that (a) the Cauchy stress is symmetric, and (b) (6.2) is satisfied. The deformation gradients admissible as varied states in testing (6.2) must satisfy (6.3); i.e., they must differ from the minimizing deformation gradient by a pure stretch. For this requirement, without precedent in earlier work, some support is given at the end of Section 8. It is assumed also that increase in entropy at constant deformation always increases internal energy, reflecting the classic idea that the entropy rate, other things being equal, is positive or negative according as "heat" is being added or taken away.

Theorems 1 and 2 in Section 8 assert conditions which, taken together, are necessary and sufficient for equilibrium according to COLEMAN & NOLL's minimal principle. First, the classical formulae (8.1) and (8.2) giving the stress and temperature in terms of the energy function must hold. Second, the energy function must satisfy the inequality (8.3), which has since been named **the Coleman-Noll condition.** As is remarked, the inequality includes as a special case the requirement that if a natural state exists, the energy must be a minimum in it. Section 9 gives an alternative formulation of these same results when internal energy rather than entropy is varied; in Section 13 the same results are presented in terms of formulae in which temperature rather than entropy appears as an independent variable.

In Section 10 the Coleman-Noll inequality is specialized to the case of infinitesimal strain superimposed on a given strain; in particular, for the classical linearized theory of elasticity it is equivalent to the requirement that the stored-energy function be positive-definite. In Section 11 the specialization to fluids is determined; in addition to the inequalities derived by GIBBS, the stronger requirement that the energy density be a convex function of the cube root of the specific volume is found. In Section 12, the Coleman-Noll inequality is shown to imply that in an isotropic material the energy density must be a convex function of the principal stretches and the entropy. Theorem 8a asserts that the greater principal force must occur in the direction of the greater principal stretch. As remarked just afterward, the Baker-Ericksen inequalities (see Paper No. 3 in this volume) follow for states of pure tension, but not for all states of stress. For a survey of further work on inequalities of this sort, see Sections 51-52 and 87 of NFTM.

Up to this point, the considerations are all local. Several concepts of **stability**, which refers to an entire body rather than to its individual parts, are introduced in Sections 14 and 15. The reader not familiar at first hand with GIBBS' work might do well to turn first to Section 16, where his assertions and verbal arguments about fluids are expressed in mathematical form and given compact, rigorous proofs. The essential new result on stability of perfect materials in general is given by **Theorem 14.**

The paper here reprinted raised thermodynamics, after its slumber of nearly half a century, to the level of a mathematical science. As with any other theory, mathematical correctness does not prove physical relevance; the range of applicability of COLEMAN & NOLL's theory is still not settled.

Offprint from "Archive for Rational Mechanics and Analysis",
Volume 4, Number 2, 1959, P. 97—128

Springer-Verlag, Berlin · Göttingen · Heidelberg

On the Thermostatics of Continuous Media

Bernard D. Coleman & Walter Noll

Contents

Introduction

In this article we regard thermostatics as being that branch of thermodynamics which deals with bodies which are at rest at the present time and which, for all practical purposes, may be regarded as having been at rest at all times in the past.

We attempt to develop here a rigorous theory of thermostatics for continuous bodies in arbitrary states of strain. The thermodynamics of chemical reactions, phase transitions, and capillarity is not discussed. Our aim is to derive some of the fundamental laws of hydrostatics and elastostatics from thermodynamic principles. Among these laws are the existence of elastic potentials for stress-strain relations, the known inequalities of hydrostatics, and some new inequalities for hydrostatics and elastostatics.

In his classic work, "On the Equilibrium of Heterogeneous Substances", J. W. Gibbs [*1*] laid down criteria for determining whether a given (global) state of a body is thermodynamically stable. He used these criteria to derive particular equations and inequalities which represent conditions (in some cases necessary and other cases sufficient) for various special states to be stable. The equations GIBBS obtained as necessary conditions for thermodynamic stability are now recognized as fundamental laws in physical chemistry. GIBBS also derived inequalities which, apparently because they are in obvious accord with everyday experience and thus might be mistakenly called trivial, have attracted relatively little attention and are sometimes not even mentioned in modern thermodynamics courses. For example, in his treatment of homogeneous systems at rest under uniform hydrostatic pressure, GIBBS showed that a necessary condition for such a system to be in a stable state is that both its heat capacity at constant volume and its adiabatic modulus of compression be non-negative. It is inequalities of this type which are emphasized in the present paper. We take, however, a point of view different from that of GIBBS.

In the classical treatments of thermostatics (*e.g.*, [*1*], [*2*]) the adjective *stable* is used in two senses. It is sometimes used as a modifier for the word *equilibrium*; *i.e.* one refers to "states of stable equilibrium"; or it is used as a modifier for the word *state*; *i.e.* one refers to "stable states". In this paper we never use the word stable in the former sense. The theory which we develop here makes a careful distinction between *local* states, referring to a material point in a body, and *global* states, referring to the body as a whole. A local thermomechanic state is specified by giving the entropy density and the local configuration at a material point. A global thermomechanic state, on the other hand, is specified only when the entropy field and the complete configuration are specified for the entire body. We regard *thermal equilibrium* to be a property of *local states*. We consider just one type of thermal equilibrium. We define a state of thermal equilibrium as a local thermomechanic state which minimizes an appropriate potential rather than as a state at which a first variation vanishes. We regard *stability* as a property of only *global states*. We consider several types of stable states, defined as global thermomechanic states which minimize certain energy integrals subject to different constraints.

Our theory is based on two physical postulates. The first asserts that, at a material point, any local thermomechanic state can be an equilibrium state provided the local temperature and local forces have appropriate values. The second postulate is essentially the assumption that, at least in continuum mechanics, absolute temperatures are never negative. We believe that these physical postulates, which are stated in terms of our definition of equilibrium, contain the physical content for the statics of continuous media of the First and Second Laws of Thermodynamics. From our postulates we prove relationships between the stress-strain equation and the caloric equation of state, and we derive various inequalities restricting the form of the caloric equation of state. We should like to propose that the inequalities which we obtain for the finite theory of elasticity answer some of the questions raised by C. TRUESDELL [*3*] in his recent article, "Das ungelöste Hauptproblem der endlichen Elastizitätstheorie".

Although our definition of thermal equilibrium is new, some of the definitions of the stability of global states which we propose for study are similar to stability definitions considered by GIBBS [*1*] and J. HADAMARD [*4*]. In particular, our concepts of isothermal and adiabatic stability *at fixed boundary* are closely related to, but not identical to, *Hadamard stability**. We briefly discuss GIBBS' theory of the stability of fluid phases in § 16. In a future article we hope to give a discussion of GIBBS' theory of the stability of fluid mixtures.

We regard the main tasks of the science of thermostatics to be, first, the exploration of the consequences for the caloric equation of state of the existence of local states of thermal equilibrium and, second, the derivation of useful necessary and sufficient criteria for global states to be stable. In the present paper, § 6—§ 13 are devoted to the first task and § 14—§ 16 deal briefly with the second. From our present point of view, we should say that the great classical thermodynamicists, GIBBS and DUHEM, devoted their main efforts to the second task.

It will be noticed that in this paper we never mention such notions as "reversible processes" and "quasi-static processes"; in fact, our theory of thermostatics, being a truly statical theory, has no need of "processes" at all.

In writing the present paper we have striven for a level of mathematical rigor comparable to that of works in pure mathematics rather than to that customary in physics.

Notation and basic mathematical concepts. We often find it convenient to distinguish between functions and their values. The basic local thermodynamic variables are denoted by light face Greek minuscules: $\varepsilon, \psi, \eta, \vartheta, \ldots$. Symbols such as $\hat{\varepsilon}, \bar{\varepsilon}, \bar{\bar{\varepsilon}} \ldots$ and $\hat{\psi}, \tilde{\psi}, \bar{\psi} \ldots$ represent real valued *functions* whose values are the thermodynamic variables ε and ψ.

We denote vectors and points of the three-dimensional Euclidean space $\mathscr{E}$ by bold face Latin minuscules: $\boldsymbol{v}, \boldsymbol{x}, \boldsymbol{y} \ldots$.

Second order tensors are denoted by light face Latin majuscules: F, U, Q, R, I. However, we reserve the symbols X and Z to represent material points of a physical body. The term tensor is used as a synonym for linear transformation. Tensors of order higher than two do not occur in this paper. For the trace of the tensor F we write $\operatorname{tr} F$ and for the determinant of F we write $\det F$. We say that F is invertible if F has an inverse F^{-1}; *i.e.* if $\det F \neq 0$. The transpose of F is denoted by F^T. The identity transformation is written I. For the composition, or product, of two linear transformations A and B we write simply AB.

* Hadamard stability requires (roughly) that the first variation of the integral of the elastic potential vanish, and that the second variation be non-negative, for all smooth variations in the state of strain which are compatible with a fixed boundary. This sort of stability is necessary but not sufficient for stability at fixed boundary as we define it here. In the theory of the propagation of waves in a perfectly elastic solid, Hadamard stability of a particular rest state implies the reality of all roots of the wave velocity equation for acceleration waves of arbitrary direction which might impinge on an object in that state. J. L. ERICKSEN & R. A. TOUPIN [*5*] have recently considered a modification of Hadamard stability in which they require that the second variation of the integral of the elastic potential be strictly positive. They use their definition of stability to prove uniqueness theorems in the theory of small deformations superimposed on large. R. HILL [*15*] also has recently discussed relationships between uniqueness and stability. In the third article of his "Recherches sur l'élasticité" P. DUHEM [*6*] formulated several definitions of stability which are applicable to bodies with fixed and partially free surfaces; he also derived several necessary conditions on the equation of state for particular states of strain to be stable.

Let $\boldsymbol{h}(\boldsymbol{x})$ be a function for which both the range and the domain consist of either vectors or points in Euclidean space $\mathscr{E}$. Assume that for $\boldsymbol{x}$ in some region the derivative

$$\frac{d}{ds}\boldsymbol{h}(\boldsymbol{x}+s\,\boldsymbol{v})\Big|_{s=0} = \nabla\boldsymbol{h}(\boldsymbol{x};\boldsymbol{v}) \tag{1}$$

exists for all $\boldsymbol{v}$ and is continuous in $\boldsymbol{x}$. It is the content of a fundamental theorem of analysis that $\nabla\boldsymbol{h}(\boldsymbol{x};\boldsymbol{v})$ is then a linear function of $\boldsymbol{v}$, and hence we can write

$$\nabla\boldsymbol{h}(\boldsymbol{x};\boldsymbol{v}) = [\nabla\boldsymbol{h}(\boldsymbol{x})]\,\boldsymbol{v}, \tag{2}$$

where $\nabla\boldsymbol{h}(\boldsymbol{x})$ is a linear transformation (tensor), called the *gradient* of $\boldsymbol{h}$ at $\boldsymbol{x}$.

Similarly, the gradient of a real valued function $\zeta(F)$ of a tensor variable F is a tensor valued function $\zeta_F(F)$ defined by the relation

$$\frac{d}{ds}\zeta(F+s\,A)\Big|_{s=0} = \operatorname{tr}[\zeta_F(F)\,A], \tag{3}$$

where A is an arbitrary tensor. If Cartesian coordinates are used, and if $\|f_{ij}\|$ is the matrix of F, then the matrix of ζ_F is given by

$$\|\zeta_F(F)\| = \left\|\frac{\partial\zeta}{\partial f_{ji}}\right\|,$$

where i is the row and j the column index.

We make frequent use of the following theorem, called the *polar decomposition theorem: Any invertible tensor F has unique decompositions*

$$F = R\,U = V\,R \tag{4}$$

where R is orthogonal (i.e., $RR^T = I$) and U, V are positive definite symmetric tensors (i.e., $U = U^T$, $V = V^T$, and the proper numbers of U and V are all real and greater than zero). In addition, we have

$$U = R^T V R, \qquad U^2 = F^T F, \qquad V^2 = F F^T. \tag{5}$$

Consider a smooth (*i.e.*, continuously differentiable) real valued function $\zeta(\boldsymbol{w})$ whose domain $\mathscr{W}$ is a region in a finite dimensional vector space. The function ζ is called *strictly convex* if either of the following two equivalent conditions are satisfied:

(a) For all $\boldsymbol{w}_1$ and $\boldsymbol{w}_2 \neq \boldsymbol{w}_1$ in $\mathscr{W}$ and all positive α, β with $\alpha+\beta=1$, the inequality

$$\zeta(\alpha\,\boldsymbol{w}_1+\beta\,\boldsymbol{w}_2) < \alpha\,\zeta(\boldsymbol{w}_1)+\beta\,\zeta(\boldsymbol{w}_2) \tag{6}$$

holds.

(b) For all $\boldsymbol{w}$ and $\boldsymbol{w}^* \neq \boldsymbol{w}$ in $\mathscr{W}$ the inequality

$$\zeta(\boldsymbol{w}^*) - \zeta(\boldsymbol{w}) - (\boldsymbol{w}^* - \boldsymbol{w})\cdot\nabla\zeta(\boldsymbol{w}) > 0 \tag{7}$$

is satisfied.

When $\mathscr{W}$ is a region in the space of all tensors, we use the notation of (3) and the convexity inequality (7) becomes

$$\zeta(F^*) - \zeta(F) - \operatorname{tr}[(F^* - F)\,\zeta_F(F)] > 0. \tag{8}$$

For a twice continuously differentiable function $\zeta(\boldsymbol{w})$ to be strictly convex in $\mathscr{W}$, it is sufficient that the second gradient $\nabla\nabla\zeta(\boldsymbol{w})$ be positive definite for $\boldsymbol{w}$ in $\mathscr{W}$. This condition is not necessary, however: if $\zeta(\boldsymbol{w})$ is convex, it follows only that $\nabla\nabla\zeta(\boldsymbol{w})$ is positive *semi*definite.

1. Mechanical preliminaries

We give a brief summary of those concepts from the mechanics of continuous media that are relevant to the present investigation. For a detailed discussion we refer to [7] and [8].

A *body* $\mathscr{B}$ is a smooth manifold of elements $X, Z, \ldots$, called *material points**. A *configuration* $\boldsymbol{f}$ of $\mathscr{B}$ is a smooth one-to-one mapping of $\mathscr{B}$ onto a region in a three-dimensional Euclidean point space $\mathscr{E}$. The point $\boldsymbol{x}=\boldsymbol{f}(X)$ is the *position* of the material point X in the configuration $\boldsymbol{f}$. The *mass distribution* m of $\mathscr{B}$ is a measure defined on all Borel subsets of $\mathscr{B}$. For the total mass of $\mathscr{B}$ we write $m(\mathscr{B})$. To each configuration $\boldsymbol{f}$ of $\mathscr{B}$ corresponds a mass density ϱ.

Consider a neighborhood $\mathscr{N}(X)$ of a material point in a body; *i.e.*, a part of the body containing X in its interior. Let $\boldsymbol{g}$ be a smooth homeomorphism of $\mathscr{N}(X)$ into the three-dimensional vector space $\mathscr{V}$ such that X itself is mapped into the zero vector $\mathbf{0}$. The inverse mapping of $\boldsymbol{g}$ is denoted by $\overset{-1}{\boldsymbol{g}}$. Let $\boldsymbol{g}_1$ and $\boldsymbol{g}_2$ be two such homeomorphisms. The composition $\boldsymbol{g}_2\circ\overset{-1}{\boldsymbol{g}}_1$ of $\boldsymbol{g}_2$ and $\overset{-1}{\boldsymbol{g}}_1$ is defined by

$$\left(\boldsymbol{g}_2\circ\overset{-1}{\boldsymbol{g}}_1\right)(\boldsymbol{x}) = \boldsymbol{g}_2\left(\overset{-1}{\boldsymbol{g}}_1(\boldsymbol{x})\right).$$

It is a mapping of a neighborhood of $\mathbf{0}$ onto another neighborhood of $\mathbf{0}$. We define an equivalence relation "$\sim$" among all these homeomorphisms by the condition that $\boldsymbol{g}_1\sim\boldsymbol{g}_2$ if the gradient of the mapping $\boldsymbol{g}_2\circ\overset{-1}{\boldsymbol{g}}_1$ at $\mathbf{0}$ is the identity I. The resulting equivalence classes will be called the *local configurations*** M of X. If M_1 is the equivalence class of $\boldsymbol{g}_1$ and M_2 the equivalence class of $\boldsymbol{g}_2$ then the gradient at $\mathbf{0}$ of $\boldsymbol{g}_2\circ\overset{-1}{\boldsymbol{g}}_1$, *i.e.*

$$G = \nabla\left(\boldsymbol{g}_2\circ\overset{-1}{\boldsymbol{g}}_1\right)(\mathbf{0}), \tag{1.1}$$

depends only on M_1 and M_2. We write

$$G = M_2 M_1^{-1}, \quad M_2 = G M_1, \tag{1.2}$$

and call G the *deformation gradient* from M_1 to M_2; G is an invertible linear transformation.

It is often convenient to employ a *local reference configuration* M_r and to characterize the other local configurations

$$M = F M_r \tag{1.3}$$

by their deformation gradients F from the local reference configuration M_r. If, in this way, two local configurations M_1 and M_2 correspond, respectively, to F_1 and F_2 then the deformation gradient G from M_1 to M_2 is given by

$$G = F_2 F_1^{-1}, \quad F_2 = G F_1. \tag{1.4}$$

* The term "particle" is often used. We prefer "material point" to avoid confusion with molecules and other physical particles.

** The term "configuration gradient" was used in [7].

The *rotation tensor* R, the *right stretch tensor** U, and the *left stretch tensor* V of a deformation gradient F are defined by the unique polar decompositions

$$F = RU = VR, \tag{1.5}$$

where R is orthogonal, while U and $V = RUR^T$ are symmetric and positive definite. We note that U and V have the same proper numbers; these proper numbers are called the *principal stretches* v_1, v_2, v_3. A deformation gradient G is called a *pure stretch* if its rotation tensor reduces to the identity I; *i.e.*, if G is symmetric and positive definite and hence coincides with its own right and left stretch tensors.

The mass densities at X corresponding to the local configurations M_1 and M_2 are denoted, respectively, by ϱ_1 and ϱ_2. We have

$$\varrho_2 = \frac{1}{|\det G|} \varrho_1, \tag{1.6}$$

where G is related to M_1 and M_2 by (1.2).

2. Thermomechanic states

A global thermomechanic state, or simply a *state*, of a body $\mathcal{B}$ is a pair $\{\boldsymbol{f}, \eta\}$ consisting of a configuration $\boldsymbol{f}$ of $\mathcal{B}$ and a scalar field η defined on $\mathcal{B}$; η is called the *entropy distribution* of the state.

A local thermomechanic state, or simply a *local state*, of a material point X is defined as a pair (M, η) consisting of a local configuration M of X and a real number η, called the *entropy density* (per unit mass) of the local state**.

In the following we often use a local reference configuration M_r and, according to (1.3), characterize the other local configurations M by the deformation gradients F from M_r. We then use the pair (F, η) to characterize the local states.

Two local states (F, η) and (F', η') will be called *equivalent* if they differ only by a change of frame of reference. The local configuration transforms under a change of frame according to the law $F' = QF$ where Q is orthogonal. We assume that the entropy density η is *objective*; *i.e.*, it remains invariant under a change of frame. Thus, the local states (F, η) and (F', η') are equivalent if and only if

$$F' = QF, \quad \eta' = \eta \tag{2.1}$$

for some orthogonal Q.

We say that two global states $\{\boldsymbol{f}, \eta\}$ and $\{\boldsymbol{f}', \eta'\}$ are equivalent if they differ by only a change of frame. This is the case if and only if

$$\eta'(X) = \eta(X), \quad F'(X) = QF(X) \tag{2.2}$$

for all X in the body and some orthogonal tensor Q independent of X. Here, $F(X)$ and $F'(X)$ are the deformation gradients at X corresponding to $\boldsymbol{f}$ and $\boldsymbol{f}'$ respectively.

---

* The term "strain tensor" was used in [7].

** In this article, pairs in braces, { }, always refer to *global* properties; the elements of such pairs are fields over $\mathcal{B}$. On the other hand, pairs in brackets, ( ), always refer to *local* properties and have elements which are either real numbers or tensors. Note that the symbol η in $\{\boldsymbol{f}, \eta\}$ and (M, η) denotes different entities; in the first case η denotes a field while in the second case it denotes a number. No confusion should arise, however.

3. The caloric equation of state

A *material* is characterized by a real valued function of local states, whose values ε are called the *energy densities* (per unit mass) of the local states. We pick a fixed local reference configuration M_r and characterize the state (M, η) by the pair (F, η) where $F = M M_r^{-1}$. We write

$$\varepsilon = \hat{\varepsilon}(F, \eta). \tag{3.1}$$

It is assumed here that the function $\hat{\varepsilon}$ has continuous derivatives with respect to F and η*.

We assume that the energy density is objective; *i.e.* invariant under a change of frame. It follows from (2.1) that the function $\hat{\varepsilon}$ must satisfy the relation

$$\hat{\varepsilon}(QF, \eta) = \hat{\varepsilon}(F, \eta) \tag{3.2}$$

for all orthogonal Q. Using the polar decomposition (1.5) and putting $Q = R^T$ in (3.2) we see that

$$\varepsilon = \hat{\varepsilon}(F, \eta) = \hat{\varepsilon}(U, \eta); \tag{3.3}$$

i.e., that the energy density is determined by the right stretch tensor U and the entropy η.

The function $\hat{\varepsilon}$ in (3.3) depends on the choice of the local reference configuration M_r. The function $\hat{\varepsilon}'$ corresponding to some other local reference configuration M_r' is related to $\hat{\varepsilon}$ by

$$\hat{\varepsilon}'(F, \eta) = \hat{\varepsilon}(FG, \eta), \tag{3.4}$$

where $G = M_r' M_r^{-1}$ is the deformation gradient from M_r to M_r'.

The equation (3.3) characterizes the thermal and mechanical properties of a material in statics. It is called the *caloric equation of state* of the material.

4. The isotropy group

It may happen that the energy function $\hat{\varepsilon}$ remains the same function if the local reference configuration M_r is changed to another local reference configuration $M_r' = H M_r$ with the same density. It follows from (3.4) that $\hat{\varepsilon}$ then satisfies the relation

$$\hat{\varepsilon}(F, \eta) = \hat{\varepsilon}(FH, \eta). \tag{4.1}$$

Since M_r' and M_r have the same density, it is clear from (1.6) that $|\det H| = 1$; *i.e.*, H is a unimodular transformation. The unimodular transformations H for which (4.1) holds form a group, called the *isotropy group* $\mathcal{G}$ of $\hat{\varepsilon}$ or of the material defined by $\hat{\varepsilon}$. This group depends, in general, on the choice of the local reference configuration, but it can be shown that the groups corresponding to two different local configurations are always conjugate and hence isomorphic.

We say that the energy function $\hat{\varepsilon}$ defines a *simple fluid* if its isotropy group $\mathcal{G}$ is the full unimodular group $\mathcal{U}$. If $\mathcal{G} = \mathcal{U}$ for one reference configuration, then $\mathcal{G} = \mathcal{U}$ for all reference configurations. A material point is called a *fluid material point* if its energy function defines a simple fluid. The caloric equation

* For the application to physical situations it is necessary to limit the domain of $\hat{\varepsilon}$ to a region in the space of local configurations and an interval on the η-axis. We do not supply the mathematical details which may arise in the consideration of limitations of this kind.

of state (3.3) then reduces to the form

$$\varepsilon = \hat{\varepsilon}(F, \eta) = \bar{\varepsilon}(v, \eta), \tag{4.2}$$

where

$$v = \frac{1}{\varrho} = |\det F| \frac{1}{\varrho_r} \tag{4.3}$$

is the *specific volume* of the local configuration $M = F M_r$; ϱ and ϱ_r are the mass densities corresponding to M and M_r. The function $\bar{\varepsilon}$ in (4.2) does not depend on the choice of the reference configuration.

We say that a material point is an *isotropic material point* if the isotropy group of its energy function $\hat{\varepsilon}$, relative to some local reference configuration, contains the orthogonal group $\mathcal{O}$. Those local reference configurations of the material point for which $\mathcal{G}$ contains $\mathcal{O}$ are said to be *undistorted*. A simple fluid is isotropic, and all of its local configurations are undistorted. For any isotropic material, it follows from (3.2) and (4.1) that $\hat{\varepsilon}$ satisfies the relation

$$\hat{\varepsilon}(Q U Q^T, \eta) = \hat{\varepsilon}(U, \eta) \tag{4.4}$$

for all symmetric and positive definite U and all orthogonal Q, provided the local reference configuration for $\hat{\varepsilon}$ is undistorted. Taking $Q = R$, so that $V = R U R^T$ is the left stretch tensor, we see that for isotropic material points the caloric equation of state (3.3) may be written in the form

$$\varepsilon = \hat{\varepsilon}(F, \eta) = \hat{\varepsilon}(V, \eta). \tag{4.5}$$

It is a further consequence of (4.4) that for each fixed value of η, ε may be expressed as a symmetric function of the three principal stretches v_1, v_2, v_3:

$$\varepsilon = \hat{\varepsilon}(F, \eta) = \hat{\varepsilon}(V, \eta) = \bar{\varepsilon}(v_1, v_2, v_3; \eta) = \bar{\varepsilon}(v_j, \eta). \tag{4.6}$$

It may also be expressed as a function of the three principal invariants I_V, II_V, III_V of V and U:

$$\varepsilon = \hat{\varepsilon}(V, \eta) = \bar{\bar{\varepsilon}}(I_V, II_V, III_V; \eta). \tag{4.7}$$

We say that the energy function $\hat{\varepsilon}$ defines a *simple solid* if its isotropy group $\mathcal{G}$ is contained as a subgroup in the orthogonal group $\mathcal{O}$. A material point is called a *solid material point* if its energy function $\hat{\varepsilon}$, relative to some local configuration as a reference, defines a simple solid. The local reference configurations with this property are again called the *undistorted* states of the solid material point. For an *isotropic simple solid*, the isotropy group $\mathcal{G}$ is identical to the orthogonal group $\mathcal{O}$.

Throughout the rest of this paper, whenever we discuss isotropic materials it is to be understood that the local reference configuration for the energy density function is undistorted, unless the reference configuration is explicitly specified.

5. Forces, stresses, and work

A *system of forces* is a system of vector valued measures, one for each part of the body $\mathcal{B}$ under consideration*. One must distinguish between contact and body forces. The contact force acting across an oriented surface element in $\mathcal{B}$ will be denoted by $d\mathbf{c}$.

* For a detailed axiomatic treatment *cf.* [8].

Definition of mechanical equilibrium. *In order that a body $\mathcal{B}$ be in* ***mechanical equilibrium*** *under a given system of forces, two conditions must be fulfilled for each part $\mathcal{P}$ of $\mathcal{B}$:* (a) *the sum of the forces acting on $\mathcal{P}$ must vanish, and* (b) *the sum of the moments, about any point, of the forces acting on $\mathcal{P}$ must vanish.*

The condition (a), called the *force condition*, depends only on the body and the force system, not on the configuration of the body. The condition (b), called the *moment condition*, does depend on the configuration of the body; *i.e.*, for a given force system, the moment condition may be satisfied for one configuration but not for another.

The force condition alone implies that, for each configuration, the contact forces $d\boldsymbol{c}$ arise from a stress-tensor S, so that

$$d\boldsymbol{c} = S\boldsymbol{n}\,dA, \tag{5.1}$$

where $\boldsymbol{n}$ is the unit normal vector of the oriented surface element and dA its area in the configuration under consideration. For fixed contact forces $d\boldsymbol{c}$, the stress tensor S will be different for different configurations.

We consider now a neighborhood $\mathcal{N}(X)$ of a material point X and assume that a system of contact forces $d\boldsymbol{c}$ is given for $\mathcal{N}(X)$. Let $\boldsymbol{f}_r$ be a fixed reference configuration and $\boldsymbol{f}$ some other configuration of $\mathcal{N}(X)$. If $d\boldsymbol{c}$ is such that the force condition is satisfied, then (5.1) is valid for all configurations; we can write for the reference configuration $\boldsymbol{f}_r$, in particular,

$$d\boldsymbol{c} = S_r\boldsymbol{n}_r\,dA_r, \tag{5.2}$$

where $\boldsymbol{n}_r$ is the unit normal of the oriented surface element in the reference configuration $\boldsymbol{f}_r$, and dA_r is the area of the surface element in $\boldsymbol{f}_r$. We denote the position vector, in the configuration $\boldsymbol{f}$, of a typical material point Z in $\mathcal{N}(X)$, relative to the position of X as origin, by $\boldsymbol{p}$, and we consider the tensor K defined by

$$K = \frac{1}{v(\mathcal{N}(X))}\int_{\overline{\mathcal{N}(X)}} \boldsymbol{p}\otimes d\boldsymbol{c}, \tag{5.3}$$

where $\overline{\mathcal{N}(X)}$ denotes the boundary surface of $\mathcal{N}(X)$ and $v(\mathcal{N}(X))$ the volume of $\mathcal{N}(X)$ in the configuration $\boldsymbol{f}$, and where $\otimes$ denotes a tensor product. If the force condition is satisfied, the relation (5.1) is valid, and we have

$$K^T = \frac{1}{v(\mathcal{N}(X))}\int_{\overline{\mathcal{N}(X)}} S\boldsymbol{n}\otimes\boldsymbol{p}\,dA.$$

In the limit as $\mathcal{N}(X)$ shrinks to X, we obtain, after using Green's theorem,

$$S^T = \lim_{\mathcal{N}(X)\to X} K. \tag{5.4}$$

The same argument, with the configuration $\boldsymbol{f}$ replaced by the reference configuration $\boldsymbol{f}_r$, gives

$$S_r^T = \lim_{\mathcal{N}(X)\to X}\frac{1}{v_r(\mathcal{N}(X))}\int_{\overline{\mathcal{N}(X)}} \boldsymbol{p}_r\otimes d\boldsymbol{c}, \tag{5.5}$$

where $v_r(\mathcal{N}(X))$ is the volume of $\mathcal{N}(X)$ in the reference configuration and $\boldsymbol{p}_r$ the position vector, in the reference configuration, of a typical material point Z

in $\mathcal{N}(X)$, relative to the position of X as origin. The position vector $\boldsymbol{p}$ of Z in the configuration $\boldsymbol{f}$ is related to $\boldsymbol{p}_r$ by the relation

$$\boldsymbol{p} = F\boldsymbol{p}_r + o(|\boldsymbol{p}_r|) \tag{5.6}$$

where F is the gradient at X of the deformation from $\boldsymbol{f}_r$ to $\boldsymbol{f}$ and where

$$\lim_{d\to 0} \frac{o(d)}{d} = 0.$$

Substitution of (5.6) into (5.3) and use of (5.4) and (5.5) yields

$$S = \frac{\varrho}{\varrho_r} F S_r, \tag{5.7}$$

where ϱ and ϱ_r are, respectively, the mass densities at X in the configurations $\boldsymbol{f}$ and $\boldsymbol{f}_r$.

The skew part of K, defined by (5.3), is the moment about X, per unit volume, of the contact forces $d\boldsymbol{c}$ acting on $\mathcal{N}(X)$ in the configuration $\boldsymbol{f}$. If the moment condition is satisfied for the configuration $\boldsymbol{f}$, then the total moment (*i.e.* the moment of the contact forces *and* the body forces) about X in $\boldsymbol{f}$ must vanish. Since the moment per unit volume about X of the body forces on $\mathcal{N}(X)$ goes to zero as $\mathcal{N}(X)$ shrinks to X, it follows from (5.4) that S must be symmetric if the moment condition is satisfied in $\boldsymbol{f}$.

We say that a material point X is in *local mechanical equilibrium*, when the body is in a given configuration and under a given force system, if the stress tensor S exists at X and is symmetric.

The local behavior at X of a system of contact forces is completely determined by the tensor S_r defined by (5.2). It is called the *Kirchhoff tensor** of the system. For a given force system, the Kirchhoff tensor depends only on the choice of the reference configuration and remains the same if the actual configuration is changed. From (5.7) we see that the existence of the Kirchhoff tensor S_r and the symmetry of $F S_r$ are necessary and sufficient conditions for local mechanical equilibrium at a material point in the local configuration determined by F.

In order that a body $\mathcal{B}$ in a configuration $\boldsymbol{f}$ be in mechanical equilibrium, it is not sufficient that all its material points be in local mechanical equilibrium; *i.e.*, that the stress tensor exist and be symmetric at each material point. Global mechanical equilibrium will prevail only if, in addition, Cauchy's law

$$\operatorname{div} S + \varrho\,\boldsymbol{b} = \boldsymbol{0} \tag{5.8}$$

is satisfied. In this equation, S, ϱ, and the density $\boldsymbol{b}$ of the body forces are to be regarded as fields with domain $\boldsymbol{f}(\mathcal{B})$.

We consider now a smooth one-parameter family of configurations $\boldsymbol{f}(s)$ with deformation gradients $F(s)$ at X. The *work per unit mass* done on $\mathcal{N}(X)$ by the contact forces $d\boldsymbol{c}$ along the path of configurations $\boldsymbol{f}(s)$ from $s = s_1$ to $s = s_2$ is defined by

$$w = \frac{1}{m(\mathcal{N}(X))} \int_{s_1}^{s_2} \left[\int_{\mathcal{N}(X)} \frac{d\boldsymbol{p}}{ds} \cdot d\boldsymbol{c} \right] ds, \tag{5.9}$$

* *Cf.* TRUESDELL [9], (26.5).

where $m(\mathcal{N}(X))$ is the mass of $\mathcal{N}(X)$ and $\boldsymbol{p}(s)$ denotes the position vector, in the configuration $\boldsymbol{f}(s)$, of a typical material point in $\mathcal{N}(X)$. Assuming that the contact forces $d\boldsymbol{c}$ are independent of s, we obtain

$$w = \frac{1}{m(\mathcal{N}(X))}\left[\int_{\partial\mathcal{N}(X)} \boldsymbol{p}(s_2)\cdot d\boldsymbol{c} - \int_{\partial\mathcal{N}(X)} \boldsymbol{p}(s_1)\cdot d\boldsymbol{c}\right]. \tag{5.10}$$

Observing (5.3), (5.4) and (5.7), and taking the limit $\mathcal{N}(X)\to X$, we get

$$\varrho_r w = \operatorname{tr}[F(s_2)\, S_r] - \operatorname{tr}[F(s_1)\, S_r]. \tag{5.11}$$

This relation shows that $-\frac{1}{\varrho_r}\operatorname{tr}(F\, S_r)$ has the physical meaning of the potential energy, per unit mass, of the local contact forces.

6. Definition of thermal equilibrium

A *force temperature pair* for a material point X is a pair (S_r, ϑ) consisting of a tensor S_r, to be interpreted as the Kirchhoff tensor of a system of contact forces at X, and a real number ϑ, to be interpreted as the temperature at X.

Let a force temperature pair (S_r, ϑ) be given and consider the function

$$\hat{\lambda}(F,\eta) = \hat{\varepsilon}(F,\eta) - \frac{1}{\varrho_r}\operatorname{tr}(F\, S_r) - \eta\,\vartheta. \tag{6.1}$$

To help motivate the definition of thermal equilibrium given below, we make the following remarks. According to (5.11) the term $-\frac{1}{\varrho_r}\operatorname{tr}(F\, S_r)$ is the potential energy, per unit mass, of the local contact forces. The term $-\eta\vartheta$ may be interpreted as a thermal potential energy. Thus, the value $\lambda = \hat{\lambda}(F,\eta)$ gives a kind of free energy per unit mass of the local state (F,η) when under the action of the force temperature pair (S_r, ϑ).

Definition of thermal equilibrium. *The local state (F,η) is called a* ***state of thermal equilibrium under a given force temperature pair*** (S_r, ϑ) *if*

(a) *the stress tensor $S = (\varrho/\varrho_r) F\, S_r$ is symmetric,*

(b) *the inequality*

$$\hat{\lambda}(F^*,\eta^*) > \hat{\lambda}(F,\eta) \tag{6.2}$$

holds for all states $(F^*,\eta^*) \neq (F,\eta)$ such that

$$F^* = G F, \tag{6.3}$$

where G is symmetric and positive definite.

The condition (a) means that F corresponds to a local configuration in local mechanical equilibrium (*cf.* § 5). The condition (b) means that a change of state increases the free energy λ provided that the configuration of the changed state is related to the original configuration by a pure stretch G (*cf.* § 1).

7. Conditions for thermal equilibrium

In this section we show that, for a local state (F,η) to be a state of thermal equilibrium under the force temperature pair (S_r, ϑ), the following three conditions are necessary and sufficient:

(α) The stress tensor $S = \frac{\varrho}{\varrho_r} F S_r$ is given by the *stress relation**

$$S = \varrho F \hat{\varepsilon}_F(F, \eta). \tag{7.1}$$

(β) The temperature ϑ is given by the *temperature relation*

$$\vartheta = \hat{\varepsilon}_\eta(F, \eta). \tag{7.2}$$

(γ) The inequality

$$\hat{\varepsilon}(F^*, \eta^*) - \hat{\varepsilon}(F, \eta) - \operatorname{tr}\left[(F^* - F)\, \hat{\varepsilon}_F(F, \eta)\right] - (\eta^* - \eta)\, \hat{\varepsilon}_\eta(F, \eta) > 0 \tag{7.3}$$

holds if $(F^*, \eta^*) \neq (F, \eta)$ and F^* is related to F by $F^* = GF$, where G is positive definite and symmetric.

We assume first that (F, η) is a state of thermal equilibrium and prove the validity of (α), (β), and (γ). By (6.2) and (6.3), the function $\hat{\lambda}(GF, \eta^*)$ of the symmetric tensor variable G and the scalar variable η^* has a minimum for $G = I$ and $\eta^* = \eta$. By a theorem of calculus, it follows that the derivatives of $\hat{\lambda}(GF, \eta^*)$ with respect to G and η^* must vanish for $G = I$ and $\eta^* = \eta$. If we set the derivative of $\hat{\lambda}(GF, \eta^*)$ with respect to η^* equal to zero at $\eta^* = \eta$, we obtain the temperature relation (7.2). The gradient of $\hat{\lambda}(GF, \eta^*)$ with respect to G may be computed using the formula (3) of the mathematical preliminaries and (6.1); we obtain the equation

$$\operatorname{tr}\left\{\left[F \hat{\varepsilon}_F(F, \eta) - \frac{1}{\varrho_r} F S_r\right] A\right\} = 0, \tag{7.4}$$

which is valid for arbitrary symmetric tensors A. Using (5.7) the equation (7.4) may be rewritten in the form

$$\operatorname{tr}\{[\varrho F \hat{\varepsilon}_F(F, \eta) - S]\, A\} = 0. \tag{7.5}$$

By the condition (a) of the definition of thermal equilibrium, S is symmetric. It follows from (3.2) and Theorem I of reference [*10*], p. 42, that $\varrho F \hat{\varepsilon}_F(F, \eta)$ is also symmetric. Thus, the tensor $\varrho F \hat{\varepsilon}_F(F, \eta) - S$ is symmetric. On the other hand, (7.5) can be valid for arbitrary symmetric A only if $\varrho F \hat{\varepsilon}_F(F, \eta) - S$ is skew; whence it follows that $\varrho F \hat{\varepsilon}_F(F, \eta) - S$ must vanish, which proves (7.1). The inequality (7.3) is obtained simply by substitution of (7.1) and (7.2) into the inequality (6.2), after $\hat{\lambda}$ is replaced by its definition (6.1).

We assume now that the conditions (α), (β), and (γ) are satisfied. It then follows from (7.1), (3.2) and the theorem of reference [*10*] mentioned above that the stress tensor S must be symmetric, so that condition (a) of the definition of thermal equilibrium is satisfied. Furthermore, the Kirchhoff tensor is given by

$$S_r = \varrho_r \hat{\varepsilon}_F(F, \eta). \tag{7.6}$$

Substitution of (7.6) and (7.2) into the inequality (7.3) gives the inequality (6.2); hence condition (b) of the definition of equilibrium is also satisfied.

---

* This is the familiar stress-strain relation of finite elasticity theory (*cf.* [*10*], (16.4)).

8. The fundamental postulates

We are now able to lay down our two fundamental postulates:

Postulate I. *For every local state (F, η) for which $\hat{\varepsilon}(F, \eta)$ is defined there exists a force temperature pair (S_r, ϑ) such that (F, η) is a state of thermal equilibrium under (S_r, ϑ).*

Postulate II. *The energy function $\hat{\varepsilon}(F, \eta)$ is strictly increasing in η for each fixed F.*

Postulate I and the results of the previous section yield the following theorems:

Theorem 1. *The force temperature pair (S_r, ϑ) which makes the local state (F, η) a state of thermal equilibrium is given by*

$$S_r = \varrho_r \hat{\varepsilon}_F(F, \eta), \tag{8.1}$$

$$\vartheta = \hat{\varepsilon}_\eta(F, \eta). \tag{8.2}$$

Theorem 2. *The energy function $\hat{\varepsilon}$ obeys the inequality*

$$\hat{\varepsilon}(F^*, \eta^*) - \hat{\varepsilon}(F, \eta) - \operatorname{tr}\left[(F^* - F)\, \hat{\varepsilon}_F(F, \eta)\right] - (\eta^* - \eta)\, \hat{\varepsilon}_\eta(F, \eta) > 0 \tag{8.3}$$

for any two local states (F, η) and (F^*, η^*), in the domain of definition of $\hat{\varepsilon}$, which are related by

$$F^* = G F, \tag{8.4}$$

where G is symmetric and positive definite.

The discussion of the previous section shows that Theorem 2 is equivalent to Postulate I. In fact, if we are given a state (F, η), we can define a force temperature pair (S_r, ϑ) according to (8.1) and (8.2) and then use the inequality (8.3) to prove that (F, η) is in equilibrium under (S_r, ϑ).

The inequality (8.3) of Theorem 2 is a restricted convexity condition on the function $\hat{\varepsilon}$. If we take, in particular, $F^* = F$, then (8.3) reduces to

$$\hat{\varepsilon}(F, \eta^*) - \hat{\varepsilon}(F, \eta) - (\eta^* - \eta)\, \hat{\varepsilon}_\eta(F, \eta) > 0 \tag{8.5}$$

for $\eta^* \neq \eta$. This inequality is the content of the following corollary to Theorem 2:

Theorem 3. *For each fixed local configuration, the energy density is given by a strictly convex function of the entropy density.*

This theorem is equivalent to the statement that $\hat{\varepsilon}_\eta(F, \eta)$ must be a strictly increasing function of η for each fixed F. It follows that the equation (8.2) can be solved for η in a unique manner:

$$\eta = \tilde{\eta}(F, \vartheta). \tag{8.6}$$

Here, $\tilde{\eta}$ is a strictly increasing function* of ϑ for each F. The fact that (8.6) is obtained by solving (8.2) for η is expressed by the identity

$$\hat{\varepsilon}_\eta\left[F, \tilde{\eta}(F, \vartheta)\right] = \vartheta. \tag{8.7}$$

---

* The specific heat c at fixed strain is given by $c = \vartheta\, \tilde{\eta}_\vartheta(F, \vartheta)$. Hence, it is a consequence of Theorem 3 that c/ϑ is never negative and, for each F, is strictly positive except possibly for a nowhere dense set of values of ϑ.

If we take $\eta^* = \eta$ in (8.3), we obtain

$$\hat{\varepsilon}(F^*, \eta) - \hat{\varepsilon}(F, \eta) - \operatorname{tr}[(F^* - F)\,\hat{\varepsilon}_F(F, \eta)] > 0; \tag{8.8}$$

this inequality holds whenever $F^* = GF$, where $G \neq I$ is symmetric and positive definite.

A local state (F, η) is called a *natural state* if the corresponding stress (8.1) vanishes. Keeping the entropy fixed, we may use the local configuration of the natural state as the reference configuration, so that $F = I$ and $\hat{\varepsilon}_F(I, \eta) = \frac{1}{\varrho} S = 0$. In this case, the inequality (8.8), by (8.4), reduces to

$$\hat{\varepsilon}(G, \eta) > \hat{\varepsilon}(I, \eta), \tag{8.9}$$

which is valid for arbitrary symmetric and positive definite $G \neq I$. Replacing G by the right stretch tensor U of an arbitrary deformation gradient F and using (3.3), we see that

$$\hat{\varepsilon}(F, \eta) \geqq \hat{\varepsilon}(I, \eta); \tag{8.10}$$

this expression becomes an equality only when F is orthogonal; *i.e.*, when (F, η) is equivalent to (I, η). Hence, the *energy density is smallest in a natural state.* It should be pointed out that this observation, though important for the theory of simple solids, is vacuous for fluids. For, we shall prove in § 11 that the stress on a fluid material point in thermal equilibrium is always a strictly positive pressure; thus, for a fluid there is no natural state.

We note that the restriction (8.4) on the inequality (8.3) of Theorem 2 is essential for application of the present theory to physical situations. This restriction means that the local configurations corresponding to F^* and F must be related by a pure stretch. If, for example, these local configurations were related by a rotation so that $F^* = QF$, with Q an orthogonal transformation, then the left side of (8.8) would reduce to $-\operatorname{tr}[(Q - I) F\, \hat{\varepsilon}_F(F, \eta)]$, since $\hat{\varepsilon}(F^*)$ would equal $\hat{\varepsilon}(F)$ by (3.2). The stress relation (7.1) shows that the left side of (8.8) would then become $-\frac{1}{\varrho}\operatorname{tr}[(Q - I)\, S]$. One can show that this expression can be made negative by an appropriate choice of Q if S has at least one negative proper number. Thus, the inequality (8.8), were it to hold for arbitrary pairs F, F^*, would exclude the possibility of thermal equilibrium under compression stresses, which is certainly not in accord with experience*.

9. An alternative axiomatization

In this section we hope to make clear our reasons for assuming Postulate II and to motivate further our definition of equilibrium.

It follows from Postulate II that, for each fixed F, the caloric equation of state has a unique solution for η:

$$\eta = \hat{\hat{\eta}}(F, \varepsilon), \tag{9.1}$$

and that the function $\hat{\hat{\eta}}$ is strictly increasing in ε for each F. This one-to-one correspondence between ε and η at each F makes it possible to give an alternative

* It has also been pointed out by HILL [15] that an assumption of unrestricted convexity of $\hat{\varepsilon}$ in the deformation gradient would lead to unacceptable physical behavior.

axiomatization of our present theory of thermostatics by taking ε and F as independent variables and defining thermal equilibrium in terms of the function $\hat{\hat{\eta}}$. In such a formulation a local thermomechanic state is characterized by a pair (F, ε), and thermal equilibrium is defined as follows:

Alternative definition of thermal equilibrium. *The local state (F, ε) is called a state of thermal equilibrium under the force temperature pair (S_r, ϑ), with $\vartheta \neq 0$, if*

(a) *the stress tensor $S = (\varrho/\varrho_r) F S_r$ is symmetric,*

(b) *the inequality*

$$\hat{\hat{\eta}}(F, \varepsilon) > \hat{\hat{\eta}}(F^*, \varepsilon^*) + \frac{1}{\vartheta \varrho_r} \operatorname{tr}[(F^* - F) S_r] - \frac{\varepsilon^* - \varepsilon}{\vartheta} \tag{9.2}$$

holds for all states $(F^*, \varepsilon^*) \neq (F, \varepsilon)$ such that $F^* = GF$, where G is symmetric and positive definite.

Theorem 4. *The definition of thermal equilibrium given in § 6 and the alternative definition of thermal equilibrium are equivalent (for $\vartheta \neq 0$) if Postulate II is assumed.*

Proof. In § 7 we showed that, under the original definition of § 6, in order for a state (F, η) to be a state of thermal equilibrium for the force temperature pair (S_r, ϑ) it is necessary that

$$\vartheta = \hat{\varepsilon}_\eta(F, \eta). \tag{9.3}$$

By a very similar argument it can be shown, using the alternative definition of thermal equilibrium, that in order for the state (F, ε) to be a state of thermal equilibrium it is necessary that

$$\frac{1}{\vartheta} = \hat{\hat{\eta}}_\varepsilon(F, \varepsilon). \tag{9.4}$$

Now, by Postulate II, the functions $\hat{\varepsilon}$ and $\hat{\hat{\eta}}$ are strictly increasing in η and ε, respectively, for fixed F. Hence, ϑ cannot be negative if (S_r, ϑ) is to be a force temperature pair for some state of thermal equilibrium, regardless of which of the two definitions is used. Since we here assume $\vartheta \neq 0$, we have $\vartheta > 0$, and (9.2) can be multiplied by ϑ and then rearranged to give

$$-\vartheta \hat{\hat{\eta}}(F^*, \varepsilon^*) - \frac{1}{\varrho_r} \operatorname{tr}(F^* S_r) + \varepsilon^* > -\vartheta \hat{\hat{\eta}}(F, \varepsilon) - \frac{1}{\varrho_r} \operatorname{tr}(F S_r) + \varepsilon. \tag{9.5}$$

Noting the relations

$$\begin{aligned} \eta^* &= \hat{\hat{\eta}}(F^*, \varepsilon^*), & \eta &= \hat{\hat{\eta}}(F, \varepsilon), \\ \varepsilon^* &= \hat{\varepsilon}(F^*, \eta^*), & \varepsilon &= \hat{\varepsilon}(F, \eta), \end{aligned} \tag{9.6}$$

and (6.1), we see that (9.5) is equivalent to (6.2). The requirement that $(F, \eta) \neq (F^*, \eta^*)$ and the requirements on $G = F^* F^{-1}$ are the same for (6.2) and (9.5). The condition (a) is obviously the same in both definitions; hence the definitions are equivalent, q.e.d.

From a certain point of view the alternative definition of thermal equilibrium given in this section is more fundamental than the original definition of § 6. The alternative definition is more closely related to the physical notion that, since entropy tends to increase, equilibrium states should be, in some sense, states of maximum entropy. The definition of § 6 is closely related to the idea, which is often used in mechanics, that equilibrium states should be, in some sense, states of minimum potential. It should be emphasized that the two definitions are equivalent only if Postulate II is assumed; *i.e.*, only if states of negative temperature are excluded. Of course, negative temperatures never occur in continuum mechanics, but there are subjects in which they do occur (*cf.* [*11*], [*12*]). Statistical mechanical considerations suggest that for systems capable of negative temperatures a practical definition of thermal equilibrium should be based on the idea of maximum entropy.

10. Infinitesimal deformations from an arbitrary state

Here we consider the classical theory of *infinitesimal deformations* from an arbitrary initial configuration. We make no attempt to justify the use of the theory of infinitesimal deformations as an approximation to the theory of finite deformations.

In the theory of infinitesimal deformations one considers cases in which $F^* = GF$ is obtained from F by superimposing an infinitesimal deformation. The *infinitesimal strain tensor* E is defined as the *symmetric part* of $G - I$.

In the special case in which G is positive definite and symmetric (*i.e.*, when F^* is related to F by a pure stretch) we have

$$E = G - I, \tag{10.1}$$

and the excess energy $\hat{\varepsilon}(GF, \eta) - \hat{\varepsilon}(F, \eta)$ is a function of E alone:

$$\sigma(E) = \hat{\varepsilon}(GF, \eta) - \hat{\varepsilon}(F, \eta). \tag{10.2}$$

Equation (10.2) is valid approximately even when G is not symmetric.

In the infinitesimal theory it is assumed (i) that (10.2) is valid exactly for all G and (ii) that the excess energy is exactly given by the sum,

$$\sigma(E) = \sigma_1(E) + \sigma_2(E), \tag{10.3}$$

of a term $\sigma_1(E)$ linear in E and a term $\sigma_2(E)$ quadratic in E.

By taking the gradient of (10.2) with respect to E and then putting $E = 0$, it is easily shown that the linear term $\sigma_1(E)$ must be given by

$$\sigma_1(E) = \operatorname{tr}[E F \hat{\varepsilon}_F(F, \eta)]. \tag{10.4}$$

Hence, using the stress relation (7.1), we have

$$\sigma_1(E) = \frac{1}{\varrho} \operatorname{tr}(E S), \tag{10.5}$$

where S is the stress of the original state (F, η).

Now, the fundamental inequality (8.8) may be written

$$\hat{\varepsilon}(GF, \eta) - \hat{\varepsilon}(F, \eta) - \operatorname{tr}[(G - I) F \hat{\varepsilon}_F(F, \eta)] > 0. \tag{10.6}$$

From (10.1), (10.2) we get

$$\sigma(E) - \operatorname{tr}[E F \hat{\varepsilon}_F(F, \eta)] > 0, \tag{10.7}$$

and it follows from (10.3), (10.4) and (10.5) that

$$\sigma_2(E) = \sigma(E) - \frac{1}{\varrho} \operatorname{tr}(E S) > 0. \tag{10.8}$$

This inequality is the content of the following theorem:

Theorem 5. *For an infinitesimal deformation superimposed, at fixed entropy, on an arbitrary state, the excess energy is the sum of a positive definite quadratic form in the infinitesimal strain tensor* E *of the superimposed strain and a linear term* $\frac{1}{\varrho}\operatorname{tr}(E\,S)$, *where* ϱ *is the density and* S *the stress corresponding to the original state.*

If the original state is a natural state in which the stress vanishes, the above theorem reduces to the familiar statement that the strain energy is a positive definite quadratic form in the infinitesimal strain tensor. For isotropic materials, this statement is equivalent to following well known inequalities for the Lamé constants:

$$\mu > 0, \quad 3\lambda + 2\mu > 0, \tag{10.9}$$

which state that the shear modulus and the compression modulus must be positive.

11. Simple fluids

For simple fluids we have, by (4.2) and (4.3),

$$\hat{\varepsilon}(F,\eta) = \bar{\varepsilon}(|\det F|\, v_r, \eta), \tag{11.1}$$

where $v_r = 1/\varrho_r$ is the specific volume in the reference configuration. Taking the gradient of (11.1) with respect to F, we obtain

$$\hat{\varepsilon}_F(F,\eta) = \bar{\varepsilon}_v(v,\eta)\, v\, F^{-1}, \tag{11.2}$$

where $v = |\det F|\, v_r$. On substituting (11.2) into the fundamental inequality (8.3) and using (8.4), we obtain

$$\bar{\varepsilon}(v^*,\eta^*) - \bar{\varepsilon}(v,\eta) - v\,\bar{\varepsilon}_v(v,\eta)\operatorname{tr}(G-I) - (\eta^*-\eta)\,\bar{\varepsilon}_\eta(v,\eta) > 0, \tag{11.3}$$

which must hold for all positive definite symmetric $G = F F^{*-1}$ whenever either $G \neq I$ or $\eta \neq \eta^*$.

We assume now that $v^* = v$; *i.e.*, that $|\det F^*| = |\det F|$, which means that G is unimodular. We also choose $\eta^* = \eta$. Then (11.3) reduces to

$$-v\,\bar{\varepsilon}_v(v,\eta)\operatorname{tr}(G-I) > 0, \tag{11.4}$$

which must be valid for all symmetric positive definite unimodular tensors $G \neq I$. Let g_1, g_2, g_3 be the proper numbers of G. We then have

$$g_i > 0, \quad g_1 g_2 g_3 = 1 \tag{11.5}$$

and

$$\operatorname{tr}(G-I) = g_1 + g_2 + g_3 - 3. \tag{11.6}$$

Using the fact that the arithmetic mean is greater than the geometric mean,

$$\frac{g_1+g_2+g_3}{3} > \sqrt[3]{g_1 g_2 g_3}, \tag{11.7}$$

we see that (11.5) and (11.6) imply

$$\operatorname{tr}(G-I) > 0. \tag{11.8}$$

Hence, it follows from (11.4) that

$$\bar{\varepsilon}_v(v,\eta) < 0 \tag{11.9}$$

for all v and η for which $\bar{\varepsilon}$ is defined. Thus, $\bar{\varepsilon}(v,\eta)$ must be a strictly decreasing function of v for each fixed η.

Substitution of (11.2) into (7.1) shows that the stress relation reduces to

$$S = -\bar{p}(v,\eta)\, I, \tag{11.10}$$

where

$$\bar{p}(v,\eta) = -\bar{\varepsilon}_v(v,\eta) \tag{11.11}$$

is the hydrostatic pressure. By (11.9) it is positive.

For further exploitation of (11.3) we choose $G = \alpha I$, $\alpha > 0$. Since

$$\alpha^3 = |\det G| = \left|\frac{\det F^*}{\det F}\right| = \frac{v^*}{v},$$

we have

$$G = \left(\sqrt[3]{\frac{v^*}{v}}\right) I. \tag{11.12}$$

Substitution of (11.12) into (11.3) yields the inequality

$$\bar{\varepsilon}(v^*,\eta^*) - \bar{\varepsilon}(v,\eta) - 3v\,\bar{\varepsilon}_v(v,\eta)\left(\sqrt[3]{\frac{v^*}{v}} - 1\right) - (\eta^* - \eta)\,\bar{\varepsilon}_\eta(v,\eta) > 0, \tag{11.13}$$

which must be valid for all v, v^*, η, η^* except, of course, when both $v = v^*$ and $\eta = \eta^*$. In order to understand the significance of this inequality we introduce the new variable

$$\nu = \sqrt[3]{v} \tag{11.14}$$

and define the function $\bar{\bar{\varepsilon}}$ by

$$\bar{\varepsilon}(v,\eta) = \bar{\bar{\varepsilon}}(\nu,\eta) = \bar{\bar{\varepsilon}}(\sqrt[3]{v},\eta). \tag{11.15}$$

A straightforward calculation shows that (11.13) is equivalent to the inequality

$$\bar{\bar{\varepsilon}}(\nu^*,\eta^*) - \bar{\bar{\varepsilon}}(\nu,\eta) - (\nu^* - \nu)\,\bar{\bar{\varepsilon}}_\nu(\nu,\eta) - (\eta^* - \eta)\,\bar{\bar{\varepsilon}}_\eta(\nu,\eta) > 0, \tag{11.16}$$

which states that $\bar{\bar{\varepsilon}}(\nu,\eta)$ is strictly convex in ν and η jointly. If $\bar{\bar{\varepsilon}}(\nu,\eta)$ happens to possess continuous second derivatives, it follows that the matrix

$$\left\|\begin{matrix} \bar{\bar{\varepsilon}}_{\nu\nu} & \bar{\bar{\varepsilon}}_{\nu\eta} \\ \bar{\bar{\varepsilon}}_{\eta\nu} & \bar{\bar{\varepsilon}}_{\eta\eta} \end{matrix}\right\| \tag{11.17}$$

must be positive semi-definite.

We summarize in the following theorem:

Theorem 6. *For a simple fluid in thermal equilibrium, the stress S reduces to a hydrostatic pressure $S = -\bar{p}(v,\eta) I$. The pressure $\bar{p}(v,\eta) = -\bar{\varepsilon}_v(v,\eta)$ is always positive. The energy density $\bar{\bar{\varepsilon}}(\nu,\eta)$ is a strictly convex function of the cube root ν of the specific volume and the entropy η jointly.*

It is not hard to show that, for simple fluids, the positivity of $\bar{p}(v,\eta)$ and the convexity of $\bar{\bar{\varepsilon}}(\nu,\eta)$ are not only necessary but also sufficient conditions for the validity of the fundamental inequality (11.3). Hence, these conditions are also sufficient conditions for the validity of Postulate I for simple fluids.

12. Isotropic materials

For isotropic materials in general, if we pick an undistorted state as reference, we have, by (4.5),

$$\hat{\varepsilon}(F,\eta) = \hat{\varepsilon}(VR,\eta) = \hat{\varepsilon}(V,\eta), \tag{12.1}$$

where V is the left stretch tensor, defined by the polar decomposition $F = VR$. On computing the gradient of (12.1) with respect to V, we find

$$\hat{\varepsilon}_F(F,\eta) = R^T \hat{\varepsilon}_V(V,\eta). \tag{12.2}$$

If we substitute (12.2) into (7.1) and again use $F = VR$, we see that the stress relation may be written in the form

$$S = \varrho V \hat{\varepsilon}_V(V,\eta) = \varrho \hat{\varepsilon}_V(V,\eta) V. \tag{12.3}$$

On substituting (8.4), (12.1) and (12.2) into the fundamental inequality (8.3) and observing that

$$\hat{\varepsilon}(F^*) = \hat{\varepsilon}(GF) = \hat{\varepsilon}(GVR) = \hat{\varepsilon}(GV),$$

we obtain

$$\hat{\varepsilon}(GV,\eta^*) - \hat{\varepsilon}(V,\eta) - \operatorname{tr}\left[(G-I)V\hat{\varepsilon}_V(V,\eta)\right] - (\eta^* - \eta)\hat{\varepsilon}_\eta(V,\eta) > 0. \tag{12.4}$$

This inequality must be valid for all η, η^* and all symmetric and positive definite G and V, except, of course, when both $\eta = \eta^*$ and $G = I$.

We consider now the special case when G and V commute; *i.e.*, when

$$V^* = GV \tag{12.5}$$

is symmetric. In this case the tensors V and V^* have an orthonormal basis of proper vectors in common. The matrices of V and V^*, relative to this basis, are

$$\|V\| = \left\| \begin{matrix} v_1 & 0 & 0 \\ 0 & v_2 & 0 \\ 0 & 0 & v_3 \end{matrix} \right\|, \quad \|V^*\| = \left\| \begin{matrix} v_1^* & 0 & 0 \\ 0 & v_2^* & 0 \\ 0 & 0 & v_3^* \end{matrix} \right\|, \tag{12.6}$$

where the v_i and the v_i^* are the proper numbers of V and V^*, respectively. The matrix of $\hat{\varepsilon}_V(V,\eta)$ is

$$\|\hat{\varepsilon}_V(V,\eta)\| = \left\| \begin{matrix} \varepsilon_1 & 0 & 0 \\ 0 & \varepsilon_2 & 0 \\ 0 & 0 & \varepsilon_3 \end{matrix} \right\|, \tag{12.7}$$

where

$$\varepsilon_i = \bar{\varepsilon}_i(v_j,\eta) = \frac{\partial}{\partial v_i}\bar{\varepsilon}(v_j,\eta) \tag{12.8}$$

are the partial derivatives of the function (4.6). Substitution of (12.5), (4.6), (12.6), and (12.7) into (12.4) gives the inequality

$$\bar{\varepsilon}(v_j^*,\eta^*) - \bar{\varepsilon}(v_j,\eta) - \sum_{i=1}^{3}(v_i^* - v_i)\bar{\varepsilon}_i(v_j,\eta) - (\eta^* - \eta)\bar{\varepsilon}_\eta(v_j,\eta) > 0, \tag{12.9}$$

which is valid except when $\eta^* = \eta$ and $v_i = v_i^*$ for all i. We have thus proved*.

* We have shown that for isotropic materials the inequality (12.9) is a *necessary* condition for validity of the fundamental inequality (8.3). At the present time, it is an open matter as to whether (12.9) is *sufficient* for the validity of (8.3) in the isotropic case, or whether further inequalities which are independent of (12.9) can be deduced from Postulate I for isotropic materials.

Theorem 7. *For an isotropic material, the energy density $\bar{\varepsilon}(v_j, \eta)$ is a strictly convex function of the principal stretches v_j and the entropy density η jointly.*

If $\bar{\varepsilon}$ happens to be twice continuously differentiable, it follows that the matrix

$$\begin{Vmatrix} \bar{\varepsilon}_{11} & \bar{\varepsilon}_{12} & \bar{\varepsilon}_{13} & \bar{\varepsilon}_{1\eta} \\ \bar{\varepsilon}_{21} & \bar{\varepsilon}_{22} & \bar{\varepsilon}_{23} & \bar{\varepsilon}_{2\eta} \\ \bar{\varepsilon}_{31} & \bar{\varepsilon}_{32} & \bar{\varepsilon}_{33} & \bar{\varepsilon}_{3\eta} \\ \bar{\varepsilon}_{\eta 1} & \bar{\varepsilon}_{\eta 2} & \bar{\varepsilon}_{\eta 3} & \bar{\varepsilon}_{\eta\eta} \end{Vmatrix} \tag{12.10}$$

is positive semidefinite. Here the indices 1, 2, 3, and η denote the derivatives of $\bar{\varepsilon}$ with respect to v_1, v_2, v_3, and η, respectively.

A corollary of the convexity inequality (12.9) is

Theorem 8. *For an isotropic material, the functions $\bar{\varepsilon}_i(v_j, \eta)$, defined by* (12.8), *have the property that $v_i > v_k$ implies $\bar{\varepsilon}_i(v_j, \eta) > \bar{\varepsilon}_k(v_j, \eta)$.*

Proof. Without loss of generality, we take $i=1$ and $k=2$. We then choose $v_1^* = v_2$, $v_2^* = v_1$, $v_3^* = v_3$, and $\eta^* = \eta$. Since $\bar{\varepsilon}(v_j, \eta)$ is a symmetric function of the principal stretches v_j (*cf.* § 4), and since the v_j^* differ from the v_j only by their order, we have

$$\bar{\varepsilon}(v_j^*, \eta) = \bar{\varepsilon}(v_j, \eta).$$

Hence (12.9) reduces to

$$-(v_2 - v_1)\,\bar{\varepsilon}_1(v_j, \eta) - (v_1 - v_2)\,\bar{\varepsilon}_2(v_j, \eta) > 0;$$

i.e.,

$$(v_1 - v_2)\left[\bar{\varepsilon}_1(v_j, \eta) - \bar{\varepsilon}_2(v_j, \eta)\right] > 0.$$

Thus, if $v_1 > v_2$, then $\bar{\varepsilon}_1(v_j, \eta) > \bar{\varepsilon}_2(v_j, \eta)$, q.e.d.

In an isotropic material, the left stretch tensor V and the stress tensor S have an orthonormal basis $\boldsymbol{e}_i$ of proper vectors in common. The $\boldsymbol{e}_i$ determine the principal axes of stress. It follows from (12.3), (12.6), and (12.7) that the principal stresses are given by

$$s_i = \varrho\, v_i\, \bar{\varepsilon}_i(v_j, \eta). \tag{12.11}$$

When measured per unit area in the undistorted reference state, these principal stresses must be replaced by

$$s_i' = \varrho_r\, \bar{\varepsilon}_i(v_j, \eta). \tag{12.12}$$

Hence Theorem 8 has the following simple physical interpretation:

Theorem 8a. *If, at a given value η, the principal stretch v_i is greater than the principal stretch v_k, then the principal stress, measured per unit area in the undistorted reference state, in the direction of v_i is greater than that in the direction of v_k.*

It should be noted that the statement of this theorem does not necessarily remain valid if the principal stresses are measured per unit area of the deformed state*, except when these stresses are all positive; *i.e.*, except in a state of pure tension.

* Such a statement was proposed as a postulate by M. BAKER & J. L. ERICKSEN [*13*]. In our theory, only the modification given by Theorem 8a is valid. Related inequalities have been studied by J. BARTA [*14*].

13. The free energy

It is often useful to employ the deformation gradient F and the temperature ϑ, rather than F and the entropy η, as the independent variables. This is possible because, by (8.2) and (8.6), there is a one-to-one correspondence between η and ϑ for each fixed F.

The *free energy function* $\tilde{\psi}$ is defined by

$$\tilde{\psi}(F,\vartheta) = \hat{\varepsilon}[F,\tilde{\eta}(F,\vartheta)] - \vartheta\,\tilde{\eta}(F,\vartheta), \tag{13.1}$$

where the entropy function $\tilde{\eta}$ is defined in (8.6) as the unique solution of the equation (8.2). The values ψ of the free energy function $\tilde{\psi}$ are called *free energy densities**.

Differentiation of (13.1) with respect to F, using the chain rule, gives

$$\tilde{\psi}_F(F,\vartheta) = \hat{\varepsilon}_F[F,\tilde{\eta}(F,\vartheta)] + \hat{\varepsilon}_\eta[F,\tilde{\eta}(F,\vartheta)]\,\tilde{\eta}_F(F,\vartheta) - \vartheta\,\tilde{\eta}_F(F,\vartheta).$$

It follows from (8.7) that the last two terms cancel, so that

$$\tilde{\psi}_F(F,\vartheta) = \hat{\varepsilon}_F[F,\tilde{\eta}(F,\vartheta)]. \tag{13.2}$$

Differentiation of (13.1) with respect to ϑ gives

$$\tilde{\psi}_\vartheta(F,\vartheta) = -\,\tilde{\eta}(F,\vartheta). \tag{13.3}$$

From Theorems 1 and 2, (13.2), and (13.3) we get

Theorem 9. *For the force temperature pair (S_r,ϑ) to make the local state (F,η) a state of thermal equilibrium, it is necessary and sufficient that S_r and η be given by*

$$S_r = \varrho_r\,\tilde{\psi}_F(F,\vartheta), \tag{13.4}$$

$$\eta = -\,\tilde{\psi}_\vartheta(F,\vartheta). \tag{13.5}$$

On multiplying (13.4) on the left by $(\varrho/\varrho_r)\,F$ and noting that $S = (\varrho/\varrho_r)F\,S_r$, we get the following form for the stress relation:

$$S = \varrho\,F\,\tilde{\psi}_F(F,\vartheta). \tag{13.6}$$

Assuming that two temperatures ϑ,ϑ^* and two deformation gradients F, F^* are given, we now put

$$\eta = \tilde{\eta}(F,\vartheta) = -\,\tilde{\psi}_\vartheta(F,\vartheta)$$
$$\eta^* = \tilde{\eta}(F^*,\vartheta^*) = -\,\tilde{\psi}_\vartheta(F^*,\vartheta^*). \tag{13.7}$$

By substituting (13.1)—(13.7) into the fundamental inequality (8.3) of Theorem 2, we obtain

Theorem 10. *The free energy function $\tilde{\psi}$ obeys the inequality*

$$\tilde{\psi}(F^*,\vartheta^*) - \tilde{\psi}(F,\vartheta) - \operatorname{tr}[(F^*-F)\,\tilde{\psi}_F(F,\eta)] - (\vartheta^*-\vartheta)\,\tilde{\psi}_\vartheta(F^*,\vartheta^*) > 0 \tag{13.8}$$

for any two pairs (F,ϑ) and $(F^*,\vartheta^*) \neq (F,\vartheta)$ in the domain of definition of $\tilde{\psi}$ which are related by

$$F^* = G F, \tag{13.9}$$

where G is symmetric and positive definite.

* The term "Helmholtz free energy per unit mass" would also be in accord with common usage.

As Theorem 2, so also Theorem 10 is equivalent to Postulate I.

If in (13.8) we take the special case $F^*=F$ and interchange ϑ and ϑ^*, we obtain

$$\tilde{\psi}(F,\vartheta^*) - \tilde{\psi}(F,\vartheta) - (\vartheta^* - \vartheta)\,\tilde{\psi}_\vartheta(F,\vartheta) > 0. \tag{13.10}$$

This inequality, which is valid for all F and all $\vartheta^* \neq \vartheta$, states that the free energy function $\tilde{\psi}(F,\vartheta)$ is *strictly concave* in ϑ for each F.

Putting $\vartheta^*=\vartheta$ in (13.8) gives the following restricted convexity of $\tilde{\psi}$ in F:

$$\tilde{\psi}(F^*,\vartheta) - \tilde{\psi}(F,\vartheta) - \operatorname{tr}\left[(F^*-F)\,\tilde{\psi}_F(F,\vartheta)\right] > 0, \tag{13.11}$$

the restriction being the condition (13.9).

The considerations and results of § 11 and § 12 on simple fluids and isotropic materials remain valid if the energy function $\hat{\varepsilon}$ is replaced by the free energy function $\tilde{\psi}$, except that the convexity of $\hat{\varepsilon}(F,\eta)$ in η corresponds to the concavity of $\tilde{\psi}(F,\vartheta)$ in ϑ. We summarize the relevant results.

For a simple fluid, the free energy density reduces to a function of the specific volume v and the temperature ϑ only:

$$\psi = \tilde{\psi}(F,\vartheta) = \overline{\psi}(v,\vartheta). \tag{13.12}$$

The stress reduces to a hydrostatic pressure given by

$$S = -\,\overline{p}(v,\vartheta)\,I, \quad \overline{p}(v,\vartheta) = -\,\overline{\psi}_v(v,\vartheta). \tag{13.13}$$

The pressure is always positive. The function $\overline{\overline{\psi}}$, giving the free energy as a function of the cube root ν of the specific volume and the temperature,

$$\overline{\overline{\psi}}(\nu,\vartheta) = \overline{\psi}(\nu^3,\vartheta), \tag{13.14}$$

satisfies the inequality

$$\overline{\overline{\psi}}(\nu^*,\vartheta^*) - \overline{\overline{\psi}}(\nu,\vartheta) - (\nu^*-\nu)\,\overline{\overline{\psi}}_\nu(\nu,\vartheta) - (\vartheta^*-\vartheta)\,\overline{\overline{\psi}}_\vartheta(\nu^*,\vartheta^*) > 0. \tag{13.15}$$

This inequality implies that $\overline{\overline{\psi}}(\nu,\vartheta)$ is strictly convex in ν for each ϑ and strictly concave in ϑ for each ν.

For isotropic materials in general, the free energy reduces to a function of the temperature ϑ and the three principal stretches v_1, v_2, v_3, computed relative to an undistorted state:

$$\tilde{\psi}(F,\vartheta) = \overline{\psi}(v_1, v_2, v_3; \vartheta). \tag{13.16}$$

The function $\overline{\psi}$ is symmetric and strictly convex in the variables v_1, v_2, v_3; $\overline{\psi}$ is strictly concave in ϑ. Theorems 8 and 8a remain valid if $\overline{\varepsilon}$ is replaced by $\overline{\psi}$; *i.e.*, if the temperature, rather than the entropy is fixed at a given value. The stress relation may be written in the form

$$S = \varrho\, V\, \tilde{\psi}_V(V,\vartheta), \tag{13.17}$$

where V is the left stretch tensor.

The forms, (13.6), (13.13), and (13.17), of the stress relation are useful in discussing experiments involving equilibrium states for which the temperature is controlled, while the forms, (7.1), (11.10), and (12.3), are appropriate for discussing experiments involving equilibrium states for which the entropy is controlled.

14. Thermal stability

Consider a body $\mathscr{B}$ and a global thermomechanic state $\{\boldsymbol{f}, \eta\}$ of $\mathscr{B}$, defined by a configuration $\boldsymbol{f}$ of $\mathscr{B}$ and an entropy distribution η of $\mathscr{B}$; (*cf.* § 2). Let the caloric equation of state of the material point X of $\mathscr{B}$ be given by

$$\varepsilon(X) = \hat{\varepsilon}[F(X), \eta(X); X]. \tag{14.1}$$

Here $F(X)$ is the deformation gradient at X of the configuration $\boldsymbol{f}$ relative to some reference configuration $\boldsymbol{f}_r$. We do not assume that the body is homogeneous, and hence the function $\hat{\varepsilon}$ may depend explicitly on X as indicated in (14.1). The *total entropy* of $\mathscr{B}$ in the given state is defined by

$$\mathsf{H} = \int_{\mathscr{B}} \eta(X)\, dm \tag{14.2}$$

and the *total internal energy* of $\mathscr{B}$ by

$$\mathsf{E} = \int_{\mathscr{B}} \hat{\varepsilon}[F(X), \eta(X); X]\, dm. \tag{14.3}$$

In this section we shall deal with situations in which the deformation gradient $F(X)$ is kept fixed at each X while the entropy field $\eta = \eta(X)$ is varied. It will not be necessary to make the dependence of ε on F explicit, and the following abbreviated notation will be convenient:

$$\hat{\varepsilon}[F(X), \eta(X); X] = \varepsilon(X, \eta(X)). \tag{14.4}$$

Definition of thermal stability. *Let $\{\boldsymbol{f}, \eta\}$ be a state of $\mathscr{B}$ and let E and H be, respectively, the total internal energy and total entropy corresponding to the state $\{\boldsymbol{f}, \eta\}$. We say that $\{\boldsymbol{f}, \eta\}$ is a **thermally stable** state of $\mathscr{B}$ if every other state $\{\boldsymbol{f}, \eta^*\}$, with the same configuration as $\{\boldsymbol{f}, \eta\}$ and the same total entropy as $\{\boldsymbol{f}, \eta\}$,*

$$\mathsf{H}^* = \int_{\mathscr{B}} \eta^*(X)\, dm = \mathsf{H} = \int_{\mathscr{B}} \eta(X)\, dm, \tag{14.5}$$

has a greater total internal energy than the state $\{\boldsymbol{f}, \eta\}$; i.e.,

$$\mathsf{E}^* = \int_{\mathscr{B}} \varepsilon(X, \eta^*(X))\, dm > \mathsf{E} = \int_{\mathscr{B}} \varepsilon(X, \eta(X))\, dm. \tag{14.6}$$

We give another condition, equivalent to the one given above, which could also be used to define thermal stability.

Theorem 11. *A state $\{\boldsymbol{f}, \eta\}$ of $\mathscr{B}$ is thermally stable if and only if every other state $\{\boldsymbol{f}, \eta^*\}$ with the same configuration as $\{\boldsymbol{f}, \eta\}$ and the same total energy as $\{\boldsymbol{f}, \eta\}$,*

$$\mathsf{E}^* = \int_{\mathscr{B}} \varepsilon(X, \eta^*(X))\, dm = \mathsf{E} = \int_{\mathscr{B}} \varepsilon(X, \eta(X))\, dm, \tag{14.7}$$

has a lower total entropy than the state $\{\boldsymbol{f}, \eta\}$; i.e.,

$$\mathsf{H} = \int_{\mathscr{B}} \eta(X)\, dm > \mathsf{H}^* = \int_{\mathscr{B}} \eta^*(X)\, dm. \tag{14.8}$$

Proof. We show that the hypothesis of Theorem 11 is necessary for thermal stability by showing that if there exists a state $\{\boldsymbol{f}, \eta_1\}$ (with η_1 not identical to η) which obeys the equation (14.7) of Theorem 11 but violates (14.8), then there must exist a state $\{\boldsymbol{f}, \eta_2\}$ (with η_2 not identical to η) which obeys the equation

(14.5) of the definition of thermal stability but which does not obey (14.6). Let η_1 be the entropy density distribution which obeys (14.7) but not (14.8); we construct η_2 as follows:

$$\eta_2(X) = \eta_1(X) + \frac{\mathsf{H} - \mathsf{H}_1}{m(\mathscr{B})}, \tag{14.9}$$

where H_1 is the total entropy corresponding to η_1. The total entropy corresponding to η_2 is

$$\mathsf{H}_2 = \int_{\mathscr{B}} \eta_2(X)\, dm = \mathsf{H}. \tag{14.10}$$

Hence, the state $\{\boldsymbol{f}, \eta_2\}$ obeys the equation (14.5) of the definition. We have assumed that η_2 is not identical to η and that $\mathsf{H}_1 \geqq \mathsf{H}$. If $\mathsf{H}_1 = \mathsf{H}$, then η_2 is the same as η_1 and hence different from η. In this trivial case of $\eta_2 = \eta_1$, it follows from the fact that η_1 obeys (14.7) that

$$\int_{\mathscr{B}} \varepsilon(X, \eta_2(X))\, dm = \int_{\mathscr{B}} \varepsilon(X, \eta_1(X))\, dm = \int_{\mathscr{B}} \varepsilon(X, \eta(X))\, dm. \tag{14.11}$$

If $\mathsf{H}_1 > \mathsf{H}$, then $\eta_2(X) < \eta_1(X)$ for all X in $\mathscr{B}$. It then follows from Postulate II of § 8 and the assumption that η_1 obeys (14.7) that

$$\int_{\mathscr{B}} \varepsilon(X, \eta_2(X))\, dm < \int_{\mathscr{B}} \varepsilon(X, \eta_1(X))\, dm = \int_{\mathscr{B}} \varepsilon(X, \eta(X))\, dm. \tag{14.12}$$

It is clear from (14.12) that η_2 is not identical to η. Hence, whenever $\mathsf{H}_1 \geqq \mathsf{H}$, we have, by the construction (14.9), a state $\{\boldsymbol{f}, \eta_2\}$ with η_2 different from η but with $\mathsf{H}_2 = \mathsf{H}$ and

$$\mathsf{E}_2 = \int_{\mathscr{B}} \varepsilon(X, \eta_2(X))\, dm \leqq \int_{\mathscr{B}} \varepsilon(X, \eta(X))\, dm = \mathsf{E}. \tag{14.13}$$

Thus, a violation of the hypothesis of Theorem 11 implies the existence of a state different from $\{\boldsymbol{f}, \eta\}$ which obeys (14.5) yet violates (14.6).

The sufficiency of the hypothesis of Theorem 11 is proved analogously by starting with a state which obeys (14.5) of the definition, but not (14.6), and then using Postulate II to construct a state which obeys (14.7) of the theorem, but which violates (14.8).

The main result of the present section is the following theorem:

Theorem 12. *A state* $\{\boldsymbol{f}, \eta\}$ *of a body is thermally stable if and only if it is of uniform temperature;* i.e., *if and only if*

$$\vartheta = \varepsilon_\eta(X, \eta(X)) \tag{14.14}$$

is a constant, independent of the material point X.

Proof. To show the necessity of $\vartheta = \text{constant}$, we observe that, by (14.6), the function $\eta(X)$ is the solution of the variational problem

$$\int_{\mathscr{B}} \varepsilon(X, \eta^*(X))\, dm = \text{Minimum} \tag{14.15}$$

subject to the constraint (14.5). It follows that the first variation of

$$\int_{\mathscr{B}} [\varepsilon(X, \eta^*(X)) - \alpha\, \eta^*(X)]\, dm \tag{14.16}$$

must vanish for $\eta^* = \eta$. Here α is a constant Lagrange parameter. We obtain

$$\alpha = \varepsilon_\eta(X, \eta(X)) = \vartheta = \text{constant}. \tag{14.17}$$

To prove the sufficiency of $\vartheta = \text{constant}$, we substitute the function values $F(X)$, $\eta(X)$ and $\eta^*(X)$ for F, η and η^* in the convexity inequality (8.5). Using the abbreviation (14.4) and the equation (14.14), we get

$$\varepsilon(X, \eta^*(X)) - \varepsilon(X, \eta(X)) - [\eta^*(X) - \eta(X)]\,\vartheta \geqq 0. \qquad (14.18)$$

This inequality must be strict for some X if η^* and η are different continuous functions. If ϑ is a constant and if (14.5) holds, then integration of (14.18) over the body $\mathscr{B}$ gives the inequality (14.6), which proves that $\{\boldsymbol{f}, \eta\}$ is thermally stable, *q.e.d.*

15. Mechanical stability

Consider a state $\{\boldsymbol{f}, \eta\}$ of a body $\mathscr{B}$. According to Postulate I of § 8 it is possible to find a temperature field ϑ and a stress field S such that every material point of $\mathscr{B}$ is in *thermal equilibrium* for the force temperature field defined by S and ϑ. In fact, S and ϑ are given by the stress relation (7.1) and the temperature relation (7.2), respectively. If a field of body forces $\boldsymbol{b}$ is given, then the state $\{\boldsymbol{f}, \eta\}$ will be a state of *mechanical equilibrium* if Cauchy's condition

$$\operatorname{Div} S + \varrho\,\boldsymbol{b} = 0 \qquad (15.1)$$

holds. If $\{\boldsymbol{f}, \eta\}$ is such that every material point is in thermal equilibrium, it is always possible to choose $\boldsymbol{b}$ such that the state $\{\boldsymbol{f}, \eta\}$ is a state of mechanical equilibrium. We need only to define $\boldsymbol{b}$ by (15.1). We say that the fields S, ϑ, and $\boldsymbol{b}$, given by (7.1), (7.2) and (15.1), make $\{\boldsymbol{f}, \eta\}$ a state of equilibrium. We call S, ϑ and $\boldsymbol{b}$, respectively, the stress, temperature, and body force fields of $\{\boldsymbol{f}, \eta\}$.

We investigate the possible meaning that can be given to the statement that an equilibrium state $\{\boldsymbol{f}, \eta\}$ is *stable*. First, we require that it be *thermally stable* which, according to Theorem 12, means that the temperature ϑ must be uniform. In addition, we require that some condition of *mechanical stability* be satisfied. One must distinguish between various types of *isothermal mechanical stability* and *adiabatic mechanical stability*.

In the case of isothermal mechanical stability, one compares the given equilibrium state $\{\boldsymbol{f}, \eta\}$ with a class of states $\{\boldsymbol{f}^*, \eta^*\}$ corresponding to the same uniform temperature $\vartheta = \hat{\vartheta}(F, \eta)$ as the given state. Each of these states is characterized by its configuration $\boldsymbol{f}^*$ alone, because the corresponding entropy distribution is then determined by

$$\eta = \tilde{\eta}(F^*, \vartheta). \qquad (15.2)$$

External forces or boundary conditions must be prescribed for each of the comparison configurations $\boldsymbol{f}^*$. The configuration $\boldsymbol{f}$ is called stable if the increase in the total free energy would always be greater than the work done on the body by the external forces if the configuration were to be deformed into any of the comparison configurations $\boldsymbol{f}^*$. We give more precise definitions in two special cases.

Definition of isothermal stability at fixed boundary (IFB stability). *An equilibrium state $\{\boldsymbol{f}, \eta\}$ is called* ***IFB stable*** *if $\{\boldsymbol{f}, \eta\}$ has a uniform temperature ϑ*

and if for every state $\{\boldsymbol{f}^*, \eta\}$ which satisfies the following conditions:

(a) $\boldsymbol{f}^*$ *lies in a prescribed neighborhood*[★] *of* $\boldsymbol{f}$,

(b) $\boldsymbol{f}^*(X) = \boldsymbol{f}(X)$, *when* X *belongs to* $\overline{\mathscr{B}}$, (15.3)

(c) *the temperature corresponding to* $\{\boldsymbol{f}^*, \eta\}$ *is equal to* ϑ *for all* X *in* $\mathscr{B}$,

the following inequality holds:

$$\int_{\mathscr{B}} \{\psi(F^*) - \psi(F) - \boldsymbol{b} \cdot (\boldsymbol{f}^* - \boldsymbol{f})\} \, dm \geqq 0. \tag{15.4}$$

Here $\overline{\mathscr{B}}$ is the boundary of $\mathscr{B}$, and $\psi(F)$ is an abbreviation for

$$\psi(F) = \tilde{\psi}(F(X), \vartheta; X); \tag{15.5}$$

$F^*(X)$ and $F(X)$ are the deformation gradients at X for the configurations $\boldsymbol{f}^*$ and $\boldsymbol{f}$, respectively, both computed relative to the same fixed reference configuration. As in § 14, we do not assume that the body is homogeneous, and hence the function $\tilde{\psi}$ may depend explicitly on X.

We say that $\{\boldsymbol{f}, \eta\}$ is *strictly* IFB *stable* if the inequality (15.4) is strict whenever $\{\boldsymbol{f}^*, \eta^*\}$ obeys (a), (b) and (c) and is such that $f^* \neq f$.

Note that the surface tractions do no work if the boundary is fixed and that $-\int_{\mathscr{B}} \boldsymbol{f}^* \cdot \boldsymbol{b} \, dm$ is a potential of the work done by the body forces if these are held at their values $\boldsymbol{b}(X)$ in the equilibrium state $\{\boldsymbol{f}, \eta\}$.

The type of stability considered is affected by the prescription of the neighborhood in the requirement (a) of the definition of IFB stability. A global state may be stable with respect to some (small) neighborhood without being stable with respect to other (larger) neighborhoods.

Definition of isothermal stability at fixed surface tractions (IFT stability). *An equilibrium state* $\{\boldsymbol{f}, \eta\}$ *is called* ***IFT stable*** *if* $\{\boldsymbol{f}, \eta\}$ *has a uniform temperature* ϑ *and if for every state* $\{\boldsymbol{f}^*, \eta\}$ *which satisfies the following conditions:*

(a) $\boldsymbol{f}^*$ *lies in a prescribed neighborhood of* $\boldsymbol{f}$,

(b) *the temperature corresponding to* $\{\boldsymbol{f}^*, \eta\}$ *is equal to* ϑ *for all* X *in* $\mathscr{B}$,

the following inequality holds:

$$\Gamma = \int_{\mathscr{B}} \{\psi(F^*) - \psi(F) - \boldsymbol{b} \cdot (\boldsymbol{f}^* - \boldsymbol{f})\} \, dm - \int_{\overline{\mathscr{B}}} (\boldsymbol{f}^* - \boldsymbol{f}) \cdot S \boldsymbol{n} \, dA \geqq 0. \tag{15.6}$$

Here $\overline{\mathscr{B}}$ is the boundary surface of the region occupied by $\mathscr{B}$ in the configuration $\boldsymbol{f}$; dA is the element of that surface; and $\boldsymbol{n}$ is the exterior unit normal.

Note that $-\int_{\overline{\mathscr{B}}} \boldsymbol{f}^* \cdot S \boldsymbol{n} \, dA$ is a potential of the work done by the surface tractions if they are held at their values in the equilibrium state $\{\boldsymbol{f}, \eta\}$.

An IFT stable state is always also IFB stable. This follows from the fact that the surface integral in (15.6) gives no contribution if the boundary condition (15.3) holds, so that the inequalities (15.4) and (15.6) become the same in this case.

[★] A neighborhood of a configuration is defined by the metric

$$\delta(\boldsymbol{f}, \boldsymbol{f}^*) = \sup_{X \in \mathscr{B}} \{|\boldsymbol{f}^*(X) - \boldsymbol{f}(X)| + |F^{*-1}(X) F(X) - I|\}$$

over the space of all configurations.

If the inequality (15.6) holds for all states which obey items (a) and (b) of the definition of IFT stability and is, furthermore, a strict inequality for all such states for which $F^*(X) \neq F(X)$ for at least one material point X, then we say that $\{\boldsymbol{f}, \eta\}$ is *strictly* IFT *stable against deformations and rotations.* For in that case (15.6) can reduce to an equality only if $\boldsymbol{f}^*$ is related to $\boldsymbol{f}$ by a simple rigid translation.

To investigate adiabatic mechanical stability, one compares the given equilibrium state $\{\boldsymbol{f}, \eta\}$ with a class of states which correspond to the same total entropy as $\{\boldsymbol{f}, \eta\}$. We again consider two special cases.

Definition of adiabatic stability at fixed boundary (AFB stability). *An equilibrium state $\{\boldsymbol{f}, \eta\}$ is called* ***AFB stable*** *if $\{\boldsymbol{f}, \eta\}$ is thermally stable and if for every state $\{\boldsymbol{f}^*, \eta^*\}$ which satisfies the following conditions:*

(a) *$\boldsymbol{f}^*$ lies in a prescribed neighborhood of $\boldsymbol{f}$,*

(b) *$\boldsymbol{f}^*(X) = \boldsymbol{f}(X)$, when X belongs to $\overline{\mathscr{B}}$,*

(c) $\int_{\mathscr{B}} \eta^*(X)\, dm = \int_{\mathscr{B}} \eta(X)\, dm,$

the following inequality holds:

$$\int_{\mathscr{B}} \{\hat{\varepsilon}\,[F^*(X), \eta^*(X); X] - \hat{\varepsilon}\,[F(X), \eta(X); X] - \boldsymbol{b} \cdot (\boldsymbol{f}^* - \boldsymbol{f})\}\, dm \geqq 0. \tag{15.7}$$

If the inequality in (15.7) is strict for all $\{\boldsymbol{f}^*, \eta^*\}$ satisfying (a), (b) and (c) and for which $\boldsymbol{f}^* \neq \boldsymbol{f}$, then we say that $\{\boldsymbol{f}, \eta\}$ is *strictly* AFB *stable.*

Theorem 13. *A thermally stable equilibrium state $\{\boldsymbol{f}, \eta\}$ is AFB stable if and only if for every state $\{\boldsymbol{f}^*, \eta^*\}$ which satisfies the following conditions:*

(a) *$\boldsymbol{f}^*$ lies in a prescribed neighborhood of $\boldsymbol{f}$,*

(b) *$\boldsymbol{f}^*(X) = \boldsymbol{f}(X)$ when X belongs to $\overline{\mathscr{B}}$,*

(c) $\int_{\mathscr{B}} \{\hat{\varepsilon}(F^*(X), \eta^*(X); X) - \boldsymbol{b} \cdot \boldsymbol{f}^*\}\, dm = \int_{\mathscr{B}} \{\hat{\varepsilon}(F(X), \eta(X); X) - \boldsymbol{b} \cdot \boldsymbol{f}\}\, dm, \quad (15.8)$

the following inequality holds:

$$\int_{\mathscr{B}} \eta^*(X)\, dm \leqq \int_{\mathscr{B}} \eta(X)\, dm. \tag{15.9}$$

Furthermore, $\{\boldsymbol{f}, \eta\}$ is strictly AFB stable if and only if (15.9) *is a strict inequality for every state $\{\boldsymbol{f}^*, \eta^*\} \neq \{\boldsymbol{f}, \eta\}$ obeying* (a), (b) *and* (c).

We omit the proof of Theorem 13 because it is analogous to that of Theorem 11. Of course, the validity of Theorem 13 requires the assumption of Postulate II.

Definition of adiabatic stability at fixed surface tractions (AFT stability). *An equilibrium state $\{\boldsymbol{f}, \eta\}$ is called* ***AFT stable*** *if it is thermally stable and if for every state $\{\boldsymbol{f}^*, \eta^*\}$ which satisfies the following conditions:*

(a) *$\boldsymbol{f}^*$ is in a prescribed neighborhood of $\boldsymbol{f}$,*

(b) $\int_{\mathscr{B}} \eta^*(X)\, dm = \int_{\mathscr{B}} \eta(X)\, dm,$

the following inequality holds:

$$\int_{\mathscr{B}} \{\hat{\varepsilon}[F^*(X), \eta^*(X); X] - \hat{\varepsilon}[F(X), \eta(X); X] - \boldsymbol{b} \cdot (\boldsymbol{f}^* - \boldsymbol{f})\}\, dm - \int_{\overline{\mathscr{B}}} (\boldsymbol{f}^* - \boldsymbol{f}) \cdot S\, \boldsymbol{n}\, dA \geqq 0. \tag{15.10}$$

It will be noticed that a state which is AFT stable is always AFB stable.

If the inequality (15.10) holds for all states which obey (a) and (b) and is a strict inequality for all such states for which $F^*(X) \neq F(X)$ for at least one X, then we say that $\{\boldsymbol{f}, \eta\}$ is *strictly* AFT *stable against deformations and rotations.*

It is clear that, in analogy to Theorem 13, an alternative, but equivalent, definition of AFT stability can be formulated in which a stable state is defined to be one of maximum entropy among all those states for which (15.10) reduces to an equality.

The definitions of IFB, IFT, AFB and AFT stability given above are applicable only to those physical situations in which the body force field $\boldsymbol{b} = \boldsymbol{b}(X)$ is independent of the comparison configuration $\boldsymbol{f}^*$. If one is interested in studying cases in which the body force on X depends on X and is also a functional of $\boldsymbol{f}^*$, one can modify the definitions of stability by connecting the comparison state $\boldsymbol{f}^*$ to $\boldsymbol{f}$ by means of a continuous one-parameter family $\boldsymbol{f}_s$, $0 \leqq s \leqq 1$, $\boldsymbol{f}_0 = \boldsymbol{f}$, $\boldsymbol{f}_1 = \boldsymbol{f}^*$ and replacing the term

$$-\int_{\mathscr{B}} \boldsymbol{b} \cdot (\boldsymbol{f}^* - \boldsymbol{f})\, dm$$

in (15.4), (15.6), (15.7), (15.8) and (15.10) by

$$-\int_{\mathscr{B}} \int_0^1 \boldsymbol{b}(X, \boldsymbol{f}_s) \cdot \frac{\partial \boldsymbol{f}_s(X)}{\partial s}\, ds\, dm.$$

If the body force on each material point is derivable from a single-valued potential, then the integral exhibited above is independent of the paramatization, and is simply the difference in the potentials at $\boldsymbol{f}$ and $\boldsymbol{f}^*$.

In the definitions of IFT and AFT stability, we assumed that not only the body forces but also the contact forces at the surface do not depend on the comparison configuration. One can also study, in a way analogous to that outlined above for the body forces, those cases in which the surface tractions depend on the comparison configuration.

Theorem 14. *A state which has isothermal stability of a certain type also has adiabatic stability of the corresponding type.*

Proof. Consider a state $\{\boldsymbol{f}, \eta\}$ which has a uniform temperature ϑ and which has isothermal stability of a particular type. Let $\boldsymbol{f}^*$ be a configuration which satisfies the boundary conditions, if any, for the appropriate comparison configurations. Define the entropy field η_1 by

$$\eta_1(X) = \tilde{\eta}\left(F^*(X), \vartheta\right), \tag{15.11}$$

where F^* is the deformation gradient field corresponding to the configuration $\boldsymbol{f}^*$. By (13.1) we have

$$\tilde{\psi}(F^*, \vartheta) - \tilde{\psi}(F, \vartheta) = \hat{\varepsilon}(F^*, \eta_1) - \hat{\varepsilon}(F, \eta) - (\eta_1 - \eta)\, \vartheta. \tag{15.12}$$

Here F corresponds to $\boldsymbol{f}$. Let η^* be any entropy distribution satisfying the condition

$$\int_{\mathscr{B}} \eta^*(X)\, dm = \int_{\mathscr{B}} \eta(X)\, dm, \tag{15.13}$$

which is required for comparison states in adiabatic stability. Define the field β by

$$\beta = \hat{\varepsilon}(F^*, \eta^*) - \hat{\varepsilon}(F^*, \eta_1) - (\eta^* - \eta_1)\, \vartheta. \tag{15.14}$$

From (8.5) we get

$$\beta(X) \geqq 0$$

for all X. From (15.12) we have

$$\tilde{\psi}(F^*, \vartheta) - \tilde{\psi}(F, \vartheta) = \hat{\varepsilon}(F^*, \eta^*) - \hat{\varepsilon}(F, \eta) - \beta - (\eta^* - \eta)\vartheta. \tag{15.15}$$

We integrate (15.15) over $\mathscr{B}$. According to (15.13) we get no contribution from the term $-(\eta^*-\eta)\vartheta$; hence, since β is non-negative,

$$\int_{\mathscr{B}} [\tilde{\psi}(F^*, \vartheta) - \tilde{\psi}(F, \vartheta)]\, dm \leqq \int_{\mathscr{B}} [\hat{\varepsilon}(F^*, \eta^*) - \hat{\varepsilon}(F, \eta)]\, dm. \tag{15.16}$$

Since the work W done by the external forces in going from $\boldsymbol{f}$ to $\boldsymbol{f}^*$ is the same in adiabatic and isothermal stability, it follows from (15.16) that if

$$\int_{\mathscr{B}} [\tilde{\psi}(F^*, \vartheta) - \tilde{\psi}(F, \vartheta)]\, dm - W \tag{15.17}$$

is non-negative, then

$$\int_{\mathscr{B}} [\hat{\varepsilon}(F^*, \eta^*) - \hat{\varepsilon}(F, \eta)]\, dm - W \tag{15.18}$$

is non-negative (and strictly positive when (15.17) is strictly positive). Hence, the isothermal stability of $\{\boldsymbol{f}, \eta\}$ implies the corresponding adiabatic stability for $\{\boldsymbol{f}, \eta\}$, *q.e.d.*

Although in writing our proof of Theorem 14 we have used a notation which implies that $\mathscr{B}$ is homogeneous, it is clear that the same argument is valid when $\mathscr{B}$ is not homogeneous.

It appears to us that the converse of Theorem 14 need not be true; *i.e.*, an equilibrium state may have adiabatic stability without being isothermally stable.

16. Gibbs' thermostatics of fluids

We now consider a type of stability which was proposed by GIBBS* for fluids free from body forces. GIBBS states** that he had in mind a physical situation in which the fluid is "enclosed in a rigid envelop which is non-conducting to heat and impermeable to all the components of the fluid". A body which may be regarded as being in such an envelop is usually called an "isolated system".

Definition of G stability*.** *An equilibrium state $\{\boldsymbol{f}, \eta\}$ of a fluid body $\mathscr{B}$ is called* ***G stable*** *if the following condition is satisfied. Let $\{\boldsymbol{f}^*, \eta^*\}$ be any other state with the same total volume and the same total entropy as $\{\boldsymbol{f}, \eta\}$,*

$$\int_{\mathscr{B}} v^*\, dm = \int_{\mathscr{B}} v\, dm, \qquad \int_{\mathscr{B}} \eta^*\, dm = \int_{\mathscr{B}} \eta\, dm, \tag{16.1}$$

---

* See the section of [*1*] which is entitled "Internal stability of homogeneous fluids as indicated by the fundamental equations", (b), pp. 100—115, particularly the subsection entitled "Stability with respect to continuous changes of phase" (b), pp. 105—111.

** [*1*] (b), p. 100.

*** In this definition we again restrict ourselves to those physical situations in which fluctuations in chemical composition are surpressed. We have in mind situations in which chemical reactions are prohibited and in which the fluid is either homogeneous or does not allow diffusion. For fluids the homogeneous case is the one of practical importance. Situations in which flow is permitted but diffusion is prohibited are rare.

then $\{\boldsymbol{f}, \eta\}$ *has a lower total internal energy than* $\{\boldsymbol{f}^*, \eta^*\}$,

$$\int_{\mathscr{B}} \bar{\varepsilon}\left[v^*(X), \eta^*(X); X\right] dm > \int_{\mathscr{B}} \bar{\varepsilon}\left[v(X), \eta(X); X\right] dm, \qquad (16.2)$$

unless $v^*(X) = v(X)$ *and* $\eta^*(X) = \eta(X)$ *for all* X *in* $\mathscr{B}$.

In (16.1) v and v^* denote the specific volume fields for $\mathscr{B}$ corresponding to the configurations $\boldsymbol{f}$ and $\boldsymbol{f}^*$.

In the following alternative definition $\boldsymbol{f}$ and ε are taken as the independent variables, and the permitted comparison states are such that the total internal energy and total volume of the body are conserved during the variations. This alternative formulation may suggest to the reader why G stability is regarded as being appropriate for discussing the physics of *isolated systems* composed of fluids:

Alternative definition of G stability. *An equilibrium state* $\{\boldsymbol{f}, \varepsilon\}$ *of a fluid body* $\mathscr{B}$ *is called G stable if any other state* $\{\boldsymbol{f}^*, \varepsilon^*\}$ *with the same total volume and the same total internal energy as* $\{\boldsymbol{f}, \varepsilon\}$,

$$\int_{\mathscr{B}} v^*\, dm = \int_{\mathscr{B}} v\, dm, \qquad \int_{\mathscr{B}} \varepsilon^*\, dm = \int_{\mathscr{B}} \varepsilon\, dm, \qquad (16.3)$$

has a higher total entropy,

$$\int_{\mathscr{B}} \hat{\bar{\eta}}\left[v^*(X), \varepsilon^*(X); X\right] dm < \int_{\mathscr{B}} \hat{\bar{\eta}}\left[v(X), \varepsilon(X); X\right] dm, \qquad (16.4)$$

unless $v^*(X) = v(X)$ *and* $\varepsilon^*(X) = \varepsilon(X)$ *for all* X *in* $\mathscr{B}$.

The function $\hat{\bar{\eta}}$ in (16.4) is obtained by solving $\varepsilon = \bar{\varepsilon}(v, \eta; X)$ for η, which is possible in a unique way because $\bar{\varepsilon}$ is strictly increasing in η.

The proof of the equivalence of the two definitions of G stability is analogous to the one given for Theorem 11 of § 14 in the case of thermal stability; one must again use Postulate II of § 8.

The main result of this section is

Theorem 15. *An equilibrium state* $\{\boldsymbol{f}, \eta\}$ *of a fluid body is G stable if and only if its temperature and pressure are uniform.*

Proof. To prove that the condition is necessary we observe that the functions v, η are solutions of the variational problem

$$\int_{\mathscr{B}} \bar{\varepsilon}(v^*, \eta^*; X)\, dm = \text{Minimum} \qquad (16.5)$$

subject to the constraints (16.1). Therefore, the first variation of

$$\int_{\mathscr{B}} \left[\bar{\varepsilon}(v^*, \eta^*; X) - \lambda \eta^* - \mu v^*\right] dm$$

must vanish for $v^* = v$ and $\eta^* = \eta$. Here λ and μ are constant Lagrange parameters. It follows that

$$\bar{\varepsilon}_\eta(v, \eta; X) = \lambda = \text{constant}, \qquad \bar{\varepsilon}_v(v, \eta; X) = \mu = \text{constant}. \qquad (16.6)$$

Hence, by (8.2) and (11.11), both the temperature, $\vartheta = \bar{\varepsilon}_\eta(v, \eta; X)$, and the pressure, $p = -\bar{\varepsilon}_v(v, \eta; X)$ are uniform over $\mathscr{B}$.

To prove the sufficiency of the condition of the theorem, we assume that ϑ and p are uniform and that (16.1) holds. From the convexity inequality (11.16), the inequality (11.9), and the fact that $v = \nu^3$, $\nu > 0$, is a convex function of ν, one can easily infer that $\bar{\varepsilon}(v, \eta)$ must be convex in v and η. Hence, the inequality

$$\bar{\varepsilon}(v^*, \eta^*; X) - \bar{\varepsilon}(v^*, \eta; X) - (v^* - v)\,\bar{\varepsilon}_v(v, \eta; X) - (\eta^* - \eta)\,\bar{\varepsilon}_\eta(v, \eta; X) \geqq 0 \quad (16.7)$$

is valid at all material points X in $\mathscr{B}$; (16.7) cannot reduce to an equality for all X unless $v(X) = v^*(X)$ and $\eta(X) = \eta^*(X)$ for all X. Since $p = -\varepsilon_v(v, \eta)$ and $\vartheta = \bar{\varepsilon}_\eta(v, \eta)$ are independent of X, integration of (16.7) over $\mathscr{B}$ gives

$$\int_{\mathscr{B}} \{\bar{\varepsilon}(v^*, \eta^*; X) - \bar{\varepsilon}(v, \eta; X)\}\,dm + p \int_{\mathscr{B}} (v^* - v)\,dm - \vartheta \int_{\mathscr{B}} (\eta^* - \eta)\,dm > 0.$$

The condition (16.1) states that the last two terms vanish and hence that (16.2) holds, q.e.d.

In his discussion of the stability of homogeneous fluids, Gibbs used a definition of stability which is identical to what we have called G stability, except that he did not demand, as we do, that $\{\boldsymbol{f}, \eta\}$ be an equilibrium state*. Gibbs was able to prove that uniform values of $\bar{\varepsilon}_\eta(v, \eta)$ and $\bar{\varepsilon}_v(v, \eta)$ are necessary for his stability and, furthermore, that the inequality (16.7) is also necessary. He also realized that the constancy of $\bar{\varepsilon}_\eta$ and $\bar{\varepsilon}_v$ over $\mathscr{B}$ and the validity of (16.7) are sufficient for his stability. If he had gone a step further and postulated that for homogeneous fluids stable states exist for every value of v and η for which $\bar{\varepsilon}$ is defined, he would have obtained (16.7) as a property of the function $\bar{\varepsilon}$. Such a procedure, however, cannot yield the statements, made in Theorem 6, that $-\bar{\varepsilon}_v$ is positive and that $\bar{\bar{\varepsilon}}$ is jointly and strictly convex in ν and η.

We conclude with

Theorem 16. *An equilibrium state $\{\boldsymbol{f}, \eta\}$ of a fluid body $\mathscr{B}$ is G stable if and only if both of the following conditions hold:*

(a) *The temperature corresponding to $\{\boldsymbol{f}, \eta\}$ is uniform.*

(b) *Any other state $\{\boldsymbol{f}^*, \eta^*\}$ with the same total volume,*

$$\int_{\mathscr{B}} v^*\,dm = \int_{\mathscr{B}} v\,dm, \quad (16.8)$$

and the same uniform temperature ϑ has a higher total free energy,

$$\int_{\mathscr{B}} \bar{\psi}(v^*, \vartheta; X)\,dm > \int_{\mathscr{B}} \bar{\psi}(v, \vartheta; X)\,dm, \quad (16.9)$$

unless $v^*(X) = v(X)$ for all X in $\mathscr{B}$.

Proof. The proof that the conditions (a) and (b) are sufficient for the G stability of $\{\boldsymbol{f}, \eta\}$ is completely analogous to the proof of Theorem 14 of § 15.

The necessity of the condition (a) for the G stability of $\{\boldsymbol{f}, \eta\}$ follows from Theorem 15. To prove that (b) is necessary we assume that $\{\boldsymbol{f}, \eta\}$ is stable. We consider another state $\{\boldsymbol{f}^*, \eta^*\}$ which obeys (16.8) and which has the uniform temperature ϑ. Since $v = \nu^3$ is a convex function of ν for $\nu > 0$, and $\bar{\psi}_v(v, \vartheta) < 0$, the inequality (13.15) implies that

$$\bar{\psi}(v^*, \vartheta; X) - \bar{\psi}(v, \vartheta; X) - (v^* - v)\,\bar{\psi}_v(v, \vartheta; X) \geqq 0; \quad (16.10)$$

---

* Gibbs does not use either our Postulate I or our definition of (local) thermal equilibrium.

(16.10) cannot reduce to equality for all X unless $v(X)=v^*(X)$ for all X. Now, since we are assuming that $\{\boldsymbol{f},\eta\}$ is stable, it follows from Theorem 15 and (13.13) that $\bar{\bar{\psi}}_v(v,\vartheta;X)$ is independent of X. Thus, by (16.8), if we compute the mass integral of (16.10) over $\mathscr{B}$, the last term on the left makes no contribution, and we get (16.9). Hence, when $\{\boldsymbol{f},\eta\}$ is G stable, the condition (b) is valid, q.e.d.

This theorem shows that for G stability of fluids adiabatic and isothermal stability are equivalent.

Acknowledgement. This research was supported in part by the Air Force Office of Scientific Research under Contract AF 49(638)-541 with the Mellon Institute and by the National Science Foundation under Grant NSF-G 5250 to Carnegie Institute of Technology.

References

[1] (a) GIBBS, J. W.: On the equilibrium of heterogeneous substances. Trans. Conn. Acad. **3**, 108—248, 343—524 (1875—1878), or (b) The Scientific Papers of J. WILLARD GIBBS **1**, 55—372, particularly 55—62 and 100—115, Longmans, Green, 1906.

[2] DUHEM, P.: Dissolutions et Mélanges. Travaux et Mémoires des Facultés de Lille **3**, No. 2, 1—136 (1893).

[3] TRUESDELL, C.: Das ungelöste Hauptproblem der endlichen Elastizitätstheorie. Z. angew. Math. u. Mech. **36**, 97—103 (1956).

[4] HADAMARD, J.: Leçons sur la Propagation des Ondes et les Équations de l'Hydrodynamique. Paris 1903.

[5] ERICKSEN, J. L., & R. A. TOUPIN: Implications of Hadamard's condition for elastic stability with respect to uniqueness theorems. Can. J. Math. **8**, 432—436 (1956).

[6] DUHEM, P.: Recherches sur l'élasticité. Troisième partie. La stabilité des milieux élastiques. Ann. École Norm. (3) **22**, 143—217 (1905).

[7] NOLL, W.: A mathematical theory of the mechanical behavior of continuous media. Arch. Rat. Mech. Anal. **2**, 197—226 (1958).

[8] NOLL, W.: The fundations of classical mechanics in the light of recent advances in continuum mechanics. Proceedings of the Berkeley Symposium on the Axiomatic Method, 266—281, 1959.

[9] TRUESDELL, C.: The mechanical foundations of elasticity and fluid dynamics. J. Rat. Mech. Anal. **1**, 125—300 (1952); **2**, 593—616 (1953).

[10] NOLL, W.: On the continuity of the solid and fluid states. J. Rat. Mech. Anal. **4**, 3—81 (1955).

[11] RAMSEY, N. F.: Thermodynamics and statistical mechanics at negative absolute temperatures. Phys. Rev. **103**, 20—28 (1956).

[12] COLEMAN, B. D., & W. NOLL: Conditions for equilibrium at negative absolute temperatures. Phys. Rev. **115**, 262—265 (1959).

[13] BAKER, M., & J. L. ERICKSEN: Inequalities restricting the form of the stress-deformation relations for isotropic elastic solids and Reiner-Rivlin fluids. J. Washington Acad. Sciences **44**, 33—35 (1954).

[14] BARTA, J.: On the non-linear elasticity law. Acta Tech. Acad. Scient. Hungaricae **18**, 55—65 (1957).

[15] HILL, R.: On uniqueness and stability in the theory of finite elastic strain. J. Mech. Phys. Solids **5**, 229—241 (1957).

Mellon Institute
Pittsburgh, Pennsylvania
and
Carnegie Institute of Technology
Pittsburgh, Pennsylvania

(Received August 24, 1959)

Druck der Universitätsdruckerei H. Stürtz AG., Würzburg

No. 12

GENERAL CONTINUUM THEORY OF DISLOCATIONS AND INITIAL STRESSES

E. Kröner

(Allgemeine Kontinuumstheorie der Versetzungen und Eigenspannungen), Archive for Rational Mechanics and Analysis, Vol. 4, pp. 273-334 (1960).

Appendix: **Remark on the fundamental geometric law of the general continuum theory of dislocations and initial stresses** (Bemerkungen zum geometrischen Grundgesetz der allgemeinen Kontinuumstheorie der Versetzungen und der Eigenspannungen), Archive for Rational Mechanics and Analysis, Vol. 7, pp. 78-80 (1961).

The treatise here reprinted was awarded a prize by the German Physical Society. It arises from a stream of influence previously distinct from the others represented in this volume, namely, solid-state physics and, in particular, molecular studies of lattice defects in crystals. In this stream a material is viewed alternatively as an assembly of little balls (atoms) or as a continuum having a peculiar non-Euclidean geometry. Motivation for the basic assumptions of the continuum theory is found in the ball model. The present essay attempts to bring the older theories of KONDO, BILBY, and others into a mathematically exact form "in which the usual methods of non-linear continuum mechanics are taken over so far as possible."

While of course the continuum is visualized as smooth and capable of smooth deformation, the gradient of the deformation carrying the body from one of its configurations to another does not alone determine the stress, in general. This fact lies behind the introduction of affine transformations of differential elements in Section 4; we are to presume that the stress is related to these transformations, which generally fail to correspond to point deformations. The particular geometric structure assumed in Section 8 is so formed as to include all earlier work along the same lines and thus to share its motivation.

As is common in works on dislocation theory, stress functions are introduced in Section 10. These functions are considered especially convenient for calculations in cases when the elastic strain is incompatible. Some of the formulae are valid in all continuous media (cf. CFT, Sections 224-230) and thus fail to show any special properties of the present theory; others rest on linearized elasticity theory and thus introduce specializing assumptions beyond those of the general theory outlined earlier.

The rest of the paper discusses physical properties of materials and special assumptions related to them.

While great attention is given to the geometry of deformation, constitutive equations for a medium affected by dislocations are mentioned only in passing. In this respect, the present essay leaves open a number of questions the answers to which would set the continuum theory of dislocations in its place within continuum mechanics as a whole. Progress in this direction has been made by NOLL in NFTM, Sections 34 and 44. Namely, NOLL shows that if a simple material (RMM, No. 12) is inhomogeneous but materially uniform, then the geometric structure assumed by KRÖNER necessarily exists. That is, the geometrical postulates of KRÖNER's theory are **proved to follow from** the general constitutive equations for the particles making up the simple body. However, in Section 9 of the paper here translated KRÖNER expresses the opinion that couple stresses as introduced by the brothers COSSERAT (cf. MF, Section 26, footnote 7, and CFT, Sections 200-205) will arise in response to dislocations. The theory of materials with couple stresses, necessarily non-simple, has not yet been developed sufficiently to provide a starting point for work aiming to include within the structure of modern continuum mechanics all current ideas about dislocations.

Allgemeine Kontinuumstheorie der Versetzungen und Eigenspannungen

Ekkehart Kröner

Vorgelegt von J. Meixner

Inhalt

This work* is both a review of the present day situation of the general non-linear continuum theory of stationary dislocations and internal stresses and a presentation of new results in that field.

By the *general* theory we mean the theory of a continuum, the deformed state of which is described by 15 functions of position and time (theory of 15 degrees of freedom). Developing further the views of Günther, one has to look at such a continuum

* Habilitationsschrift zur Erlangung der Lehrberechtigung für *Theoretische Physik* an der Technischen Hochschule Stuttgart.

as a generalization of the Cosserat continuum (6 degrees of freedom) the state of which is characterized by elastic displacements (3) and independent elastic rotations (3) of the geometric structure (in the case of crystals: of the lattice structure). Instead of displacements and rotations one can use in the geometric description also elastic deformations and structure curvatures, both of which have tensor character. The extension of the Cosserat theory, leading to the general theory, implies that both the deformations and the curvatures become incompatible, *i.e.*, the possibility of deriving them from displacement and rotation fields is abandoned. The number of degrees of freedom increases to $6+9=15$. The connection with dislocation theory and with general differential geometry follows from the fact that the dislocation density is equivalent on one hand with the Cosserat structure curvatures (NYE, GÜNTHER), on the other hand with CARTAN'S torsion (KONDO; BILBY, BULLOUGH & SMITH).

Instead of the geometric characterization of the state, it is possible to employ a static description, which likewise needs 15 functions: 6 functions for the (force-) stresses, 9 for what are called Cosserat torque stresses. It is shown in the present work that torque stresses enable us to describe the *microscopically* fluctuating stresses of macroscopically continuous distributions of dislocations in a *macroscopic* way. When the constitutive law connecting stresses and torque stresses with deformations and curvatures is known, the geometric and static functions can be converted into each other.

The geometric part of the theory, given in Chapter II, is the main part of the present work. First of all we give the theory in a new elementary form in which the usual methods of non-linear continuum mechanics are taken over so far as possible. The concepts developed in the linear continuum theory of dislocations and internal stresses are completely incorporated within this non-linear form. Secondly we give a presentation of the theory based on differential geometry which partly follows the ideas developed by KONDO and by BILBY, BULLOUGH & SMITH. However, we go further in the physical interpretation. The general (incompatible) Cosserat continuum proves to be identical with a medium the geometric state of which is described by the general Riemann-Cartan (= metric) affine connexion Γ_{mlk} (15 degrees of freedom). A new feature is the introduction of the "matter tensor" which forms the right-hand side of the "Einstein equations of continuum mechanics", the generalization of the de St. Venant compatibility equations. The symmetric part of the matter tensor describes the inserted foreign matter (in crystals, *e.g.* distributions of interstitial atoms) whereas the antisymmetric part characterizes some kind of rotation matter which is connected with the ending of dislocations inside the body.

If torque stresses are neglected, the integration of the Einstein equations leads to the determination of the state, given the actions (*e.g.*, forces, dislocations, *etc.*). In the non-linear theory, also, the most important resource for the integration is the stress function tensor. The non-linear integration problem can be linearized by an iteration procedure. The resulting linear summation problem has been solved previously and will be briefly described. In Chapter III we discuss in more detail the second boundary value problem. The usefulness of SCHAEFER'S stress functions is demonstrated by the example of a body bounded by two infinite parallel planes: It is possible to reduce this problem for any distributions of surface forces to a pair of standard problems, one of potential theory and the other of bi-potential theory.

Chapter IV contains an elementary account of the previously sketched concept of a para and dia-elastic continuum which has practical importance for solid state physics. The lattice defects appearing macroscopically as point defects can be characterized mechanically to a large extent as elastic dipoles (double forces) or polarizable substances. Very general and simple formulae hold for the potential energy of these defects in an elastic field and for the forces and torques exerted on the defect by the fields.

In the discussion at the end of this work we point out the intimate relations to general theory of relativity. It is hoped that they will have favorable effects on the further development of both theories.

I. Einleitung und Übersicht

Der Aufgabenkreis, der von der Kontinuumsmechanik des festen Körpers bewältigt wird oder zumindest bewältigt werden sollte, hat sich in den letzten dreißig Jahren außerordentlich erweitert. Dies ist in erster Linie mit dem gewaltigen Aufstieg der Festkörperphysik zu demjenigen Zweig der Physik zu erklären, der heute neben der Kernphysik mit dem größten Aufwand betrieben wird. Der Aufschwung der Festkörperphysik begann in den frühen zwanziger Jahren, als man gelernt hatte, Kristalle einheitlicher Gitterorientierung (Einkristalle) zu züchten, und erkannte, daß man zuerst die Eigenschaften dieser Einkristalle zu erforschen hatte, bevor an ein Verständnis der normalerweise im vielkristallinen Zustand vorliegenden Gebrauchswerkstoffe zu denken war.

Einige wichtige Stationen auf diesem Wege, die vor allem vom mechanischen Standpunkt interessant sind, mögen genannt werden:

a) Die theoretische Berechnung der kritischen Schubspannung des *idealen* Kristalls durch FRENKEL (1926) [*1*], die sich nach SCHMID und POLANYI (1929) [*2*] selbst bei sehr tiefen Temperaturen um mehr als drei Zehnerpotenzen größer als die experimentell an *realen* Kristallen gemessene kritische Schubspannung erwies.

b) Die Überlegungen von DEHLINGER [*3*] über die Wirkung der Kristallbaufehler als Eigenspannungsquellen (1929). Es wurde damals erst klar, warum in einem Kristall überhaupt Eigenspannungen möglich sind.

c) Die Einführung des Versetzungsbegriffs in die Theorie der plastischen Verformung durch TAYLOR, OROWAN und POLANYI (1934) [*4—6*], die sich als ungewöhnlich fruchtbar erwiesen hat und als ersten großen Erfolg die Beseitigung der oben erwähnten Schwierigkeiten mit der kritischen Schubspannung brachte.

d) Die elastizitätstheoretische Behandlung der singulären Versetzung durch BURGERS (1939) [*7*], die zu einer mathematisch einwandfreien Definition der Versetzung führte.

e) Die Schaffung der Kontinuumstheorie der Versetzungen und Eigenspannungen durch die Arbeiten mehrerer Autoren, die im folgenden zu nennen sein werden. Wie früher ausgeführt wurde [*8*], soll diese Theorie die zwischen der Elastizitätstheorie und der phänomenologischen Plastizitätstheorie klaffende Lücke schließen und gleichzeitig die Brücke zwischen der letztgenannten Theorie und der in der Festkörperphysik so wichtigen *atomistischen* Plastizitätstheorie darstellen.

Die fundamentale Bedeutung der Kristallbaufehler (Gitterfehler) im festen Körper ist heute allgemein anerkannt. Von den vielen sich im festen Zustand abspielenden Vorgängen mit Materietransport — z.B. Phasenumwandlungen, Ausscheidungen, plastische Verformung, Diffusion u. v. a. — gibt es keinen einzigen, der ohne Beteiligung irgendwelcher Gitterfehler ablaufen könnte. Die Rolle der Gitterfehler besteht dabei kurz gesagt in folgendem (vgl. z.B. DEHLINGER [*9*]):

Nur unter Mitwirkung der Gitterfehler können die genannten Vorgänge als Reaktionen niedriger Ordnung ablaufen, und nur deshalb können sie überhaupt stattfinden. Sie gehen dann so vor sich, daß die freie Energie möglichst erniedrigt wird. Nun macht die Energie der inneren Spannungsfelder einen sehr wesentlichen, ja oft geradezu den entscheidenden Anteil an der freien Energie aus, und die Quellen der inneren Spannungsfelder sind gerade die Gitterfehler. Daher geben diese nicht nur Anlaß zu mehr oder weniger starken elektrischen bzw. magnetischen Wirkungen, sondern auch zu sehr bedeutsamen mechanischen Effekten.

Im Zuge der oben skizzierten Entwicklung stellte sich heraus, daß die Kontinuumsmechanik des Festkörpers in ihrem früheren Umfang d.h. mit ihren Zweigen Elastizitätstheorie und phänomenologische Plastizitätstheorie, den neuen Anforderungen bei weitem nicht gewachsen war. Die wichtigsten, in der Kontinuumsmechanik des Festkörpers immer wieder auftretenden Probleme sind vorwiegend von einem der folgenden drei Typen:

(1) Gegeben irgendwelche äußere Einwirkungen auf den Körper (Kräfte, Drehmomente, Temperaturschwankungen usw.) als Funktionen des Ortes und der Zeit, gesucht der Zustand des Körpers, ebenfalls als Funktion des Ortes und der Zeit.

(2) Gegeben eine Quellenverteilung von Eigenspannungen — z.B. die Versetzungsdichte mit dem Grenzfall der singulären Versetzung — gesucht der Zustand des Körpers (etwa charakterisiert durch die Eigenspannungen, Gitterkrümmungen und elastische Energie).

(3) Gegeben ein elastisches Feld in einem Körper, gesucht die elastische Energie eines bestimmten Gitterfehlers in diesem Feld bzw. die von dem Feld auf diesen Gitterfehler ausgeübte Kraft. Hierzu gehören auch die gegenseitigen Kraftwirkungen zwischen Gitterfehlern.

Aufgabe (1) verlangt die Heranziehung aller drei unter e) genannten Zweige der Kontinuumsmechanik des Festkörpers und ist heute nur in Spezialfällen streng lösbar. Die Aufgaben (3) und insbesondere (2), die typisch für die Kontinuumstheorie der Versetzungen und Eigenspannungen sind, stellen oft Teilaufgaben innerhalb des Problems (1) dar, sie bilden jedoch auch häufig den kontinuumsmechanischen Bestandteil allgemeinerer physikalischer Fragestellungen, die vielfach den Rahmen der Mechanik weit überschreiten. Der Leser sei dieserhalb auf die einschlägige Literatur verwiesen [*10*—*14*].

In den §§ 1—3 werden wir versuchen, einen kurzen Überblick über die neue Situation in der Kontinuumsmechanik des Festkörpers zu geben, wobei wir gleichzeitig die Gelegenheit haben werden, die Unzulänglichkeit der älteren Kontinuumsmechanik näher zu kennzeichnen. Dabei werden wir auf dynamische Effekte nicht eingehen, doch ist klar, daß die Grundlagen der Theorie, die hier besprochen werden, zugleich auch zu den Grundlagen der noch zu entwickelnden dynamischen Theorie der Versetzungen und Eigenspannungen gehören werden. Auf den zusammenfassenden Bericht des Verfassers [*8*] über die *lineare* Näherung in dem Buch *Kontinuumstheorie der Versetzungen und Eigenspannungen* wird öfter Bezug genommen. Die vorliegende Arbeit soll indessen vornehmlich zusammenfassende Darstellung und Ausbau der *nicht-linearen* Theorie sein[1]. Sie liegt in der Linie der kürzlich erschienenen Arbeit von Kröner und Seeger [*19*], in welcher

[1] Sofern der Leser die Erläuterung der Methoden der nicht-linearen Elastizitätstheorie in der vorliegenden Arbeit als unzureichend empfindet, sei er auf die schönen Darstellungen von Truesdell, Murnaghan, Sokolnikoff sowie Doyle und Ericksen [*15*—*18*] verwiesen.

die nicht-Riemannsche Geometrie der Versetzungen von KONDO [20, 21] sowie von BILBY, BULLOUGH und SMITH [22—26] zu einer nicht-linearen Elastizitätstheorie der Versetzungen und Eigenspannungen ausgebaut wurde.

§ 1. Die allgemeinen Zusammenhänge: Geometrie

In ihrem im Jahre 1909 erschienenen Buch [27] haben die Gebr. COSSERAT die Theorie eines Körpers entwickelt, dessen „Punkte" nicht nur elastisch verschoben, sondern darüber hinaus in meßbarer Weise elastisch verdreht werden konnten. Schon damals dachte man an kristalline Körper als Anwendungsgebiet, doch blieb unklar, wie man sich z.B. den Zustand eines Kristalls vorzustellen hatte, dessen Bausteine zwar Drehungen, aber keine Verschiebungen erlitten hatten.

Es ist seit etwa zehn Jahren bekannt, daß nach gewisser Vorbehandlung[2] Kristalle, die frei von Lastspannungen und makroskopischen Eigenspannungen sind, bei röntgenographischer oder ggfs. optischer Durchstrahlung eine Krümmung der Gitterebenen, d.h. der „geometrischen Struktur" des Kristalles erkennen lassen, wie sie einer örtlich veränderlichen Drehung kleinster Kristallbereiche entsprechen würde. In vielen Fällen kann man erkennen, daß die makroskopisch stetig gekrümmt erscheinenden Gitterebenen mikroskopisch polygonisiert sind (CAHN, GUINIER, CRUSSARD *et al.* 1949 [28]).

Man kann sich das Zustandekommen einer makroskopisch spannungsfreien Drehung der Gitterstruktur eines Massenelements heute gut veranschaulichen. Wie BURGERS und BRAGG [7, 29] gefunden haben, gibt es gewisse flächenhafte Anordnungen von Versetzungen (sog. *Korngrenzenanordnungen*), die keine makroskopischen Spannungsfelder hervorrufen, sondern nur Orientierungsänderungen zwischen benachbarten Kristallbereichen vermitteln. Wirken beispielsweise auf das Massenelement Momente ein, die seine Orientierung drehen wollen, so kann es diesem Zwang nachgeben, wenn sich in bestimmter Anordnung Versetzungsschleifen bilden, die das Element verdrehen und gleichzeitig als Korngrenzen den Übergang zu den Nachbarelementen vermitteln. Die Versetzungsbildung, oder noch besser, die damit äquivalente Drehung der Massenelemente kann elastisch genannt werden, wenn nach Wegnahme der Drehmomente eine zur Rückdrehung führende Annihilation der Versetzungsschleifen erfolgt. Wirken auf *alle* Massenelemente des Körpers Momente wie oben, jedoch in verschiedener Stärke, so werden sich ortsveränderliche Drehungen der Gitterstruktur ergeben, die in einer makroskopisch spannungsfreien Gitterkrümmung resultieren.

NYE [30] hat im Jahre 1953 eine Kontinuumstheorie der (makroskopisch spannungsfreien) Gitterkrümmungen entworfen, doch erst GÜNTHER [31] erkannte im Jahre 1958, daß ein derart gekrümmter Kristall kontinuumstheoretisch betrachtet die Verifikation des Cosserat-Kontinuums darstellt, d.h. die oben beschriebenen Gitterdrehungen und -Krümmungen haben genau die von den

---

[2] Zum Beispiel nach plastischer Biegung. Diese makroskopisch spannungsfreien Gitterkrümmungen müssen gut von den etwa durch *elastische* Biegung zu erhaltenden, mit Spannungen verbundenen Gitterkrümmungen unterschieden werden. Die weiter unten erwähnte Polygonisation erhält man durch Glühen des Werkstückes. Dadurch werden die Versetzungen in sog. Korngrenzenanordnungen gebracht (s. unten), deren elastische Energie besonders gering ist. Die makroskopische Gitterkrümmung ist schon vor der Polygonisation vorhanden.

Cosserats erläuterten Charakteristiken. Wir bezeichnen sie als *Cosserat-Nyesche Drehungen* und *Krümmungen* oder auch als *Strukturdrehungen* und *-Krümmungen*. Die bis jetzt besprochenen Krümmungen nennen wir außerdem *kompatibel*, da sie sich aus einem Drehfeld herleiten.

Ein geeignetes Maß für die Cosserat-Nyeschen Krümmungen stellt der *Cosserat-Nyesche Tensor* $K^{i}_{.j}$ dar, der die Relativdrehung der Gitterstruktur ($d\theta^i$) an zwei um dx^j auseinander liegenden Punkten angibt (also $d\theta^i = K^{i}_{.j}\, dx^j$). Jedoch sind die Krümmungen auch vollständig durch den Tensor $\alpha^{i}_{.j} = K^k_k\, \delta^i_j - K^{i}_{.j}$ charakterisiert. $\alpha^{i}_{.j}$ wird als *Tensor der Versetzungsdichte* bezeichnet, er mißt den *Burgers-Vektor* $d b_j$ der ein Flächenelement dF_i durchsetzenden Versetzungen (also $d b_j = \alpha^{i}_{.j}\, dF_i$).

Zur geometrischen Kennzeichnung des verformten Körpers benötigen wir weiterhin noch den *elastischen Distorsionstensor* β_{ij}, welcher die elastische Relativverschiebung zweier um $d x^i$ auseinander liegender Flächenelemente angibt (also $d s_j = \beta_{ij}\, d x^i$). Im Falle kleiner Distorsion ist der symmetrische Teil des Distorsionstensors mit dem gebräuchlichen Deformationstensor identisch [*8*].

Wir denken uns nun den Körper aus einem idealen Anfangszustand in einen verformten Endzustand gebracht. Diesen beschreiben wir geometrisch durch die Tensoren $\boldsymbol{\beta}$ und $\boldsymbol{K}$ bzw. $\boldsymbol{\alpha}$. Soll nun der zu Anfang kompakte, d.h. als zusammenhängendes Kontinuum vorliegende Körper diese Eigenschaft auch nach der Verformung haben (also keine Risse oder Doppelraumerfüllung zeigen — nur dann kann man von einer Kontinuumstheorie sprechen —), so muß, wie später gezeigt wird, in der Gleichung

$$\mathrm{Rot}\,\boldsymbol{\beta} - \boldsymbol{\alpha} = \boldsymbol{\delta} \tag{1}$$

der asymmetrische Tensor $\boldsymbol{\delta}$ i. allg. verschwinden. Er braucht nur dann nicht zu verschwinden, wenn in den zunächst aus lauter „regulären" Atomen aufgebauten Idealkristall des Anfangszustands „irreguläre Materie" (wir nennen sie auch „Extramaterie") eingebaut wird, die nun der Körper im Endzustand zusätzlich enthält. Der Tensor $\boldsymbol{\delta}$ ist ein Maß dieser Extramaterie, für die die sog. Fremdatome (als Zwischengitter- oder Substitutionsatome) das wichtigste Beispiel sind.

Gl. (1) läßt einen für die allgemeine Kontinuumstheorie der Versetzungen und Eigenspannungen wesentlichen Zug gut erkennen: Der Distorsionstensor und der Krümmungstensor bzw. der Versetzungstensor werden als „innere" Größen betrachtet, die direkt den geometrischen Zustand des Kontinuums beschreiben. Die Extramaterie dagegen wird als „äußerer" Einfluß angesehen, der zu Distorsionen und Krümmungen Anlaß gibt. Dies entspricht vollkommen dem Bild, das man sich von einem Realkristall, welcher ja den verformten Zustand unseres Körpers repräsentiert, zu machen hat: Man kann in Gedanken einen Idealkristall, ohne von außen etwas hinzuzufügen oder wegzunehmen, zu einem Realkristall machen, indem man Versetzungen erzeugt. Der so entstandene Realkristall enthält dann nur reguläre Atome. Man könnte die Versetzungen daher als *innere Gitterfehler* bezeichnen. Dagegen müssen Fremdatome in den Idealkristall (oder in den Realkristall mit Versetzungen) von außen eingeführt werden, sie wären daher als *äußere Gitterfehler* zu bezeichnen. Dem entspricht, daß in Gl. (1) links nur innere, rechts nur äußere Größen stehen. Eine analoge Darstellung werden wir in der Statik erhalten.

Die Gl. (1) gilt für endliche Verformungen nur in der sog. *Lagrangeschen* Beschreibungsweise, d.h. unter dx^i hat man die relative Lage im Anfangszustand zu verstehen [*8*]. Wir nennen das durch Gl. (1) mathematisch formulierte Gesetz das *geometrische Grundgesetz* (der allgemeinen Kontinuumsmechanik). Es gilt bemerkenswerterweise auch noch dann, wenn man zuläßt, daß die elastische Distorsion (bzw. Deformation) und die Strukturkrümmung inkompatibel werden, d.h. sich nicht mehr aus einem Verschiebungs- bzw. Drehfeld ableiten lassen. Dies bedeutet eine wesentliche Erweiterung der ursprünglichen Cosseratschen Theorie. Die Zahl der funktionalen Freiheitsgrade, mit welcher der Körper geometrisch beschrieben wird, wächst dadurch von sechs auf fünfzehn (sechs elastische Deformationen, neun Strukturkrümmungen)[3].

Die Lagrangesche Beschreibungsweise ist für die wichtige Aufgabe der Bestimmung des Zustands aus den physikalischen Gegebenheiten ziemlich ungeeignet. Man bevorzugt daher die *Eulersche* Darstellung in der Geometrie des Kontinuums. Es ist nun höchst bemerkenswert, daß die Eulersche Formulierung der erweiterten (d.h. inkompatiblen) Cosseratschen Theorie in geometrischer Hinsicht mit der Riemann-Cartanschen Geometrie des Festkörpers von Kondo [*20, 21*] sowie Bilby, Bullough und Smith [*22—26*] äquivalent ist. Es gibt nach Ansicht des Verfassers keine elegantere Formulierung der geometrischen Grundgleichungen des nicht-linearen Problems der Kontinuumsmechanik, als eben diejenige der allgemeinen Differentialgeometrie. Nicht allein werden die Gleichungen selbst so einfach, wie es bei der bekannten Kompliziertheit des nicht-linearen Problems überhaupt möglich ist, sondern auch die hieran anschließende Methode der Bestimmung des Zustands aus den physikalischen Gegebenheiten gestaltet sich entsprechend günstig.

Mit der starken Betonung des geometrischen Aspekts der Kontinuumstheorie der Versetzungen und Eigenspannungen soll auf einen entscheidenden Unterschied zur klassischen Elastizitätstheorie hingedeutet werden: In letzterer ist die Geometrie Euklidisch und daher trivial, der geometrische Teil der Theorie wird weitgehend damit erledigt, daß man dem Körper ein elastisches Verschiebungsfeld zuschreibt, welches seine Punkte vom Anfangs- in den Endzustand bringt. Oder mathematisch ausgedrückt: Die Kompatibilitätsbeziehungen für die elastischen Deformationen als geometrische Grundgleichungen der Elastizitätstheorie werden mit Hilfe des Vektorfeldes der Verschiebungen identisch erfüllt.

Die Geometrie eines Körpers mit Versetzungen und Extramaterie ist dagegen prinzipiell nicht-Euklidisch. Es ist hier nicht möglich, ein elastisches Verschiebungsfeld (bzw. Drehfeld) zu definieren; an die Stelle der Kompatibilitätsgleichungen treten die allgemeineren Gleichungen (1), zu deren Lösung neue Methoden benötigt werden.

Die Cosserat-Nyeschen Krümmungen schließlich werden mit der Cartanschen Geometrie, vor allem mit dem Cartanschen Begriff der *Torsion* beschrieben, wie im II. Kapitel eingehend ausgeführt wird. Insbesondere wird die Identität des in der Versetzungstheorie zur Definition der Versetzung benützten Frankschen Burgers-Umlaufs und des in der Differentialgeometrie seit langem bekannten

[3] Die Drehungsanteile von β_{ij} folgen, wie man zeigen kann, aus den elastischen Deformationen und den Strukturkrümmungen, sie liefern also keine eigenen Freiheitsgrade.

Cartan-Umlaufs detailliert nachgewiesen. Diese Identität bildet ein Fundament der differentialgeometrischen Fassung unserer Kontinuumstheorie und besagt, daß die Versetzungsdichte (also auch die Cosserat-Nyeschen Krümmungen) und die Cartansche Torsion exakt das gleiche Phänomen darstellen.

Wir haben in diesem Überblick den *Zustand* des Mediums in den Vordergrund gerückt, sind dagegen auf den früher ausführlich behandelten *Vorgang*, der zu diesem Zustand führte, nicht näher eingegangen [*8*]. Dies wird zum Teil im II. Kapitel nachgeholt. Hier mag die folgende Bemerkung genügen: Jede Bewegung von Versetzungen gibt Anlaß zu einer plastischen Distorsion des Mediums, die, soweit sie makroskopischen Charakter hat, durch einen Distorsionstensor ($\boldsymbol{\beta}^P$) beschrieben werden kann. Dieser hängt mit der Versetzungsdichte $\boldsymbol{\alpha}$ unmittelbar durch die Beziehung

$$\text{Rot}\, \boldsymbol{\beta}^P = -\boldsymbol{\alpha} \tag{2}$$

zusammen, die auch als Definition der Versetzungsdichte angesehen werden kann. Damit schreibt sich z.B. Gl. (1) im Fall $\boldsymbol{\delta} = 0$, wenn man die Summe von elastischer und plastischer Deformation (in der Lagrangeschen Beschreibungsweise) als Gesamtdistorsion $\boldsymbol{\beta}^G$ bezeichnet,

$$\text{Rot}\, \boldsymbol{\beta}^G = 0, \tag{3}$$

in Worten: Die Gesamtdistorsion des Körpers erfolgt so, daß weder Doppelraumerfüllung noch Risse entstehen. Gl. (3) ist eine besonders einfache Formulierung des geometrischen Grundgesetzes in der (durch $\boldsymbol{\delta} = 0$) „beschränkten" Theorie. Sie enthält insbesondere die Möglichkeit verschwindender elastischer Distorsion [*32*], d.h. die plastische Verformung kann makroskopisch spannungsfrei erfolgen. Dies ist von erheblicher praktischer Bedeutung.

§ 2. Die allgemeinen Zusammenhänge: Statik

Die Besonderheit der Cosseratschen Statik gegenüber der klassischen Elastostatik besteht in dem Auftreten der sog. *Momentenspannungen* τ^{ij}. Diese sind definiert als die auf das Flächenelement bezogenen Drehmomente, die man an einer Schnittfläche anzubringen hat, wenn in dieser keine Drehungen stattfinden sollen. Die sonst in der Elastizitätstheorie benützten *Kraftspannungen* oder *Spannungen* schlechthin (σ^{ij}) sind bekanntlich analog definiert: Man hat Kräfte anzubringen, wenn keine Verschiebungen stattfinden sollen.

Wie die Gebr. COSSERAT gezeigt haben, gelten die folgenden *statischen Grundgleichungen* (= Gleichgewichtsbedingungen für Kräfte und Momente) in Eulerscher Schreibweise[4]:

$$\text{Div}\, \boldsymbol{\sigma} = -\mathfrak{F}, \tag{4}$$

$$\text{Div}\, \boldsymbol{\tau} + \vec{\sigma} = \mathfrak{M} \tag{5}$$

(vgl. z.B. GÜNTHER [*31*]). Hier bedeuten $\mathfrak{F}$ und $\mathfrak{M}$ die Dichten der äußeren Kräfte und Drehmomente. Sowohl der (Kraft-)Spannungstensor $\boldsymbol{\sigma}$ als auch der Momentenspannungstensor $\boldsymbol{\tau}$ sind i. allg. asymmetrisch, $\vec{\sigma}$ sei der mit dem antisymmetrischen Teil von $\boldsymbol{\sigma}$ äquivalente Vektor.

---

[4] Eine der Hauptschwierigkeiten der nicht-linearen Theorie liegt bekanntlich darin, daß die statischen Grundgleichungen nur in der Eulerschen, die geometrischen Grundgleichungen nur in der Lagrangeschen Beschreibungsweise eine einfache Form an-

Es ist klar, daß die den Momentenspannungen zuzuordnenden geometrischen Größen die im letzten Paragraphen beschriebenen Strukturkrümmungen sind. An einem in der Praxis häufigen Beispiel werden wir dies erläutern.

Ein Kristallstab werde bei hinreichend hoher Temperatur plastisch so gebogen, daß er am Ende alle Versetzungen in Nyescher, d.h. Korngrenzenanordnung hat. Dieser Stab ist nach Wegnahme der äußeren Biegemomente ohne makroskopische Spannungsfelder, enthält jedoch (makroskopisch) stetige Gitterkrümmungen. Infolge der übrig gebliebenen kurzreichenden Verzerrungswirkung der Versetzungen ist der Energieinhalt dieses Stabes mit Gitterkrümmungen höher als der Energieinhalt eines gleichgeformten Stabes mit idealem Gitteraufbau. Man kann dies so verstehen, daß mit den Gitterkrümmungen gemäß einem Materialgesetz Momentenspannungen verbunden sind. Führt man nämlich irgendwo einen Schnitt, so werden die unmittelbar benachbarten Versetzungen aus der Schnittfläche heraustreten, wie wir an Abb. 1 erläutern.

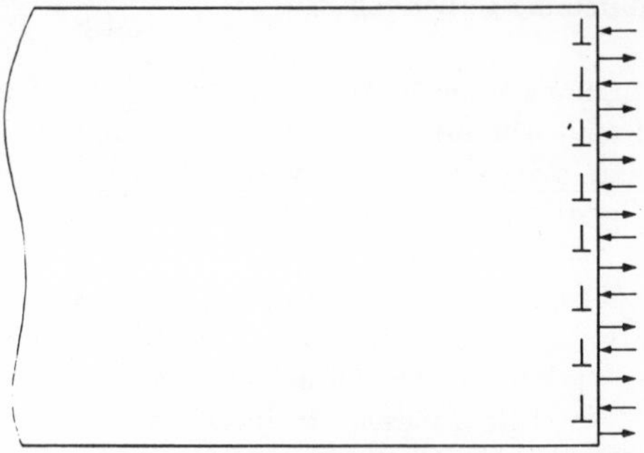

Abb. 1. Zur physikalischen Bedeutung der (makroskopischen) Momentenspannungen

Diese zeigt eine Feinkorngrenze aus Stufenversetzungen (Symbol ⊥) nahe der Schnittfläche. Durch die Spiegelwirkung dieser Fläche (d.h. durch ihre eigenen Spannungsfelder) werden die Versetzungen aus dem Körper herausgezogen, wenn man nicht (von der Schnittfläche her) am Ort der einzelnen Versetzungen eine Schubspannung erzeugt, welche auf jene eine Kraft in der entgegengesetzten Richtung ausübt, die das Austreten der Versetzungen verhindert. Die Pfeile auf der Schnittfläche geben den Typ der dort anzubringenden Einwirkungen an: *Mikroskopisch* betrachtet sind es Kräfte, *makroskopisch* betrachtet Momente. Sie verhindern, daß durch das Austreten (oder auch nur durch Verrückung) der Versetzungen an der Schnittfläche Gitterdrehungen stattfinden. Wir haben damit (hier erstmals) das wichtige Ergebnis gewonnen:

Die mikroskopischen Spannungsfelder der Nyeschen Versetzungsanordnungen lassen sich makroskopisch als Momentenspannungsfelder beschreiben.

Die auf die eben dargelegte Weise im Schnittversuch zu messenden Momentenspannungen bestehen bei Abwesenheit von äußeren Einwirkungen, sie sind daher nach dem in der Elastizitätstheorie üblichen Sprachgebrauch als innere oder Eigenspannungen zu bezeichnen. Daß sie bestehen können, rührt von dem anelastischen Verhalten der Versetzungen her: Diese bedürfen zur Wanderung einer Aktivierung. Könnten die Versetzungen beliebig leicht durch den Kristall wandern, so würden sie nach Wegnahme der äußeren Einwirkungen sofort sämtlich aus dem Kristall herausgehen.

Wir hatten früher den Zustand des verformten Körpers *geometrisch* durch Angabe von fünfzehn Funktionen, den sechs elastischen Deformationen und den neun Strukturkrümmungen charakterisiert. Statt dessen können wir den Zustand auch *statisch* durch Angabe von fünfzehn Funktionen kennzeichnen: Den sechs

Funktionen, die den symmetrischen Teil des Spannungstensors darstellen, und den neun Momentenspannungen [5]. Ist das Materialgesetz, das Spannungen mit Deformationen und Momentenspannungen mit Strukturkrümmungen verbindet, bekannt, so kann man die beiden Sätze von Funktionen ineinander umrechnen [6].

Nur falls die Verformungen vollständig elastisch verlaufen, kann man den Zustand des Körpers eindeutig mit den äußeren Einwirkungen verbinden. Diese werden wiederum durch fünfzehn Funktionen beschrieben, man findet die entsprechenden Größen auf den rechten Seiten der Gln. (1), (4) und (5). Es sind: Extramaterie (9), äußere Kräfte (3) und Drehmomente (3). Wegen der physikalischen Realität der letzteren, die heute gesichert ist, vgl. z.B. [*33*], [*8*] S. 87.

Die eben durchgeführte Betrachtung der funktionalen Freiheitsgrade des Zustands und der äußeren Einwirkungen sollten vor allem einen Überblick über die Reichweite der allgemeinen Theorie geben; sie sind uns zugleich der Anlaß zu der Bezeichnung *Theorie der fünfzehn Freiheitsgrade*. Wir werden diese Theorie in der vorliegenden Arbeit in einer eingeschränkten Form bringen: Da die Cosserat-sche Statik noch nicht genügend bearbeitet wurde und die „Krümmungsenergie" i. allg. nicht sehr groß ist, werden wir die Momentenspannungen nicht beachten, dagegen werden wir die fünfzehn geometrischen Freiheitsgrade voll berücksichtigen [7].

Bevor wir jedoch in den §§ 7, 8 die *allgemeine* Theorie darstellen, werden wir in den §§ 4—6 noch eine *beschränkte* Theorie geben, die wir auch die *Theorie der neun Freiheitsgrade* nennen: Diese Theorie ist dadurch gekennzeichnet, daß die Extramaterie $\boldsymbol{\delta}$ und die äußeren Drehmomente $\mathfrak{M}$ verschwinden, daß ferner die Versetzungsdichte $\boldsymbol{\alpha}$ formal als äußerer Einfluß (und somit als gegeben) angesehen wird. Die Feldgleichungen dieser Theorie lauten in der früher gewählten Beschreibungsweise

$$\operatorname{Rot} \boldsymbol{\beta} = \boldsymbol{\alpha}, \qquad \operatorname{Div} \boldsymbol{\sigma} = -\mathfrak{F}, \tag{6}$$

aus der die neun Freiheitsgrade hinreichend deutlich abzulesen sind. Als Materialgesetz genügen die in der klassischen Elastizitätstheorie verwendeten Gesetze, die Spannungen und Deformationen verbinden. Die in Wirklichkeit auch hier vorhandenen Momentenspannungen werden wiederum nicht beachtet. Diese beschränkte Theorie gestattet bereits die Lösung einer großen Zahl praktisch wichtiger Probleme und hat in letzter Zeit in zunehmendem Maße Anwendung gefunden.

Es mag nun noch eine Bemerkung zu der grundsätzlichen Bedeutung der Spannungsfunktionen in der (allgemeinen und beschränkten) Kontinuumstheorie der Versetzungen und Eigenspannungen folgen, die nach dem heutigen Stand

[5] Wie man zeigen kann, ist mit dem symmetrischen Teil der Spannungen und mit den Momentenspannungen auch zugleich der antisymmetrische Teil der Spannungen bekannt, dieser hat also keine eigenen Freiheitsgrade.

[6] Gemäß Gl. (5) sind die Tensoren $\boldsymbol{\sigma}$ und $\boldsymbol{\tau}$ gekoppelt. Ob sie auch im Materialgesetz gekoppelt vorkommen können, bedarf noch weiterer Untersuchung. Sicher ist, daß sich die neuen Materialkonstanten nicht aus den Hookeschen Konstanten allein ausrechnen lassen.

[7] Eine etwas andere Rolle als in der Versetzungstheorie spielen die Momentenspannungen in gewissen ein- und zweidimensionalen Problemen (Balken, Schale, Platte). Vgl. hierzu etwa ERICKSEN und TRUESDELL [*34*], SCHAEFER [*35*], GÜNTHER [*31*].

der Theorie unentbehrlich erscheinen und hier dieselbe Rolle spielen, wie das Vektorpotential in der Elektrodynamik.

Wir denken den Beitrag der äußeren Kräfte und Drehmomente bereits durch eine Rechnung, die sich eines Verschiebungs- bzw. Drehfeldes bedient, berücksichtigt, wir behandeln also den Fall, daß die rechten Seiten der Gln. (4, 5) verschwinden. Dann lassen sich diese Gleichungen mit Hilfe eines Spannungsfunktionsansatzes befriedigen, den in voller [auch die Gln. (5) berücksichtigenden Allgemeinheit] zuerst GÜNTHER [*31*] angegeben hat. Falls man die Momentenspannungen nicht beachtet, genügt *ein* Spannungsfunktionstensor, mit Hilfe dessen die Gln. (4) identisch befriedigt werden.

Die in der Physik der Eigenspannungen anfallenden Probleme sind nun oft wesentlich dreidimensionaler Natur. Bis vor kurzem galten die Spannungsfunktionen als unbrauchbar bei der Behandlung dreidimensionaler Probleme. Dies hat sich in den letzten Jahren grundlegend geändert. So konnte zunächst gezeigt werden, daß sich im unendlich ausgedehnten, elastisch isotropen Medium bei vorgegebenen Eigenspannungsquellen die Spannungsfunktionen aus inhomogenen Bipotentialgleichungen ergeben [*36*]. In einer richtungsweisenden Arbeit hat ferner SCHAEFER [*35*] gezeigt, daß sich auch für die Behandlung des dreidimensionalen Randwertproblems mit Spannungsfunktionen durchaus günstige Aspekte ergeben, soweit man bei der bekannten Kompliziertheit des dreidimensionalen Randwertproblems überhaupt von „günstig" sprechen kann. Man hat drei durch die Randbedingungen gekoppelte Laplacesche Gleichungen zu lösen. In manchen Fällen können diese Gleichungen entkoppelt werden. Die Methode hat bei der Berechnung von Eigenspannungen gewisse Vorzüge gegenüber derjenigen von PAPKOVITCH und NEUBER [*37*, *38*].

Angesichts der zentralen Bedeutung der Spannungsfunktionen in der Kontinuumstheorie der Versetzungen und Eigenspannungen erschien es angebracht, diesen ein besonderes Kapitel zu widmen (III. Kapitel).

§ 3. Par- und Dielastizität

Par- und Dielastizität sind Erscheinungen, die der klassischen Elastizitätstheorie fremd sind und die sehr eng mit dem atomaren bzw. kristallinen Aufbau unserer Festkörper zusammenhängen. Wir sprechen daher zunächst von Kristallen.

Ideale Kristalle, die aus *einer* Sorte von Atomen bestehen, zeigen weder Par- noch Dielastizität. Dagegen sind alle realen, mikroskopisch kristallin aufgebauten Festkörper dielastisch, viele darüber hinaus parelastisch. Die Abweichungen der realen Kristallstruktur von der idealen, die Gitterfehler, bilden den Sitz der Par- und Dielastizität.

Zu den wichtigsten Gitterfehlern gehören neben den Versetzungen Fremdatome. Hat ein Kristall sehr viele Fremdatome, so bezeichnet man diese meist nicht mehr als Gitterfehler, sondern man spricht von Mischkristallen, im Falle von Metallen auch von Legierungen. Doch besteht von unserem Standpunkt kein prinzipieller Unterschied z.B. zwischen dem Fremdatom als Verunreinigungsatom und dem Fremdatom als Legierungsatom. Dieses wollen wir daher im folgenden auch zu den Gitterfehlern rechnen.

Das Ziel der Theorie der Par- und Dielastizität ist eine konsequente Behandlung der besonderen mechanischen Effekte, die mit Gitterfehlern verbunden sind. Dabei sind die Konzeptionen und Begriffe ganz von den so bewährten Vorstellungen der Elektro- und Magnetostatik materieller Körper übernommen. Dies wird in den eingeführten Bezeichnungen so deutlich zum Ausdruck kommen, daß wir darauf verzichten können, die Analogie im Einzelnen zu beschreiben. So ist ein dielastischer Körper dadurch gekennzeichnet, daß in ihm bei Anlegen einer mechanischen Spannung „elastische Dipole induziert" werden, wodurch er „elastisch polarisiert" wird. Ein parelastischer Körper enthält dagegen „permanente" Dipole, welche sich in die Richtung des elastischen Feldes eindrehen können. Permanente und auch induzierte Dipole erfahren im elastischen Feld Kräfte, von denen sie bei hinreichend großer Beweglichkeit zur Wanderung angetrieben werden. So ist z.B. die Wanderung der als permanente elastische Dipole zu kennzeichnenden Kohlenstoffatome im Eisen von großer Bedeutung in der Technik. Die Theorie der Parelastizität gibt die Möglichkeit, diese Wanderung quantitativ zu verfolgen.

Es wird vorgeschlagen, die makroskopisch punktförmig erscheinenden Gitterfehler mechanisch durch ihre Polarisierbarkeit bzw. Dipolstärke zu charakterisieren. Beide Größen sind experimentellen Messungen zugänglich. Durch diese Größen ist das mechanische Verhalten der Gitterfehler weitgehend bestimmt. Für die Wechselwirkung der Gitterfehler untereinander und mit den inneren Spannungsfeldern des Kristalls erhält man auf diese Weise höchst einfache und weittragende Formeln, die bereits eine große Zahl von praktisch wichtigen Problemen zu erledigen gestatten.

Wohl der wichtigste Gitterfehler ist die Versetzung. Die mechanische Theorie der Versetzungen verhält sich zur Theorie der Par- und Dielastizität etwa wie die Theorie der Magnetfelder stationärer Ströme zur Magnetostatik materieller Körper. Insbesondere kann jeder punktförmige Gitterfehler formal als (induzierte oder permanente) infinitesimale Versetzungsschleife (genauer: drei zueinander senkrechte Versetzungsschleifen) beschrieben werden, entsprechend der Ampèreschen Auffassung der magnetischen Dipole als elementare Kreisströme. Hierüber ist indessen an anderer Stelle ausführlich geschrieben worden [*8*]. In der Behandlung der Par- und Dielastizität des IV. Kapitels ist daher vorwiegend an die makroskopisch punktförmig erscheinenden Gitterfehler gedacht.

II. Die geometrische Theorie

Der Versuchskörper dieser Arbeit ist das sog. Cosserat-Kontinuum, das sich von dem sonst in der Elastizitätstheorie gebrauchten Körper durch das Auftreten einer meßbaren geometrischen Struktur unterscheidet. Das soll heißen: An jedem Punkt des Mediums lassen sich drei nicht-planare, jedoch nicht notwendig zueinander senkrechte ausgezeichnete Richtungen nachweisen. Es ist oft nützlich, sich dieses Kontinuum als einen kubischen Kristall mit verschwindender Gitterkonstanten vorzustellen.

Wir werden einfachheitshalber als Ausgangszustand den Idealzustand wählen, in dem die ausgezeichneten Richtungen im ganzen Körper zueinander parallel sind. Da indessen nicht diese Richtungen selbst, sondern die *Krümmungen* der geometrischen Struktur den Zustand des Körpers bestimmen, stellt diese besondere

Wahl des Ausgangszustands keine Einschränkung der Allgemeinheit unserer Formeln dar. Insbesondere gelten diese unverändert auch dann, wenn der Ausgangszustand ein ungestörter Polykristall ist.

In diesem Kapitel benützen wir fast durchgehend die für die Anwendungen besonders wichtige Eulersche, d.h. auf die Endkoordinaten bezogene Schreibweise. Wir geben zunächst (§ 4) die in § 1 definierte beschränkte Theorie (neun Freiheitsgrade). Dabei begehen wir den gleichen Weg wie früher in der linearen Theorie. Die erforderliche Trennung der Distorsion in Deformation und Drehung ist im Fall endlicher Verformungen nicht mehr durch Zerlegung des Distorsionstensors in symmetrischen und antisymmetrischen Teil möglich. Anstelle detaillierter geometrischer Betrachtungen hierzu benützen wir einen Kunstgriff, der zunächst etwas unmotiviert erscheint, dann aber in der differentialgeometrischen Fassung der Theorie (§ 5) seine Erklärung findet. § 6 bringt den detaillierten Nachweis der auch in der allgemeinen Theorie als Fundament anzusehenden Identität von Versetzungsdichte und Cartanscher Torsion. In § 7 erläutern wir qualitativ die Konzeptionen der allgemeinen Theorie, die in § 8 ihre mathematische Form erhält. In § 9 besprechen wir u. a. den Zusammenhang mit der linearen Theorie.

§ 4. Die elementare Fassung der beschränkten Theorie

In der beschränkten Theorie werden drei Zustände des Mediums betrachtet:

Der Ideal- oder Anfangszustand ($\mathfrak{k}$),
der natürliche oder Zwischenzustand ($\varkappa$),
der deformierte oder Endzustand (k).

Mit ($\mathfrak{k}$), ($\varkappa$), (k) sei auch das dem betr. Zustand zugeordnete Koordinatensystem symbolisch bezeichnet. $dx^{\mathfrak{k}}$, $dx^{\varkappa}$, dx^{k} sei die gegenseitige Lage zweier Punkte innerhalb eines Masseneiements, es soll sich dabei jeweils um die gleichen materiellen Punkte handeln, die in allen drei Zuständen verfolgt werden. Ihr Abstandsquadrat sei resp.

$$ds^2_{(\mathfrak{k})} = b_{\mathfrak{k}\mathfrak{l}}\, dx^{\mathfrak{k}}\, dx^{\mathfrak{l}}, \qquad ds^2_{(\varkappa)} = g_{\varkappa\lambda}\, dx^{\varkappa}\, dx^{\lambda}, \qquad ds^2_{(k)} = a_{kl}\, dx^{k}\, dx^{l} \tag{1}$$

(Summationskonvention!). Der Zusammenhang zwischen den drei Zuständen wird durch die Beziehungen[8]

$$\begin{aligned} dx^{\varkappa} &= A^{\varkappa}_{\mathfrak{k}}\, dx^{\mathfrak{k}}, & dx^{\mathfrak{k}} &= A^{\mathfrak{k}}_{\varkappa}\, dx^{\varkappa} \\ dx^{k} &= A^{k}_{\varkappa}\, dx^{\varkappa}, & dx^{\varkappa} &= A^{\varkappa}_{k}\, dx^{k} \\ dx^{\mathfrak{k}} &= A^{\mathfrak{k}}_{k}\, dx^{k}, & dx^{k} &= A^{k}_{\mathfrak{k}}\, dx^{\mathfrak{k}} \end{aligned} \tag{2}$$

gegeben, wobei die Bedeutung der A-Größen die von Transformationen der Zustände ineinander ist. Wir wollen sie als Distorsionen (= Überlagerung von Deformation und Drehung) bezeichnen und sie bald genauer charakterisieren. Zwischen ihnen bestehen die Inversionsbeziehungen

$$\begin{gathered} A^{\varkappa}_{\mathfrak{k}} A^{\mathfrak{l}}_{\varkappa} = \delta^{\mathfrak{l}}_{\mathfrak{k}}, \quad A^{\varkappa}_{\mathfrak{k}} A^{\mathfrak{k}}_{\lambda} = \delta^{\varkappa}_{\lambda}, \quad A^{k}_{\varkappa} A^{\varkappa}_{l} = \delta^{k}_{l}, \quad A^{k}_{\varkappa} A^{\lambda}_{k} = \delta^{\lambda}_{\varkappa} \\ A^{\mathfrak{k}}_{k} A^{l}_{\mathfrak{k}} = \delta^{l}_{k}, \quad A^{\mathfrak{k}}_{k} A^{k}_{\mathfrak{l}} = \delta^{\mathfrak{k}}_{\mathfrak{l}}. \end{gathered} \tag{3}$$

[8] An die Verwendung des gleichen Kernbuchstaben A für sechs verschiedene Transformationen gewöhnt man sich sehr rasch, da die Indizes in deutlicher Weise angeben, welcher Übergang gemeint ist.

Es sollen jetzt die drei Zustände erklärt werden. Es sind die auch in der linearen Theorie [8] gebrauchten, wo wegen näherer Einzelheiten und Illustration nachgesehen werden kann.

($\mathfrak{l}$): Der Idealzustand soll einem spannungsfreien Idealkristall (mit verschwindender Gitterkonstanten) entsprechen. In diesem Zustand sind die ausgezeichneten Richtungen im ganzen Körper dieselben, die Strukturkrümmung ist Null.

($\varkappa$): Der natürliche Zustand ist ein gedachter Zustand, der von dem Idealzustand aus wie folgt erreicht wird: Es wird zunächst jedem Massenelement des Körpers eine spannungsfreie *eingeprägte* oder *plastische* Distorsion $A_{\mathfrak{l}}^{\varkappa}$ zugeordnet, die durch eine Versetzungsbildung und -wanderung zu realisieren sei. Vor der Durchführung der Distorsionen sollen die Massenelemente numeriert und auseinandergeschnitten werden. Läßt man beliebige Variation der $A_{\mathfrak{l}}^{\varkappa}$ von Element zu Element zu, so werden die Massenelemente i. allg. nach der Distorsion nicht mehr lückenlos aneinander passen[9]. Durch die plastische Distorsion wird zwar die Form des einzelnen Massenelements geändert, nicht aber sein Zustand und seine Orientierung, wie früher ausführlich erläutert wurde [8]. Es ist wichtig zu bemerken, daß auch im Zwischenzustand die ausgezeichneten Richtungen aller Massenelemente definitionsgemäß Euklidisch parallel sind, dagegen kommt es in unserer Analyse auf den Ort des einzelnen Massenelementes nicht an. Bei dem Koordinatensystem ($\varkappa$) dieses Zustands handelt es sich um ein sog. anholonomes System, es hat zwar $dx^{\varkappa}$ einen Sinn, es gibt aber keine Koordinaten $x^{\varkappa}$[10]

(k): Der deformierte Zustand schließlich wird von dem idealen Zustand aus erreicht, wenn man die oben vorgeschriebene Versetzungswanderung ohne Zerschneiden des Körpers im Euklidischen Raum ablaufen läßt. Der Zwang zum Verbleiben im Euklidischen Raum bewirkt dabei, daß sich den plastischen Distorsionen $A_{\mathfrak{l}}^{\varkappa}$ elastische Distorsionen $A_{\varkappa}^{k}$ überlagern. (Wir verzichten i. allg. auf die besondere Erwähnung der Massenkräfte, die in trivialer Weise berücksichtigt werden können.)

Insgesamt stellt sich die Distorsion eines Massenelements vom Anfangszustand in den Endzustand als Überlagerung von plastischer ($A_{\mathfrak{l}}^{\varkappa}$) und elastischer ($A_{\varkappa}^{k}$) dar:

$$A_{\mathfrak{l}}^{k} = A_{\mathfrak{l}}^{\varkappa} A_{\varkappa}^{k}. \tag{4}$$

---

[9] Anstelle des natürlichen Zustands als Konglomerat von plastisch distordierten Massenelementen ist die gleichwertige Vorstellung zulässig, daß die isolierten Massenelemente spannungsfrei in einen gedachten nicht-Euklidischen Raum gebracht werden, in dem sie nunmehr lückenlos aneinanderpassen. Bei dieser Vorstellung können wir auf das Auseinanderschneiden der Massenelemente vor der Distorsion verzichten. Man kann die einzelnen Massenelemente des Aggregats als (materielle) Euklidische Räume ansehen, welche den (materiellen) nicht-Euklidischen Raum des Gesamtkörpers an der entsprechenden Stelle tangieren.

[10] Bezieht man den in Fußnote 9 erwähnten nicht-Euklidischen Standpunkt, so hat man einen kontinuierlichen Körper und kann diesen mit einem (nicht-Euklidischen) Koordinatensystem $x^{\varkappa}$ beschreiben. Man nennt dieses Koordinatensystem dann *anholonom in Bezug auf das System* $x^{\mathfrak{l}}$, weil es keine Transformation gibt, die $x^{\mathfrak{l}}$ in $x^{\varkappa}$ überführt (vgl. Schouten [39]). Man hat vielmehr nur die Pfaffsche anholonome Transformation $dx^{\varkappa} = A_{\mathfrak{l}}^{\varkappa}\, dx^{\mathfrak{l}}$. Die Bedingung, daß $x^{\varkappa}$ in Bezug auf $x^{\mathfrak{l}}$ holonom sei, lautet offenbar $\partial_{\mathfrak{m}} A_{\mathfrak{l}}^{\varkappa} - \partial_{\mathfrak{l}} A_{\mathfrak{m}}^{\varkappa} = 0$, sie ist zugleich die Bedingung dafür, daß die Massenelemente nach der plastischen Distorsion noch zusammenpassen.

Die reziproken Distorsionen überlagern sich gemäß

$$A^{\mathfrak{k}}_{k} = A^{\mathfrak{k}}_{\varkappa} A^{\varkappa}_{k}. \tag{5}$$

Als geometrisches Grundgesetz der Theorie hatten wir gefordert: Bei der Distorsion $A^{k}_{\mathfrak{k}}$ vom Anfangs- in den Endzustand darf in dem Körper weder Rißbildung noch Doppelraumerfüllung stattfinden. Hierfür ist notwendig und hinreichend, daß ein makroskopisch stetiges Verschiebungsfeld existiert, welches die Punkte des Körpers aus dem idealen in den deformierten Zustand bringt (dann gibt es auch ein stetiges Verschiebungsfeld, welches sie wieder zurück in den Anfangszustand bringt). Die Existenz der „Vorwärtsverschiebung" verlangt (vgl. Fußnote 10)

$$\partial_{\mathfrak{m}} A^{k}_{\mathfrak{l}} - \partial_{\mathfrak{l}} A^{k}_{\mathfrak{m}} = 0, \tag{6}$$

diejenige der „Rückwärtsverschiebung" dagegen

$$\partial_{m} A^{\mathfrak{k}}_{l} - \partial_{l} A^{\mathfrak{k}}_{m} = 0. \tag{7}$$

Mit den Gln. (6) und (7) haben wir zwei Fassungen des geometrischen Grundgesetzes vor uns, die erste bezogen auf den Anfangszustand, die zweite auf den Endzustand. Weitere Formulierungen dieses Gesetzes werden wir bald kennenlernen.

Beziehungen der Art (6, 7) gelten nur für die Gesamtdistorsion, da nur diese den Zusammenhang des Körpers grundsätzlich wahrt. Der Grund für die mögliche Zusammenhangsstörung bei der rein plastischen Distorsion ist das Auftreten von Versetzungen. Es gibt im wesentlichen zwei Definitionen der Versetzung, eine differentielle und eine Integraldefinition. In der ersten wird die Versetzung als Randlinie zwischen dem abgeglittenen (d.h. plastisch verschobenen) und dem nicht-abgeglittenen Bereich einer Netzebene definiert und durch Gleitvektor und Tangentenvektor gekennzeichnet. Die zweite Definition erfolgt mit Hilfe des sog. Frankschen Burgers-Umlaufs um die Versetzung. In die Linie der momentanen Darstellung gehört die differentielle Definition, während die Integraldefinition der differentialgeometrischen Betrachtungsweise der Theorie näher steht.

Wir kümmern uns hier nicht um Details, wegen derer auf [*8*] verwiesen wird, sondern definieren die Versetzungsdichte $\alpha_{\mathfrak{m}\mathfrak{l}\cdot}{}^{\varkappa}$ bzw. $\alpha^{\mathfrak{n}\varkappa}$ als Maß der Zusammenhangsstörung bei der rein plastischen Distorsion durch

$$\alpha_{\mathfrak{m}\mathfrak{l}\cdot}{}^{\varkappa} \equiv -\varepsilon_{\mathfrak{m}\mathfrak{l}\mathfrak{n}}\, \alpha^{\mathfrak{n}\varkappa}/2 \equiv (\partial_{\mathfrak{m}} A^{\varkappa}_{\mathfrak{l}} - \partial_{\mathfrak{l}} A^{\varkappa}_{\mathfrak{m}})/2. \tag{8}$$

(In $\alpha^{\mathfrak{n}\varkappa}$ gibt bekanntlich $\mathfrak{n}$ die Linienrichtung, $-\varkappa$ die Gleitrichtung an.) Diese Definition ist, wenn sie auf eine singuläre Versetzung angewandt wird, mit der obigen Grenzliniendefinition identisch[11]. Geht man zur linearen Näherung über, indem man $A^{\varkappa}_{\mathfrak{l}} = \delta^{\varkappa}_{\mathfrak{l}} + \beta^{P}{}^{\varkappa}_{\mathfrak{l}}$ setzt, so erhält man bei Vernachlässigung der in den β's quadratischen Glieder die Definition in der in [*8*] angeschriebenen Form

$$\boldsymbol{\alpha} \equiv -\operatorname{Rot} \boldsymbol{\beta}^{P}. \tag{9}$$

$\boldsymbol{\alpha}$ und $\boldsymbol{\beta}^{P}$ sind die Tensoren (zweiter Stufe) der Versetzungsdichte bzw. der plastischen Distorsionen.

---

[11] Beachte: Die Randlinie einer Fläche ist deren „Wirbellinie".

Die Form (8, 9) der Definition als Rotation der plastischen Distorsion ist sehr eindringlich, (8) hat jedoch für Anwendungen den Nachteil, daß in $\alpha_{\mathfrak{m}\mathfrak{l}}{}^{\varkappa}$ die Indizes des Anfangs- und Zwischenzustands vorkommen. Benötigt wird meistens eine ganz in den Endkoordinaten gehaltene (d.h. Eulersche) Darstellung. Die Umrechnung ergibt [12]

$$\alpha_{ml}{}^{k} \equiv A^{\mathfrak{m}}_{m} A^{\mathfrak{l}}_{l} A^{k}_{\varkappa} \alpha_{\mathfrak{m}\mathfrak{l}}{}^{\varkappa} \equiv - A^{k}_{\mathfrak{k}} (A^{\varkappa}_{l} \partial_{m} A^{\mathfrak{k}}_{\varkappa} - A^{\varkappa}_{m} \partial_{l} A^{\mathfrak{k}}_{\varkappa})/2 . \tag{10}$$

Wir werden diese Form der Definition benötigen, wenn wir jetzt die Fassung (7) des Grundgesetzes durch die Einführung des Versetzungsbegriffes erweitern. Dazu ersetzen wir in Gl. (7) $A^{\mathfrak{k}}_{l}$, $A^{\mathfrak{k}}_{m}$ nach Gl. (5) und multiplizieren mit $A^{k}_{\mathfrak{k}}/2$, es bleibt dann

$$A^{k}_{\varkappa} (\partial_{m} A^{\varkappa}_{l} - \partial_{l} A^{\varkappa}_{m})/2 + A^{k}_{\mathfrak{k}} (A^{\varkappa}_{l} \partial_{m} A^{\mathfrak{k}}_{\varkappa} - A^{\varkappa}_{m} \partial_{l} A^{\mathfrak{k}}_{\varkappa})/2 = 0 , \tag{11}$$

und mit (10) erhalten wir die um den Versetzungsbegriff erweiterte Fassung

$$A^{k}_{\varkappa} (\partial_{m} A^{\varkappa}_{l} - \partial_{l} A^{\varkappa}_{m})/2 = \alpha_{ml}{}^{k} \tag{12}$$

der geometrischen Grundgleichungen. Linearisiert lautet sie ($A^{k}_{\varkappa} = \delta^{k}_{\varkappa} + \beta^{k}_{\varkappa}$, $A^{\varkappa}_{l} = \delta^{\varkappa}_{l} - \beta^{\varkappa}_{l}$)

$$\mathrm{Rot}\, \boldsymbol{\beta} = \boldsymbol{\alpha} .$$

Der Anwendung dieser Gleichung auf praktische Probleme, insbesondere die Spannungsbestimmung bei gegebener Versetzungsverteilung steht im Wege, daß in Gl. (12) die elastischen *Distorsionen* vorkommen, während das Materialgesetz die elastischen *Deformationen* mit den Spannungen verbindet. Es gelingt nun mit Hilfe von Gl. (12) eine Gleichung herzuleiten, die nur noch Deformationen und Versetzungsdichte enthält, und die sich als geeignet zur Spannungsbestimmung erweist. Dazu wenden wir den in der Einleitung zu diesem Kapitel erwähnten Kunstgriff an. Ausgangspunkt ist die Identität

$$\begin{aligned} B_{mlk} \equiv A_{k\varkappa} \partial_{m} A^{\varkappa}_{l} \equiv\; & A_{k\varkappa} (\partial_{m} A^{\varkappa}_{l} + \partial_{l} A^{\varkappa}_{m})/2 + A_{k\varkappa} (\partial_{m} A^{\varkappa}_{l} - \partial_{l} A^{\varkappa}_{m})/2 - \\ & - A_{l\varkappa} (\partial_{k} A^{\varkappa}_{m} - \partial_{m} A^{\varkappa}_{k})/2 + A_{l\varkappa} (\partial_{k} A^{\varkappa}_{m} - \partial_{m} A^{\varkappa}_{k})/2 + \\ & + A_{m\varkappa} (\partial_{l} A^{\varkappa}_{k} - \partial_{k} A^{\varkappa}_{l})/2 - A_{m\varkappa} (\partial_{l} A^{\varkappa}_{k} - \partial_{k} A^{\varkappa}_{l})/2 . \end{aligned} \tag{13}$$

Die rechts stehenden Terme sind nach Gl. (12) gleich

$$\alpha_{mlk} + \alpha_{kml} - \alpha_{lkm} \equiv h_{mlk} . \tag{14}$$

Von den links stehenden sechs Summanden formen wir die ersten drei durch partielle Differentiation um, z.B. ist

$$A_{k\varkappa} \partial_{m} A^{\varkappa}_{l} = \partial_{m} (A_{k\varkappa} A^{\varkappa}_{l}) - A^{\varkappa}_{l} \partial_{m} A_{k\varkappa} = \partial_{m} g_{kl} - A_{l\varkappa} \partial_{m} A^{\varkappa}_{k} . \tag{15}$$

Hier ist g_{kl} durch

$$d s^{2}_{(\varkappa)} \equiv g_{kl}\, d x^{k}\, d x^{l} \tag{16}$$

definiert, die benützte Beziehung

$$A_{k\varkappa} A^{\varkappa}_{l} = g_{kl} \tag{17}$$

---

[12] Schreibe $A^{k}_{\varkappa} = A^{\mathfrak{k}}_{\varkappa} A^{k}_{\mathfrak{k}}$ und differenziere partiell ($A^{\mathfrak{k}}_{\varkappa} \partial_{\mathfrak{m}} A^{\varkappa}_{\mathfrak{l}} = - A^{\varkappa}_{\mathfrak{l}} \partial_{\mathfrak{m}} A^{\mathfrak{k}}_{\varkappa}$ usw.). Setze weiter $A^{\mathfrak{m}}_{m} \partial_{\mathfrak{m}} = \partial_{m}$ ([*39*], S. 70).

folgt leicht aus dem Vergleich von (16) mit (1) unter Benützung von (2). Insgesamt bleibt somit übrig [13]

$$B_{mlk} = (\partial_m g_{kl} + \partial_l g_{mk} - \partial_k g_{lm})/2 + h_{mlk} \equiv \Gamma_{mlk}. \tag{18}$$

Wir definieren nun wie in [*19*] die Ausdrücke

$$\begin{aligned} g'_{mlk} &\equiv (\partial_m g_{kl} + \partial_l g_{mk} - \partial_k g_{lm})/2, \\ g_{mlk} &\equiv (\nabla_m g_{kl} + \nabla_l g_{mk} - \nabla_k g_{lm})/2. \end{aligned} \tag{19}$$

Diese Definitionen sollen auch dann gelten, wenn man überall g durch a, b oder ε ersetzt. Ferner brauchen wir die Größen a^{hk} und g^{hk}, die durch

$$a^{hk} a_{kl} \equiv \delta^h_l, \qquad g^{hk} g_{kl} \equiv \delta^h_l \tag{20}$$

definiert seien. ∇_n sei das Symbol für kovariante Differentiation im deformierten Zustand bezüglich der a_{kl}-Metrik [14]. Schließlich definieren wir die Eulerschen, d.h. auf den Endzustand bezogenen Deformationen in der in der nicht-linearen Theorie üblichen Weise durch

$$\begin{gathered} d s^2_{(k)} - d s^2_{(\mathfrak{t})} \equiv 2 \overset{G}{\varepsilon}_{kl}\, d x^k\, d x^l, \qquad d s^2_{(\varkappa)} - d s^2_{(\mathfrak{t})} \equiv 2 \overset{P}{\varepsilon}_{kl}\, d x^k\, d x^l, \\ d s^2_{(k)} - d s^2_{(\varkappa)} \equiv 2 \varepsilon_{kl}\, d x^k\, d x^l. \end{gathered} \tag{21}$$

Wir erhalten so

$$\overset{G}{\varepsilon}_{kl} = (a_{kl} - b_{kl})/2, \qquad \overset{P}{\varepsilon}_{kl} = (g_{kl} - b_{kl})/2, \qquad \varepsilon_{kl} = (a_{kl} - g_{kl})/2 \tag{22}$$

für den Tensor der Gesamtdeformation, der plastischen und der elastischen Deformation. Somit ist

$$g'_{mlk} = a'_{mlk} - 2\varepsilon'_{mlk}. \tag{23}$$

Wir kommen nun zurück zu Gl. (18). Man rechnet leicht nach, daß der Ausdruck

$$B^{ij} \equiv \tfrac{1}{2}\, \varepsilon^{jnm}\, \varepsilon^{ilk} (\partial_n B_{mlk} - g^{pq} B_{nkq} B_{mlp}) \tag{24}$$

identisch verschwindet, demnach gilt

$$\Gamma^{ij} \equiv \tfrac{1}{2}\, \varepsilon^{jnm}\, \varepsilon^{ilk} (\partial_n \Gamma_{mlk} - g^{pq} \Gamma_{nkq} \Gamma_{mlp}) = 0. \tag{25}$$

Es läßt sich zeigen [*19*], daß der antisymmetrische Teil dieser Gleichungen mit der aus der Definition (8) der Versetzungsdichte folgenden Divergenzbedingung

$$\nabla_{\mathfrak{n}}\, \alpha^{\mathfrak{n}\varkappa} = 0 \tag{26}$$

identisch ist, welche besagt, daß Versetzungen im Innern eines Kontinuums nicht enden können.

[13] Gl. (18) enthält außer der Grundgleichung noch die Aussage (17). Faßt man diese so auf, daß an den Distorsionen, die von ($\varkappa$) nach (k) führen, nur elastische Deformationen (keine quasiplastischen Distorsionen, wie in § 8) beteiligt sein dürfen, so kann man (allerdings etwas künstlich) die Beziehung (17) als beteiligt an der Zusammenhangswahrung ansehen und Gl. (18) anstelle von Gl. (12) als vollständigen Ausdruck des Grundgesetzes werten. In der allgemeinen Theorie (§ 8) werden wir entsprechend vorgehen.

[14] Zum Beispiel $\nabla_n I^{kl}_{\cdot\cdot m} = \partial_n I^{kl}_{\cdot\cdot m} + a'_{np\cdot}{}^{k}\, I^{pl}_{\cdot\cdot m} + a'_{np\cdot}{}^{l}\, I^{kp}_{\cdot\cdot m} - a'_{nm\cdot}{}^{p}\, I^{kl}_{\cdot\cdot p}$

Bildet man den symmetrischen Teil der Tensorgleichung (25)[15], so erhält man, wenn man noch ∂_n gemäß Fußnote 13 durch ∇_n ausdrückt[16], die *Grundgleichungen der Eigenspannungsbestimmung in der beschränkten Theorie* [*19*]

$$\Gamma^{(ij)} \equiv \tfrac{1}{2}\{\varepsilon^{jnm}\varepsilon^{ilk}[\nabla_n(-2\varepsilon_{mlk}+h_{mlk}) - \\ - g^{pq}(-2\varepsilon_{nkq}+h_{nkq})(-2\varepsilon_{mlp}+h_{mlp})]\}_{(ij)} = 0. \tag{27}$$

Für $h_{mlk}=0$ sind dies die bekannten nicht-linearen Kompatibilitätsbedingungen für die elastischen Deformationen [*17*, *40*]. In linearisierter Form wurden die Gln. (27) früher [*8*]

$$\mathrm{Ink}\,\boldsymbol{\epsilon} \equiv \nabla\times\boldsymbol{\epsilon}\times\nabla = (\boldsymbol{\alpha}\times\nabla)^S \equiv \boldsymbol{\eta} \tag{28}$$

geschrieben (für Ink lies „Inkompatibilität von").

Wir deuten die Verwendung dieser Gleichungen kurz an ([*8*, *19*], vgl. auch § 8)*. Mit Hilfe des Spannungsfunktionsansatzes werden die Gleichgewichtsbedingungen für die Spannungen bei Abwesenheit von Massenkräften identisch erfüllt. Unter Benützung des Materialgesetzes wird danach ε_{kl} bzw. ε_{mlk} in den Spannungsfunktionen ausgedrückt, so daß die Grundgleichungen der Eigenspannungsbestimmung zu Gleichungen werden, die nur Spannungsfunktionen und Versetzungsdichte enthalten. Die Lösung dieser Gleichungen unter Berücksichtigung der Randbedingungen liefert die Spannungsfunktionen, damit auch die Spannungen und elastischen Deformationen. Wie wir in § 5 erläutern, ist die physikalische Bedeutung von h_{mlk} diejenige der Cosserat-Nyeschen Strukturkrümmungen, die sich somit bei gegebener Versetzungsdichte trivial ergeben. Danach ist die auf S. 276 unter (2) gestellte Aufgabe im Rahmen der beschränkten Theorie gelöst.

Hiermit wollen wir die elementare Fassung der Theorie verlassen und zur differentialgeometrischen Betrachtungsweise übergehen.

§ 5. Die differentialgeometrische Fassung der beschränkten Theorie

Für die Verwendung der allgemeinen Differentialgeometrie in der Kontinuumsmechanik ist die folgende Betrachtungsweise typisch: $B^{\mathfrak{k}}(1)$ sei ein Vektor, der zwei Punkte innerhalb des Massenelements 1 im Anfangszustand verbindet. $B^{\mathfrak{k}}(2)$ sei ein dazu paralleler, gleichlanger Vektor in einem benachbarten Element 2. Den Vektor, der im Endzustand die gleichen Punkte wie $B^{\mathfrak{k}}$ im Anfangszustand verbindet, also das Abbild von $B^{\mathfrak{k}}$, nennen wir B^k. Kann man nun den Wert von dB^k für alle Nachbarelemente im Endzustand angeben, so ist damit auch die Gesamtdistorsion, die der Körper erlitten hat, gekennzeichnet.

---

* *Zusatz bei der Korrektur.* Das in [*19*] zur Berechnung des Spannungsfeldes der Schrauben- und Stufenversetzungen verwendete quadratische Elastizitätsgesetz (54) enthält leider einen Fehler. Daher sind in den Formeln der §§ 5, 6 von [*19*] kleinere Korrekturen nötig, die demnächst zusammen mit einer auch die Randbedingungen berücksichtigenden Behandlung des Problems der Schrauben- und Stufenversetzungen angegeben werden sollen (voraussichtlich H. PFLEIDERER et al., Z. Naturforschung **15**a (1960)).

[15] Wir deuten an, daß wir den symmetrischen oder antisymmetrischen Teil bezüglich zweier Indizes nehmen, indem wir diese in runde bzw. eckige Klammern setzen.

[16] Wählt man zur Beschreibung des Endzustands kartesische Koordinaten, so ist $a'_{nk}{}^{p}=0$ und $\nabla_n=\partial_n$.

$d\,B^k$ wird dem Vektor B^k selbst proportional sein und auch dem Abstand $d\,x^m$ der Punkte, an denen B^k verglichen wird, d.h.

$$dB^k = -\,b'_{ml\cdot}{}^{k}\,B^l\,d\,x^m. \tag{29}$$

Vergleicht man in entsprechender Weise einen Vektor $C^\varkappa$ im natürlichen Zustand, den wir uns jetzt gemäß Fußnote 9, 10 als (materiellen) nicht-Euklidischen Raum vorstellen, mit seinem Abbild C^k im deformierten Zustand, so erhält man entsprechend

$$d\,C^k = -\,\Gamma_{ml\cdot}{}^{k}\,C^l\,d\,x^m \tag{30}$$

oder auch[17]

$$d\,C_k = -\,\Gamma_{mlk}\,C^l\,d\,x^m. \tag{31}$$

Man bezeichnet zwei Vektoren C^k an zwei um $d\,x^m$ auseinanderliegenden Punkten, für die Gl. (30) gilt, als (nicht-Euklidisch) parallel bezüglich $\Gamma_{ml\cdot}{}^{k}$, ihr kovariantes Differential

$$\delta C^k \equiv d\,C^k + \Gamma_{ml\cdot}{}^{k}\,C^l\,d\,x^m \tag{32}$$

verschwindet.

Wir werden sehen, daß Γ_{mlk} sowohl die elastischen Deformationen als auch die Strukturkrümmungen enthält, also in dem von uns angestrebten Umfang den Endzustand des Körpers kennzeichnet. Die Größen Γ_{mlk} bzw. b'_{mlk} heißen *lineare* oder *affine Konnexion* (auch *Affinität*). Die affine Konnexion stellt die zentrale Größe des von uns beanspruchten Teils der allgemeinen Differentialgeometrie dar. Wir haben uns jetzt mit ihren Eigenschaften zu beschäftigen.

Schon allein aus den Symmetrieeigenschaften von Γ_{mlk} kann man wichtigen Aufschluß über die Verformung des Körpers bekommen. Zunächst führt der in l, k antisymmetrische Teil $\Gamma_{m[lk]}$ der Konnexion Γ_{mlk} immer zu einer infinitesimalen Drehung des Vektors C^k beim Fortschreiten um $d\,x^m$, denn es ist $C^k\,d\,C_k = -\,\Gamma_{m[lk]}\,C^l\,C^k\,d\,x^m \equiv 0$. Untersucht man die Distorsion eines Dreibeins bei der bezüglich $\Gamma_{m[lk]}$ parallelen Verschiebung um $d\,x^m$, so stellt man fest, daß dieses ebenfalls gedreht, jedoch nicht deformiert wird. Dagegen gibt der in l, k symmetrische Teil $\Gamma_{m(lk)}$ von Γ_{mlk} Anlaß zu einer reinen Deformation des Dreibeins. Es besteht also bei gegebener Konnexion die einfache Möglichkeit, die Deformations- und Drehungsanteile additiv zu trennen, was daher rührt, daß der in der Konnexion betrachtete *Unterschied* der Deformation bzw. Drehung in zwei Nachbarelementen infinitesimal ist.

Als dreifach indizierte Größe könnte die Konnexion Γ_{mlk} im Dreidimensionalen prinzipiell 27 funktionale Freiheitsgrade besitzen. Diese Zahl reduziert sich indessen auf 15, wenn man sich auf metrische Räume beschränkt, das sind solche, in denen der Abstand zweier beliebiger Punkte definiert ist. Nur solche Räume kommen bis jetzt in der Kontinuumsmechanik vor (s. § 9).

In den Lehrbüchern der Differentialgeometrie erfährt man, daß die allgemeinste metrische Konnexion Γ_{mlk} die Form

$$\Gamma_{mlk} \equiv g'_{mlk} + h_{mlk} \tag{33}$$

---

[17] Wir werden den ausgezeichneten Index in den Konnexionen (immer der dritte) je nach Bedarf als oberen oder unteren Index schreiben. Für das Heben und Senken der Indizes muß der richtige Metriktensor verwendet werden, z.B. $b'_{mlk} = b_{kh}\,b'_{ml\cdot}{}^{h}$, aber $\Gamma_{mlk} = g_{kh}\,\Gamma_{ml\cdot}{}^{h}$. Dabei ist $b_{kh} = A^{\mathfrak{k}}_{k} A^{\mathfrak{h}}_{h}\, b_{\mathfrak{k}\mathfrak{h}}$, $g_{ki} = A^{\varkappa}_{k} A^{\iota}_{i}\, g_{\varkappa\iota}$. In Zweifelsfällen werden wir den Metriktensor besonders angeben.

mit den Abkürzungen

$$g'_{mlk} = (\partial_m g_{lk} + \partial_l g_{mk} - \partial_k g_{lm})/2, \tag{34}$$

$$h_{mlk} = \Gamma_{[ml]k} + \Gamma_{[km]l} - \Gamma_{[lk]m} \tag{35}$$

hat. Dabei folgt die Bedeutung von g_{kl} aus

$$d s_{(\times)}^2 = g_{kl}\, d x^k\, d x^l. \tag{36}$$

($d s_{(\times)}$ ist der Abstand zweier Punkte im natürlichen Zustand, deren gegenseitige Lage im deformierten Zustand durch $d x^k$ gekennzeichnet ist. Demnach ist

$$\varepsilon_{kl} = (a_{kl} - g_{kl})/2 \tag{37}$$

der schon in § 4 benützte (Eulersche) elastische Deformationstensor.)

Wie man sieht, ist h_{mlk} antisymmetrisch in l, k, beschreibt also eine reine Drehung des Dreibeins beim Fortschreiten zum Nachbarelement.

Die von h_{mlk} beschriebenen Relativdrehungen zwischen den Massenelementen bestehen zunächst unabhängig von den elastischen Deformationen des Körpers, die wegen (37) ganz durch den Anteil g'_{mlk} von Γ_{mlk} beschrieben werden. Insbesondere können die Deformationen verschwinden, d.h. $\varepsilon'_{mlk} = 0$ werden, und die Drehungen bestehen bleiben. Betrachtet man das gemäß der Beziehung (31) verschobene Dreibein als das *trièdre mobile* der Gebr. COSSERAT, so hat man unmittelbar die Beziehung gefunden: Der Anteil h_{mlk} von Γ_{mlk} beschreibt die Cosseratschen Relativdrehungen bzw. die daraus resultierenden Strukturkrümmungen.

Der in m, l antisymmetrische Teil $\Gamma_{[ml]k}$ einer Konnexion Γ_{mlk} wird nach CARTAN [*41*] als Torsion bezeichnet. Er hat die Transformationseigenschaften eines Tensors dritter Stufe, während Γ_{mlk} selbst sich nach einer komplizierteren Formel transformiert.

Wir werden die Beziehung

$$\Gamma_{[ml]k} \equiv \alpha_{mlk} \tag{38}$$

in § 6 ableiten, d.h. es ist die Cartansche Torsion mit der Versetzungsdichte identisch. Damit folgt aber aus (35) unmittelbar die frühere Beziehung (14). Infolgedessen sind die Cosseratschen Strukturkrümmungen direkt mit den Versetzungen verbunden, sie können ohne Versetzungen nicht realisiert werden. NYE [*30*] hat diese Krümmungen mit Hilfe des mit h_{mlk} äquivalenten Tensors

$$K^{n}_{\cdot m} \equiv - \varepsilon^{nlk} h_{mlk}/2 \tag{39}$$

beschrieben, der durch die Definition

$$d\theta^n \equiv K^{n}_{\cdot m}\, d x^m \tag{40}$$

eingeführt wurde, wo $d\theta^n$ die Relativdrehung zwischen zwei Nachbarelementen ist. Den Zusammenhang mit COSSERAT hat dann GÜNTHER [*31*] hergestellt. Es ist sehr eindrucksvoll zu sehen, in welch einfacher Weise die in dem Cosseratschen Buch so kompliziert erscheinenden Krümmungen in der modernen differentialgeometrischen Darstellung auftreten. Da mit gegebener Versetzungsdichte gleichzeitig auch die Strukturkrümmungen gegeben sind, ist das Hauptproblem die Bestimmung der zu den Versetzungen gehörigen Eigenspannungen.

Diese hängen sehr eng mit den g'_{mlk} zusammen, die ein Maß für die elastische Deformation sind. Bei der Deutung der g'_{mlk} können wir uns demnach auf die Betrachtung des Ausdrucks

$$-(\partial_m \varepsilon_{kl} + \partial_l \varepsilon_{mk} - \partial_k \varepsilon_{lm}) \tag{41}$$

beschränken. Der erste Summand ist symmetrisch in k, l und gibt daher Anlaß zu einer reinen Deformation, nämlich

$$d\,C_k^{(\mathrm{def})} = C^l d\,\varepsilon_{kl}. \tag{42}$$

Dagegen ist der Rest $-(\partial_l \varepsilon_{mk} - \partial_k \varepsilon_{lm})$ in k, l antisymmetrisch und gibt Anlaß zu einer reinen Drehung. Es wird

$$d\,C_k^{(\mathrm{rot})} = C^l(\partial_l \varepsilon_{mk} - \partial_k \varepsilon_{lm})\,d\,x^m \equiv \epsilon_{lkh} C^l(\epsilon^{fgh}\partial_f \varepsilon_{gm}\,d\,x^m), \tag{43}$$

wobei der in dem rechten Term in Klammern stehende Ausdruck als Drehung von C^k beim Fortschreiten um $d\,x^m$ zu interpretieren ist. (Falls ε_{gm} aus einem Verschiebungsfeld herrührt, also $\varepsilon_{gm} = (\nabla_g s_m + \nabla_m s_g)/2$ ist, wird dieser Ausdruck einfach d (rot $\mathfrak{s}$).)

Die eben beschriebenen Drehungen bzw. die zugehörigen Krümmungen sind unmittelbar mit den elastischen Deformationen gekoppelt, sie verschwinden mit der Entspannung (etwa durch Auseinanderschneiden). Entsprechendes hat man ja in der geometrisch einfacheren Theorie der Lastspannungen, wo mit den Deformationen zugleich die Drehungen festgelegt sind. Man muß die zu (43) gehörigen Krümmungen gut von den weiter oben erklärten (makroskopisch) spannungsfreien Strukturkrümmungen unterscheiden.

Differenziert man die Konnexion $\Gamma_{ml\cdot}^{\;\;\;k}$ bzw. Γ_{mlk} kovariant bezüglich des ausgezeichneten Index k (und bezüglich $\Gamma_{ml\cdot}^{\;\;\;k}$), und bildet man von dem Ergebnis den antisymmetrischen Teil (Symbol $[n\,m]$), so erhält man mit dem Riemann-Christoffelschen Krümmungstensor

$$\Gamma_{nml\cdot}^{\;\;\;\;\;k} \equiv 2[\partial_n \Gamma_{ml\cdot}^{\;\;\;k} + \Gamma_{np\cdot}^{\;\;\;k}\Gamma_{ml\cdot}^{\;\;\;p}]_{[nm]}, \tag{44}$$

$$\Gamma_{nmlk} \equiv 2[\partial_n \Gamma_{mlk} - g^{pq}\Gamma_{nkq}\Gamma_{mlp}]_{[nm]} \tag{45}$$

eine weitere wichtige Größe der Theorie. Im Falle metrischer Konnexion Γ_{mlk} ist Γ_{nmlk} antisymmetrisch sowohl im ersten als auch im zweiten Indexpaar, während Symmetrie bezüglich der Vertauschung von n, m mit l, k nur unter einschränkenden Bedingungen für $\Gamma_{[ml]k}$ gilt. Wegen der erwähnten Antisymmetrie ist der aus Γ_{nmlk} gemäß [18]

$$\Gamma^{ij} \equiv \tfrac{1}{4}\,\epsilon^{jmn}\,\epsilon^{ilk}\,\Gamma_{nmlk} \tag{46}$$

gebildete Einstein-Tensor Γ^{ij} mit Γ_{nmlk} gleichwertig. Für Γ^{ij} gilt die Divergenzbedingung (SCHOUTEN [*39*], S. 146)

$$\nabla_i \Gamma^{ij} = \epsilon_{mlk}\,\alpha^{kl}\,\Gamma^{mj}, \tag{47}$$

die als Bedingung für Γ_{nmlk} geschrieben, auch Bianchi-Identität heißt. Die rechte Seite von (47) verschwindet in einer linearisierten Theorie.

[18] Diese Formel gilt nur im Dreidimensionalen. Die für beliebig-dimensionale Räume gültige Definition des Einstein-Tensors erfolgt über den sog. Ricci-Tensor, man findet sie in allen Lehrbüchern der Differentialgeometrie und Relativitätstheorie.

Ein bekannter Satz der Differentialgeometrie besagt: Verschwindet der Krümmungstensor Γ_{nmlk}, so hat die Konnexion Γ_{mlk} die Form

$$\Gamma_{mlk} = A_{k\varkappa}\partial_m A_l^{\varkappa}. \tag{48}$$

Falls nun die Identität (38) gilt, ist der antisymmetrische Teil der Gl. (48) die geometrische Grundgleichung [19] (vgl. (12)), und die Gleichung

$$\Gamma^{(ij)} = 0, \tag{49}$$

wo Γ_{mlk} nach Gl. (33, 34, 37) einzusetzen ist, die Grundgleichung der Eigenspannungsbestimmung (vgl. (14) und (27)). Die Gleichung

$$\Gamma^{[ij]} = 0 \tag{50}$$

ist wieder die Divergenzbedingung für die Versetzungsdichte. Damit ist die Beziehung zwischen der elementaren und der differentialgeometrischen Fassung der Theorie weitgehend hergestellt.

Die Gl. (49) stellt eine Kopplung zwischen dem Krümmungsanteil h_{mlk} und dem Deformationsanteil g'_{mlk} der Konnexion Γ_{mlk} her, welche bewirkt, daß eine gegebene Versetzungsdichte zu Spannungen führt.

Ersichtlich erscheint hier Gl. (48) bzw. (49, 50) als eine Forderung, die zusätzlich zu der geometrischen Grundgleichung (12) besteht. Wir haben nun zu fragen, was uns dazu berechtigt, Γ_{nmlk} bzw. Γ^{ij} gleich Null zu setzen. Diese Frage war bei der elementaren Behandlung der Theorie gar nicht aufgetaucht, die Gl. (25) ergab sich hier ganz von selbst aus der entwickelten Vorstellung über den Verformungsvorgang. Man erkennt an dieser Stelle, daß der differentialgeometrische Standpunkt der allgemeinere ist, und es erhebt sich die Frage nach der physikalischen Bedeutung eines nicht-verschwindenden Krümmungstensors (bzw. Einstein-Tensors). Kondo, der diese Frage aufwarf [*20, 21*], sprach in diesem Zusammenhang von „Krümmungsfehlstellen“ im Gegensatz zu den „Torsionsfehlstellen“ (Versetzungen), doch blieb in der Frage der physikalischen Bedeutung der Krümmungsfehlstellen noch einiges offen.

Im (allerdings nur scheinbaren) Gegensatz zu Kondo waren Bilby und Smith [*24*] auf Grund ähnlicher Vorstellungen, wie sie oben entwickelt wurden, zu der Beziehung $\Gamma_{nmlk}=0$ gekommen, die sie als physikalisches Erfordernis bezeichneten, damit ein Kristallgitter an jedem Punkt des Mediums definiert sei. Wir werden diese wichtigen Fragen in § 6—9 besprechen. Zuvor soll im nächsten Paragraphen die Identität von Versetzungsdichte und Cartanscher Torsion bewiesen werden, die das Fundament der differentialgeometrischen Theorie der Versetzungen bildet.

§ 6. Die Identität von Versetzungsdichte und Cartanscher Torsion [20]

Wir zeigen in diesem Paragraphen, daß der zur (Integral-)Definition der Versetzung vielbenützte Franksche Burgers-Umlauf [*42*] mit dem in der Differentialgeometrie schon vor der Einführung des Versetzungsbegriffs bekannten Cartan-Umlauf identisch ist. Dazu beschreiben wir zunächst kurz die Franksche Versetzungsdefinition.

[19] Daß man unter $A_{\varkappa}^{k}$ wieder die elastischen Distorsionen zu verstehen hat, läßt sich leicht zeigen, vgl. § 6.

[20] Vgl. zu diesem Paragraphen insb. Bilby [*26*].

Abb. 2a zeigt einen Realkristall (*a*) mit einer Versetzung (entsprechend unserem deformierten Zustand). Durch Zahlen ist in diesem ein die Versetzung umfassender geschlossener Umlauf, beginnend und endend beim Punkt P, angedeutet. In dem idealen Kristall (*b*) der Abb. 2b (der nichts mit unserem Anfangszustand zu tun haben soll) sei von einem Bildpunkt P' von P ausgehend das korrespondierende Umlaufprogramm durchgeführt (gestrichene Zahlen). Jedem Schritt in *a* entspricht ein Schritt in *b*. Nach demjenigen Schritt, mit dem in *a* der Umlauf geschlossen ist, bleibt in *b* noch ein Rest, der sog. Schließungsfehler $\overrightarrow{Q'P'}$ bis zum Bildpunkt P'. Mit Hilfe dieses „Burgers-Vektors" definiert FRANK die Versetzung.

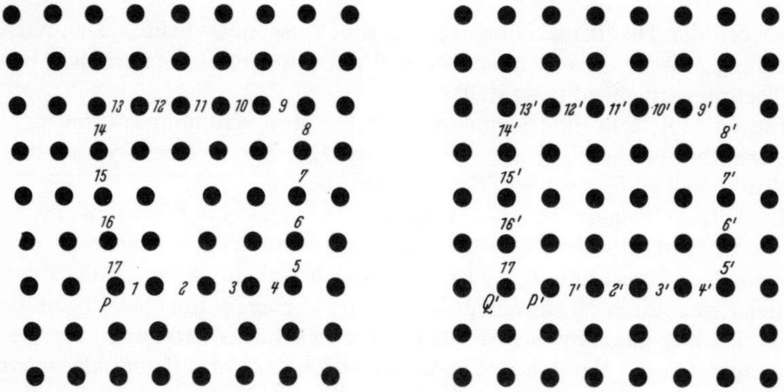

a b

Abb. 2 a u. b. Zur Frankschen Definition der Versetzung im Kristall

Wir wollen nun den Schließungsfehler mit Hilfe der Konnexion ausdrücken. Dazu betrachten wir den Realkristall *a* von einem nicht-Euklidischen Standpunkt, womit wir die Basis von CARTAN beziehen. Es wird festgesetzt, daß zwei Vektoren an zwei um dx^m auseinander liegenden Punkten, die sich um

$$dC^k = -\Gamma_{ml.}^{\;\;\;\,k} C^l \, dx^m \tag{51}$$

unterscheiden, gleichlang und parallel sein sollen (BILBY, BULLOUGH und SMITH [*23*]). Von diesem Standpunkt aus wird der Realkristall zum nicht-Euklidischen Idealkristall, d.h. seine kleinsten Gittervektoren sind alle gleichlang und, soweit sie gleiches k haben, parallel ($k = 1, 2, 3$). (Auf die singulären Verhältnisse im Zentrum der Versetzung brauchen wir uns nicht einzulassen, da der Umlauf dieses nicht berührt.)

Wir geben nun eine etwas abgeänderte Beschreibung des Frankschen Umlaufs, von der man jedoch sofort erkennt, daß sie mit der ursprünglichen gleichwertig ist (vgl. hierzu SCHOUTEN [*39*], S. 127). Wir denken uns den Idealkristall *b* so auf den Realkristall *a* gelegt, daß der Punkt P' mit P zusammenfällt und das Idealgitter *b* tangential an dem Realgitter *a* liegt. Der erste Schritt des Umlaufs bringe die Punkte 1′ und 1 zur Deckung, wobei nun *b* in 1 tangential an *a* liegen möge. Wir nennen diese Stellung symbolisch (1′1). Der zweite Schritt des Umlaufs bringe *b* in die Stellung (2′2), die analog wie (1′1) zu beschreiben sei.

Wir versuchen jetzt die Lage des Punktes P' in der jeweiligen Stellung zu berechnen, und zwar nehmen wir das kartesische Koordinatensystem ($\varkappa$) des Idealgitters a in der betr. Stellung mit dem Kontaktpunkt (z. B. n' in Stellung $(n'n)$) als Ursprung zu Hilfe. Es soll jedoch versucht werden, anstelle der Koordinaten $x^\varkappa$ des Idealgitters die Koordinaten des Realgitters soweit wie möglich zu verwenden.

In der $(1'1)$-Stellung hat P' in dem oben beschriebenen kartesischen Gitter die Koordinaten $-\underset{1}{d}x^\varkappa$. (Das Subskript 1 kennzeichne die Nummer des Schrittes.) Wir werden sehen, daß es allgemein erlaubt ist, $\underset{m}{d}x^\varkappa$ durch $\underset{n}{d}x^k$ zu ersetzen, wenn $n=m$ ist.

Bei der folgenden Verschiebung von $(1'1)$ nach $(2'2)$ bekommt zunächst der Punkt $1'$ im kartesischen Gitter mit Ursprung in $2'$ gemessen die Koordinate $-\underset{2}{d}x^\varkappa$ bzw. $-\underset{2}{d}x^k$. Bei dieser Verschiebung ist jedoch der Vektor $\overrightarrow{1'P'}$, d. h. $-\underset{1}{d}x^k$ parallel über $\underset{2}{d}x^k$ verschoben worden, d. h. er hat sich um $d\underset{1}{d}x^k = -\Gamma_{ml\cdot}^{\ \ k}\underset{1}{d}x^l\underset{2}{d}x^m$ geändert. Somit sind die Koordinaten von P' (bezüglich des Punktes $2'=2$) $-\underset{1}{d}x^k - \underset{2}{d}x^k + \Gamma_{ml\cdot}^{\ \ k}\underset{1}{d}x^l\underset{2}{d}x^m$. Beim nächsten Schritt wird der eben hingeschriebene Vektor über $\underset{3}{d}x^k$ parallel verschoben, man erhält als Ortsvektor von P' bezüglich $3'$ nun $-\underset{1}{d}x^k - \underset{2}{d}x^k - \underset{3}{d}x^k + \Gamma_{ml\cdot}^{\ \ k}\underset{1}{d}x^l\underset{2}{d}x^m + \Gamma_{ml\cdot}^{\ \ k}\underset{1}{d}x^l\underset{3}{d}x^m + \Gamma_{ml\cdot}^{\ \ k}\underset{2}{d}x^l\underset{3}{d}x^m$ (die Anteile dritten Grades in den dx^k sind weggelassen).

Man sieht, wie es weiter geht. Mit der Ankunft in der Stellung $(Q'P)$ haben wir einen vollen Cartan-Umlauf ausgeführt. Zur Berechnung des Schließungsfehlers $\overrightarrow{Q'P'}$ haben wir eine kompliziert aussehende Summe auszurechnen.

An dieser Stelle machen wir nun den Übergang zur Kontinuumstheorie. Wir lassen die Gitterkonstante gegen Null gehen und ersetzen die einzelne Versetzung durch eine Anordnung kontinuierlich verteilter Versetzungen infinitesimaler Stärke. Machen wir den Umlauf genügend klein, so können wir $\Gamma_{ml\cdot}^{\ \ k}$ in dem betreffenden Bereich als konstant ansehen (ein Schluß, wie er auch sonst in der Kontinuumsphysik oft benützt wird). Dann schreibt sich der Schließungsfehler $\overrightarrow{Q'P'}$

$$\Delta b^k = \sum_n \underset{n}{d}x^k + \Gamma_{ml\cdot}^{\ \ k}\left\{\begin{array}{r} \underset{1}{d}x^l\underset{2}{d}x^m + \underset{1}{d}x^l\underset{3}{d}x^m + \underset{1}{d}x^l\underset{4}{d}x^m + \cdots \\ + \underset{2}{d}x^l\underset{3}{d}x^m + \underset{2}{d}x^l\underset{4}{d}x^m + \cdots \\ + \underset{3}{d}x^l\underset{4}{d}x^m + \cdots \\ + \cdots \end{array}\right\} \tag{52}$$

Die erste Summe hätte genau genommen $\sum_n \underset{n}{d}x^\varkappa$ geheißen, doch erkennt man an dieser Stelle, daß zwischen beiden Summen kein Unterschied besteht, man braucht nur die Länge der Schritte gegen Null gehen zu lassen (man vgl. etwa die Umfangsberechnung eines Kreises mit Hilfe eines Polygons, dessen Eckenzahl gegen unendlich geht). Zugleich sieht man, daß der obige Ersatz von $\underset{n}{d}x^\varkappa$ durch $\underset{n}{d}x^k$ die zweite Summe in (52) nur um Glieder dritten Grades in $\underset{n}{d}x^k$ ändern konnte, da die Differenz von $\underset{n}{d}x^\varkappa$ und $\underset{n}{d}x^k$ in $\underset{n}{d}x^k$ quadratisch ist. Somit ist der oben vorgenommene Ersatz von $\underset{n}{d}x^\varkappa$ durch $\underset{n}{d}x^k$ voll gerechtfertigt.

Die erste Summe in (52) verschwindet, die zweite ergibt gerade das von dem Umlauf berandete Flächenelement ΔF^{ml} (Vorzeichen gemäß Rechtsschraubenregel). Wegen der Antisymmetrie von ΔF^{ml} trägt offenbar der symmetrische Teil von $\Gamma_{ml}{}^{k}_{\cdot}$ nichts zum Schließungsfehler bei, es bleibt

$$\Delta b^k \equiv \Gamma_{[ml]}{}^{k}_{\cdot}\, \Delta F^{ml}. \tag{53}$$

Da

$$\Delta b^k \equiv \alpha_{ml}{}^{k}_{\cdot}\, \Delta F^{ml} \equiv \alpha^{nk}\, \Delta F_n \tag{54}$$

die Kontinuumsversion der Frankschen Versetzungsdefinition ist, haben wir die Identität (38) von Versetzungsdichte und Cartanscher Torsion bewiesen. Dabei sind wir ganz ohne den Begriff der Distorsion ausgekommen.

Man kann nun nach BILBY, BULLOUGH und SMITH [23] (etwas weniger allgemein) den Schließungsfehler leicht auch in der elastischen Distorsion ausdrücken. Schreibt man die Koordinaten von P' in der $(n'n)$-Stellung $-\sum_{i=1}^{n} \underset{i}{d x^{\varkappa}}\, \mathfrak{e}_{\varkappa}$, wo $\mathfrak{e}_{\varkappa}$ die kartesischen Basisvektoren des Idealgitters in der $(n'n)$-Stellung sind, so hat man $d x^{\varkappa} = A^{\varkappa}_{k}\, d x^k$. Für den geschlossenen Umlauf $(n' = Q')$ ist dann

$$b^{\varkappa}\, \mathfrak{e}_{\varkappa} \equiv \overrightarrow{Q' P'} = -\sum_i \underset{i}{d x^k}\, A^{\varkappa}_{k}\, \mathfrak{e}_{\varkappa}. \tag{55}$$

Da die $\mathfrak{e}_{\varkappa}$ kartesisch sind, können wir sie außerhalb der Summe stellen, d.h. wir können sie in Gl. (55) überhaupt streichen. Der Grenzübergang zur Kontinuumstheorie liefert mit Hilfe des Stokesschen Satzes

$$b^{\varkappa} = -\oint d x^k A^{\varkappa}_{k} = \tfrac{1}{2} \iint (\partial_m A^{\varkappa}_{l} - \partial_l A^{\varkappa}_{m})\, dF^{ml}, \tag{56}$$

und wenn der Umlauf ein genügend kleines Flächenelement ΔF^{ml} umschließt,

$$\Delta b^{\varkappa} = \tfrac{1}{2} (\partial_l A^{\varkappa}_{m} - \partial_m A^{\varkappa}_{l})\, \Delta F^{ml}. \tag{57}$$

Das Abbild von $\Delta b^{\varkappa}$ im deformierten Zustand ist $\Delta b^k \equiv A^k_{\varkappa}\, \Delta b^{\varkappa}$, somit wird

$$\Delta b^k \equiv \alpha_{ml}{}^{k}_{\cdot}\, \Delta F^{ml}, \tag{58}$$

$$\alpha_{ml}{}^{k}_{\cdot} = A^k_{\varkappa} (\partial_l A^{\varkappa}_{m} - \partial_m A^{\varkappa}_{l})/2. \tag{59}$$

Man kann dies als Beweis für die Behauptung von Fußnote 19 in Verbindung mit Gl. (48) ansehen.

Zum Schluß haben wir noch ein Ergebnis zu erwähnen, das in vielen Lehrbüchern der Differentialgeometrie oder Relativitätstheorie abgeleitet wird und den Riemannschen Krümmungstensor betrifft. Verschiebt man einen Vektor C^k parallel längs des Randes eines Flächenelements ΔF^{nm} einmal herum bis zum Ausgangspunkt, so erfährt der Vektor eine Änderung

$$\Delta C^k = \tfrac{1}{2} R_{nml}{}^{k}_{\cdot}\, C^l\, \Delta F^{nm}. \tag{60}$$

In unserem Falle metrischer Konnexion ist R_{nmlk} in l, k antisymmetrisch, infolgedessen ist $\Delta C^k \perp C^l$. Verschiebt man statt eines einzelnen Vektors ein Dreibein, so sieht man, daß dieses gedreht, aber nicht deformiert wird. Man kann daher die Gl. (60) leicht in die Form

$$\Delta \omega_{lk} = -R_{nmlk}\, \Delta F^{nm} \tag{61}$$

oder in die Einsteinsche Form (vgl. [8], S. 130)[21]

$$\Delta\omega^i = -R^{ij}\Delta F_j \tag{62}$$

bringen. Dabei ist ω_{lk} der antisymmetrische Tensor, welcher die Drehungen beschreibt, ω^i der äquivalente Vektor.

Die Beziehung (62) hat zu einer anschaulichen Deutung des in der linearen Theorie der Eigenspannungen in letzter Zeit viel benützten Inkompatibilitätstensors $\boldsymbol{\eta}$ geführt, der auch ein Einstein-Tensor ist (vgl. Gl. (86)). Schneidet man aus dem Körper mit Eigenspannungen einen geschlossenen, ein Flächenelement ΔF_j berandeten Ring heraus, und schneidet man diesen dann auf, so erleiden die Enden Drehsprung $\Delta\omega^i = -\eta^{ij}\Delta F_j$ (MORIGUTI [43], ESHELBY [44], KRÖNER [8], S. 38).

Aus (61) folgt: Da in einem Kristall, wie er auch immer deformiert sei, die Gitterorientierung an jedem Punkt definiert werden kann (sonst hat man keinen Kristall mehr), muß der Riemann-Tensor einer Konnexion, die *Gitter*distorsionen beschreibt, verschwinden (BILBY und SMITH [24]).

§ 7. Die Konzeptionen der allgemeinen Theorie

Wir hatten in § 4 den deformierten Zustand mit Hilfe des Tensorfeldes der elastischen Distorsionen $A^k_\varkappa$ gekennzeichnet. Mit $A^k_\varkappa$ ist auch $A^k_\varkappa\,\partial_m A^\varkappa_l$ bestimmt, und damit folgen über Gl. (17) und (18) die Deformationen und Strukturkrümmungen. Die $A^k_\varkappa$ brauchen a priori keinerlei Einschränkungen zu unterliegen, sie enthalten also i. allg. neun funktionale Freiheitsgrade. Aus der Versetzungstheorie ist bekannt, daß Versetzungslinien im Innern eines Körpers nicht enden können; wir hatten dies durch die Divergenzbedingung (26) zum Ausdruck gebracht. Somit hat die Versetzungsdichte sechs funktionale Freiheitsgrade. Die Zahl der Freiheitsgrade der Ursachen (Versetzungsdichte, Massenkräfte) ist damit, wie es sein muß, gleich der Zahl der Freiheitsgrade der Wirkungen (gekennzeichnet etwa durch elastische Distorsionen), nämlich neun.

Im Gegensatz hierzu hat die allgemeine metrische Konnexion fünfzehn funktionale Freiheitsgrade. Die Beschränkung auf neun erfolgte in der differentialgeometrischen Theorie durch Nullsetzen des Riemann- bzw. Einstein-Tensors. Diese Maßnahme erscheint vom allgemeineren Standpunkt der Differentialgeometrie als sehr willkürlich, und man hat daher im metrischen Körper Zustände zu erwarten, die allgemeiner sind als die in § 4, 5 gemeinten. Zur Beschreibung dieser Zustände haben wir die Konnexion Γ_{mlk}, diese besteht aus dem Deformationsanteil g'_{mlk} (sechs Freiheitsgrade) und dem Strukturkrümmungsanteil h_{mlk} (neun Freiheitsgrade). Die wichtige Frage ist nun diejenige nach den Ursachen dieser allgemeineren Zustände, d.h. nach der physikalischen Bedeutung des Tensorfeldes B^{ij}, das dem Einstein-Tensorfeld Γ^{ij} gleichzusetzen ist.

Wie erwähnt, ist die Gleichung, die man erhält, wenn man den antisymmetrischen Teil des Einstein-Tensors für sich Null setzt, mit der Divergenzbedingung für die Versetzungsdichte im deformierten Zustand identisch. Man wird also

[21] Der Bericht [8] enthält die Vorstellung, daß R_{nmlk} in l, k nicht antisymmetrisch zu sein braucht. Alle diesbezüglichen Bemerkungen müssen korrigiert werden, wenn die Konnexion metrisch sein soll. Insbesondere sind dann in Fußnote 1, S. 135 von [8] die Distorsionen durch die Drehungen zu ersetzen.

damit zu rechnen haben, daß Versetzungen auch im Innern eines Körpers aufhören können. Allerdings hat man dann offenbar die Versetzungsdichte allgemeiner zu definieren, als in § 4. Es sei betont, daß die Definition der Versetzung mit Hilfe des Cartan-Umlaufs nicht das Verbot des Aufhörens im Körper enthält.

Während bei verschwindender Versetzungsdichte auch der antisymmetrische Teil des Einstein-Tensors verschwindet, trifft dies für den symmetrischen Teil i. allg. nicht zu. Wir schreiben hierfür

$$\Gamma^{(ij)} = B^{(ij)}, \tag{63}$$

wobei g'_{mlk} für Γ_{mlk} einzusetzen ist.

Die $B^{(ij)}$ führen also zu einer elastischen Deformation und somit zu Eigenspannungen. Dabei tritt jedoch keine Cosserat-Nyesche Strukturkrümmung auf, denn wir hatten $h_{mlk} = 0$. Wir wollen jetzt zeigen, daß man solche Eigenspannungen durch Einschieben von Materie in den sich im Idealzustand befindlichen Körper realisieren kann. Das wesentliche läßt sich wieder am besten am Kristall erklären.

Dieser bestehe aus nur einer Sorte von Atomen und befinde sich im Idealzustand. Zum Beispiel können wir ihn mit dem Kristall in Abb. 2b identifizieren. Schieben wir in diesen Kristall Materie etwa in Form einer neuen, im Innern aufhörenden Netzebene ein, so erhalten wir den Realkristall von Abb. 2a: Wir haben eine Versetzungslinie in dem Idealkristall erzeugt. Dies gerade brauchen wir aber nicht, da mit der Versetzung die Struktur verändert wird, in dem Sinn, daß die Cosserat-Nyeschen Krümmungen h_{mlk} nicht mehr überall verschwinden

Wir können jedoch noch auf andere Weise Materie in den Körper einschieben, nämlich auf sog. Zwischengitterplätze. Dann werden die regulären Atome elastisch verschoben, wobei die Netzebenen natürlich auch gekrümmt werden. Dies ist jedoch die mit dem Anteil g'_{mlk} verbundene, mit den elastischen Deformationen fest gekoppelte Krümmung, die wir durch Gl. (43) beschrieben hatten. Wir haben also zweierlei Arten von Materie zu unterscheiden: Die *reguläre Materie*, die den Idealzustand aufbaut, und die *Extramaterie*, die Anlaß zu einer elastischen Deformation des Körpers gibt, ohne daß dabei Versetzungen gebildet werden. Keine der regulären Netzebenen des mit Extramaterie gefüllten Körpers endet in dessen Innern.

Die spannungserzeugende Wirkung der Extramaterie besteht darin, daß die umliegende reguläre Materie auseinander gedrückt und dadurch elastisch deformiert wird. Jedes einzelne Zwischengitteratom kann als ein elastischer Dipol angesehen werden, wie wir ihn im IV. Kap. ausführlicher beschreiben. Solch ein Dipol ist ein *symmetrischer* Tensor[22] (symmetrisch, da von ihm keine Drehmomente auf seine Umgebung ausgeübt werden). Infolgedessen läßt sich die Extramaterie durch das symmetrische Tensorfeld einer stetigen Verteilung elastischer Dipole beschreiben.

[22] Ein Zwischengitteratom drückt i. allg. nach verschiedenen Richtungen nicht gleichstark, daher kommt die tensorielle Wirkung der Extramaterie. In ganz ähnlicher Weise wirken natürlich auch substitutionell eingebaute Fremdatome und Leerstellen. Diese sind daher in die Extramaterie eingeschlossen. Insbesondere kann bei diesen Gitterfehlern das Vorzeichen der Extramaterie auch negativ werden.

Wir schneiden nun die einzelnen Massenelemente auseinander, sie können sich dann frei dehnen, d.h. die Spannungen verschwinden, übrig bleibt eine von Massenelement zu Massenelement sich ändernde spannungsfreie (deshalb auch *quasiplastisch* genannte) Deformation $\overset{Q}{\varepsilon}_{ij}$ gegenüber dem Zustand ohne Extramaterie. Man kann auch das symmetrische Tensorfeld dieser quasiplastischen Deformation verwenden, um die Extramaterie zu kennzeichnen.

Das nicht-homogene Einfüllen von Extramaterie verändert die reguläre Kristallstruktur derart, daß die Gitterkonstanten von Ort zu Ort variabel werden, jedoch bleibt die Orientierung erhalten. In einem gewissen nicht-Euklidischen (Riemannschen) Raum könnte ein solches Gitter spannungsfrei bestehen. Zwingt man es jedoch im Euklidischen Raum z.B. in eine solche Position, daß seine regulären Atome die Plätze eines Idealgitters einnehmen, so ist dieser Zustand nicht (kraft-)spannungsfrei.

Man kann nun andererseits an eine Substanz denken, die, in einen Idealkristall eingefüllt, bewirkt, daß der Körper nur in einem nicht-Euklidischen (Cartanschen) Raum momentenspannungsfrei sein kann, bzw. daß er in der Position des Idealkristalls (wie oben) nicht momentenspannungsfrei ist. Eine detaillierte Vorstelllung über das Wesen dieser Substanz besteht zur Zeit nicht, man könnte an gewisse mikroskopisch schwankende Verteilungen von Zwischengittermasse denken, entsprechend der im ersten Kapitel hervorgehobenen Äquivalenz von makroskopischen Momentenspannungen und mikroskopischen Kraftspannungen. Wir lassen diese Frage offen und wollen die genannte Substanz provisorisch als *Drehmaterie* bezeichnen. Sie hat sechs Freiheitsgrade (im Gegensatz zu der makroskopischen Extramaterie, die drei hat) und wird daher durch den antisymmetrischen Teil $B^{[ij]}$ von B^{ij} nur zur Hälfte beschrieben.

Für die qualitative Diskussion der Drehmaterie eignet sich besonders die geometrische Grundgleichung in der im I. Kapitel benützten Lagrangeschen Schreibweise:

$$\operatorname{Rot} \boldsymbol{\beta} - \boldsymbol{\alpha} = \boldsymbol{\delta}.$$

Zerlegt man $\boldsymbol{\delta}$ gemäß

$$\boldsymbol{\delta} = \operatorname{Rot} \overset{Q}{\boldsymbol{\epsilon}} + \operatorname{Rot} \overset{Q}{\boldsymbol{\omega}} + \operatorname{Grad} \mathfrak{a},$$

wo $\overset{Q}{\boldsymbol{\epsilon}}$ der oben genannte Tensor der quasiplastischen Deformation ist, welcher die makroskopische Extramaterie beschreibt, so stellen das Drehtensorfeld $\overset{Q}{\boldsymbol{\omega}}$ und das Vektorfeld $\mathfrak{a}$ die Drehmaterie dar. Wegen $\operatorname{Div} \boldsymbol{\alpha} = -\operatorname{Div} \operatorname{Grad} \mathfrak{a}$ ist der Gradientenanteil von $\boldsymbol{\delta}$ mit $B^{[ij]}$ gleichwertig, während der Anteil $\operatorname{Rot} \overset{Q}{\boldsymbol{\omega}}$ von $\boldsymbol{\delta}$, wie aus den Rechnungen des nächsten Paragraphen folgt, bei der Bildung des Einstein-Tensors verloren geht.

Wenn wir die Theorie der neun Freiheitsgrade um die neun Freiheitsgrade der Extramaterie erweitern, sollten wir, so möchte es scheinen, zu einer Theorie der achtzehn Freiheitsgrade kommen. Tatsächlich trifft dies nicht zu, in der erstgenannten Theorie hatten wir ja die Versetzungsdichte künstlich als äußere Einwirkung und damit als gegeben betrachtet. In Wirklichkeit ist es unzulässig, Extramaterie und Versetzungsdichte unabhängig voneinander vorzugeben. Unsere Konzeption in der allgemeinen Theorie wird es vielmehr sein, den *Materietensor* B^{ij} (6), die Versetzungsdichte (6) und die Massenkräfte (3) unabhängig voneinander vorzugeben. Dabei haben wir der Versetzungsdichte nur sechs Freiheitsgrade zugeschrieben, da Div $\boldsymbol{\alpha}$ ja mit $B^{[ij]}$ äquivalent ist. Wir kommen so wieder zu der richtigen Zahl von fünfzehn Freiheitsgraden.

Zunächst werden wir uns sogar noch weiter einschränken, indem wir $B^{[ij]}=0$ annehmen. Dies entspricht dem derzeitigen Bedürfnis: Die Drehmaterie wird erst in einer Theorie interessant werden, die auch die Momentenspannungen voll berücksichtigt.

Die im nächsten Paragraphen zu gebende mathematische Fassung der allgemeinen Theorie soll an die folgenden Vorstellungen geknüpft werden: Ausgangspunkt sei der Idealkristall ($\mathfrak{k}$). Diesen bringen wir wie früher durch eine plastische Distorsion $A^{\varkappa}_{\mathfrak{k}}$ in den Zwischenzustand ($\varkappa$), den man sich als Konglomerat isolierter Massenelemente oder als nicht-Euklidischen Zustand vorstellen mag. In die Massenelemente bringen wir nun Extramaterie ein, womit das ideale Kristallgitter von außen her verändert wird. Der neue Zwischenzustand heiße ($\varkappa'$), die Formänderungen der Massenelemente beim Übergang $(\varkappa)\rightarrow(\varkappa')$ nennen wir $A^{\varkappa'}_{\varkappa}$. Vom Zustand ($\varkappa'$) gelangen wir wie früher durch eine elastische Distorsion $A^{k}_{\varkappa'}$ in den Endzustand.

§ 8. *Die mathematische Fassung der allgemeinen Theorie*

Zu Beginn einige Bezeichnungen. Wir nennen die Metriktensoren der vier Zustände ($\mathfrak{k}$), ($\varkappa$), ($\varkappa'$), (k) resp. $b_{\mathfrak{k}\mathfrak{l}}$, $c_{\varkappa\lambda}$, $g_{\varkappa'\lambda'}$, a_{kl} oder z.B., indem wir die zwei Punkte, deren Abstand gemessen werden soll, durch ihre gegenseitige Lage im Endzustand (dx^k) kennzeichnen, b_{kl}, c_{kl}, g_{kl}, a_{kl}. Die auf den Endzustand bezogenen Tensoren der Gesamtdeformation ($\mathfrak{k}\rightarrow k$), der resultierenden Gitterdeformation ($\varkappa\rightarrow k$), der elastischen ($\varkappa'\rightarrow k$), der plastischen ($\mathfrak{k}\rightarrow\varkappa$), und der quasiplastischen ($\varkappa\rightarrow\varkappa'$) Deformation sind dann[23]

$$\overset{G}{\varepsilon}_{kl}=(a_{kl}-b_{kl})/2,\quad \overset{R}{\varepsilon}_{kl}=(a_{kl}-c_{kl})/2,\quad \varepsilon_{kl}=(a_{kl}-g_{kl})/2$$
$$\overset{P}{\varepsilon}_{kl}=(c_{kl}-b_{kl})/2,\quad \overset{Q}{\varepsilon}_{kl}=(g_{kl}-c_{kl})/2. \tag{64}$$

Für die Dreiindizessymbole mögen die Definitionen vom Typ (19) gelten. Jede der Deformationen (64) ist Bestandteil einer Distorsion, für die wir wie früher den Kernbuchstaben A und die betr. Indizes verwenden, welche den gemeinten Übergang angeben.

Unser erstes Ziel sei nun die Beschreibung des Kristall*gitters* im deformierten Zustand. Da der Übergang $(\mathfrak{k})\rightarrow(\varkappa)$ die Kristallstruktur nicht ändert (vgl. § 4), haben wir von ($\varkappa$) auszugehen. $B^{\varkappa}(1)$ und $B^{\varkappa}(2)$ seien etwa zwei primitive Gittervektoren in zwei benachbarten Massenelementen, ihr Abstand sei dx^{λ}, sie seien Euklidisch parallel und gleichlang, so daß $dB^{\varkappa}=0$, wenn ($\varkappa$) ein kartesisches Koordinatensystem ist. Durch die Distorsion $A^{\varkappa'}_{\varkappa}$ wird nun ($\varkappa$) nach ($\varkappa'$) gebracht, und durch $A^{k}_{\varkappa'}$ ($\varkappa'$) nach (k). Bei beiden Operationen handelt es sich um eine Distorsion des Kristallgitters, im ersten Fall um eine spannungsfreie (quasiplastische), im zweiten Fall um eine elastische Distorsion. Infolgedessen ist die

[23] Auf Grund der Additivität der Deformationen kann man leicht z.B. eine Meßvorschrift für $\overset{Q}{\varepsilon}_{kl}$ angeben: Es ist die Deformation, welche das herausgeschnittene Massenelement des Endzustands erleidet, wenn ihm unter Konstanthaltung der Schnittkräfte plötzlich die Extramaterie entzogen wird.

gesamte Distorsion des regulären Gitters gleich

$$A^k_\varkappa = A^{\varkappa'}_\varkappa A^k_{\varkappa'}. \tag{65}$$

Berechnen wir den Unterschied der obigen Gittervektoren, für die $d B^\varkappa = 0$ galt, im Endzustand, so erhalten wir unter Berücksichtigung von $B^\varkappa = A^\varkappa_l B^l$, $B^k = A^k_\varkappa B^\varkappa$

$$d B^k = B^\varkappa d A^k_\varkappa = A^\varkappa_l B^l (\partial_m A^k_\varkappa) d x^m, \tag{66}$$

$$d B^k = - A_{m l.}{}^k B^l d x^m, \tag{67}$$

$$A_{m l.}{}^k \equiv A^k_\varkappa \partial_m A^\varkappa_l. \tag{68}$$

A_{mlk} ist die Konnexion, welche die resultierende Distorsion des Gitters beschreibt. Sie hat die Form, die zu einem verschwindenden Riemann-Tensor führt, was nach § 6 bedeutet, daß die Kristallorientierung an jedem Punkt des Körpers auch im deformierten Zustand eindeutig bestimmt ist.

Die Gitterstruktur im deformierten Zustand und damit die Konnexion A_{mlk} kann im Prinzip z.B. röntgenographisch ausgemessen werden. Mit einer solchen Ausmessung ist jedoch der Zustand des Körpers noch nicht bestimmt, da sich nicht ergibt, wie groß die quasiplastischen und die elastischen Anteile an der Distorsion des Gitters sind. Daher können auch die Eigenspannungen bei Anwesenheit von Extramaterie röntgenographisch nicht gemessen werden. Experimentell könnte man nachträglich im Zerschneideversuch die elastischen Deformationen bestimmen und so den Zustand vollends festlegen (wir sehen von den im letzten Paragraphen besprochenen Drehmaterie einstweilen ab).

Die Gitterkonnexion A_{mlk} läßt sich in derselben Weise wie in § 4 oder 5 (vgl. z.B. Gl. (13) ff.), in die Form

$$A_{mlk} = c'_{mlk} + h_{mlk} \tag{69}$$

bringen, womit sie in ihre Deformations- und Krümmungsanteile zerlegt erscheint. Nun setzt sich gemäß (64) die resultierende Gitterdeformation additiv aus quasiplastischer und elastischer Deformation zusammen, d.h.

$$c'_{mlk} = a'_{mlk} - 2\overset{R}{\varepsilon}{}'_{mlk} = a'_{mlk} - 2\varepsilon'_{mlk} - 2\overset{Q}{\varepsilon}{}'_{mlk} = g'_{mlk} - 2\overset{Q}{\varepsilon}{}'_{mlk}. \tag{70}$$

Damit können wir die Beziehung (69) in die Form

$$\Gamma_{mlk} \equiv g'_{mlk} + h_{mlk} = A_{mlk} + 2\overset{Q}{\varepsilon}{}'_{mlk} \equiv B_{mlk} \tag{71}$$

setzen. Hier repräsentiert g'_{mlk} den elastischen Deformationsanteil, h_{mlk} den infolge der Versetzungswanderung entstandenen Cosserat-Nyeschen Krümmungsanteil des deformierten Zustands. Es kommt richtig heraus, daß das Einfüllen von Extramaterie zu keinen spannungsfreien Strukturkrümmungen führt. Bildet man nämlich den antisymmetrischen Teil von Gl. (71), so fällt $\overset{Q}{\varepsilon}{}'_{mlk}$ heraus. Die übrig bleibende Gleichung

$$\Gamma_{[ml]k} \equiv \alpha_{mlk} = A_{k\varkappa}(\partial_m A^\varkappa_l - \partial_l A^\varkappa_m)/2, \tag{72}$$

welche in der beschränkten Theorie Ausdruck des geometrischen Grundgesetzes war, vermag hier den Zusammenhang des Körpers nur soweit zu garantieren, als die Versetzungen betroffen sind. Die Sicherung des Zusammenhanges bei

Anwesenheit von Versetzungen *und* Extramaterie wird durch die vollständige Gl. (71) gegeben, die daher als der Ausdruck des geometrischen Grundgesetzes in der allgemeinen Theorie anzusehen ist[24].

Die Terme g'_{mlk} und h_{mlk} erscheinen in Gl. (71) genau wie in der beschränkten Theorie (vgl. Gl. (33)). Jedoch besteht ein wesentlicher Unterschied: Der Riemann-Tensor der Konnexion Γ_{mlk} verschwindet nicht, da zu A_{mlk} das Glied $2\overset{Q}{\varepsilon}'_{mlk}$ hinzugetreten ist, die Konnexion also nicht mehr die zu einem verschwindenden Riemann-Tensor gehörige beschränkte Form hat.

Wir können jetzt im wesentlichen auf zwei Wegen fortschreiten.

(a) Wir schreiben Gl. (71) in der Form

$$A_{mlk} = g'_{mlk} + h_{mlk} - 2\overset{Q}{\varepsilon}'_{mlk} \tag{73}$$

und bilden von beiden Seiten den Riemann-Tensor. Die linke Seite liefert

$$A_{nmlk} \equiv 2[\partial_m A_{mlk} - c^{pq} A_{nkq} A_{mlp}]_{[nm]} \equiv 0, \tag{74}$$

somit wird

$$[\partial_n(\Gamma_{mlk} - 2\overset{Q}{\varepsilon}'_{mlk}) - c^{pq}(\Gamma_{nkq} - 2\overset{Q}{\varepsilon}'_{nkq})(\Gamma_{mlp} - 2\overset{Q}{\varepsilon}'_{mlp})]_{[nm]} = 0, \tag{75}$$

wobei $c^{pq}\ c_{qr} \equiv \delta^p_r$. Setzen wir

$$H_{mlk} \equiv h_{mlk} - 2\overset{Q}{\varepsilon}_{mlk}, \tag{76}$$

so können wir Gl. (75) leicht in die zu Gl. (27) entsprechende Form bringen. Es wird

$$\tfrac{1}{2}\{\varepsilon^{jnm}\varepsilon^{ilk}[\nabla_n(-2\varepsilon_{mlk}+H_{mlk}) - c^{pq}(-2\varepsilon_{nkq}+H_{nkq})(-2\varepsilon_{mlp}+H_{mlp})]\}_{(ij)} = 0. \tag{77}$$

Die im Anschluß an Gl. (27) besprochene Methode der Eigenspannungsbestimmung kann daher praktisch unverändert auch hier angewendet werden, mit den Eigenspannungen sind aber auch die elastischen Deformationen, damit die g'_{mlk} und nach Gl. (71) die Gitterkrümmungen und die Konnexion A_{mlk} bekannt, so daß der Zustand des Körpers aus der Versetzungsdichte und der durch $\overset{Q}{\varepsilon}_{kl}$ beschriebenen Extramaterie vollständig bestimmt ist.

(b) Der zweite Weg steht den Überlegungen von Kondo näher. Wir bilden direkt von Gl. (71) den Riemann-Tensor. Die linke Seite lautet

$$\Gamma_{nmlk} \equiv 2[\partial_n \Gamma_{mlk} - g^{pq}\Gamma_{nkq}\Gamma_{mlp}]_{[nm]}. \tag{78}$$

Man beachte den wesentlichen Unterschied zwischen A_{nmlk} und Γ_{nmlk}: Er besteht in dem Auftreten von g^{pq} anstelle von c^{pq} und besagt, daß Γ_{nmlk} zur Metrik des Zwischenzustands ($\varkappa'$) gehört, während für A_{nmlk} die Metrik des Zwischenzustands ($\varkappa$) zuständig ist. Bilden wir also jetzt den Riemann-Tensor der rechten Seite von (71), so liefert auch A_{mlk} einen nicht-verschwindenden Anteil. Es wird

$$B_{nmlk} \equiv 2[\partial_n B_{mlk} - g^{pq} B_{nkq} B_{mlp}]_{[nm]} \tag{79}$$

[24] Sie enthält die über (72) hinausgehende Beziehung $A_{k\varkappa}A^{\varkappa}_{l} = a_{kl} - 2\varepsilon_{kl} - 2\overset{Q}{\varepsilon}_{kl}$, welche eine Bedingung für ε_{kl} darstellt, die für die Wahrung des Zusammenhangs erfüllt sein muß. Vgl. Fußnote 13.

und nach einer kurzen Zwischenrechnung

$$B_{nmlk} = (2\overset{0}{\varepsilon})_{nmlk} - 4\left[(c^{pq} - g^{pq})\, A_{nkq} A_{mlp} - g^{pq}(\overset{0}{\varepsilon}'_{nkq} A_{mlp} + A_{nkq}\overset{0}{\varepsilon}'_{mlp})\right]_{[nm]}, \quad (80)$$

$$(2\overset{0}{\varepsilon})_{nmlk} = 2\left[2\partial_n \overset{0}{\varepsilon}'_{mlk} - 4g^{pq}\overset{0}{\varepsilon}'_{nkq}\overset{0}{\varepsilon}'_{mlp}\right]_{[nm]}. \quad (81)$$

Multiplizieren wir (78) und (80) mit $\varepsilon^{jnm}\,\varepsilon^{ilk}/4$, so erhalten wir die *Einsteinschen Gleichungen der Kontinuumsmechanik*

$$\Gamma^{ij} = B^{ij}, \quad (82)$$

die, symmetrisiert, mit den Gl. (77) gleichwertig sind und daher auch als Grundgleichungen für die Eigenspannungsbestimmung bei gegebener Versetzungsdichte und Extramaterie angesehen werden können. Wir werden die Gln. (82) im nächsten Paragraphen noch explizit anschreiben.

Daß in B^{ij} die zunächst unbekannten Größen A_{mlk} vorkommen, stört relativ wenig, wenn man z.B. ein Iterationsverfahren zur Lösung der Einsteinschen Gleichungen verwendet, wie es für die Lösung der Gln. (27) vorgeschlagen wurde [*19*]. Da die A_{mlk} von derselben Ordnung klein sind wie die $\overset{0}{\varepsilon}_{kl}$, kann man die linearen Glieder berechnen, indem man $B^0_{nmlk} = (2\overset{0}{\varepsilon})_{nmlk}$ setzt. Die lineare Rechnung liefert u.a. A^0_{mlk}, die erste Näherung von A_{mlk}. Bei dem zweiten Schritt berechnet man zunächst B^1_{nmlk} mit Hilfe von A^0_{mlk} usw. Wir können hier auf eine detaillierte Darstellung der Lösung der Grundgleichungen für die Eigenspannungsbestimmung verzichten, da eine solche bei KRÖNER und SEEGER gegeben worden ist [*19*], s. auch § 10.

§ 9. Diskussion

Wir haben bisher nicht von Massenkräften gesprochen, deren Berücksichtigung im Vergleich zu den hier zur Diskussion stehenden Problemen trivial ist. Man kann die Aufgabe schrittweise zunächst für den Fall verschwindender Massenkräfte lösen und dann anschließend durch eine rein elastische Zusatzrechnung die Massenkräfte berücksichtigen. Denken wir diese Möglichkeit in der Darstellung von § 8 implizit enthalten, so ist die Theorie des § 8 die Theorie der zwölf Freiheitsgrade. Man könnte diese Theorie vollends zu der Theorie der fünfzehn Freiheitsgrade machen, wenn man zu B_{mlk} in Gl. (71) noch einen Anteil $\overset{0}{h}_{mlk}$ addierte, der die in § 7 angedeutete Drehmaterie beschreibt. Formal erhält man dann asymmetrische Einsteinsche Gleichungen.

Man überzeugt sich leicht, daß die Gleichungen der beschränkten Theorie aus denen der allgemeinen Theorie hervorgehen, wenn man dort $\overset{0}{\varepsilon}_{kl} = 0$ setzt (woraus $c^{pq} = g^{pq}$ folgt), d.h. bei Abwesenheit von Extramaterie. Zunächst wird $B_{nmlk} = 0$, die Konnexion Γ_{mlk} also integrabel, in Übereinstimmung mit Gl. (71). Gl. (82) wird mit Gl. (77) und (27) identisch.

BILBY und SMITH [*24*] hatten in Hinblick auf Gl. (60) das Verschwinden des Riemann-Tensors A_{nmlk} als ein physikalisches Erfordernis bezeichnet, das erfüllt sein muß, wenn an jedem Punkt des Kristalls ein Gitter eindeutig definiert sein soll.

Dieses Postulat bleibt auch in der allgemeinen Theorie gültig. Es gilt für die *Gitterkonnexion* A_{mlk}, aber nicht für die allgemeinere Konnexion Γ_{mlk}, für welche vielleicht der Name *Zustandskonnexion* passend wäre, da sie im Gegensatz zu A_{mlk} den Zustand eindeutig bestimmt. Diese Zustandskonnexion ist es, die KONDO benützt. Falls man diese beiden Konnexionen nicht verwechselt, besteht keinerlei Widerspruch zwischen den Theorien von KONDO sowie von BILBY, BULLOUGH und SMITH. Insbesondere existiert auch in der allgemeineren Theorie die Gitterkonnexion, welche die Distorsion des Gitters mit Hilfe des zugehörigen Parallelverschiebungsgesetzes in anschaulicher Weise charakterisiert. Leider besteht diese Anschaulichkeit bei der Zustandskonnexion nur noch beschränkt, da es sich hier nicht mehr um eine Parallelverschiebung von *Gitter*vektoren handelt. Doch ist diese Konnexion in ihrer additiven Zusammensetzung aus dem elastischen Deformationsanteil und dem Strukturkrümmungsanteil auch sehr nützlich, da man dieser Additivität letzten Endes die Möglichkeit der Abtrennung der elastischen Deformation von den übrigen Effekten verdankt, wodurch die Eigenspannungsbestimmung erst realisierbar wird.

Die zu dem Glied $(2\overset{Q}{\varepsilon})_{nmlk}$ hinzutretenden Summanden in dem Ausdruck (80) des Riemann-Tensors R_{nmlk} bzw. die entsprechenden Glieder in dem Einstein-Tensor B^{ij} mögen zunächst als ein Schönheitsfehler erscheinen, da sie von den Gitterdistorsionen $A^k_\varkappa$ abhängen. Denselben „Mangel" hatten wir früher bei der Definition (10) der lokalen Versetzungsdichte. Voraussichtlich verschwindet diese Abhängigkeit, wenn man die Einsteinschen Gleichungen in den Koordinaten des Anfangszustandes ($\mathfrak{k}$) formuliert, doch ist dies mit einigen Schwierigkeiten verbunden und bisher noch nicht verifiziert worden.

Der Begriff der quasiplastischen Deformation bzw. Distorsion war bereits in der linearen Theorie benützt worden (vgl. RIEDER [*45*] und KRÖNER [*46*]). Die beschränkte Theorie wurde hier durch die Gleichung

$$\nabla\times\boldsymbol{\beta} = -\nabla\times\boldsymbol{\beta}^P = \boldsymbol{\alpha} \tag{83}$$

beherrscht. Die Versetzungsdichte war als Maß der durch die plastische Verformung bewirkten Zusammenhangsstörung definiert worden. Bei der Spannungsbestimmung kann es keine Rolle spielen, ob die spannungsfreien Distorsionen $\boldsymbol{\beta}^P$ durch Versetzungswanderung oder durch andere Einflüsse, also Einfüllen von Materie, Temperaturschwankungen, Elektro- und Magnetostriktion usw. zustande kommen. Man kann also anstelle einer Versetzungstheorie auch eine Theorie solcher Quasidistorsionen machen und eine Quasiversetzungsdichte[25]

$$\overset{Q}{\boldsymbol{\alpha}} = -\nabla\times\boldsymbol{\beta}^Q \tag{84}$$

definieren. Hat man gleichzeitig Versetzungen und Quasiversetzungen (= allgemeine Theorie), so bekommt man die Gleichung

$$\nabla\times\boldsymbol{\beta} = \boldsymbol{\alpha} + \overset{Q}{\boldsymbol{\alpha}}. \tag{85}$$

Hier hat man i. allg. $\boldsymbol{\alpha}$, $\overset{Q}{\boldsymbol{\alpha}}$ aus den physikalischen Gegebenheiten des Problems zu berechnen. Bildet man von rechts die Rotation und nimmt dann den symmetri-

[25] Diese Definition der Quasiversetzungsdichte verzichtet allerdings auf die drei mit $\mathrm{Div}\,\boldsymbol{\alpha}$ verbundenen Freiheitsgrade.

schen Teil (Symbol S), so bleibt

$$\nabla\times\boldsymbol{\epsilon}\times\nabla=\boldsymbol{\eta}+\overset{Q}{\boldsymbol{\eta}},\qquad \boldsymbol{\eta}\equiv(\boldsymbol{\alpha}\times\nabla)^S,\qquad \overset{Q}{\boldsymbol{\eta}}\equiv(\overset{Q}{\boldsymbol{\alpha}}\times\nabla)^S. \tag{86}$$

Man verifiziert leicht, daß diese erweiterten Kompatibilitätsgleichungen mit den symmetrisierten Einsteinschen Gln. (82) identisch werden, falls man diese linearisiert. Wir schreiben die Gln. (82) zum Vergleich explizit an:

$$\tfrac{1}{2}\{\varepsilon^{jnm}\varepsilon^{ilk}[\nabla_n(-2\varepsilon_{mlk}+h_{mlk})-g^{pq}(-2\varepsilon_{nkq}+h_{nkq})(-2\varepsilon_{mlp}+h_{mlp})]\}_{(ij)}=B^{ij}. \tag{87}$$

Linearisiert man diese Gleichungen, so erhält man (vgl. (80, 81))

$$\tfrac{1}{2}\{\varepsilon^{jnm}\varepsilon^{ilk}\nabla_n(-2\varepsilon_{mlk}+h_{mlk}-2\overset{Q}{\varepsilon}_{mlk})\}_{(ij)}=0. \tag{88}$$

Offenbar entspricht der erste Summand dem Term $\nabla\times\boldsymbol{\epsilon}\times\nabla$ in (86), der zweite Summand entspricht $\boldsymbol{\eta}$ und der dritte $\overset{Q}{\boldsymbol{\eta}}$.

Indem wir in Gl. (76) zu der die Versetzungen beschreibenden Größe h_{mlk} die die Extramaterie kennzeichnende Größe $-2\overset{Q}{\varepsilon}_{mlk}$ addiert und so getan haben, als hätten wir eine resultierende Versetzungsdichte, haben wir effektiv auch in der nicht-linearen Theorie die Vorstellung der Quasiversetzungen benützt. In der nicht-linearen Theorie treten üblicherweise Kopplungsglieder zwischen Größen verschiedener Bedeutung, z.B. Produkte von h_{mlk} mit $\overset{Q}{\varepsilon}_{mlk}$ usw., auf. Sieht man von diesen typisch nicht-linearen Erscheinungen ab, so ist der physikalische Inhalt der nicht-linearen Gleichungen derselbe wie derjenige der linearen Gleichungen, und man kann sich die meisten grundsätzlichen Fragen an den linearen Gleichungen klarmachen. Es ist eines der Ziele dieser Arbeit, darauf hinzuweisen, daß das Verständnis der linearen Theorie bereits zu einem erheblichen Maße das Verständnis der grundsätzlichen Konzeptionen nicht nur der beschränkten, sondern auch der allgemeinen nicht-linearen Kontinuumstheorie der Versetzungen und Eigenspannungen einbegreift.

Wir beschließen diese Diskussion mit einer Bemerkung zu der auch in der allgemeinen Theorie geübten Beschränkung auf metrische Körper. Wir hatten den deformierten Zustand durch die Konnexion Γ_{mlk} beschrieben und für diese die Form

$$\Gamma_{mlk}=g'_{mlk}+h_{mlk} \tag{89}$$

gefunden. Hierin enthält g'_{mlk} die (i. allg. inkompatiblen) elastischen Deformationen und h_{mlk} die (i. allg. inkompatiblen) Cosserat-Nyeschen Strukturkrümmungen mit zusammen fünfzehn Freiheitsgraden. Aus der Differentialgeometrie ist bekannt, daß die allgemeinste *metrische* Konnexion gerade die Form (89) hat. Das allgemeinste metrische Kontinuum ist also das in Bezug auf Deformationen und Krümmungen inkompatible Cosserat-Kontinuum.

Metrisch heißt: Der Abstand zwischen zwei beliebigen Punkten des Körpers ist definiert. Diese Forderung erfüllt z.B. ein Körper, der aus lauter Fasern besteht, oder ein kontinuierlich von Rissen durchzogener Körper, wie man ihn etwa beim Walzen eines Metallstückes erhält, wenn man die Stiche zu groß wählt, nicht. Ein solcher Körper ist kein Kontinuum im üblichen Sinn mehr. Diese Feststellung war es, die uns zu der (provisorischen) Bezeichnung „Allgemeine Theorie" veranlaßt hat.

III. Die Integration der Grundgleichungen

In diesem Kapitel handelt es sich um die Integration der Einsteinschen Gleichungen. Das wichtigste Hilfsmittel hierzu ist der Spannungsfunktionstensor $\boldsymbol{\chi}$. Auf die prinzipielle Bedeutung des Tensorfeldes der Spannungsfunktionen in der Kontinuumstheorie der Versetzungen und Eigenspannungen ist bereits früher mehrfach hingewiesen worden [*8*, *19*]. Von SCHAEFER [*47*] stammt eine physikalische Deutung der Spannungsfunktionen, die dem differentialgeometrischen Standpunkt der Theorie besonders angepaßt erscheint: Die Spannungsfunktionen stellen die Reaktionen (im Sinne von LAGRANGE) auf die Zwangsbedingung dar, daß der Körper im Euklidischen Raum bleiben muß.

In [*19*] wurde gezeigt, wie das nicht-lineare Summationsproblem der Eigenspannungen auf eine Reihe iterativ zu behandelnder linearer Summationsaufgaben zurückgeführt werden kann. Es ist klar, daß man in ähnlicher Weise auch das zweite Randwertproblem[26] bzw. das kombinierte Problem (Eigenspannungsquellen und Randkräfte gegeben) iterativ linear behandeln kann. Man löst dazu zuerst die Aufgabe linear, das so erhaltene Tensorfeld der Spannungsfunktionen $\boldsymbol{\chi}^0$ befriedigt die Randbedingungen, aber nicht die nicht-linearen Differentialgleichungen (das sind die Einsteinschen Gleichungen, in denen die elastischen Deformationen mit Hilfe des Materialgesetzes durch die Spannungsfunktionen ersetzt sind). Man hat also zu $\boldsymbol{\chi}^0$ ein zweites Tensorfeld zu addieren, welches die Bedingungen eines freien Randes erfüllt und für die Befriedigung der Differentialgleichungen sorgt. Wir werden dies w. u. etwas mehr im Detail ausführen.

Nun ist bereits das lineare dreidimensionale Randwertproblem sehr schwierig, so daß man zunächst von der Lösung mehrerer solcher Probleme, wie sie bei der Iteration benötigt werden, zurückschrecken könnte. Indessen sind die zu lösenden Teilaufgaben alle vom gleichen Typ, sie betreffen immer den gleichen Rand, so daß die Zwischenergebnisse der ersten Rechnung weitgehend bei der Lösung der folgenden Aufgaben verwendet werden können. Will man also etwa die Rechnung mit Hilfe der Greenschen Funktion durchführen, so kommt man für sämtliche Iterationsschritte mit der gleichen Funktion aus. Benützt man die praktisch wichtigere Methode der Reihenentwicklung, so ist die Hauptarbeit die Berechnung der Matrixelemente, diese kann man dann aber wiederum für alle Iterationen verwenden. Schließlich sind die modernen Rechenanlagen gerade für die Durchführung von Iterationsprozessen besonders geeignet. Die zur Programmierung benötigte Zeit hängt von der Anzahl der Schritte nicht ab, die Rechenzeit der Maschine selbst geht linear mit dieser Zahl. Von diesem Standpunkt erscheint daher die Durchrechnung des nicht-linearen Problems kaum noch komplizierter als diejenige des linearen Problems.

Wir bringen im folgenden Parapraphen Allgemeines über den Spannungsfunktionsansatz und eine kurze Darstellung des Iterationsprozesses. In § 11 wird das zweite Randwertproblem der linearen Theorie behandelt.

[26] Wir beschränken uns durchgehend auf das besonders wichtige zweite Randwertproblem (Randkräfte gegeben), welches auch den Fall des freien Randes einschließt.

§ 10. Der Spannungsfunktionsansatz

Die Gleichgewichtsbedingungen für die Spannungen schreiben sich in den Koordinaten des deformierten Zustands

$$\nabla_i \sigma^{ij} = 0. \tag{1}$$

Sie werden durch den Ansatz

$$\sigma^{ij} = -\varepsilon^{ilk} \nabla_l \varphi_{k\cdot}^{\ j}, \qquad \varphi_{k\cdot}^{\ j} = \varepsilon^{jnm} \nabla_n \chi_{km} \tag{2}$$

oder auch

$$\sigma^{ij} = -\varepsilon^{jnm} \varepsilon^{ilk} \nabla_n \nabla_l \chi_{mk} \tag{3}$$

identisch befriedigt, wie zuerst BELTRAMI [*48*] gezeigt hat. Für den Spannungsfunktionstensor 1. Ordnung $\varphi_{k\cdot}^{\ j}$ gelten offenbar die Gleichungen

$$\nabla_j \varphi_{k\cdot}^{\ j} = 0, \qquad \varphi_{j\cdot}^{\ j} = 0. \tag{4}$$

Da wegen der Bedingung (1) der symmetrische Tensor σ^{ij} drei funktionale Freiheitsgrade hat, kann man dem symmetrischen Spannungsfunktionstensor 2. Ordnung χ_{ij} drei Bedingungen auferlegen, ohne die Mannigfaltigkeit der aus χ_{ij} abzuleitenden Spannungszustände einzuschränken. Diese Bedingungen sind allerdings nicht beliebig. Uns interessieren nur „zulässige" Bedingungen, das sind solche, welche keine Einschränkung für die Spannungen bedeuten. Zulässig sind z.B. die Bedingungen $\chi_{xx} = \chi_{yy} = \chi_{zz} = 0$ (MORERA [*49*]), $\chi_{xy} = \chi_{yz} = \chi_{zx} = 0$ (MAXWELL [*50*]), $\chi_{xz} = \chi_{yz} = \chi_{zz} = 0$, $\chi_{xy} = \chi_{yy} = \chi_{zz} = 0$, $\chi_{xy} = \chi_{xz} = \chi_{zz} = 0$ (BLOCH [*51*]). Andere zulässige Kombinationen mit drei verschwindenden kartesischen Komponenten von χ_{ij} gibt es nicht [*51*]. Rechnet man mit nicht-kartesischen Komponenten des Spannungsfunktionstensors, so kann die Frage nach der Zulässigkeit sehr schwierig werden. Wir kommen hierauf noch zurück.

Die Spannungsfunktionen genügen gewissen Differentialgleichungen, die man erhält, wenn man sie mit Hilfe des Materialgesetzes in die (erweiterten) Kompatibilitätsgleichungen

$$-\varepsilon^{jnm} \varepsilon^{ilk} \nabla_n \nabla_l \varepsilon_{mk} = \eta^{ij} \tag{5}$$

einführt. (Diese Gleichungen sind ja nach § 8 die linearisierten Einsteinschen Gleichungen.) Anstelle der Gln. (5) benützt man vorteilhaft die (erweiterte) Beltramische Form ([*8*], S. 55)[27]

$$\Delta' \sigma^{ij} + \frac{1}{1+\nu} (\nabla^i \nabla^j - a^{ij} \Delta) \sigma_k^k = 2G \eta^{ij}, \qquad \Delta' \equiv \nabla^l \nabla_l. \tag{6}$$

Diese Gleichungen gelten nur bei Gültigkeit von (1).

Es ist nun vor wenigen Jahren gelungen, die oben genannten Nebenbedingungen für die Spannungsfunktionen so festzusetzen, daß man auf Probleme der Bipotentialtheorie oder der Potentialtheorie geführt wird. Dabei gibt es zwei wesentlich verschiedene Möglichkeiten, von denen die eine zur Lösung des Summationsproblems führt, während die andere bei der Behandlung des Randwertproblems gewisse Vorteile zu bieten scheint. Beide Ansätze sind im Gegensatz zu den oben genannten kovariant, womit sich ihre Erfolge erklären.

[27] Beachte: Nur für kartesische Koordinatensysteme ist $\nabla^l \nabla_l = \partial^l \partial_l$, und nur bei der Anwendung auf skalare Größen ist Δ' gleich dem üblicherweise mit Δ bezeichneten Laplaceschen Operator.

a) Um den Ansatz von KRÖNER-MARGUERRE [*36, 52*] zu beschreiben, führen wir die Abkürzungen

$$\chi'_{ij} \equiv \left(\chi_{ij} - \frac{\nu}{1+2\nu}\chi^k_k a_{ij}\right)\Big/2G, \qquad \eta'^{ij} \equiv 2G\left(\eta^{ij} + \frac{\nu}{1-\nu}\eta^k_k a^{ij}\right) \tag{7}$$

mit den Umkehrungen

$$\chi_{ij} \equiv 2G\left(\chi'_{ij} + \frac{\nu}{1-\nu}\chi'^k_k a_{ij}\right), \qquad \eta^{ij} \equiv \left(\eta'^{ij} - \frac{\nu}{1+2\nu}\eta^k_k a^{ij}\right)\Big/2G \tag{8}$$

ein. Setzen wir als Nebenbedingung (in Analogie zu der bekannten Lorentz-Konvention der Elektrodynamik)

$$\nabla_i \chi'^{ij} = 0, \tag{9}$$

(woraus auch $\nabla_i \varphi^{ij} = 0$ folgt), so gehen die Beltramischen Gleichungen bei Einsetzen von (3) in

$$\Delta' \Delta' \chi'^{ij} = \eta^{ij} \tag{10}$$

bzw., gleichwertig, in

$$\Delta' \Delta' \chi^{ij} = \eta'^{i} \tag{11}$$

über. Im unendlichen Medium ist

$$\chi'^{ij}(\mathfrak{x}) = -\frac{1}{8\pi}\iiint \eta^{ij}(\mathfrak{x}')\,|\mathfrak{x} - \mathfrak{x}'|\,dV' \tag{12}$$

die allgemeine Lösung von (1O) und (9), also zugleich die Lösung des Summationsproblems der Eigenspannungen bei gegebener Quelldichte η^{ij}. Im endlich ausgedehnten Medium ist die Nebenbedingung (9) nicht automatisch erfüllt, doch läßt sie sich einfach berücksichtigen [*8*].

b) Der Ansatz von SCHAEFER eignet sich zur Behandlung von Randwertproblemen, d.h. zur Lösung der zu (6) gehörigen homogenen Gleichung, das ist die übliche Form der Beltramischen Gleichungen

$$\Delta' \sigma^{ij} + \frac{1}{1+\nu}\nabla^i \nabla^j \sigma^k_k = 0. \tag{13}$$

Man zerlegt den Spannungsfunktionstensor χ^{ij} in einen Kugeltensor $(\Omega + \Theta^k_k/3)\,a^i$ und einen harmonischen Deviator $\Theta^{ij} - \Theta^k_k a^{ij}/3$, also

$$\chi^{ij} = \Theta^{ij} + \Omega\, a^{ij}. \tag{14}$$

Führt man dies unter Benützung von (3) in (13) ein, so ergibt sich

$$\Delta' \Theta^{ij} = 0, \qquad \Delta \Omega = \frac{1}{1-\nu}\nabla_i \nabla_j \Theta^{ij}, \tag{15}$$

woraus

$$\Delta \Delta \Omega = 0 \tag{16}$$

folgt. Da Ω nur zu dem antisymmetrischen Teil von φ^{ij} beiträgt, ist auch

$$\Delta' \varphi^{(ij)} = 0. \tag{17}$$

Die rechte Gl. (15) läßt sich elementar integrieren, eine mögliche Form der allgemeinen Lösung ist z.B.

$$\Omega = \frac{\frac{1}{2}}{1-\nu} x_i \nabla_j \Theta^{ij} + v, \tag{18}$$

so daß Ω durch die Θ^{ij} und eine weitere harmonische Funktion v ausgedrückt werden kann. Da das dreidimensionale Randwertproblem dreifach harmonisch ist, die Θ^{ij} aber sechs harmonische Funktionen darstellen, kann noch über vier harmonische Funktionen weitgehend verfügt werden. Zum Beispiel ist es zulässig, $\Theta_{xy}=\Theta_{yz}=\Theta_{zx}=v=0$ zu setzen, man behält dann drei harmonische Funktionen übrig, der Ansatz bekommt die Maxwellsche Form [*36*]. Die in der Überzahl an harmonischen Funktionen begründete Freiheit kann dazu benützt werden, sich einem vorliegenden Problem so gut wie möglich anzupassen. Sie erscheint als ein gewisser Vorzug gegenüber der Methode von PAPKOVITCH-NEUBER [*37*, *38*], der nur *eine* überzählige harmonische Funktion enthält. Wie SCHAEFER gezeigt hat [*47*], stehen seine Spannungsfunktionen in enger Beziehung zu denjenigen von PAPKOVITCH-NEUBER, diese Autoren benützen die Funktionen Ω, $\nabla_i\Theta^{ij}$. Die letztgenannten sind keine Spannungsfunktionen — im Gegensatz zu den Θ^{ij} —, da mit ihrer Hilfe die Gleichgewichtsbedingungen nicht *identisch* erfüllt werden können.

Nach der i. allg. sehr einfachen Integration der rechten Gl. (15) braucht man auf keine Nebenbedingungen mehr zu achten. Dies ist vielleicht ein gewisser Vorzug des Schaeferschen Ansatzes gegenüber demjenigen von KRÖNER und MARGUERRE bei der Behandlung des Randwertproblems, zu dem wir im folgenden Paragraphen übergehen.

Hier soll noch kurz das Iterationsverfahren für den Fall eines Körpers erläutert werden, der von Randkräften beansprucht wird und gleichzeitig Eigenspannungen enthält, als deren gegebene Quellen wir die Versetzungen α^{kl} und die Extramaterie B^{ij} ansehen. Das Elastizitätsgesetz denken wir in der Form

$$\varepsilon_{kl}=s_{ijkl}\sigma^{ij}+s_{ghijkl}\sigma^{ij}\sigma^{gh}+\cdots \tag{18a}$$

vorliegen, jedoch spezialisieren wir uns auf isotrope Medien.

Führen wir mit Hilfe des Gesetzes (18a) die Spannungsfunktionen in die Einsteinschen Gleichungen (II, 87) ein, so erhalten wir wie in [*19*]

$$\Delta'\Delta'\chi^{ij}=\eta_0'^{ij}+P'^{ij}+Q'^{ij}. \tag{18b}$$

Hier sollen die gestrichenen Größen auf der rechten Seite mit den entsprechenden ungestrichenen Größen in derselben Weise zusammenhängen, wie η'^{ij} mit η^{ij} gemäß Gl. (7). Die P^{ij} und Q^{ij} seien definiert wie in [*19*] (sie enthalten die χ^{ij}, die Q^{ij}, außerdem die α^{kl} in nicht-linearer Form). In η_0^{ij} haben wir jetzt den Materietensor B^{ij} mit hineingenommen, der in [*19*] nicht berücksichtigt worden war. Die Gl. (18b) bekommt damit exakt die gleiche Form wie Gl. (44) in [*19*], die hieran anschließende Methode der Spannungsbestimmung kann weitgehend übernommen werden. Wir setzen also für den ersten Näherungsschritt $P'^{ij}=Q'^{ij}=0$ und bestimmen die lineare Näherung des Spannungsfunktionstensors χ_0^{ij}, indem wir das partikuläre Integral der Gleichung

$$\Delta'\Delta'\overset{S}{\chi}{}_0^{ij}=\eta_0'^{ij} \tag{18c}$$

aufsuchen und zu diesem eine solche Lösung der homogenen Gleichung

$$\Delta'\Delta'\overset{R}{\chi}{}_0^{ij}=0 \tag{18d}$$

addieren, daß $\chi_0^{ij}=\overset{S}{\chi}{}_0^{ij}+\overset{R}{\chi}{}_0^{ij}$ die Randbedingungen befriedigt. Die Methode der Bestimmung von $\overset{R}{\chi}{}_0^{ij}$ folgt im nächsten Paragraphen.

Hiernach können wir $P_0'^{ij}$ und $Q_0'^{ij}$ aus χ_0^{ij} berechnen [19], und wir haben als nächsten Näherungsschritt das partikuläre Integral der Gleichung

$$\Delta' \Delta' \overset{S}{\chi}{}_1^{ij} = P_0'^{ij} + Q_0'^{ij} \tag{18e}$$

aufzusuchen und durch $\overset{R}{\chi}{}_1^{ij}$ zu einer die Randbedingungen befriedigenden Funktion χ_1^{ij} zu ergänzen. $\chi_0^{ij} + \chi_1^{ij}$ ist die quadratische Näherung des Spannungsfunktionstensors. Der nächste Schritt verlangt

$$\Delta' \Delta' \overset{S}{\chi}{}_2^{ij} = P_1'^{ij} + Q_1'^{ij} \tag{18f}$$

usw. Da heute die für den dritten und die weiteren Schritte benötigten elastischen Konstanten höherer Ordnung noch nicht experimentell bestimmt sind, hat man sich einstweilen mit der quadratischen Näherung zu begnügen. Falls anstelle von B^{ij} etwa $\overset{Q}{\varepsilon}_{kl}$ gegeben ist, ergeben sich geringfügige Komplikationen, die durch die Bemerkungen am Schluß von § 8 als erledigt gelten können*.

§ 11. Die Behandlung des dreidimensionalen zweiten Randwertproblems mit Hilfe von Spannungsfunktionen

Der Erfolg bei der Behandlung des dreidimensionalen Randwertproblems mit Hilfe des Schaeferschen Spannungsfunktionsansatzes hängt weitgehend von einer geschickten Ausnützung der durch die Überzahl der harmonischen Funktionen Θ^{ij} gegebenen Freiheit ab. Wir wollen auf das damit verbundene Zulässigkeitsproblem, das vor allem bei der Benützung krummliniger Komponenten von Θ^{ij} recht schwierig werden kann, hier nicht eingehen, Anhaltspunkte findet man etwa in [*51*] oder [*36*].

Wir schreiben die Randbedingungen

$$\mathfrak{n} \cdot \boldsymbol{\sigma} = -\mathfrak{n} \cdot (\nabla \times \boldsymbol{\varphi}) = -(\mathfrak{n} \times \nabla) \cdot \boldsymbol{\varphi} = (\mathfrak{n} \times \nabla) \cdot [\mathfrak{n} \times (\mathfrak{n} \times \boldsymbol{\varphi})] = \mathfrak{A}, \tag{19}$$

wobei $\mathfrak{A}$ die Flächendichte der Randkräfte, $\mathfrak{n}$ der äußere Normaleneinheitsvektor sein soll. Diese Bedingungen sind erfüllt, wenn man

$$\mathfrak{n} \times (\mathfrak{n} \times \boldsymbol{\varphi}) = \mathfrak{n} \times \nabla \mathfrak{H} + \mathfrak{n} \times (\mathfrak{n} \times \nabla)\, \mathfrak{a} \tag{20}$$

setzt, falls nur

$$(\mathfrak{n} \times \nabla) \cdot (\mathfrak{n} \times \nabla)\, \mathfrak{H} = \mathfrak{A} \tag{21}$$

gilt. Die Lösung dieser Gleichungen kann man nach SCHAEFER [*35*] als Lösung eines Gleichgewichtsproblems in der Randschicht („Krustenschale") auffassen. Der hierzu erforderliche Arbeitsaufwand ist im Vergleich zu der Gesamtrechnung geringfügig. Wir nehmen daher $\mathfrak{H}$ als gegeben an.

Wie man sieht, fällt $\mathfrak{a}$ beim Einsetzen von (20) in (19) heraus, es kann also völlig beliebig gewählt werden. Das Auftreten von $\mathfrak{a}$ wird verständlich, wenn man bedenkt, daß man zu $\boldsymbol{\varphi}$ ein beliebiges Feld der Form $\nabla \mathfrak{a}$ addieren kann, ohne die Spannungen zu ändern. Hieraus ist zu schließen, daß die Freiheit in der Wahl von $\mathfrak{a}$ eng mit der erwähnten Freiheit bezüglich der Θ^{ij} gekoppelt ist, durch bestimmte Festsetzungen über die Θ^{ij} wird $\mathfrak{a}$ weitgehend festgelegt und umgekehrt.

* *Zusatz bei der Korrektur.* Es hat sich inzwischen ergeben, daß es genügt, die Randbedingungen nur einmal, nämlich beim letzten Näherungsschritt, zu berücksichtigen.

Wir werden uns im folgenden auf Körper beschränken, deren Rand ausschließlich aus (beliebig vielen) Stücken kartesischer Koordinatenflächen $x, y, z=$ const. besteht. Dies ist keine wirkliche Einschränkung, da man jeden Körper auf diese Weise beliebig gut annähern kann. Machen wir die zulässige Festsetzung $\Theta_{xy}=\Theta_{yz}=\Theta_{zx}=0$, d.h. rechnen wir mit Maxwell-Funktionen, so lassen sich die Randbedingungen in der folgenden Weise schreiben, die leicht zu verifizieren ist, indem man (20) explizit anschreibt. Es gilt auf den Flächen

$x=$ const.:

$$\begin{aligned} &\partial_{zz}\chi_{yy}+\partial_{yy}\chi_{zz}=-A_x && \text{(a)}\\ &\partial_x\chi_{yy}=\partial_z H_z+\partial_y\int dz(\partial_y H_z) && \text{(b)}\\ &\partial_x\chi_{zz}=\partial_y H_y+\partial_z\int dy(\partial_z H_y) && \text{(c)} \end{aligned} \qquad (22')$$

$y=$ const.:

$$\begin{aligned} &\partial_{xx}\chi_{zz}+\partial_{zz}\chi_{xx}=-A_y && \text{(a)}\\ &\partial_y\chi_{zz}=\partial_x H_x+\partial_z\int dx(\partial_z H_x) && \text{(b)}\\ &\partial_y\chi_{xx}=\partial_z H_z+\partial_x\int dz(\partial_x H_z) && \text{(c)} \end{aligned} \qquad (22'')$$

$z=$ const.:

$$\begin{aligned} &\partial_{yy}\chi_{xx}+\partial_{xx}\chi_{yy}=-A_z && \text{(a)}\\ &\partial_z\chi_{xx}=\partial_y H_y+\partial_x\int dy(\partial_x H_y) && \text{(b)}\\ &\partial_z y_{yy}=\partial_x H_x+\partial_y\int dx(\partial_y H_x) && \text{(c)}. \end{aligned} \qquad (22''')$$

(Die Integrale geben den Beitrag von α an.) Dabei folgen die H_i ($i=x, y, z$) eindeutig aus den Gleichungen vom Typ

$$(\partial_{xx}+\partial_{yy})H_i=A_i \quad \text{für} \quad x=\text{const.} \qquad (23)$$

usw. Es ist bisher nicht gelungen, von hieraus allgemein auf Standardprobleme der Potential- oder Bipotentialtheorie zu kommen, d.h. die Randbedingungen zu entkoppeln (die Differentialgleichungen für die kartesischen Θ^{ij} sind ja entkoppelt). In dem speziellen Fall des von zwei unendlich ausgedehnten parallelen Ebenen $z=$ const. begrenzten Körpers gelingt eine solche Entkopplung, wie jetzt gezeigt werden soll, da hier die Randbedingungen für $x=$ const. und $y=$ const. entfallen.

Zunächst berechnet man die harmonische Funktion $\chi_{xx}-\chi_{yy}$ aus ihren Normalableitungen auf dem Rand

$$\partial_z(\chi_{xx}-\chi_{yy})=\partial_y H_y-\partial_x H_x+\partial_x\int dy(\partial_x H_y)-\partial_y\int dx(\partial_y H_x). \qquad (24)$$

Man kann diese Aufgabe nach Belieben als erstes oder zweites Randwertproblem der Potentialtheorie gestalten. Wählt man das erstere, so berechnet man $\partial_z(\chi_{xx}-\chi_{yy})$ im Volumen und hat damit auch

$$\chi_{xx}-\chi_{yy}=\int dz[\partial_z(\chi_{xx}-\chi_{yy})]+f(x,y), \qquad (25)$$

wo $f(x,y)=0$ zu setzen ist, wenn die Spannungen im Unendlichen verschwinden sollen.

Mit der Kenntnis von $\chi_{xx}-\chi_{yy}$ sind wir in der Lage, durch Integration der Randbedingung (a)

$$(\partial_{xx}+\partial_{yy})\chi_{xx}=-A_z+\partial_{xx}(\chi_{xx}-\chi_{yy}) \qquad (26)$$

die Funktion χ_{xx} auf dem Rand auszurechnen. Da auch die Normalableitung von χ_{xx} auf dem Rand gegeben ist (b), folgt χ_{xx} im ganzen Volumen durch Lösung eines Standardproblems der Bipotentialtheorie. Damit ist aber auch χ_{yy} bekannt.

Die Spannungsfunktion χ_{zz} schließlich bekommt man in elementarer Weise aus der zweiten Bedingung (15), die man wegen $\Delta\Omega = \Delta\chi_{xx}$ in die Form

$$\Delta\chi_{xx} = \frac{-1}{1-\nu}\left[\partial_{yy}(\chi_{xx}-\chi_{yy}) + \partial_{zz}(\chi_{xx}-\chi_{zz})\right] \tag{27}$$

setzen kann. Hieraus folgt

$$\chi_{zz} = \chi_{xx} + \int dz \int dz \left[\partial_{yy}(\chi_{xx}-\chi_{yy}) + (1-\nu)\,\Delta\chi_{xx}\right] + z\,g(x,y) + h(x,y). \tag{28}$$

Da aus dem gleichen Grunde wie oben $f(x, y)$ jetzt $g(x, y)$ und $h(x, y)$ Null zu setzen ist, haben wir auch χ_{zz} ermittelt. Es sind sämtliche Differentialgleichungen und Randbedingungen befriedigt.

Eine Spezialisierung des hier behandelten Körpers ist der elastische Halbraum $z \leqq 0$. Setzt man $\chi_{xx} = zu + v$ mit $\Delta u = \Delta v = 0$, so hat man anstelle des Bipotentialproblems zwei Standardaufgaben der Potentialtheorie zu lösen. Die Möglichkeit, das Problem des elastischen Halbraums auf drei Standardprobleme der Potentialtheorie zurückzuführen, ist seit langem bekannt [*53*]. Durch ausschließliche Verwendung von Spannungsfunktionen ist sie dagegen erst kürzlich von SCHAEFER realisiert worden [*35*], der im Gegensatz zu uns χ_{yz}, χ_{zx} und $\chi_{xx} - \chi_{yy}$ gleich Null setzte.

Die Rückführung des dreidimensionalen Randwertproblems für beliebigen Rand auf Standardaufgaben der Potential- oder Bipotentialtheorie (oder auch vielleicht einer „Tripotentialtheorie") wäre vor allem vom Standpunkt der modernen Rechenmaschinen sehr vorteilhaft, da sich diese Standardaufgaben natürlich viel besser programmieren lassen, als Aufgaben mit gekoppelten Randbedingungen. Zwar ist es sehr fraglich, ob eine solche Rückführung auf Standardprobleme überhaupt allgemein möglich ist, doch wäre es bereits ein großer Erfolg, wenn man diese Vereinfachung wenigstens für einige wichtige Körperformen realisieren könnte. Entsprechende Untersuchungen wären auch für speziellere Kräfteverteilungen nützlich, z. B. vereinfachen sich die Randbedingungen (22), wenn man $\partial_i A_j - \partial_j A_i = 0$ setzt, wesentlich.

In den Fällen, in denen die Rückführung auf Standardprobleme nicht gelingt, wird man meist zur Methode der Reihenentwicklung der Θ^{ij} nach harmonischen Funktionen greifen. Dann ersetzt man zweckmäßig die χ_{ij} in den Randbedingungen (22) durch die Θ^{ij}, wobei vielleicht die Lösung (18) für Ω passend ist. Bei krummem Rand wird man sich den gegebenen Bedingungen so gut wie möglich anpassen.

Es soll nun auf einen Vorteil hingewiesen werden, den die Spannungsfunktionsmethode speziell bei der Berechnung der Eigenspannungen eines endlichen Körpers mit freiem Rand bietet. Wie in § 10 bemerkt, erhält man durch Lösung des Summationsproblems zunächst die Spannungsfunktionen $\overset{S}{\chi}_{ij}$, z. B. als Maxwell-Funktionen [*8*]. Diese befriedigen die Randbedingungen noch nicht. Es seien nun $\overset{R}{\chi}_{ij}$ die durch Lösung des Randwertproblems zu ermittelnden Spannungsfunktionen, die man zu den $\overset{S}{\chi}_{ij}$ zu addieren hat, um die resultierenden Spannungsfunktionen χ_{ij} zu erhalten, welche die Bedingungen des freien Randes erfüllen.

Indem man $\chi_{ij} = \overset{S}{\chi}_{ij} + \overset{R}{\chi}_{ij}$ in diese Bedingungen einsetzt, bekommt man fast unmittelbar die Randbedingungen zur Bestimmung der $\overset{R}{\chi}_{ij}$. Man kann also das Randwertproblem direkt an das Summationsproblem anschließen, ohne erst die zu den $\overset{S}{\chi}_{ij}$ gehörigen Spannungen zu ermitteln, die ja gar nicht interessieren. Dadurch spart man viel elementare Rechenarbeit, auch die Integrationen (23) entfallen. Es wäre offensichtlich sehr unpraktisch, nach der Lösung der Summationsaufgabe zum Zwecke der Behandlung des Randwertproblems zu den Verschiebungen überzugehen.

Schließlich sei noch besonders hervorgehoben, daß der Spannungsfunktionsansatz im Gegensatz zu der Methode des Verschiebungsfeldes seine einfachste Formulierung in den Koordinaten des Endzustands hat. Dies ist zweifellos für viele nicht-lineare Probleme ein großer Vorzug, z.B. immer dann, wenn die äußeren Einwirkungen als Funktionen des Endkoordinaten gegeben sind. Natürlich kommen andererseits Probleme vor, bei denen eine Behandlung in den Anfangskoordinaten natürlicher erscheint. Diese Art von Aufgaben scheint indessen in der Minderzahl zu sein.

IV. Par- und Dielastizität [28]

Die Erscheinung der Par- und Dielastizität ist sehr eng mit der im zweiten Kapitel behandelten Extramaterie verknüpft. Wir hatten in § 7 bemerkt, daß sich die eingeschobene Extramaterie als eine elastische Dipoldichte beschreiben läßt. Der permanente oder induzierte elastische Dipol (= Doppelkrafttensor) ist aber der zentrale Begriff in der Theorie der Par- und Dielastizität (§ 12).

Streng genommen ist in der allgemeinen Theorie bereits alles enthalten. Wenn wir jetzt gesondert von einer Theorie der Par- und Dielastizität sprechen, so deshalb, weil wir hier spezielle Anwendungen im Auge haben, die bereits durch die Namensgebung weitgehend umrissen sind: Wir sehen das parelastische bzw. dielastische Kontinuum als das Analogon zu dem paramagnetischen bzw. diamagnetischen Körper an. Es liegt auf der Hand, daß in einer solchen Theorie im Gegensatz zu der Theorie des II. Kap. vor allem auch Probleme mit singulären Eigenspannungsquellen interessieren. Durch die besondere Aufmerksamkeit gegenüber solchen Problemen bekommt die Theorie der Par- und Dielastizität ihr von der allgemeinen Kontinuumstheorie stark abweichendes Gepräge. Leider müssen wir uns in diesem Kapitel ganz auf die lineare Näherung beschränken.

§ 12. Der elastische Dipol [29]

Der wichtigste Begriff in der Theorie der Di- und Parelastizität ist der elastische Dipol. Er wurde von Boussinesq in anderem Zusammenhang eingeführt und wird heute meist als Doppelkraft bezeichnet. Für unsere Zwecke empfiehlt sich mehr der oben genannte Name. Er läßt die Analogie zu den elektro-magnetischen Verhältnissen besser hervortreten, auch spielen in den beabsichtigten Anwendungen die Kraftwirkungen auf elastische Singularitäten eine große Rolle;

[28] Herrn Dr. J. D. Eshelby, von dem die Theorie der Par- und Dielastizität viele Anregungen erhalten hat, möchte ich für Korrespondenz zu diesem Thema herzlich danken.

[29] Vgl. zu diesem Paragraphen die Darstellung in Love's Mathematical Theory of Elasticity [*54*].

es ist sehr bequem und vertraut, von Kräften zu sprechen, die auf einen Dipol ausgeübt werden.

Wir geben jetzt die *mikroskopische* Definition des (einachsigen) Dipols in einem elastischen Kontinuum. In diesem mögen an zwei verschiedenen Punkten, deren gegenseitige Lage durch den Vektor $\mathfrak{l}$ beschrieben wird, zwei Einzelkräfte $\pm\mathfrak{P}$ gleichen Betrags in entgegengesetzter Richtung angreifen (Abb. 3). Diese Kräfte sollen nun längs ihrer Verbindungslinie zusammenrücken und ihr Betrag sich so vergrößern, daß das dyadische Produkt $\mathfrak{l}\,\mathfrak{P}$ endlich bleibt. Man definiert dann als elastischen Dipol den Grenzwert

$$\boldsymbol{P} \equiv \lim \mathfrak{l}\,\mathfrak{P}. \qquad (1)$$

Abb. 3. Zur Definition des allgemeinen einachsigen elastischen Dipols

Im Gegensatz zum elektrischen und magnetischen Dipol ist der elastische Dipol ein Tensor zweiter Stufe, entsprechend der Tatsache, daß auch die elastischen Felder (Spannung und Deformation) Tensorcharakter haben. (Wir werden sehen, daß im elastischen Fall eine Dipoldichte ein Spannungsfeld darstellt, so wie etwa eine magnetische Dipoldichte ein Magnetfeld). Der Dipol in (1) ist als einfaches dyadisches Produkt ein Spezialfall des allgemeinen (dreiachsigen) Dipoltensors. Diesen hätte man etwa als Summe über drei dyadische Produkte zu schreiben, also

$$\boldsymbol{P} \equiv \lim (\mathfrak{l}'\,\mathfrak{P}' + \mathfrak{l}''\,\mathfrak{P}'' + \mathfrak{l}'''\,\mathfrak{P}'''). \qquad (2)$$

Hierin kennzeichnet z.B. P_{xx} zwei in der x-Richtung um, sagen wir, dx auseinander liegende, in $+$ und $-x$-Richtung weisende Kräfte entsprechend einer

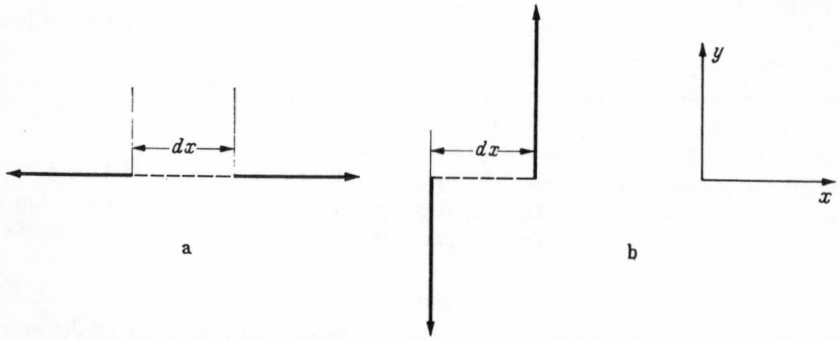

Abb. 4 a u. b. Der einachsige elastische Dipol ohne (a) und mit (b) Drehmoment

Doppelkraft *ohne* Moment (Abb. 4a), während P_{xy} zwei in der x-Richtung um dx auseinander liegende, in $+$ und $-y$-Richtung weisende Kräfte entsprechend einer Doppelkraft mit Moment um die z-Richtung repräsentiert. Hat man einen Dipol mit $P_{xy} = P_{yx}$, so heben sich die beiderseitigen Momente gerade auf, der symmetrische Doppelkrafttensor ist also momentenfrei. Er kann auf Hauptachsen transformiert werden und hat dann die Form wie in Abb. 5.

Begnügt man sich mit makroskopischer Beobachtung, so ist bei hinreichend kleinem $\mathfrak{l}$ der Grenzübergang in (2) nicht mehr wesentlich. Man kann dann z.B.

in Abb. 5 alle sechs Kräfte der Reihe nach durchnumerieren und erhält, wenn man die Ortsvektoren ihrer Angriffspunkte mit $\mathfrak{x}^{(i)}$ bezeichnet,

$$\boldsymbol{P} = \sum_{i=1}^{6} \mathfrak{x}^{(i)}\, \mathfrak{P}^{(i)} \tag{3}$$

als makroskopisch beobachtbaren Dipol.

Wichtig wird nun die folgende Verallgemeinerung: Innerhalb des Kontinuums sei eine kleine geschlossene Fläche f abgegrenzt. Auf dieser werde eine flächenhafte Kraftdichte $\mathfrak{A}(\mathfrak{x})$ mit $\int_f d\mathfrak{A} = 0$ angebracht. Diese wirkt auf große Entfernungen wie ein Gesamtdipol

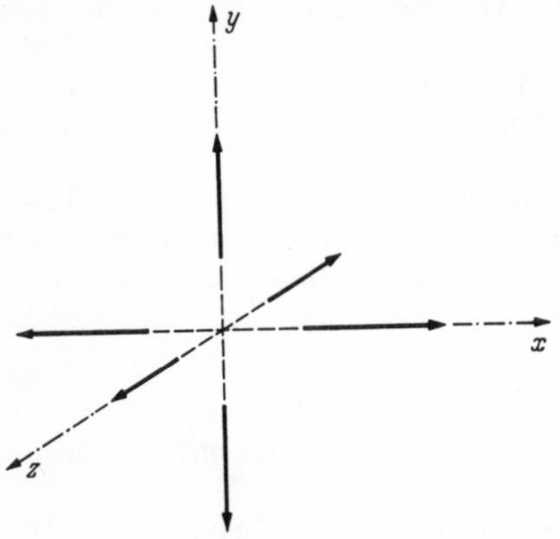

Abb. 5. Der dreiachsige symmetrische elastische Dipol in Hauptachsendarstellung

$$P^{ij} = \int_f x^i\, dA^j. \tag{4}$$

Es muß hier betont werden, daß die Definition (4) des Dipols $\boldsymbol{P}$ nur in einem Kontinuum gelten soll, das in der näheren Umgebung des Dipols elastisch homogen ist. Insbesondere sollen die elastischen Konstanten innerhalb von f die gleichen wie außerhalb sein. Denn ändert man etwa bei angelegten Kräften $\mathfrak{A}$ die elastischen Konstanten innerhalb von f ab, so ändert sich gleichzeitig das Verschiebungsfeld außerhalb von f auch bei noch so kleinem Volumen des durch f abgegrenzten Bereichs. Von einer sinnvollen Definition muß man aber verlangen, daß das nach außen abklingende Feld des Dipols durch die Angabe von P^{ij} und die elastischen Konstanten außerhalb von f eindeutig bestimmt ist[30].

Bei den beabsichtigten Anwendungen sind die Verhältnisse in der Umgebung des Dipols meist sehr unübersichtlich. Man kann dann trotzdem zuverlässige Aussagen über den Dipol machen, wenn man etwa das von ihm in größerer Entfernung hervorgerufene elastische Verschiebungsfeld beobachtet.

Bekanntlich erzeugt eine Einzelkraft P^i im Ursprung eines unendlich ausgedehnten homogenen elastischen Mediums ein Verschiebungsfeld

$$s_j(\mathfrak{x}) = S_{ij}(\mathfrak{x})\, P^i \tag{5}$$

mit

$$S_{ij}(\mathfrak{x}) = F_{ij}(\vartheta, \varphi)/r. \tag{6}$$

(r, ϑ, φ seien Kugelkoordinaten.) $F_{ij}(\vartheta, \varphi)$ ist wie S_{ij} ein Tensor zweiter Stufe. S_{ij} hat im isotropen Medium die Form (λ, μ = Lamésche Konstante)

$$S_{ij} = \frac{1}{8\pi\mu}\left(-\frac{\lambda+\mu}{\lambda+2\mu}\, \nabla_i \nabla_j + a_{ij}\,\Delta\right) r. \tag{7}$$

[30] Auf nahe Entfernungen kann das zu $\mathfrak{A}$ gehörige elastische Feld auch Quadrupol-, Oktupolanteile usw. enthalten. Ein elastischer Quadrupol wäre analog zu (1) durch $\lim l\,\boldsymbol{P}$ zu definieren. Die Verallgemeinerung der Theorie auf solche Multipole bietet keine besonderen Schwierigkeiten. Wir werden hier darauf verzichten, da sich bisher keine Anwendungen für Multipole gefunden haben.

Das Verschiebungsfeld eines elastischen Dipols ist dann

$$s_k = P^{ij} \nabla_i S_{jk}, \tag{8}$$

es fällt im Unendlichen wie $1/r^2$ ab. Gl. (8) zeigt die Möglichkeit, einen elastischen Dipol durch das Verschiebungsfeld zu definieren, das er in großer Entfernung von seinem Standpunkt hervorruft. Wir nennen die Definition des Dipols durch Gl. (8) die *makroskopische* Definition. Sie ist auch meßtechnisch von Bedeutung, da man bei den Anwendungen die in der Definition (2) oder (4) vorkommenden Kräfte i. allg. nicht kennt, während das Verschiebungsfeld (8) einer Messung zugänglich ist (genauer: das zu der Verschiebung (8) gehörige Deformationsfeld).

Es sollen jetzt kurz die wichtigsten Formeln für die Wechselwirkung des Dipols mit einem elastischen Deformationsfeld ε_{kl}, das von anderen Quellen herrührt, abgeleitet werden.

Ein homogenes, nicht notwendig isotropes Kontinuum K sei derart von Randkräften beansprucht, daß es eine homogene Deformation erfährt. An beliebiger Stelle werde nun ein Dipol der Art (4) angebracht, der für sich allein das Spannungsfeld σ'^{ij} erzeugen würde. Die Wechselwirkungsenergie mit dem Feld ist dann

$$\int_K \sigma'^{ij} \varepsilon_{ij} dV = \varepsilon_{ij} \int_K \sigma'^{ij} dV. \tag{9}$$

Anwendung des Gaußschen Satzes für die Bereiche innerhalb und außerhalb f ergibt

$$\int_K \sigma'^{ij} dV = \int_f x^i \sigma'^{jk}_{(i)} df_k - \int_f x^i \sigma'^{jk}_{(a)} df_k + \int_F x^i \sigma'^{jk} dF_k, \tag{10}$$

weil keine Massenkräfte wirken ($\nabla_i \sigma'^{ij} = 0$). Mit ($i$) und ($a$) sei angedeutet, daß die Werte unmittelbar innerhalb bzw. außerhalb f zu nehmen sind. Das dritte Integral über den Rand F des Körpers verschwindet, da zu σ'^{ij} allein die Bedingungen des freien Randes gehören. Die beiden anderen Integrale ergeben $-\int x^i dA^j$, denn $(\sigma'^{jk}_{(i)} - \sigma'^{jk}_{(a)}) df_k = -dA^j$ sind ja gerade die Bedingungen für die Spannungen in der Grenzfläche f. Somit ergibt sich die Wechselwirkungsenergie zwischen Dipol und Deformationsfeld, das ist die potentielle Energie des Dipols im Deformationsfeld ε_{ij} zu

$$E = -P^{ij} \varepsilon_{ij}. \tag{11}$$

Diese Formel gilt auch bei variablem Deformationsfeld, da es bei der Anbringung des Dipols in einem bereits vorhandenen Feld nur auf die Deformationen am Ort des Dipols ankommen kann.

Bei der hier erstmalig gegebenen *elementaren* Ableitung der Formel (11) hatten wir die Kräfte $\mathfrak{A}$ als äußere Kräfte angenommen. Wir werden im folgenden Paragraphen begründen, daß die Gl. (11) auch gilt, wenn die A^j innere Kräfte sind, es sich also sozusagen um einen Eigenspannungsdipol handelt.

Anschaulich gesprochen ist E auch die Energie, die man gewinnt, wenn man den Dipol von einer Stelle mit der Deformation Null nach einer Stelle mit der Deformation ε_{ij} bringt. Hat man ein inhomogenes Feld ε_{ij}, so gewinnt man laut Gl. (11) die Energie $dE = P^{ij} d\varepsilon_{ij}$, wenn man den Dipol um dx^i verrückt, und die Deformation sich in beiden Lagen um $d\varepsilon_{ij}$ unterscheidet. Somit wirkt in einem inhomogenen Deformationsfeld auf einen elastischen Dipol die Kraft

$$K_i = P^{jk} \nabla_j \varepsilon_{ki}. \tag{12}$$

Aus Gl. (11) folgt ferner leicht die Formel für das in einem homogenen Deformationsfeld auf einen Dipol ausgeübte Drehmoment zu

$$L^k = 2\varepsilon^{ikl} P_l^j \varepsilon_{ij}. \tag{13}$$

Bei unserer Behandlung des Problems ist die Kraftwirkung, die der Dipol über die Oberfläche auf sich selbst ausübt, nicht zur Sprache gekommen. Diese Kraftwirkung kommt dadurch zustande, daß die Eigenenergie des Dipols, also der Ausdruck $\frac{1}{2}\int_K \sigma'^{ij} \varepsilon'_{ij} dV$ bei fester Dipolstärke vom Ort des Dipols im Körper abhängt. Man kann diese Kraft nach Eshelby [*55*] auch als Wirkung von gedachten „Bildkräften" verstehen, welchen man die Erfüllung der durch den Ausdruck (8) für das Verschiebungsfeld des Dipols noch nicht befriedigten Randbedingungen zuschreibt. Die variable Eigenenergie des Dipols hat mit der in Gl. (11) gemeinten Energie natürlich nichts zu tun. In der Formel (12) hat man dagegen zu ε_{ki} das „Bildfeld" zu addieren, wenn man die „Kraft des Dipols auf sich selbst" berücksichtigen will.

Zum Gültigkeitsbereich der Gln. (11) bis (13) bemerken wir noch: Da das Elastizitätsgesetz in der Ableitung dieser Formeln nicht vorkam, gelten sie auch bei beliebiger Anisotropie der elastischen Konstanten. Es erscheint darüber hinaus möglich, daß sie auch im Bereich der nicht-linearen Theorie gelten, doch ist dies bisher nicht verifiziert worden.

Die Gln. (11) bis (13) beziehen sich alle auf symmetrische Dipole. Über das Auftreten antisymmetrischer Dipole kann zur Zeit nicht viel gesagt werden, es sei dieserhalb auf [*46*] verwiesen.

§ 13. *Das parelastische Kontinuum*

Ein elastisches Kontinuum wird als parelastisch bezeichnet, wenn es (mikroskopisch) regelmäßig oder regellos angeordnete permanente elastische Dipole enthält, die drehbar sind, d.h. sich in eine (elastische) Feldrichtung eindrehen können.

Für das Weitere nehmen wir an, daß die einzelnen Dipole so dicht beisammen liegen, daß man sie makroskopisch nicht unterscheiden kann, sie also durch eine Dipoldichte zu beschreiben hat, welche außerdem ortsunabhängig sein möge, solange der Körper makroskopisch nicht beansprucht wird. Diese Festsetzungen vereinfachen die weiteren Untersuchungen, ohne deren Allgemeinheit einzuschränken.

Die Beweglichkeit der Dipole soll zunächst noch nicht betrachtet werden. Einen einzelnen permanenten Dipol können wir in einem Kontinuum etwa durch die folgenden Operationen erzeugen:

Man schneide einen kleinen Bereich B vom Volumen V aus und verforme diesen homogen und spannungsfrei (etwa plastisch, mit oder ohne Volumenänderung) um $\overset{P}{\varepsilon}_{kl}$. Mit Hilfe von Oberflächenkräften $-A^i$ mache man diese Deformation rein elastisch rückgängig ($\varepsilon_{kl} = -\overset{P}{\varepsilon}_{kl}$), so daß die Gesamtdeformation von B

$$\overset{P}{\varepsilon}_{kl} + \varepsilon_{kl} = 0 \tag{14}$$

wird. Hiernach setze man B wieder in den Hohlraum ein und denke es mit seiner Umgebung verwachsen. Noch ist die Gesamtdeformation des ganzen Mediums Null. Dieses soll nun verformt werden, indem in der Trennfläche eine äußere flächenhafte Kraftdichte A^j angebracht wird. Da die elastischen Konstanten im ganzen Medium die gleichen sind, ist das zugehörige Verschiebungsfeld, wenigstens auf große Entfernungen, dasjenige des elastischen Dipols

$$P^{ij} = \int_f x^i \, d A^j. \tag{15}$$

Der Körper liegt jetzt in einem reinen Eigenspannungszustand vor, da die äußeren Kräfte, welche zunächst die elastischen Deformationen des inneren Bereichs $(\varepsilon_{kl} = -\overset{P}{\varepsilon}_{kl})$ aufrechterhielten, nun durch die Kräfte A^j kompensiert sind.

Der permanente Dipol drückt sich sehr einfach durch die „eingeprägte" Deformation $\overset{P}{\varepsilon}_{kl}$ aus, wie man erkennt, wenn man noch einmal zum Zustand der Gl. (14) zurückgeht. Es ist dann zunächst mit Hilfe des Gaußschen Satzes $(\nabla_k \sigma^{jk} = 0,\ \nabla_k x^i = \delta^i_k)$

$$\int_f x^i \, d A^j = -\int_f x^i \sigma^{jk} \, d f_k = -\int_B \sigma^{ij} \, dV = \int_B \overset{P}{\sigma}{}^{ij} \, dV, \tag{16}$$

also

$$P^{ij} = \int_B \overset{P}{\sigma}{}^{ij} \, dV, \tag{17}$$

wenn

$$\sigma^{ij} = c^{ijkl} \varepsilon_{kl}, \qquad \overset{P}{\sigma}{}^{ij} \equiv c^{ijkl} \overset{P}{\varepsilon}_{kl} \tag{18}$$

ist. Gl. (17) zeigt, daß man den Dipol P^{ij} auch als den Gesamtdipol auffassen kann, der einer Dipoldichte

$$\overset{P}{\sigma}{}^{ij} = d P^{ij} / dV \tag{19}$$

im Volumen V entspricht. Wegen der Beziehung zwischen $\overset{P}{\sigma}_{ij}$ und $\overset{P}{\varepsilon}_{ij}$ liegt es nahe, $\overset{P}{\sigma}_{ij}$ als „eingeprägte Spannung" zu bezeichnen, vgl. auch RIEDER [*45*].

Durch Einsetzen von (18) in (17) erhält man das wichtige Ergebnis:

Zwängt man in einen beliebig geformten Hohlraum (Volumen V) eines elastischen Kontinuums (Elastizitätsmoduln c^{ijkl}) ein Stück gleichartiger Materie ein, dessen Form sich von der des Hohlraums um eine homogene Deformation $\overset{P}{\varepsilon}_{kl}$ unterscheidet, so erhält man Eigenspannungen, die auf große Entfernungen die Spannungen des permanenten elastischen Dipols

$$P^{ij} = c^{ijkl} \overset{P}{\varepsilon}_{kl} V \tag{20}$$

sind. Unterscheiden sich Hohlraum und Einschluß um eine inhomogene Deformation $\overset{P}{\varepsilon}_{kl}$, so tritt anstelle von $\overset{P}{\varepsilon}_{kl}$ in Gl. (20) offenbar der Mittelwert $\int_B \overset{P}{\varepsilon}_{kl} \, dV / V$ von $\overset{P}{\varepsilon}_{kl}$.

Das parelastische Kontinuum kann man danach herstellen, indem man in einem homogenen spannungsfreien Kontinuum sehr viele kleine Hohlräume ausschneidet und in diese Materie der gleichen Art einzwängt.

Wir wollen jetzt begründen, daß die im letzten Paragraphen abgeleiteten Formeln (11) bis (13) auch für die in diesem Paragraphen besprochenen „inneren" Dipole (Eigenspannungsdipole) gelten. Zunächst ist klar, daß der Zustand des Kontinuums außerhalb von f in beiden Fällen gleich ist, wenn man die Flächen f, die Kräfte A^j, das Feld ε_{kl} und den Ort x^i der Dipole als gleich annimmt. Hieraus folgt, daß der Rand des von Randkräften beansprucht gedachten Kontinuums in beiden Fällen dieselbe Verschiebung erfährt, wenn man den Dipol von x^i nach x^i+dx^i verrückt. Bei dieser Operation leisten die Randkräfte jeweils die gleiche Arbeit, welche gleich der Änderung des elastischen Energieinhalts des Körpers ist; und zwar gilt diese Feststellung auch im Falle des „äußeren" Dipols, da dessen Bildungskräfte A^j wegen $\int_f dA^j = 0$ insgesamt keine Arbeit leisten. Somit folgt, daß die Dipole selbst durch die Randkräfte (Fernwirkung) bzw. durch das Deformationsfeld (Nahewirkung) die gleichen Kräfte erfahren, d.h. die Gl. (12) gilt auch für den inneren Dipol. Von hieraus kommt man leicht zu Gl. (11), wenn man die Arbeit ausrechnet, welche von der Kraft K_k bei der Verschiebung von einem Punkt mit der Deformation Null nach einem Punkt mit der Deformation ε_{ij} geleistet wird. Man erhält

$$\int_{\varepsilon_{ij}=0}^{\varepsilon_{ij}} K_k\,dx^k = \int P^{ij}\,\nabla_k\,\varepsilon_{ij}\,dx^k = P^{ij}\int \nabla_k\,\varepsilon_{ij}\,dx^k = P^{ij}\,\varepsilon_{ij}, \tag{21}$$

und das Ergebnis hängt vom Wege selbst nicht ab. Daher kann man die Gl. (11) als potentielle Energie des Dipols im Deformationsfeld auch im Falle des inneren Dipols deuten.

Es sei nun noch auf den Unterschied des Zustands im Falle des äußeren und inneren Dipols hingewiesen. Innerhalb von f hat man z.B. beim äußeren Dipol eine Dilatation, wenn die Richtung der A^j nach außen geht. Für den inneren Dipol gilt offenbar das Umgekehrte. So ist es zu erklären, daß das Integral (9) für den inneren Dipol Null ergibt, in Einklang mit dem bekannten Satz von Colonnetti [*56*], wonach die Wechselwirkungsenergie (definiert durch Gl. (9)) zwischen inneren und äußeren Spannungen verschwindet. Daher konnte die potentielle Energie des inneren Dipols nicht so wie in § 12 definiert werden, sondern wir hatten die Arbeit der äußeren Kräfte zu betrachten (was auch im Falle des äußeren Dipols zum Ziel führt). Man vergleiche zu diesen Problemen die sorgfältigen Überlegungen von Eshelby ([*55*] und insb. [*44*], S. 95ff., auch [*8*], § 19).

Die Methode von Eshelby zur Behandlung der auf elastische Singularitäten ausgeübten Kräfte sowie der Wechselwirkungsenergien ist allgemeiner als die unsere, da nicht nur Dipole betrachtet werden. Dasselbe gilt für die Untersuchungen von Rieder [*57*], die als Weiterführung der Eshelbyschen Arbeiten anzusehen sind. Demgegenüber hat die in § 12 gebrachte Ableitung, wie wir glauben, den Vorzug besonderer Einfachheit.

Es sei noch erwähnt, daß die Gln. (11, 12) zuerst auf einem dritten Weg gewonnen wurden [*46*]. Wegen der schon bemerkten Äquivalenz von elastischen Dipol und infinitesimaler Versetzungsschleife erhält man z.B. (12) bequem aus der Peach-Koehlerschen Formel ([*58*], [*8*], S. 86) für die durch ein Spannungsfeld auf das Linienelement einer Versetzung ausgeübte Kraft nach Integration längs der Schleife. Wir wollen die Peach-Koehlersche Formel, die das Analogon zur Formel für die Lorentzkraft in der Elektrodynamik darstellt und in der Versetzungstheorie fundamental ist, wenigstens anschreiben: Im Spannungsfeld $\boldsymbol{\sigma}$ erfährt das Linienelement $d\mathfrak{L}$ mit Burgersvektor $\mathfrak{b}$ die Kraft

$$d\mathfrak{K} = d\mathfrak{L} \times \boldsymbol{\sigma}\cdot\mathfrak{b}. \tag{22}$$

Wir kommen nun auf die Beweglichkeit der Dipole zu sprechen. Die Körper I und II seien zwei stabförmige parelastische Kontinua mit je gleichvielen und gleichgroßen (etwa kugelförmigen) Einschlüssen. In I seien alle Einschlüsse durch $\overset{P}{\varepsilon}_{zz}=a>0$ gekennzeichnet, im II seien je gleichviel Einschlüsse $\overset{P}{\varepsilon}_{xx}=a$, $\overset{P}{\varepsilon}_{yy}=a$, $\overset{P}{\varepsilon}_{zz}=a$ vorhanden. Waren die beiden Körper vor Einbringen der Einschlüsse gleich lang, so ist nachher der Körper I länger als II. (Man denke die Herstellung der Parelastizität etwa durch Einsetzen von auf Kugelform gestauchten Ellipsoiden in kugelförmige Hohlräume bewerkstelligt. Bei der teilweisen Entspannung nach dem Einsetzen verlängern sich die in z-Richtung gestauchten Ellipsoide in z-Richtung und nehmen dabei gewissermaßen die Umgebung mit. Entsprechendes gilt für die in x- und y-Richtung gestauchten Ellipsoide.)

Legt man nun eine homogene äußere Spannung σ^{ij} an die Proben, etwa einen homogenen Zug σ_{zz} in z-Richtung, so mißt man für beide dieselbe zusätzliche Deformation, d.h. die gleichen Elastizitätsmoduln. Denn, wie bemerkt, gibt es im Bereich der linearen Elastizitätstheorie keine integrale Wechselwirkung zwischen inneren und äußeren Spannungen (Satz von COLONNETTI).

Die Verhältnisse ändern sich jedoch, wenn man jetzt den Dipolen die Freiheit gibt, sich zu drehen. (Man denke etwa vorübergehend den Zusammenhang zwischen Dipol und Umgebung gelöst und drehe den Dipol etwa um 90°.) Zum Beispiel kann man durch Eindrehen aller $\overset{P}{\varepsilon}_{xx}$- und $\overset{P}{\varepsilon}_{yy}$-Dipole des Körpers II in die z-Richtung erreichen, daß dieser mit dem Körper I gleich lang wird, er sich also plastisch (oder, wenn man will, quasiplastisch) verlängert. (Plastisch, weil dabei keine elastische Energie gespeichert wird.) Das Eindrehen der Dipole ist also nichts anderes als eine plastische Deformation. Erfolgt dieses Eindrehen bei angelegten äußeren Zugkräften, so können diese Arbeit leisten, sie üben also auf die Dipole einen Zwang zum Eindrehen in die Feldrichtung aus.

In den meisten Anwendungen sind für die Dipole nur gewisse diskrete Orientierungen möglich, und hängt die Zahl der „umklappenden" Dipole linear von der Größe der angelegten Spannung ab. Für unser Beispiel können wir also annehmen, daß ein der äußeren Spannung proportionaler Bruchteil der Einschlüsse $\overset{P}{\varepsilon}_{xx}$, $\overset{P}{\varepsilon}_{yy}$ beim Anlegen der Spannung σ_{zz} in den Zustand $\overset{P}{\varepsilon}_{zz}$ übergeht. Der makroskopisch beobachtete Elastizitätsmodul zeigt sich somit erniedrigt, anstelle des gewöhnlichen Hookeschen Gesetzes

$$\sigma^{ij} = c^{ijkl}\,\varepsilon_{kl} \tag{23}$$

erhält man das Gesetz

$$\sigma^{ij} = (c^{ijkl} + r_P^{ijkl})\,\varepsilon_{kl}. \tag{24}$$

ε_{kl} ist die makroskopisch beobachtete Deformation, r_P^{ijkl} die parelastische Suszeptibilität der Probe.

Die Bedeutung der Konzeption des parelastischen Kontinuums liegt darin, daß sich viele reale Körper parelastisch benehmen. Wir werden in § 15 hierfür Beispiele nennen.

§ 14. Das dielastische Kontinuum

Ein elastisches Kontinuum wird als dielastisch bezeichnet, wenn in ihm bei Anlegen eines elastischen Feldes in (mikroskopisch) regelmäßiger oder regelloser Verteilung elastische Dipole induziert werden. Man spricht auch von der elastischen Polarisation des Mediums.

Über die Anordnung der induzierten Dipole machen wir die gleichen vereinfachenden Annahmen wie im Falle der permanenten Dipole im parelastischen Kontinuum. Das Medium erscheint dann wieder makroskopisch homogen.

Ein einfaches Beispiel zeigt das Wesentliche. Beansprucht man ein Kontinuum mit einem kleinen kugelförmigen Hohlraum auf hydrostatischen Druck, so zieht sich dieses Loch mehr zusammen, als aus der Größe des Drucks durch Anwendung des Hookeschen Gesetzes folgt. Die in diesem Fall sehr einfache elastizitätstheoretische Rechnung zeigt, daß das elastische Feld des Mediums sich zusammensetzt aus dem homogenen Feld, welches man bei Abwesenheit des Loches erhalten hätte, und dem Feld eines im Mittelpunkt des Loches gedachten elastischen Dipols, und zwar in diesem besonders symmetrischen Fall eines sog. Kompressionszentrums (d.h. der Dipoltensor ist hier ein Kugeltensor, vgl. LOVE [*54*]). Man sagt, durch Anlegen der Spannung wird in dem Loch ein elastischer Dipol induziert.

Enthält der Körper kein Loch, sondern einen kleinen kugelförmigen Einschluß mit abgeänderten elastischen Konstanten (eine „Inhomogenität"), so gilt ebenfalls das eben Gesagte für den Restkörper. Die induzierte Dipolstärke ist dann allerdings etwas anders, und zwar hat sie das gleiche Vorzeichen wie im Falle des Loches, wenn der Einschluß weicher, das entgegengesetzte, wenn er härter ist als der Rest. In dem Einschluß herrscht eine homogene Spannung.

Ein sinngemäßes Ergebnis gilt, wenn man den Körper mit kugelförmiger Inhomogenität nicht einem hydrostatischen Druck, sondern irgendwelchen äußeren Kräften unterwirft, die bei Abwesenheit der Inhomogenität eine konstante Spannung $\overset{A}{\sigma}{}^{ij}$ hervorrufen würden (NIESEL [*59*], ESHELBY [*60*]). Auch dann wird das Spannungsfeld im Einschluß homogen ($\overset{I}{\sigma}{}^{ij}$) und im Außenraum überlagert sich dem Spannungsfeld $\overset{A}{\sigma}{}^{ij}$ das Feld eines im Mittelpunkt der Kugel gedachten elastischen Dipols P^{ij}_{ind}.

Um $\overset{I}{\sigma}{}^{ij}$ und die Dipolstärken P^{ij}_{ind} zu ermitteln, muß jetzt ein kompliziertes Randwertproblem gelöst werden. Ist $\overset{P}{\varepsilon}{}^{ij}$ die eingeprägte (spannungsfreie) Deformation (§ 13), die ein Einschluß der gleichen elastischen Konstanten wie die Matrix haben muß, um gerade als permanenter Dipol der gleichen Art und Stärke wie P^{ij}_{ind} zu erscheinen (s. Gl. (20)), so erhält man beispielsweise bei elastischer Isotropie von Einschluß und Restkörper (vgl. ESHELBY [*60*], S. 389—390)

$$\operatorname{Spur}(\overset{P}{\varepsilon}{}^{ij}) = A \operatorname{Spur}(\overset{A}{\varepsilon}{}^{ij}), \qquad \operatorname{Dev}(\overset{P}{\varepsilon}{}^{ij}) = B \operatorname{Dev}(\overset{A}{\varepsilon}{}^{ij}), \tag{25}$$

$$\operatorname{Spur}(\overset{I}{\varepsilon}{}^{ij}) = (A\alpha + 1) \operatorname{Spur}(\overset{A}{\varepsilon}{}^{ij}), \qquad \operatorname{Dev}(\overset{I}{\varepsilon}{}^{ij}) = (B\beta + 1) \operatorname{Dev}(\overset{A}{\varepsilon}{}^{ij}) \tag{26}$$

mit

$$A = \frac{K_I - K}{(K - K_I)\alpha - K}, \qquad B = \frac{G_I - G}{(G - G_I)\beta - G},$$
$$\alpha = \frac{K}{K + 4G} = \frac{1}{3}\frac{1+\nu}{1-\nu}, \qquad \beta = \frac{2}{5}\frac{K + 6G}{K + 4G} = \frac{2}{15}\frac{4 - 5\nu}{1-\nu}. \tag{27}$$

Dev steht für Deviator, K_I, G_I und K, G sind die Kompressions- und Schubmoduln in Einschluß und Matrix resp., ν die Poissonzahl der Matrix. $\overset{I}{\varepsilon}{}^{ij}$ schließlich ist die elastische Deformation im Einschluß, also $\overset{I}{\sigma}{}^{ij} = c^{ijkl} \overset{I}{\varepsilon}_{kl}$. Für α und β gilt $\frac{1}{3} \leqq \alpha \leqq 1$, $\frac{6}{15} \leqq \beta \leqq \frac{8}{15}$.

Man überzeugt sich leicht, daß $\overset{I}{\varepsilon}_{kl}$ und $\overset{A}{\varepsilon}_{kl}$ dasselbe Vorzeichen haben, während das Vorzeichen von $\overset{P}{\varepsilon}_{kl}$ (also des induzierten Dipols) nur dann das gleiche ist, wenn der Einschluß weicher als der Restkörper ist. Ferner ist $\overset{I}{\varepsilon}_{kl}$ größer oder kleiner als $\overset{A}{\varepsilon}_{kl}$, je nachdem ob der Einschluß weicher oder härter ist. Für die zugehörigen Spannungen gilt das Umgekehrte.

Alle diese Aussagen, insbesondere die der Homogenität des Zustands im Einschluß, gelten qualitativ auch für ellipsoidförmige Einschlüsse, und auch bei Anisotropie der elastischen Konstanten in einem oder beiden der Teilkörper. Quantitativ treten dann wesentlich kompliziertere Formeln anstelle der Gln. (25) und (26).

Das dielastische Kontinuum kann man nun herstellen, indem man in einem homogenen spannungsfreien Kontinuum sehr viele kleine Hohlräume ausschneidet und diese mit Materie von anderen elastischen Eigenschaften spannungsfrei ausfüllt oder sie auch leer läßt. Die Dielastizität gibt Anlaß zu einer Erniedrigung der effektiven (oder makroskopischen) Moduln der Probe, falls die Einschlüsse weicher sind als der Restkörper, andernfalls erhält man eine Modulerhöhung. Der Erniedrigungseffekt z.B. kommt wie folgt zustande: Wir setzen makroskopische homogene Spannungen σ^{ij} in der Probe voraus. Dann ist σ^{ij} unabhängig von den elastischen Eigenschaften der Probe allein durch die äußeren Kräfte gegeben (beim Zugversuch in z-Richtung hat man z.B. $\sigma_{zz}=\text{const.}$, alle anderen Spannungskomponenten verschwinden). Wie schon oben festgestellt, ist die mittlere Deformation der (weichen) Einschlüsse größer als diejenige des Restkörpers, während für die mittleren Spannungen das Umgekehrte gilt. Infolgedessen müssen die mittleren Spannungen des Restkörpers natürlich auch größer als die Spannungen σ^{ij} sein. Der Überschuß sind gerade die Spannungen, die der Polarisation des Mediums entsprechen, die Spannungen $\sigma^{ij}_{\text{ind}}=c^{ijkl}\overset{P}{\varepsilon}_{kl}$ (vgl. § 13, etwa Gl. (20)). Dank dieser induzierten Spannungen ist die mittlere Deformation des Restkörpers größer als die makroskopische Deformation des Körpers ohne Einschlüsse, und noch größer ist die mittlere Deformation der Einschlüsse. Für die makroskopische Deformation ε_{kl} gilt also nicht mehr das Hookesche Gesetz

$$\sigma^{ij}=c^{ijkl}\,\varepsilon_{kl} \tag{28}$$

des Kontinuums ohne Einschlüsse, sondern das Gesetz

$$\sigma^{ij}=(c^{ijkl}+r_D^{ijkl})\,\varepsilon_{kl} \tag{29}$$

mit r_D^{ijkl} als dielastischer Suszeptibilität.

Im Falle der härteren Einschlüsse wird offenbar r_D^{ijkl} in Gl. (29) positiv.

Die Bedeutung der Konzeption des dielastischen Kontinuums liegt wieder darin, daß sich viele reale Körper dielastisch verhalten.

Wir hatten in den bisherigen Gedankenexperimenten in gewisse Hohlräume spannungsfreier elastischer Kontinua entweder Materie mit *gleichen* elastischen Eigenschaften *eingezwängt* oder Materie mit *anderen* elastischen Eigenschaften *spannungsfrei* eingefüllt. Die Kontinua sind dann rein parelastisch bzw. dielastisch. Allgemeiner könnte man in diese Hohlräume Materie mit *anderen* elastischen Eigenschaften *einzwängen*. Dies gibt dann, wenn die Einschlüsse beweglich sind, Anlaß zu einer parelastischen Modulerniedrigung, doch auch gleichzeitig zu einer dielastischen Modulerniedrigung bzw. -erhöhung, je nachdem, ob die Einschlüsse weicher oder härter als der Restkörper sind.

§ 15. *Die physikalische Realität der Par- und Dielastizität*

Es sollen nun Beispiele für das Vorkommen von Par- und Dielastizität besprochen werden. Die in der Natur vorhandenen festen Stoffe sind i. allg. kristallin aufgebaut. Ein idealer Kristall zeigt weder Par- noch Dielastizität. Bringt man jedoch in einen Idealkristall etwa Zwischengitteratome, so wird das Kräfteverhältnis zwischen den angrenzenden Atomen verändert, diese werden i. allg. etwas auseinander gedrückt. Es kommt so zu einer elastischen Deformation in der Umgebung des Zwischengitteratoms, die in größerer Entfernung wie $1/r^3$ abfällt. Man kann also das Zwischengitteratom makroskopisch als einen elastischen Dipol ansehen.

Im allgemeinen drückt das Zwischengitteratom nicht nach allen Seiten gleich stark. Zum Beispiel stellt das Kohlenstoffatom in Eisen einen elastischen Dipol mit tetragonaler Symmetrie dar. Die Komponenten dieses Dipols lassen sich experimentell bestimmen, man erhält ([8], S. 153)

$$P_{xx} = 11{,}2\,[\mathrm{eV}], \qquad P_{yy} = P_{zz} = 4{,}6\,[\mathrm{eV}], \qquad P_{xy} = P_{yz} = P_{zx} = 0, \tag{30}$$

wenn man die kubischen Achsen des Eiseneinkristalls mit x, y, z bezeichnet. Während ein kugelsymmetrischer Dipol nach Gl. (12) nur durch den hydrostatischen Anteil der Deformation eine Kraft erfährt, reagiert der tetragonale Dipol (30) z.B. auch auf die reine Schubdeformation $\varepsilon_{xx} - \varepsilon_{yy}$. Beispielsweise ist das Deformationsfeld einer Schraubenversetzung reiner Schub. Die in früheren Näherungen versuchte Beschreibung des Kohlenstoffatoms im Eisen als (kugelsymmetrisches) Kompressionszentrum führte daher zu keiner Wechselwirkung zwischen Schraubenversetzung und Kohlenstoffatom im Eisen. Dies wurde von Cochardt, Schöck und Wiedersich [*61*] quantitativ durch die Berücksichtigung der Tetragonalität der von dem Kohlenstoffatom hervorgerufenen Verzerrungen berichtigt. Dabei stellte sich heraus, daß die genannte Wechselwirkung von derselben Größenordnung wie diejenige eines Kohlenstoffatoms mit einer Stufenversetzung ist, die ja ein Deformationsfeld mit starker hydrostatischer Komponente erzeugt. Dies als Beispiel für einen Typ von Aufgaben, die immer wieder auftreten.

Die Rolle des Kohlenstoffatoms ist für viele Materialeigenschaften des Gebrauchseisens geradezu entscheidend. Das durch die Gln. (11) bis (13) weitgehend beschriebene elastische Verhalten hilft bei der Erklärung vieler makroskopisch beobachteter Eigenschaften des Eisens. Großen Erfolg hatte man bisher z.B. bei der Deutung des bekannten Streckgrenzeneffekts Cottrell [*12*], Schöck und Seeger [*62*], und des Snoek-Effekts [*63*], [*64*], s. auch [*8*], § 31. Für den ersteren ist die Bewegung des Kohlenstoffatoms im Deformationsfeld der Versetzung des Eisens maßgebend, die zu einer Blockade der für das Fließen des Körpers verantwortlichen Versetzungen führen kann, für den letzteren das Umklappen der Dipole in Feldrichtung bei Anlegen einer Zugspannung, das u. a. Anlaß zu einer starken mechanischen Dämpfung des Körpers geben kann. Der Snoek-Effekt ist genau die Verifikation des im § 13 beschriebenen parelastischen Umklappvorgangs.

Wir wollen uns mit diesen Beispielen der Auswirkungen von Zwischengitteratomen begnügen. Das Kohlenstoffatom im Eisen ist ein typisches Beispiel für die zahlreichen anderen möglichen Kombinationen, deren mechanisches Verhalten ebenfalls weitgehend durch die Gln. (11) bis (13) beherrscht wird.

Weitere wichtige punktförmige Gitterfehler sind Substitutions-Fremdatome und Leerstellen. Diese sitzen auf den regulären Gitterplätzen und verändern ebenfalls das Kräfteverhältnis in ihrer Umgebung. Im einfachen kubischen Gitter haben sie kubische Symmetrie und können daher als Kugeldipole beschrieben werden. Ein Kugeldipol erfährt aber als nach Gl. (13) kein Drehmoment, so daß diese Gitterfehler keinen Anlaß zur Parelastizität geben. Dies kann sich in weniger symmetrischen Gittern und vor allem auch dann ändern, wenn etwa zwei solcher Fremdatome oder Leerstellen zu Paaren zusammentreten. Solche Paare haben — auch im kubischen Gitter — höchstens tetragonale Symmetrie und können daher zu ähnlichen Effekten führen, wie sie oben am Beispiel der Zwischengitteratome besprochen wurden (vgl. z.B. ZENER [*64*]).

Alle bisher genannten Gitterfehler sind auch dielastisch, da sie einen Bereich mit abgeänderten elastischen Konstanten darstellen (eine „Inhomogenität"). Diese Dielastizität kann indessen i. allg. nur dann nachgewiesen werden, wenn nicht zugleich auch Parelastizität besteht, da die permanenten Dipolmomente i. allg. weitaus stärker sind, als die induzierten. Beispielsweise üben zwei Kugeldipole im isotropen Medium keine Kräfte aufeinander aus, weil das Deformationsfeld eines Kompressionszentrums nach Gl. (8) keinen hydrostatischen Anteil hat. In diesem Fall geht die Wechselwirkung zwischen zwei solchen Fehlstellen über die gegenseitige elastische Polarisation der Gitterfehler (CRUSSARD [*65*], TELTOW [*66*], ESHELBY [*67*]). Der dielastische Effekt ist also bei Substitutions-Fremdatomen und Leerstellen etwa im kubisch flächenzentrierten Gitter wichtig.

Es gibt zahlreiche weitere makroskopisch punktförmige Gitterfehler, die ähnliches elastisches Verhalten wie die bisher beschriebenen erwarten lassen. Darunter sind so interessante Fehler wie die *F*-Zentren in den Alkalihalogeniden (JACOBS [*68*]). Auch der von BASS [*69*] erklärte Mechanismus der mechanischen Relaxation im Eis beruht letzten Endes auf ähnlichen Effekten. Wir können auf die Vielfalt der Erscheinungen hier nicht weiter eingehen, sondern verweisen auf den demnächst erscheinenden Übersichtsartikel von ESHELBY [*70*].

Ein weiteres Anwendungsgebiet für die Theorie der Par- und Dielastizität sind Körper mit mikroskopisch größeren Einschlüssen, die von der Grundmaterie abweichende Eigenschaften haben. Bei der Behandlung solcher Körper haben sich die Ergebnisse von NIESEL [*59*] und insb. ESHELBY [*60*] für kugel- und ellipsoidförmige Einschlüsse als besonders nützlich gezeigt. Wir verweisen auch wegen dieser Anwendungen auf den Artikel von ESHELBY [*70*] und erwähnen hier noch zwei eigene Ergebnisse.

Die elastischen Konstanten des makroskopisch isotropen Vielkristalls lassen sich aus den Konstanten des Einkristalls exakt aus der Bedingung ausrechnen, daß die Polarisierbarkeit der den Vielkristall aufbauenden Kristallite im Mittel verschwindet [*71*].

b) Die gegenseitige Behinderung der Kristallite bei der plastischen Verformung des Vielkristalls, die dadurch zustande kommt, daß günstig orientierte Kristallite früher zu fließen anfangen, als die weniger günstig orientierten, spielt nur bei Verformungen unter 1% eine wesentliche Rolle. Die Methode, nach der eine solche Rechnung anzulegen ist, folgt aus der Bemerkung, daß sich die zuerst fließenden Kristallite zu elastischen Dipolen herausbilden, entsprechend ihrer plastischen Verformung $\overset{p}{\varepsilon}_{kl}$ innerhalb einer sich nur elastisch verformenden Grundsubstanz (vgl. Gl. (20)). Die so entstehenden Eigenspannungen behindern die günstig orientierten und fördern die ungünstig orientierten Kristallite in solch starkem Maße, daß nach weniger als 1% Deformation praktisch alle Kristallite gleichmäßig fließen können. Die von Greenough [72] entwickelte, mehr qualitative Theorie dieser Erscheinungen spielt also ihre Hauptrolle bei sehr kleinen Verformungen (Kröner und Debatin, unveröffentlicht).

Wir konnten hier nur einen kleinen Ausschnitt aus der Vielfalt der par- und dielastischen Erscheinungen geben, hoffen aber, daß diese kurze Darstellung genügt, um einen Eindruck von dem Nutzen und den Anwendungsmöglichkeiten der Theorie der Par- und Dielastizität zu geben.

V. Rückblick und Ausblick

§ 16. Die Versetzung als elementare Eigenspannungsquelle

In der linearen Behandlung der Kontinuumstheorie der Versetzungen und Eigenspannungen [8] nahm der Satz „Die Versetzung ist die elementare Eigenspannungsquelle" eine zentrale Stellung ein. Diesem Satz lagen die folgenden Vorstellungen zugrunde:

In einer linearen Theorie der Eigenspannungen genügt das Tensorfeld der Spannungen der Divergenzbedingung

$$\mathrm{Div}\,\boldsymbol{\sigma} = 0 \tag{1}$$

und das Materialgesetz hat die auch sonst in der linearen Elastizitätstheorie übliche Form

$$\sigma^{ij} = c^{ijkl}\,\varepsilon_{kl}. \tag{2}$$

Den Bedingungen (1) genügt jedes symmetrische Tensorfeld $\boldsymbol{\sigma}$, das die Form $\mathrm{Rot}\,\boldsymbol{\varphi}$ hat. Daher gibt es auch im unendlich ausgedehnten Medium Spannungen, ohne daß äußere Kräfte wirken, eben die Eigenspannungen. Offensichtlich sind die Gln. (1) und (2) noch unvollständig, um den Zustand des Mediums festzulegen; es fehlt die Bedingung, daß wir es mit einem Kontinuum zu tun haben, daß also der betrachtete Körper zusammenhängend sein muß. Wir haben uns an dieser Stelle irgendeine Vorstellung über das Zustandekommen des Zustands mit Eigenspannungen zu machen. Wir nehmen an, daß der zunächst in einem idealen Zustand vorliegende Körper irgendwelchen Operationen oder Vorgängen unterworfen wird, an deren Ende er in einem veränderten Zustand, eben dem Eigenspannungszustand zurückbleibt. Welcher Art die genannten Operationen und Vorgänge sind, ist zunächst nicht wichtig, die Möglichkeiten sind vielfältig. Wir verlangen jedoch, da wir eine Kontinuumstheorie machen,

a) daß der Körper am Anfang und Ende als Kontinuum also zusammenhängend vorliegt,

b) daß man den Körper des Endzustands noch mit dem Körper des Anfangszustands identifizieren kann. Diese Bedingung hatten wir bisher nicht gesondert hervorgehoben, da sie sich sozusagen von selbst versteht. Für den Augenblick ist es jedoch gut, hierauf etwas einzugehen.

Wir wollen die Bedingung b) wie folgt verstehen: Fassen wir ein beliebiges Massenelement des Körpers im Anfangszustand ins Auge (färben wir es etwa ein), so soll sich dieses Element auch im Endzustand wieder finden, sei es auch noch so verändert. Wir schließen also aus, daß sich das Massenelement in kleinere Bestandteile auflöst, die nachher nicht mehr zusammenhängen. Ferner sollen Massenelemente, die im Anfangszustand benachbart sind, dies auch im Endzustand sein, und schließlich wird nicht zugelassen, daß ganze Massenelemente verschwinden oder neu entstehen. Dagegen soll das Einschieben oder Wegnehmen von Materie *im* Massenelement gestattet sein. Dies sind die Forderungen, die man vernünftigerweise an eine Kontinuumstheorie des festen Körpers zu stellen hat. Sie lassen sich mathematisch in die Form

$$\mathrm{Rot}\,\boldsymbol{\beta}^G = 0 \tag{3}$$

zusammenfassen, in der $\boldsymbol{\beta}^G$ der sich in der linearen Theorie als Summe von Gesamtdeformation $\overset{G}{\boldsymbol{\epsilon}}$ und Gesamtdrehung $\overset{G}{\boldsymbol{\omega}}$ ergebende Tensor der Gesamtdistorsion ist.

Man kann nun ein Massenelement des Endzustands herausschneiden, dessen elastische Deformation $-\boldsymbol{\epsilon}$ bei der Entspannung und danach die Drehung $\boldsymbol{\omega}$ messen, die seine Struktur (das Gitter) gegenüber dem Anfangszustand erlitten hat. Die Summe von $\boldsymbol{\epsilon}$ und $\boldsymbol{\omega}$ nennen wir (in der linearen Theorie) den elastischen Distorsionstensor $\boldsymbol{\beta}$ und schreiben anstelle von Gl. (3)

$$\mathrm{Rot}\,\boldsymbol{\beta} = -\,\mathrm{Rot}\,(\boldsymbol{\beta}^G - \boldsymbol{\beta}) \equiv \boldsymbol{\gamma}. \tag{4}$$

Es stellt sich heraus, daß man die rechte Seite dieser Gleichung ausrechnen kann, wenn man genügend genau über die Operationen und Vorgänge orientiert ist, die den Körper vom Anfangs- in den Endzustand bringen. Wir nehmen daher Gl. (4) als drittes Gesetz zu den Gln. (1) und (2) hinzu. Das so erhaltene Gleichungssystem ist dann, wie man leicht zeigen kann, vollständig für die Bestimmung des Eigenspannungszustands aus den „Quellen“ $\boldsymbol{\gamma}$. Die zugehörige Rechnung geht über den Inkompatibilitätstensor $(\boldsymbol{\gamma} \times \nabla)^S$ und die Spannungsfunktionen und ist immer die gleiche, was auch für Ursachen zu $\boldsymbol{\gamma}$ geführt haben mögen. Waren dies z.B. plastische Distorsionen, so ist $\boldsymbol{\beta}^G - \boldsymbol{\beta}$ der plastische Distorsionstensor $\boldsymbol{\beta}^P$ und $\boldsymbol{\gamma}$ mit der kristallographischen Versetzungsdichte $\boldsymbol{\alpha}$ identisch. Handelte es sich um Einschieben von Extramaterie oder um sonstige quasiplastische Distorsionen, so ist $\boldsymbol{\beta}^G - \boldsymbol{\beta}$ der quasiplastische Distorsionstensor $\boldsymbol{\beta}^Q$ und $\boldsymbol{\gamma}$ die quasiplastische Versetzungsdichte $\overset{Q}{\boldsymbol{\alpha}}$ [31].

Es liegt nun nahe, unter $\boldsymbol{\gamma}$ eine verallgemeinerte Versetzungsdichte zu verstehen, und diese als Ursprung der Eigenspannungen anzusehen. Von diesem Standpunkt aus gilt also der Satz: Die Versetzung ist die elementare Eigenspannungsquelle. In diesem Bild erscheint z.B. der elastische Dipol als äquivalent mit einer infinitesimalen Versetzungsschleife (der vollständige Dipoltensor ist mit drei Versetzungsschleifen äquivalent), wie in [*8*] ausgeführt wurde.

---

[31] Auf die Möglichkeit des Endens von Versetzungen im Innern des Körpers, die zur Zeit noch problematisch ist, gehen wir in diesem Paragraphen nicht ein.

Es sei betont, daß dies nur ein möglicher Standpunkt ist, der in der Theorie der Magnetfelder stationärer Ströme sein Analogon in der Ampèreschen Äquivalenz von magnetischem Dipol und infinitesimaler Stromschleife hat[32].

Ein anderer Standpunkt ist es, wenn man unter einer Versetzungsdichte nur den einer plastischen Distorsion zuzuschreibenden Teil von $\boldsymbol{\gamma}$ versteht: Dies sind dann die in der Kristallphysik gebrauchten kristallographischen Versetzungen, deren Burgers-Vektor prinzipiell ein Gittervektor sein muß. Von diesem Standpunkt aus hat man dann weitere Eigenspannungsquellen, nämlich, solange man in der Mechanik bleibt (also Temperaturschwankungen und magnetische Wirkungen usw. außer acht läßt bzw. die zugehörigen Spannungen nicht zu den Eigenspannungen rechnet) die punktförmigen Gitterfehler, welche elastische Elementardipole sind. Dies ist der Standpunkt, welcher der allgemeinen differentialgeometrischen Theorie am nächsten kommt, in der wir die Extramaterie von den Versetzungen deutlich unterschieden hatten. Doch war in § 9 bemerkt worden, daß auch der erste Standpunkt in der allgemeinen Theorie seine Berechtigung hat.

Schließlich läßt sich leicht zeigen, daß es Verteilungen der Dichte gibt, die zu keinen Eigenspannungen, sondern nur zu Strukturkrümmungen führen. Nur wenn der Inkompatibilitätstensor $(\boldsymbol{\gamma}\times\nabla)^S$ nicht verschwindet, erhält man Eigenspannungen. Deshalb kann man mit dem gleichen Recht wie $\boldsymbol{\gamma}$ auch die Inkompatibilitäten $(\boldsymbol{\gamma}\times\nabla)^S$ als die elementaren Eigenspannungsquellen erklären. Da auch dieser Standpunkt in der allgemeinen Theorie seine Berechtigung behält — ein Verschwinden von $(\boldsymbol{\gamma}\times\nabla)^S$ bedeutet hier das Verschwinden des zu dem Christoffel-Symbol g'_{mlk} gehörigen Einstein-Tensors — haben wir gezeigt, daß sich die Grundkonzeptionen der linearen Theorie in der allgemeinen Theorie vollauf bewährt haben. Welchen von den drei Standpunkten man in einem speziellen Fall wählt, wird von den physikalischen Besonderheiten des Problems abhängen. Beispielsweise ist der in der Theorie der Par- und Dielastizität zu beziehende Standpunkt offensichtlich der zweite.

§ 17. Die ungelösten Probleme

In diesem Paragraphen soll die Aufmerksamkeit auf einige Probleme der allgemeinen Theorie gelenkt werden, deren Lösung einige heute als sehr störend empfundene Lücken schließen würde.

Bleiben wir zunächst bei der stationären Theorie und beginnen wir mit der Geometrie. Es ist wohl berechtigt zu sagen, daß in diesem Rahmen die beschränkte Theorie (neun Freiheitsgrade) praktisch abgeschlossen vorliegt. Grundlegende ungelöste Probleme sind nicht zurückgeblieben.

Etwas weniger weitreichend sind unsere Erkenntnisse über die drei Freiheitsgrade, die zu der (makroskopischen) Extramaterie gehören. Vor allem ist hier das in § 9 erwähnte Problem der Formulierung der Einsteinschen Gleichungen im Anfangszustand übrig geblieben, von dessen Lösung zu hoffen ist, daß sie den Zusammenhang zwischen der die Extramaterie beschreibenden quasiplasti-

[32] Dieser Standpunkt wird auch von Dehlinger in seiner auf die speziellen Bedürfnisse der Metallkunde zugeschnittenen Darstellung [*73*] eingenommen, die besonders die Anwendungsmöglichkeiten herausstellt.

schen Deformation $\overset{Q}{\varepsilon}_{\mathfrak{kl}}$ und dem Materietensor $B^{\mathfrak{ij}}$ ohne die Mithilfe von irgendwelchen Distorsionstensoren (wie wir sie in (80) hatten) bringen wird, etwa in der Form

$$B^{\mathfrak{ij}} = \tfrac{1}{4}\, \varepsilon^{\mathfrak{inm}}\, \varepsilon^{\mathfrak{jlk}} (2\overset{Q}{\varepsilon})_{\mathfrak{nmlk}}. \tag{5}$$

Im wesentlichen ungelöst ist das Problem der letzten drei Freiheitsgrade. Das Auftreten von Versetzungen, die im Innern des Körpers enden, bereitet der Vorstellung große Schwierigkeiten. Da bisher bei den Anwendungen das Bedürfnis nach solchen Versetzungen noch nicht aufgetaucht ist, erscheint deren Erforschung vielleicht nicht sehr vordringlich, obwohl sie vom Standpunkt der Grundlagenforschung natürlich wünschenswert ist.

Aktuell wäre dagegen eine eingehendere Untersuchung der mit den Cosseratschen Momentenspannungen verbundenen Probleme, insbesondere die Frage des Materialgesetzes und die Frage der Lösung der Feldgleichungen. Die Möglichkeit, auf diese Weise nicht nur die makroskopischen, sondern gleichzeitig die mikroskopischen Eigenspannungen der Versetzungen kontinuumsmechanisch zu erfassen ist sehr anziehend, wenn auch zur Zeit über die möglichen Auswirkungen wenig gesagt werden kann.

Sicher der größte Mangel in der heutigen Situation ist das Fehlen der dynamischen Theorie, welche vor allem die Bewegung der Versetzungen und Fremdatome (Extramaterie) behandeln sollte. Bei der Wichtigkeit der Gitterfehler für alle Vorgänge in festen Körpern ist ein reiches Anwendungsgebiet einer solchen Theorie von vornherein gesichert.

Die dynamische Theorie muß wesentlich über die bisherige Elastodynamik hinausgehen; es ist zweifellos unmöglich, mit einer Theorie auszukommen, die sich ganz auf einem Vektorfeld der Verschiebungen bzw. Geschwindigkeiten aufbaut, d.h. auf drei funktionale Freiheitsgrade beschränkt ist.

Eine solche dynamische Theorie kann mancherlei interessante Effekte zutage fördern. So ist es zuerst FRANK gelungen [*74*][33], die Bewegung einer einzelnen Versetzung zu berechnen, und es hat sich als Grenzgeschwindigkeit die Schallgeschwindigkeit ergeben, welche die Versetzung so wenig erreichen kann, wie ein Teilchen mit nicht-verschwindender Ruhemasse die Lichtgeschwindigkeit. Mit zunehmender Geschwindigkeit tritt eine Kontraktion des Spannungsfeldes der Versetzung auf, die durch ganz entsprechende Formeln beschrieben wird, wie man sie im Falle des zu hoher Geschwindigkeit beschleunigten Elektrons hat. Es gilt also eine Art spezielle Relativitätstheorie, bei der die Schallgeschwindigkeit an die Stelle der Lichtgeschwindigkeit getreten ist. Da man i. allg. verschiedene Schallgeschwindigkeiten hat, ist die Vielfalt der Erscheinungen sehr groß.

Andererseits ist es durch Bestrahlung von Proben in den Reaktoren heute möglich, leichte Atome mit Überschallgeschwindigkeit durch den Körper zu bringen, was u. a. zu einem „Schall-Tscherenkow-Effekt“ Anlaß gibt. Die zugehörigen Machschen Wellen fallen bei „langsamen Teilchen“ in den Hyperschallbereich. Die neuesten Fortschritte auf diesem Gebiet lassen hoffen, daß es in absehbarer Zeit möglich sein wird, diese Wellen und damit die sie erzeugenden

---

[33] Eine zusammenfassende Darstellung hat SAÉNZ gegeben [*75*].

Teilchen experimentell nachzuweisen (z.B. auch zu zählen). Das heute so wichtig gewordene Gebiet der Strahlungsschädigung fester Körper stellt jetzt schon in zunehmendem Maße Anwendungsmöglichkeiten nicht nur für die stationäre, sondern auch für die noch zu schaffende dynamische Theorie zur Verfügung.

Schließlich erwähnen wir noch eine weitere große und dringliche ungelöste Aufgabe, nämlich die endgültige Herstellung der Verbindung zwischen der Kontinuumstheorie der Versetzungen und Eigenspannungen und der phänomenologischen Plastizitätstheorie bzw. die Vereinigung der beiden Gebiete. Erst durch die gemeinsame Anwendung dieser Theorien läßt sich die in der Einleitung unter (1) genannte Aufgabe, die man als das Grundproblem der Kontinuumsmechanik des Festkörpers bezeichnen könnte, lösen. Die Herstellung dieser Verbindung sollte etwa entlang der von Bilby, Gardner und Stroh [*25*] gezeichneten Linien erfolgen, auf deren Arbeit wir verweisen. Dasselbe Ziel auf etwas anderem Weg verfolgt Kondo [*21*].

§ 18. Beziehungen zur allgemeinen Relativitätstheorie

Jedem Kenner der allgemeinen Relativitätstheorie wird bei einem Studium der allgemeinen Kontinuumstheorie der Versetzungen und Eigenspannungen die große Ähnlichkeit zwischen den beiden Theorien auffallen und ihm das Verständnis der letzteren sehr erleichtern. Die allgemeine Kontinuumstheorie hat der Relativitätstheorie sehr viel zu verdanken: Durch das Aufkommen dieser Theorie wurde die Entwicklung der höheren Differentialgeometrie außerordentlich gefördert, sie bekam ihre heutige elegante Form, die es erlaubt, auch komplizierte Zusammenhänge in einfachster Weise darzustellen.

Im Gegensatz zu der allgemeinen Relativitätstheorie bzw. deren Erweiterungen ist die allgemeine Kontinuumstheorie frei von jeglichen Spekulationen. Es wurden nur bestehende, sicher fundierte Gesetze zu ihrer Ableitung verwendet. Somit zeigt uns diese Theorie, wie eine in sich widerspruchsfreie Theorie von physikalischer Realität aussehen kann, die sich der Begriffe Konnexion, Einstein-Tensor usw. bedient.

Es ist seit langem bekannt, daß Eigenspannungen etwas mit Riemannscher Geometrie zu tun haben, doch wußte man früher mit dieser Erkenntnis nichts anzufangen. Bemerkenswerterweise hat sich nun ergeben, daß für die allgemeine Kontinuumsmechanik die Riemannsche Geometrie viel zu eng ist. Die Zahl der funktionalen Freiheitsgrade mußte um neun auf fünfzehn erhöht werden: An die Stelle der Christoffel-Symbole trat die allgemeinste metrische Konnexion Γ_{mlk}. Alle durch Γ_{mlk} zugelassenen Zustände des Kontinuums kommen in der Natur auch vor.

Die sich hier aufdrängende Frage ist: Gibt es irgendeinen physikalisch vernünftigen Grund, der uns gestattet, dem Weltall die einschneidende Beschränkung auf eine Riemannsche Geometrie aufzuerlegen? Gibt es einen Grund anzunehmen, daß das Weltall durch eine Konnexion beschrieben wird, die weniger allgemein ist, als die allgemeinste metrische Konnexion? In der Kontinuumsmechanik gab es keinen solchen Grund, und es dürfte schwer fallen, ihn für das Weltall zu finden.

Wir hatten schon früher das Kontinuum im deformierten Zustand von einem nicht-Euklidischen Standpunkt aus betrachtet, indem wir im Anschluß an Bilby und Mitarbeiter die Konnexion zur Definition eines nicht-Euklidischen Parallelverschiebungsgesetzes benützten. In dem so erhaltenen Riemann-Cartanschen Kontinuum bewegen sich z.B. einzelne Zwischengitteratome, wie die Sterne im nicht-Euklidischen Weltall. Es ist zwar noch nicht nachgerechnet, doch besteht wohl kein Zweifel, daß wie letztere, so auch die Zwischengitteratome den geodätischen Linien folgen, solange sie keinen Kräften ausgesetzt sind. Die von den Spannungen auf die Zwischengitteratome ausgeübten Kräfte rechnen hierbei nicht mit, sie erscheinen (aller Voraussicht nach) durch die Einführung des neuen Parallelverschiebungsgesetzes wegtransformiert, wie die Gravitationskräfte durch Einführung der Riemannschen Parallelität. (Von den durch die Gitterstruktur des realen Kontinuums bedingten Besonderheiten im Fall der Zwischengittermaterie soll hier abgesehen werden.) Dieses Bild zeigt sehr eindringlich auch die physikalische Ähnlichkeit der beiden Theorien.

Wir wollen uns hier nicht in irgendwelchen Spekulationen ergehen, wir haben vielmehr diese Ausführungen gebracht, weil wir glauben, daß eine eingehende Untersuchung der Zusammenhänge zwischen der allgemeinen Relativitätstheorie und der allgemeinen Kontinuumstheorie der Versetzungen und Eigenspannungen für beide Theorien mancherlei Nutzen bringen kann.

Meinen verehrten Lehrern, den Herren Professoren E. Fues, U. Dehlinger und A. Seeger möchte ich für ihr freundliches Interesse und die Förderung dieser Arbeit herzlich danken. Herrn Prof. A. Seeger gilt mein besonderer Dank für zahlreiche Besprechungen zu allgemeinen und Detailproblemen im Rahmen des behandelten Themas. Darüber hinaus erfuhr die vorliegende Arbeit mancherlei Anregungen aus Diskussionen mit den Herren Professoren K. Kondo, H. Schaefer, W. Günther und den Herren Doktoren J. D. Eshelby, B. A. Bilby und G. Rieder.

Literatur

[1] Frenkel, J.: Zur Theorie der Elastizitätsgrenze und der Festigkeit kristallinischer Körper. Z. Phys. **37**, 572—609 (1926).

[2] Polanyi, M., u. E. Schmid: Zur Frage der Plastizität. Verformung bei tiefen Temperaturen. Naturwiss. **17**, 301—304 (1929).

[3] Dehlinger, U.: Zur Theorie der Rekristallisation reiner Metalle. Ann. Phys., V. F. **2**, 749—793 (1929).

[4] Taylor, G. I.: The mechanism of plastic deformation of crystals. Proc. Roy. Soc. London, Ser. A **145**, 362—415 (1934).

[5] Orowan, E.: Zur Kristallplastizität. Z. Phys. **89**, 605—659 (1934).

[6] Polanyi, M.: Über eine Art Gitterstörung, die einen Kristall plastisch machen könnte. Z. Phys. **89**, 660—664 (1934).

[7] Burgers, J. M.: Some considerations of the field of stress connected with dislocations in a regular crystal lattice. Proc. Kon. Nederl. Akad. Wetensch. **42**, 293—325, 378—399 (1939).

[8] Kröner, E.: Kontinuumstheorie der Versetzungen und Eigenspannungen. Erg. angew. Math. **5**, 1—179 (1958).

[9] Dehlinger, U.: Umwandlungen und Ausscheidungen im kristallinen Zustand. Handbuch der Physik, Bd. VII/2, S. 211—253. Berlin-Göttingen-Heidelberg: Springer 1958.

[10] Seeger, A.: Theorie der Gitterfehlstellen. Handbuch der Physik, Bd. VII/2, S. 383—665. Berlin-Göttingen-Heidelberg: Springer 1955.

[11] Seeger, A.: Kristallplastizität. Handbuch der Physik, Bd. VII/2, S. 1—210. Berlin-Göttingen-Heidelberg: Springer 1958.

[12] COTTRELL, A. H.: Dislocations and plastic flow in crystals. Oxford: Clarendon Press 1953.

[13] FRIEDEL, J.: Les dislocations. Paris: Gauthier-Villars 1956.

[14] HAASEN, P., u. G. LEIBFRIED: Die plastische Verformung von Metallkristallen und ihre physikalischen Grundlagen. Fortschr. Physik **2**, 73—163 (1954).

[15] TRUESDELL, C.: The mechanical foundations of elasticity and fluid dynamics. J. Rat. Mech. Anal. **1**, 125—300 (1952); **2**, 593—616 (1953).

[16] MURNAGHAN, F. D.: Finite deformation of an elastic solid. New York: J. Wiley & Sons; London: Chapman & Hall 1951.

[17] SOKOLNIKOFF, I. S.: Tensor Analysis. New York: J. Wiley & Sons; London: Chapman & Hall 1951.

[18] DOYLE, T. C., & J. L. ERICKSEN: Nonlinear elasticity. Adv. Appl. Mech. **4**, 53—115 (1956).

[19] KRÖNER, E., u. A. SEEGER: Nicht-lineare Elastizitätstheorie der Versetzungen und Eigenspannungen. Arch. Rat. Mech. Anal. **3**, 97—119 (1959).

[20] KONDO, K.: On the geometrical and physical foundations of the theory of yielding. Proc. 2. Japan Nat. Congress of Appl. Mech. 1952, S. 41—47.

[21] KONDO, K.: Memoirs of the unifying study of the basic problems in engineering by means of geometry, vol. I u. II. Tokyo: Gakujutsu Bunken Fukyu-Kai 1955 u. 1958.

[22] BILBY, B. A.: Types of dislocation source, Defects in crystalline solids. Report of 1954 Bristol conference, S. 123—133. London: The Physical Society 1955.

[23] BILBY, B. A., R. BULLOUGH & E. SMITH: Continuous distributions of dislocations: a new application of the methods of non-Riemannian geometry. Proc. Roy. Soc. London, Ser. A **231**, 263—273 (1955).

[24] BILBY, B. A., & E. SMITH: Continuous distributions of dislocations III. Proc. Roy. Soc. London, Ser. A **236**, 481—505 (1956).

[25] BILBY, B. A., L. R. T. GARDNER & A. N. STROH: Continuous distributions of dislocations and the theory of plasticity, Extrait des actes du IXe congrès international de mécanique appliquée, S. 35—44. Brüssel 1957.

[26] BILBY, B. A.: Continuous distributions of dislocations. Progr. in solid mechanics **1** (1959), im Druck.

[27] COSSERAT, E. & F.: Théorie des corps déformables, S. 122ff. Paris: A. Hermann et Fils 1909.

[28] CAHN, R. W; A. GUINIER & J. TENNEVIN; C. CRUSSARD, F. AUBERTIN, B. JAOUL & G. WYON: Symposium on polygonization. Progr. Met. Phys. **2**, 151—202 (1950).

[29] BRAGG, W.: Internal strains in solids, Diskussion. Proc. Phys. Soc. London **52**, 54—55 (1940).

[30] NYE, J. F.: Some geometrical relations in dislocated crystals. Acta metallurgica **1**, 153—162 (1953).

[31] GÜNTHER, W.: Zur Statik und Kinematik des Cosseratschen Kontinuums. Abh. Braunschw. Wiss. Ges. **10**, 195—213 (1958).

[32] KRÖNER, E., u. G. RIEDER: Kontinuumstheorie der Versetzungen. Z. Phys. **145**, 424—429 (1956).

[33] RIEDER, G.: Plastische Verformung und Magnetostriktion. Z. angew. Phys. **9**, 187—202 (1957).

[34] ERICKSEN, J. L., & C. TRUESDELL: Exact theory of stress and strain in rods and shells. Arch. Rat. Mech. Anal. **1**, 295—323 (1957/58).

[35] SCHAEFER, H.: Die Spannungsfunktionen des dreidimensionalen Kontinuums; statische Deutung und Randwerte. Ing.-Arch. **28**, 291—305 (1959).

[36] KRÖNER, E.: Die Spannungsfunktionen der dreidimensionalen isotropen Elastizitätstheorie. Z. Phys. **139**, 175—188 (1954).

[37] PAPKOVITCH, P. F.: Solution générale des équations différentielles fondamentales d'élasticité exprimée par trois fonctions harmoniques. C. R. Paris **195**, 513—515 (1932); Berichtigung: ebenda S. 836.

[38] NEUBER, H.: Kerbspannungslehre. Berlin-Göttingen-Heidelberg: Springer 1958.

[39] SCHOUTEN, J. A.: Ricci-Calculus, insb. Kap. III, § 1—5. Berlin-Göttingen-Heidelberg: Springer 1954.
[40] GREEN, A. E., & W. ZERNA: Theoretical elasticity. Oxford: Clarendon Press 1954.
[41] CARTAN, É.: Sur les variétés à connexion affine et la théorie de la relativité généralisée. Ann. Sc. de l'École Norm. Sup. III. Ser. **40**, 325—412 (1923).
[42] FRANK, F. C.: Crystal dislocations–Elementary concepts and definitions. Phil. Mag., VII. Ser. **42**, 809—819 (1951).
[43] MORIGUTI, S.: Fundamental theory of dislocations of an elastic body. Oyo Sugaku Rikigaku (Appl. Math. Mech.) **1**, 29—36 u. 87—90 (1947) [Japanisch].
[44] ESHELBY, J. D.: The continuum theory of lattice defects. Solid state physics, vol. III, p. 79—144. New York: Academic Press Inc. Publ. 1956.
[45] RIEDER, G.: Spannungen und Dehnungen im gestörten Medium. Z. Naturforschung **11**a, 171—173 (1956).
[46] KRÖNER, E.: Die Versetzung als elementare Eigenspannungsquelle. Z. Naturforschung **11**a, 969—985 (1956).
[47] SCHAEFER, H.: Die Spannungsfunktionen des dreidimensionalen Kontinuums und des elastischen Körpers. Z. angew. Math. Mech. **33**, 356—362 (1953).
[48] BELTRAMI, E.: Osservazioni sulle nota precedente (Morera). Atti Accad. Naz. Lincei, Rend. Cl. Sci. Fis. Mat. Natur., V. Ser. **1** (1), 141—142 (1892).
[49] MORERA, G.: Soluzione generale delle equazione indefinite dell'equilibrio di un corpo continuo. Atti Accad. Naz. Lincei, Rend. Cl. Fis. Mat. Natur., V. Ser. **1** (1), 137—141 (1892).
[50] MAXWELL, J. C.: On reciprocal figures, frames and diagrams of forces. Trans. Roy. Soc. Edinburgh **26**, 1—40 (1870).
[51] BLOCH, W. I.: Die Spannungsfunktionen in der Elastizitätstheorie. Prikl. Mat. Mech. **14**, 415—422 (1950) [Russisch].
[52] MARGUERRE, K.: Ansätze zur Lösung der Grundgleichungen der Elastizitätstheorie. Z. angew. Math. Mech. **35**, 242—263 (1955).
[53] TREFFTZ, E.: Mathematische Elastizitätstheorie. In H. GEIGER u. K. SCHEEL, Handbuch der Physik, Bd. VI, S. 47—140. Berlin: Springer 1928.
[54] LOVE, A. E. H.: Mathematical Theory of Elasticity. Cambridge: University Press 1952. Deutsch: A. Timpe. Berlin: Teubner 1907.
[55] ESHELBY, J. D.: The force on an elastic singularity. Phil. Trans. Roy. Soc. London, Ser. A **244**, 87—112 (1951).
[56] COLONNETTI, G.: Su di una reciprocità tra deformazioni e distorsioni. Atti Accad. Naz. Lincei, Rend. Cl. Fis. Mat. Natur., V. Ser. **24** (1), 404—408 (1915).
[57] RIEDER, G.: Mechanische Arbeit bei plastischen Vorgängen. Z. angew. Phys. **10**, 140—150 (1958).
[58] PEACH, M. O., & J. S. KOEHLER: The forces exerted in dislocations and the stress field produced by them. Phys. Rev., II. Ser. **80**, 436—439 (1950).
[59] NIESEL, W.: Über elastische ellipsoidische Einschlüsse in homogenen Medien. Inaug.-Diss., Karlsruhe 1953.
[60] ESHELBY, J. D.: The determination of the elastic field of an ellipsoidal inclusion and related problems. Proc. Roy. Soc. London, Ser. A **241**, 376—396 (1957).
[61] COCHARDT, A. W., G. SCHÖCK & H. WIEDERSICH: Interaction between dislocations and interstitial atoms in body centered cubic metals. Acta metallurgica **3**, 533—537 (1955).
[62] SCHÖCK, G., & A. SEEGER: The flow stress of iron and its dependence on impurities. Acta metallurgica **7**, 469—477 (1959).
[63] SNOEK, D. L.: Effect of small quantities of carbon and nitrogen on the elastic and plastic properties of iron. Physica **8**, 711—733 (1941).
[64] ZENER, C.: Elasticity and anelasticity of metals. Chicago: University Press 1948.
[65] CRUSSARD, C.: L'interaction élastique d'atomes en solution solide. Acta metallurgica **4**, 555—556 (1956).
[66] TELTOW, J.: Zum elastischen Störstellenmodell. Ann. Phys., VI. F. **19**, 169—174 (1956).

[67] Eshelby, J. D.: The elastic model of lattice defects. Ann. Phys., VII. F. **1**, 116—121 (1958).
[68] Jacobs, I. S.: Effect of pressure on *F*-center absorption in alkali halides. Phys. Rev. **93**, 993—1004 (1954).
[69] Bass, R.: Zur Theorie der mechanischen Relaxation des Eises. Z. Phys. **153**, 16—37 (1958).
[70] Eshelby, J. D.: Elastic inclusions and inhomogeneities. Progr. in Solid Mechanics **2** (1960), im Druck.
[71] Kröner, E.: Berechnung der elastischen Konstanten des Vielkristalls aus den Konstanten des Einkristalls. Z. Phys. **151**, 504—518 (1958).
[72] Greenough, G. B.: Residual lattice strains in plastically deformed polycristalline metal aggregates. Proc. Roy. Soc. London, Ser. A **197**, 556—567 (1949).
[73] Dehlinger, U.: Die Entstehung von inneren Spannungen bei Vorgängen in Metallen. Z. Metallkunde **50**, 126—130 (1959).
[74] Frank, F. C.: On the equation of motion of crystal dislocations. Proc. Phys. Soc., Sect. A **62**, 131—134 (1949).
[75] Sáenz, A. W.: Uniformly moving dislocations in anisotropic media. J. Rat. Mech. Anal. **2**, 83—98 (1953).

Institut für theoretische und angewandte Physik
Technische Hochschule Stuttgart

(Eingegangen am 26. Oktober 1959)

See Addendum on page 308.

Bemerkung zum geometrischen Grundgesetz der allgemeinen Kontinuumstheorie der Versetzungen und Eigenspannungen, by E. KRÖNER

No. 13

HYPO-ELASTICITY AND ELASTICITY

B. Bernstein

Archive for Rational Mechanics and Analysis, Volume 6, pp. 89-104 (1960).

After NOLL's proof (RMM, No. 5) that every isotropic elastic material with invertible stress-strain relation is hypo-elastic it became natural to seek to delimit the overlap of elasticity and hypo-elasticity. BERNSTEIN saw that it is meaningless to ask whether a given hypo-elastic material is elastic, because the underlying, unformulated concept of "material" is different in the two theories. To see this clearly, turn to Section 3 of the paper here reprinted. Every "perfect gas" satisfies (3.7) and hence is a hypo-elastic material. On the other hand, the differential system (3.7) has infinitely many other solutions, in which the stress can at no time become hydrostatic. A solution of hypo-elastic constitutive equations, as is clear from examples given in Nos. 5, 6, and 7 in this volume, is in general a stress-strain relation depending on the initial stress as a parameter, while the concept of "material" underlying the definition of an elastic material regards the stress as determined by a sufficient amount of information about deformation alone. There is no reason to expect, **a priori,** that the two concepts of material ever be compatible. As the first step toward seeing if they can be, BERNSTEIN in Section 3 gives a new definition of a hypo-elastic material in terms of equivalence classes of stress-configuration pairs satisfying the hypo-elastic constitutive equations.

The main theorem, in Section 4, obtains the integrability conditions (4.4) as necessary and sufficient that a given solution to the hypo-elastic equations correspond to an elastic material. These conditions are equations to be satisfied **by the stress tensor.** Thus the example given earlier is typical: While some assignments of initial stress may yield elastic solutions, others will not.

The theorems concerning hyperelastic materials ("elasticity in the sense of Green") are really reinterpretations of results known in the theory of elasticity itself. The paper closes with a specific example of an anisotropic hyperelastic material that is not hypo-elastic.

BERNSTEIN's results are somewhat more complicated than need be, since he makes no use of the fact, which follows from the principle of material indifference, that the tensor-valued function $A_{ijkl}\, d_{kl}$ in (3.1) must be an isotropic function of both $\mathbf{t}$ and $\mathbf{d}$. Doubtless (4.4) could be simplified thereby. Certainly the proof that not all elastic materials are hypo-elastic can be: One has only to remark that when the stress vanishes, the right-hand side of (3.1) must consequently reduce to an isotropic function of $\mathbf{d}$, showing that no elastic material whose response to small strain is anisotropic can be hypo-elastic.

BERNSTEIN's paper is not as well known as it should be since "proofs" that all elastic materials are hypo-elastic have been published.

Offprint from "Archive for Rational Mechanics and Analysis"
Volume 6, Number 2, 1960, P. 89—104

Springer-Verlag, Berlin · Göttingen · Heidelberg

Hypo-Elasticity and Elasticity

BARRY BERNSTEIN

Communicated by C. TRUESDELL

1. Introduction

When TRUESDELL [1955, 6] introduced the equations of hypo-elasticity, he stated that it was his intention to find a new concept of elastic behavior, mutually exclusive with the theory of finite strain, which reduces to the classical linearized theory of elasticity under the assumptions appropriate to the latter. However, he remarked that NOLL had shown him privately, and published simultaneously [1955, 2] a proof that every isotropic Cauchy-elastic material for which the stress-strain relations are invertible is hypo-elastic.

A question then arises whether a given hypo-elastic material is elastic. And this inquiry is the theme of our discussion below. In seeking to answer this question I was impeded by a difficulty: The equations of hypo-elasticity in themselves were not sufficient to define a material well enough to enable me to proceed with my inquiry. This hurdle was overcome by the means described in § 3 below, in which are set down the stipulations which, in addition to the equations of hypo-elasticity, I feel are required in general to define a hypo-elastic material.

In the second section we introduce our notation for discussing motions of materials and define elasticity in the sense of CAUCHY and of GREEN. In the fourth and fifth sections we derive criteria, based on the equations of hypo-elasticity, for a hypo-elastic material to be elastic in the senses of CAUCHY and of GREEN. These criteria are obtained by means of seeking integrability conditions.

The sixth section is devoted to showing that unless there exist motions of a given hypo-elastic material for which the initial and final configurations are the same and the work done by the stresses is negative, the given material must necessarily be elastic in the sense of GREEN. The existence of a result of this type was suggested by the work of CAPRIOLI [1955, 1] and of BERNSTEIN & ERICKSEN [1958, 1].

In the final section, § 7, we prove that a material which is both hypo-elastic and Cauchy-elastic is isotropic with respect to a given reference configuration if and only if the stress is a uniform hydrostatic pressure for that reference configuration. We then indicate that this result implies that there exist anisotropic Green-elastic materials which are not hypo-elastic.

A summary of our results is given by BERNSTEIN [1960].

2. The constitutive equations of elasticity

We follow generally the notation of TRUESDELL [1952], letting X^A, $A=1, 2, 3$, denote material or Lagrangean coordinates, x^i, $i=1, 2, 3$, stand for spatial or Eulerian coordinates, and t for time. A (kinematically possible) *motion* is defined by a continuous, piecewise smooth mapping

$$x^i = \hat{x}^i(X^A, t), \tag{2.1}$$

where carats, bars, *etc.*, over a letter indicate that it stands for a function, a distinction which will be made when the context requires it. Marks appearing under or to the right of a kernel letter will be taken to be part of the kernel letter. Henceforth all spatial coordinates will be considered cartesian. Components of tensors in spatial coordinate systems will be written with lower case Latin kernel letters and lower case Latin indices, while those in material coordinate systems will be written with upper case Latin kernel letters and upper case Latin indices. Since all spatial coordinate systems are to be cartesian, cartesian tensor notation will be used in these systems, and lower case Latin indices may be transferred between the upper and lower positions at will. A *material point* will be denoted by X, $\underset{0}{X}$, *etc.*, when no reference is made to coordinates.

The derivatives of (2.1) with respect to the X^A, called the *displacement gradients*, will be written

$$x^i_A = \frac{\partial \hat{x}^i}{\partial X^A}. \tag{2.2}$$

It is assumed that (2.1) may be solved for the X^A, yielding

$$X^A = \hat{X}^A(x^i, t), \tag{2.3}$$

which leads to the definition of the *inverse displacement gradients*, X^A_i by

$$X^A_i = \frac{\partial \hat{X}^A}{\partial x^i}, \tag{2.4}$$

and the subsequent relations

$$X^A_i\, x^i_B = \delta^A_B, \quad x^i_A\, X^A_j = \delta^i_j, \quad x^i_A = X^A_i \det |x^j_L|. \tag{2.5}$$

By differentiation of (2.5) we get

$$\frac{\partial}{\partial x^j_A} \det |x^i_B| = X^A_j \det |x^i_B|, \qquad \frac{\partial X^A_i}{\partial x^j_L} = -X^A_j\, X^L_i. \tag{2.6}$$

When $\hat{x}^i_A$, $\tilde{x}^i_A$, *etc.*, denotes an assignment of the displacement gradients as functions of given variables, $\hat{X}^A_i$, $\tilde{X}^A_i$ *etc.* will respectively denote the corresponding inverse displacement gradients determined by (2.5) as functions of the same variables.

The symbols δ^i_j and δ^A_B appearing in (2.5) are the usual Kronecker deltas. We also adopt the Kronecker symbols δ^i_A and δ^A_i, which take the value unity when A and i are numerically equal, and take the value zero otherwise*.

* See [1954], footnote on page 14.

The *mass density*, ϱ, is given from the principle of conservation of mass by

$$\varrho_0 \det |x^i_A| = \varrho, \tag{2.7}$$

where ϱ_0 depends only on X and in fact is the density for any value of x^i_A such that $\det |x^i_A| = 1$.

If at each point of a smooth manifold $\mathfrak{M}$ of material points* the stress, t^{ij}, is given as a function of the displacement gradients,

$$t^{ij} = \hat{t}^{ij}(x^i_A, X^B), \tag{2.8}$$

we say that we have a *representation* of a material which is *elastic in the sense of* CAUCHY, or *Cauchy-elastic*. These representations form equivalence classes if we say that, for fixed $\mathfrak{M}$, two representations

$$t^{ij} = \hat{t}^{ij}(x^k_A, X^B) \quad \text{and} \quad t^{ij} = \hat{\hat{t}}^{ij}(x^k_A, X^B)$$

are equivalent if there is a transformation of material coordinates

$$X^{B'} = \hat{X}^{B'}(X^B) \tag{2.9}$$

such that

$$\hat{t}^{ij}(x^k_A, X^B) = \hat{\hat{t}}^{ij}(x^k_{A'}, X^{B'}) \tag{2.10}$$

where

$$x^k_{A'} \equiv \frac{\partial \hat{x}^k}{\partial X^{A'}} = x^k_A \frac{\partial \hat{X}^A}{\partial X^{A'}}.$$

An equivalence class of representations of Cauchy-elastic materials will be called by us a *Cauchy-elastic material*. Such a material is well defined by one of its representations.

The possible relations (2.8) are restricted by the requirement that material properties be invariant under rigid motions. This requirement has been given the name of the principle of *isotropy of space*, or *objectivity* [1955, 2] [1958, 2]. It has also been formulated as *invariance under Euclidean transformations*, and it has been shown [1958, 3] that (2.8) will be consistent with this principle if and only if it takes the form

$$t^{ij} = [\det |x^k_M|]^{-1} x^i_A x^j_B \hat{T}^{AB}(C^{KL}, X^A), \tag{2.11}$$

where

$$C^{KL} \equiv X^K_i X^L_j \delta^{ij}, \tag{2.12}$$

and $\hat{T}^{AB}$ are scalar functions with respect to time-dependent orthogonal transformations of spatial coordinates.

In case (2.8) has the form

$$t^i_j = \frac{\varrho}{\varrho_0} x^A_j \frac{\partial \hat{\Sigma}}{\partial x^i_A}, \tag{2.13}$$

where

$$\hat{\Sigma}(x^i_A, X)$$

is, at each X, a scalar function of the displacement gradients, then we say that the material defined by $\mathfrak{M}$ and (2.13) is *elastic in the sense of* GREEN, or *Green-*

* $\mathfrak{M}$ is the same as the body $\mathscr{B}$ of [1958, 2].

elastic. (If (2.8) has the form (2.13) for one representation, it has that form for all equivalent representations.)

The principle of isotropy of space is fulfilled, for materials elastic in the sense of GREEN, if and only if $\hat{\Sigma}$ is a function of the C^{KL} and X [1955, 2].

3. Hypo-elastic materials

The constitutive equations of hypo-elasticity may be written [1955, 2, 4, 5]

$$\dot{t}_{ij} = t_{ik}\,\omega_{jk} + t_{jk}\,\omega_{ik} + \hat{A}_{ijkl}(t_{pq})\,d_{kl}, \tag{3.1}$$

where, if a quantity f is expressed as a function of X and t, $f = \hat{f}(X, t)$, then $\dot{f} \equiv \partial\hat{f}/\partial t$ is called the material derivative of f; where

$$\omega_{jk} = \tfrac{1}{2}\,(v_{j,k} - v_{k,j}), \qquad d_{kl} = \tfrac{1}{2}\,(v_{k,l} + v_{l,k}), \tag{3.2}$$

v_i denoting the velocity, which is defined, using (2.1), by

$$v_i = \frac{\partial \hat{x}^i}{\partial t}; \tag{3.3}$$

and where $\hat{A}_{ijkl}(t_{pq})$ is an invariant or isotropic tensor function of the stress and possesses the symmetries $\hat{A}_{ijkl} = \hat{A}_{jikl} = \hat{A}_{jilk}$. Using (3.3), (2.1), (2.2) and (2.4), we may write the velocity gradients as

$$v^i{}_{,j} = X^A_j\,\dot{x}^i_A. \tag{3.4}$$

Substitution of (3.4) into (3.1), using (3.2), yields

$$\dot{t}_{ij} = \hat{B}_{ijkl}(t_{pq})\,X^A_l\,\dot{x}^k_A, \tag{3.5}$$

where

$$\hat{B}_{ijkl} = \tfrac{1}{2}\,[t_{il}\,\delta_{jk} + t_{jl}\,\delta_{ik} - t_{ik}\,\delta_{jl} - t_{jk}\,\delta_{il}] + \hat{A}_{ijkl}. \tag{3.6}$$

In the spirit of differential geometry, we shall assume that $\hat{A}_{ijkl}$, and hence $\hat{B}_{ijkl}$, is differentiable as many times as required, and that we have enough continuity conditions to insure existence and uniqueness of solutions to the initial-value problem for (3.1) or (3.6) in which the velocity gradients, or the displacement gradients, are assigned as continuous piecewise smooth functions of time, stress is assigned initially, and it is required to solve for stress as a function of time at each X. Our theorems are local unless obviously global.

We do not feel that equations (3.1) or (3.5) suffice to define a hypo-elastic material. The following example will bring out the difficulty which we have in mind.

Consider the particular case of (3.1) given by

$$\dot{t}_{ij} = t_{ik}\,\omega_{jk} + t_{jk}\,\omega_{ik} - \delta_{ij}\,\frac{t_{pp}}{3}\,d_{ll},$$

i.e.,

$$\hat{A}_{ijkl} = -\,\delta_{ij}\,\frac{t_{pp}}{3}\,\delta_{kl}. \tag{3.7}$$

One set of solutions to (3.7) is given by

$$t_{ij} = -\,\varkappa\,\varrho\,\delta_{ij}, \tag{3.8}$$

where $\varkappa$ is an arbitrary constant. Hence if initially the stress is a hydrostatic pressure with a given assigned value, $\varkappa$ may be adjusted so that the right-hand side of (3.8) takes that value initially and, by uniqueness, (3.8) must be the solution. It follows that if ever the stress is a hydrostatic pressure, it is always a hydrostatic pressure, and if the stress is once not a hydrostatic pressure, it may never become a hydrostatic pressure during any motion. Thus it would seem that (3.7) entails at least two essentially different types of materials, one for which the shear must vanish and one for which the shear cannot vanish. And we shall see (in the closing comments of §§ 4 and 5) that this difference is even more profound.

What is clear from the foregoing discussion is that in some way the possible initial conditions must be specified. And we now proceed to formalize this idea.

Let $\mathfrak{M}$ be a smooth manifold of material points as in § 2. A function $\hat{x}^i_A(X^B)$ over $\mathfrak{M}$, *i.e.*, an assignment of displacement gradients over $\mathfrak{M}$, subject to the compatibility conditions

$$\frac{\partial \hat{x}^i_A}{\partial X^B} = \frac{\partial \hat{x}^i_B}{\partial X^A}, \tag{3.9}$$

will be called a *configuration* (of $\mathfrak{M}$). An assignment of both a value of stress at each material point in $\mathfrak{M}$ and a configuration will be called a *stress-configuration pair* and will be denoted by

$$\{t_{ij}, x^k_A\}. \tag{3.10}$$

Now (3.10) is a function over $\mathfrak{M}$. Its value at one point X of $\mathfrak{M}$ will be denoted by

$$[t_{ij}, x^k_A](X). \tag{3.11}$$

The symbol

$$[t_{ij}, x^k_A] \tag{3.12}$$

will denote a possible set of values of stress and displacement gradients at a material point. It will be called a *stress-displacement gradient pair*. The expression (3.11) is necessarily associated with a given stress-configuration pair, while (3.12) is not.

Given two stress-configuration pairs

$$\{\overset{1}{t}_{ij}, \overset{1}{x}{}^k_A\} \quad \text{and} \quad \{\overset{2}{t}_{ij}, \overset{2}{x}{}^k_A\},$$

the following statement may or may not be true: There exist continuous piecewise smooth functions

$$\hat{t}_{ij}(t, X), \quad \hat{x}^k_A(t, X) \quad X \in \mathfrak{M}, \quad t_1 \leqq t \leqq t_2$$

satisfying (3.5) and (3.9) such that

$$[\hat{t}_{ij}(t_l, X), \hat{x}^k_A(t_l, X)] = [\overset{l}{t}_{ij}, \overset{l}{x}{}^k_A](X), \qquad l = 1, 2$$

for all $X \in \mathfrak{M}$.

If this statement is true, we shall say that the two stress-configuration pairs are equivalent,

$$\{\overset{1}{t}_{ij}, \overset{1}{x}{}^k_A\} \sim \{\overset{2}{t}_{ij}, \overset{2}{x}{}^k_A\},$$

and if not, then the stress-configuration pairs are not equivalent. It is readily verified that this is an equivalence relation. And an equivalence class of stress-configuration pairs will be called a *stress-configuration class.* A stress-configuration class for a hypo-elastic material is, then, the class of all stress-configuration pairs which may be reached from a given stress-configuration pair. Further, these stress-configuration classes themselves may be separated into equivalence classes as follows: Two stress-configuration classes are equivalent if one may be obtained from the other by a transformation of material coordinates.

In other words, given two stress-configuration classes, say Γ_1 and Γ_2, Γ_1 is equivalent to Γ_2 if there exists a coordinate transformation

$$X^{\bar{A}} = \bar{X}^{\bar{A}}(X^A) \tag{3.13}$$

such that if

$$\{t_{ij}, x^i_A\} \in \Gamma_1,$$

then

$$\{t_{ij}, x^i_{\bar{A}}\} \in \Gamma_2$$

and conversely, where

$$x^i_A = x^i_{\bar{A}} \frac{\partial \bar{X}^{\bar{A}}}{\partial X^A}.$$

From equation (3.5) it is readily verified that

$$\dot{t}_{ij} - B_{ijkl}(t_{pq})\, X^A_l\, x^k_A = \dot{t}_{ij} - B_{ijkl}(t_{pq})\, X^{\bar{A}}_l\, x^k_{\bar{A}}, \tag{3.14}$$

where

$$X^{\bar{A}}_l = \frac{\partial \bar{X}^{\bar{A}}}{\partial x^l} = \frac{\partial \bar{X}^{\bar{A}}}{\partial X^A} X^A_l.$$

Thus if any stress-configuration pair from Γ_1 may be transformed into a stress-configuration pair from Γ_2 by a transformation (3.12), it is immediate from (3.13) that every stress-configuration pair in Γ_2 is a transform under (3.12) of a stress-configuration pair in Γ_1, and conversely. Hence, necessary and sufficient that Γ_1 and Γ_2 be equivalent is that one stress-configuration pair in Γ_1 may be transformed into some stress-configuration pair in Γ_2 by a transformation of material coordinates.

By a hypo-elastic material we shall mean the assignment of a set of equations (3.1) *or* (3.5) *and a corresponding equivalence class of stress-configuration classes. By a representation of a hypo-elastic material we shall mean an assignment of a set of equations* (3.1) *or* (3.5) *and a corresponding stress-configuration class.*

It may be noted that in a representation of a hypo-elastic material which is also Cauchy-elastic there is only one value of stress for each value of the displacement gradients at each X, and hence a representation of such a material consists of an assignment of stress as a function of x^i_A and X. Also the equivalence classes of stress-configuration classes must be those obtained by considering classes of equivalent representations of an elastic material. Hence our definitions of a representation and a material are consistent for the case of a material which is both Cauchy-elastic and hypo-elastic.

4. Elasticity in the sense of Cauchy

Suppose that we are given a set of hypo-elastic equations (3.1) or (3.5), and we ask whether any hypo-elastic material corresponding to them is elastic in the sense of CAUCHY. If (2.8) defines such a material, then by substitution of (2.8) into (3.5) we see that $\hat{t}_{ij}$ must satisfy

$$\frac{\partial \hat{t}_{ij}}{\partial x^k_A} \dot{x}^k_A = \hat{B}_{ijkl} X^A_l \dot{x}^k_A \tag{4.1}$$

for arbitrary motions. But since x^k_A and $\dot{x}^k_A$ are in general independent, (2.8) must satisfy (4.1) for arbitrary $\dot{x}^k_A$ and hence must satisfy

$$\frac{\partial \hat{t}_{ij}}{\partial x^k_A} = \hat{B}_{ijkl} X^A_l. \tag{4.2}$$

Conversely, if we have a solution (2.8) of (4.2), then (4.1) and hence (3.5) is satisfied by this solution and, because of uniqueness of solution of the initial value problem for (3.5) as stated in § 3, the stress-configuration class determined by any single stress-configuration pair satisfying (2.8) must be identical with the totality of stress-configuration pairs satisfying (2.8). And thus this stress-configuration class, together with (3.5), determines a representation of a material which is both hypo-elastic and Cauchy-elastic. Thus our question reduces to that of whether (4.2) admits a solution. We therefore apply the standard method of answering this question as outlined in textbooks on differential geometry*.

The first integrability condition for (4.2) is obtained by writing

$$\begin{aligned} 0 &= \frac{\partial^2 \hat{t}_{ij}}{\partial x^p_L \, \partial x^k_A} - \frac{\partial^2 \hat{t}_{ij}}{\partial x^k_A \, \partial x^p_L} \\ &= \frac{\partial \hat{B}_{ijkl}}{\partial t_{rs}} \frac{\partial \hat{t}_{rs}}{\partial x^p_L} X^A_l + \hat{B}_{ijkl} \frac{\partial X^A_l}{\partial x^p_L} - \frac{\partial \hat{B}_{ijpl}}{\partial t_{rs}} \frac{\partial \hat{t}_{rs}}{\partial x^k_A} X^L_l - \hat{B}_{ijpl} \frac{\partial X^L_l}{\partial x^k_A}. \end{aligned} \tag{4.3}$$

By substituting (4.2) for the derivatives of $\hat{t}_{rs}$ and using $(2.6)_2$, we get a set of relations involving X^A_k and t_{pq}. From these X^A_k may be eliminated using $(2.5)_2$, so that the first integrability conditions for (4.2) take the form

$$\frac{\partial \hat{B}_{ijkl}}{\partial t_{rs}} \hat{B}_{rspq} - \frac{\partial \hat{B}_{ijpq}}{\partial t_{rs}} \hat{B}_{rskl} - \hat{B}_{ijkq} \delta_{pl} + \hat{B}_{ijpl} \delta_{kq} = 0. \tag{4.4}$$

For t_{ij} to satisfy (4.2) it is necessary that its components be related in such a way as to satisfy (4.4). If (4.4) is not satisfied identically in t_{ij} and does not consist of more than six independent relations, we may differentiate (4.4) with respect to x^k_A, substitute the right-hand side of (4.2) for the derivatives of t_{ij}, and again eliminate X^A_k by the use of $(2.5)_2$ to obtain the second integrability conditions as relations among the t_{ij}. If the second integrability conditions introduce new relations not contained among the first integrability conditions, and if the total number of independent relations among the first and second integrability conditions does not exceed six, we obtain the third integrability conditions by applying to the second integrability conditions the same process

* See, for example, § 23 of [1947].

that we applied to the first. And we continue this process till either we obtain more than six independent relations, or at some stage no new relations are introduced and the total number of independent relations is $r \leqq 6$. In the former case there is no solution of (4.2). In the latter case there are solutions for which $6-r$ components of t_{ij} may be assigned arbitrarily for one value of x_A^k at each X. And for each such assignment the solution is unique.

In case (4.4) consists of more than six independent relations there is, according to the above discussion, no solution of (4.2). On the other hand if and only if (4.4) is satisfied identically in t_{ij} is there a solution of (4.2) for any arbitrary assignment of t_{ij} for one value of x_A^k at each X. Thus, because of the uniqueness of solutions to the initial value problem for (3.5), we have the following:

Theorem I. *Necessary and sufficient that every hypo-elastic material corresponding to* (3.1) *or* (3.5) *be Cauchy-elastic is that* (4.4) *be satisfied identically in* t_{ij}.

As an example to illustrate the foregoing discussion, we consider the equations (3.7), for which the totality of independent integrability conditions may be written

$$t_{ij} = \frac{t_{kk}}{3}\,\delta_{ij}, \tag{4.5}$$

showing that a hypo-elastic material corresponding to (3.7) is elastic in the sense of CAUCHY if and only if the stress is a hydrostatic pressure.

5. Elasticity in the sense of Green

Given a material which is both hypo-elastic and Cauchy-elastic, we now ask for a criterion that it be elastic in the sense of GREEN. We ask, in other words, if there exists a function $\hat{\Sigma}(x_A^i, X^B)$ satisfying (2.13). We rewrite (2.13) as

$$\frac{\partial \hat{\Sigma}}{\partial x_A^i} = \frac{\varrho_0}{\varrho}\, t_{ij}\, X_j^A. \tag{5.1}$$

Since we are assuming that (2.8) is satisfied, a necessary and sufficient condition for the existence of a solution $\hat{\Sigma}$ to (5.1) is

$$0 = \frac{\partial^2 \hat{\Sigma}}{\partial x_L^k\, \partial x_A^i} - \frac{\partial^2 \hat{\Sigma}}{\partial x_A^i\, \partial x_L^k} = \frac{\partial}{\partial x_L^k}\left[\frac{\varrho_0}{\varrho}\, t_{ij}\, X_j^A\right] - \frac{\partial}{\partial x_A^i}\left[\frac{\varrho_0}{\varrho}\, t_{ij}\, X_j^L\right]. \tag{5.2}$$

From (2.7) and (2.6) we get

$$\frac{\partial}{\partial x_A^i}\,\frac{\varrho_0}{\varrho} = \frac{\varrho_0}{\varrho}\, X_i^A. \tag{5.2}$$

Since we are also assuming that (3.5) is satisfied, we get from (5.1), using (5.2), (3.5) and $(2.6)_2$,

$$\hat{B}_{ijpk}\, X_p^L\, X_j^A - \hat{B}_{kjpi}\, X_p^A\, X_j^L + t_{ij}\, X_k^L\, X_j^A - t_{kj}\, X_i^A\, X_j^L - X_k^A\, X_j^L\, t_{ij} + X_i^L X_j^A\, t_{kj} = 0,$$

which, using $(2.5)_2$, may be written

$$\hat{B}_{ijkl} - \hat{B}_{lkji} + t_{ij}\,\delta_{kl} - t_{lk}\,\delta_{ji} - t_{ik}\,\delta_{jl} + t_{ki}\,\delta_{lj} = 0. \tag{5.3}$$

Using (3.6), we see that (5.3) may also be written

$$\hat{A}_{ijkl} + t_{ij}\,\delta_{kl} = \hat{A}_{klji} + t_{kl}\,\delta_{ji}. \tag{5.4}$$

We state our results now as two theorems:

Theorem II. *Necessary and sufficient that a given hypo-elastic material which is Cauchy-elastic be also Green-elastic is that* (5.4) *be satisfied for all values of stress that occur.*

Theorem III. *Necessary and sufficient that all hypo-elastic materials corresponding to* (3.1) *or* (3.5) *be elastic in the sense of Green is that* (4.4) *and* (5.4) *be satisfied identically in* t_{ij}.

We see that (3.7) satisfies (5.4) for Cauchy-elastic solutions, *i.e.*, when (4.5) is satisfied. Hence Theorem II implies that hypo-elastic materials corresponding to (3.7) are elastic in the sense of GREEN if ever the stress is a hydrostatic pressure, which is to be expected since they are perfect fluids in that case. If ever, on the other hand, the stress is not a hydrostatic pressure, then the material is not elastic even in the sense of CAUCHY. Thus the stress-configuration class can be very important in determining the nature of the material corresponding to a given set of hypo-elastic equations.

6. An energetic condition for elasticity in the sense of Green

The work done by the stresses* in any material during a motion occuring in the time interval $t_1 \leqq t \leqq t_2$ is given by

$$\int_{t_1}^{t_2}\int_V t_{ij}\, d_{ij}\, dV\, dt = \int_{t_1}^{t_2}\int_{V_0} t_{ij}\, d_{ij}\, \frac{\varrho_0}{\varrho}\, dV_0\, dt, \tag{6.1}$$

where V is the volume of material at time t and V_0 is the volume for some fixed reference configuration, for which the density is ϱ_0. In this section we shall prove the following:

Theorem IV. *If for a given hypo-elastic material the work done by the stresses is non-negative for all (kinematically possible) motions for which the initial and final configurations are the same, then this material is elastic in the sense of Green.*

Before proving the theorem, we shall make some observations and establish some lemmas.

Consider a given representation of a hypo-elastic material and a given material point $\underset{0}{X}$. Let $\{'t_{ij}, 'x^k_A\}$ be an element of the corresponding stress-configuration class. Suppose that $["t_{ij}, "x^k_A]$ is a stress-displacement gradient pair for which there exist piecewise smooth functions $\hat{\hat{t}}_{ij}(t)$, $\hat{\hat{x}}^k_A(t)$, $t_1 \leqq t \leqq t_2$, satisfying (3.5) and such that

$$[\hat{\hat{t}}_{ij}(t_1), \hat{\hat{x}}^k_A(t_1)] = ['t_{ij}, 'x^k_A]\,(\underset{0}{X}),$$

and

$$[\hat{\hat{t}}_{ij}(t_2), \hat{\hat{x}}^k_A(t_2)] = ["t_{ij}, "x^k_A].$$

Then we may find an element $\{"t_{ij}, "x^k_A\}$ of the stress-configuration class corresponding to our given representation which takes the value $["t_{ij}, "x^k_A]$ at $\underset{0}{X}$, as we shall now demonstrate.

* § 27 of [1952].

Let ${}'\tilde{x}^k_A(X)$ be the values of the displacement gradients corresponding to $\{{}'t_{ij}, {}'x^k_A\}$, and let ${}'\underset{0}{X}{}^A_k$ be a set of numbers defined by

$$ {}'\underset{0}{X}{}^A_k\, {}'\tilde{x}^k_B(\underset{0}{X}) = \delta^A_B, $$

i.e., the inverse displacement gradients at $\underset{0}{X}$ corresponding to $\{{}'t_{ij}, {}'x^k_A\}$. Then define the function

$$ \hat{\tilde{x}}^k_A(X,t) \equiv \hat{\tilde{x}}^k_B(t)\, {}'\underset{0}{X}{}^B_l\, {}'\tilde{x}^l_A(X), \qquad t_1 \leqq t \leqq t_2. \tag{6.2} $$

We see that (6.2) satisfies (3.9), since ${}'\tilde{x}^l_A(X)$ does by assumption; that

$$ \hat{\tilde{x}}^k_A(\underset{0}{X},t) = \hat{\tilde{x}}^k_A(t); $$

and that

$$ \hat{\tilde{x}}^k_A(X,t_1) = {}'\tilde{x}^k_A(X) $$

for all X. Hence (6.2) defines a kinematically possible motion in which the values of the displacement gradients are prescribed at $\underset{0}{X}$. And to find the stress-configuration pair $\{{}''t_{ij}, {}''x^k_A\}$ we have but to put (6.2) into (3.5), take $\{{}'t_{ij}, {}'x^k_A\}$ as initial conditions at $t=t_1$, solve (3.5) for $t_1 \leqq t \leqq t_2$, and determine the stress-configuration pair at $t=t_2$.

For a given representation of a hypo-elastic material, we may speak of the allowable stress-displacement gradient pairs at each material point as the possible values that the stress-configuration pairs may take there. And, from the foregoing discussion, these allowable stress-displacement gradient pairs will be precisely all those which may be reached from any one of them along a solution of (3.5).

Moreover, an examination of (6.2) will show that an assignment of $\hat{\tilde{x}}^k_A(t)$ at $\underset{0}{X}$ such that $\hat{\tilde{x}}^k_A(t_1) = \hat{\tilde{x}}^k_A(t_2)$ may be imbedded in a motion of the entire set of material points for which the initial and final configurations coincide. Thus if it were possible to find a solution $[\tilde{\tilde{t}}_{ij}(t), \tilde{\tilde{x}}^k_A(t)]$, $t_1 \leqq t \leqq t_2$, of (3.5), where $[\tilde{\tilde{t}}_{ij}(t_1), \tilde{\tilde{x}}^k_A(t_1)]$ is an allowable stress-displacement gradient pair at some given material point $\underset{0}{X}$ for some given representation of a hypo-elastic material, such that ${}^{\approx}w < 0$, where

$$ {}^{\approx}w \equiv \int_{t_1}^{t_2} \tilde{\tilde{t}}_{ij}\, \tilde{\tilde{d}}_{ij}\, \frac{\varrho_0}{\tilde{\tilde{\varrho}}}\, dt, \tag{6.3} $$

then for some material volume containing $\underset{0}{X}$ it would, by (6.1) and our foregoing remarks, be possible to find a motion for which, though the initial and final configurations are the same, the work done by the stresses is negative. Hence we may make the following

Remark 1. *Suppose given a representation of a hypo-elastic material for which the hypotheses of Theorem* IV *hold, henceforth called a* representation IV. *Then the quantity* ${}^{\approx}w$ *defined in* (6.3), *and henceforth called the* work density, *must be non-negative for any set of continuous, piecewise smooth functions* $\tilde{\tilde{t}}_{ij}(t)$, $\tilde{\tilde{x}}^k_A(t)$, $t_1 \leqq t \leqq t_2$, *satisfying* (3.5) *for which* $[\tilde{\tilde{t}}_{ij}(t_1), \tilde{\tilde{x}}^k_A(t_1)]$ *is an allowable stress-displacement gradient pair at any given material point* X *such that* $\tilde{\tilde{x}}^k_A(t_1) = \tilde{\tilde{x}}^k_A(t_2)$.

And this shall be our starting point to establish Theorem IV.

Note that (6.3) may be written

$$\tilde{\tilde{w}} = \int_{t_1}^{t_2} \det|\tilde{\tilde{x}}^k_B|\, \tilde{\tilde{t}}_{ij}\, \tilde{\tilde{X}}^A_j \frac{d\tilde{\tilde{x}}^i_A}{dt}\, dt, \tag{6.4}$$

the total derivative replacing the material derivative because, since X is fixed, x^i_A becomes a function of t alone. We now proceed to our lemmas.

Lemma 1. *If $[\hat{t}_{ij}(t), \hat{x}^k_A(t)]$ satisfy (3.5), $t_1 \leqq t \leqq t_2$, and if $\overset{*}{t}(t)$ is a smooth function of t, $t_1 \leqq t \leqq t_2$, $d\overset{*}{t}/dt \neq 0$ with, say, $\overset{*}{t}(t_1) = \underset{*}{t}_1$, $\overset{*}{t}(t_2) = \underset{*}{t}_2$, then $\overset{*}{t}_{ij}(\underset{*}{t})$, $\overset{*}{x}{}^k_A(\underset{*}{t})$ defined by*

$$\overset{*}{t}_{ij}(\underset{*}{t}) = \hat{t}_{ij}(t), \quad \overset{*}{x}{}^k_A(\underset{*}{t}) = \hat{x}^k_A(t), \quad \underset{*}{t} = \overset{*}{t}(t),$$

satisfy (3.5) for $\min(\underset{*}{t}_1, \underset{*}{t}_2) \leqq \underset{*}{t} \leqq \max(\underset{*}{t}_1, \underset{*}{t}_2)$. Also the corresponding values of the work density, namely

$$\hat{w} \equiv \int_{t_1}^{t_2} \det|\hat{x}^k_B|\, \hat{t}_{ij}\, \hat{X}^A_j \frac{d\hat{x}^i_A}{dt}\, dt,$$

and (6.5)

$$^{*}w \equiv \int_{\underset{*}{t}_1}^{\underset{*}{t}_2} \det|\overset{*}{x}{}^k_B|\, \overset{*}{t}_{ij}\, \overset{*}{X}{}^A_j \frac{d\overset{*}{x}{}^i_A}{d\underset{*}{t}}\, d\underset{*}{t},$$

are related by

$$^{*}w = \hat{w} \quad \text{if} \quad \frac{d\overset{*}{t}}{dt} > 0 \quad (\text{i.e. } \underset{*}{t}_1 < \underset{*}{t}_2)$$

or

$$^{*}w = -\hat{w} \quad \text{if} \quad \frac{d\overset{*}{t}}{dt} < 0 \quad (\text{i.e. } \underset{*}{t}_2 < \underset{*}{t}_1).$$

Proof. This lemma is readily verified by substitution in (3.5) and (6.5). *q.e.d.*

It follows from Lemma 1 that, without loss of generality, we may assume that $t_1 = 0$ and $t_2 = 1$ where convenient. We proceed to

Lemma 2. *Consider a representation* IV *and any material point $\underset{0}{X}$. Let $[\hat{t}_{ij}(t), \hat{x}^k_A(t)]$, $t_1 \leqq t \leqq t_2$, be any solution of (3.5) with $[\hat{t}_{ij}(t_1), \hat{x}^k_A(t_1)]$ an allowable stress-displacement gradient pair, and $\hat{x}^k_A(t_1) = \hat{x}^k_A(t_2)$. Then $\hat{w} = 0$, where $\hat{w}$ is the corresponding value of the work density.*

Proof. Using Lemma 1 we may obtain a second solution of (3.5), $[\overset{*}{t}_{ij}(\underset{*}{t}), \overset{*}{x}{}^k_A(\underset{*}{t})]$, $t_1 \leqq \underset{*}{t} \leqq t_2$, obeying the hypotheses of Lemma 2, by writing

$$\overset{*}{t}(t) \equiv t_1 + t_2 - t.$$

Let $^{*}w$ be the value of the work density corresponding to this second solution. Then by Lemma 1 $w = -{}^{*}w$. But, because of Remark 1, $w \geqq 0$ and $^{*}w \geqq 0$. Hence $w = {}^{*}w = 0$. *q.e.d.*

Lemma 3. *Consider a representation* IV. *Let $[\underset{1}{t}_{ij}, \underset{1}{x}{}^k_A]$ and $[\underset{2}{t}_{ij}, \underset{2}{x}{}^k_A]$ be two allowable stress-displacement gradient pairs at a given material point. Suppose* *that* $[\widehat{t}_{ij}(t), \widehat{x}^k_A(t)]$ *and* $[\widehat{\widehat{t}}_{ij}(\tau), \widehat{\widehat{x}}^k_A(\tau)]$ *are two solutions of* (3.5), $t_1 \leqq t \leqq t_2$, $\tau_1 \leqq \tau \leqq \tau_2$, *such that* $[\widehat{t}_{ij}(t_1), \widehat{x}^k_A(t_1)] = [\underset{1}{t}_{ij}, \underset{1}{x}^k_A] = [\widehat{\widehat{t}}_{ij}(\tau_1), \widehat{\widehat{x}}^k_A(\tau_1)]$, $\widehat{x}^k_A(t_2) = \underset{2}{x}^k_A = \widehat{\widehat{x}}^k_A(\tau_2)$. *Let the corresponding values of the work density be* $\widehat{\ }w$ *and* $\widehat{\widehat{\ }}w$ *respectively. Then* $\widehat{\ }w = \widehat{\widehat{\ }}w$.

Proof. By Lemma 1 we may, without loss of generality, take $t_1 = \tau_1 = 0$ and $t_2 = \tau_2 = 1$. Then we define another solution of (3.5), $[\breve{t}_{ij}('t), \breve{x}^k_A('t)]$, $0 \leqq 't \leqq 2$, as follows:

$$\begin{aligned} \breve{t}_{ij}('t) &= \widehat{t}_{ij}(1-'t), & \breve{x}^k_A('t) &= \widehat{x}^k_A(1-'t), & 0 &\leqq 't \leqq 1, \\ \breve{t}_{ij}('t) &= \widehat{\widehat{t}}_{ij}('t-1), & \breve{x}^k_A('t) &= \widehat{\widehat{x}}^k_A('t-1), & 1 &\leqq 't \leqq 2. \end{aligned}$$

That this is a solution in each of the intervals $0 \leqq 't \leqq 1$ and $1 \leqq 't \leqq 2$ may be verified immediately with the use of Lemma 1. Also it is continuous at $'t = 1$ because, by the hypotheses of our lemma and the definition of this solution, $[\widehat{t}_{ij}(0), \widehat{x}^k_A(0)] = [\widehat{\widehat{t}}_{ij}(0), \widehat{\widehat{x}}^k_A(0)] = [\breve{t}_{ij}(1), x^k_A(1)]$. Hence, since $\breve{x}^k_A(0) = \widehat{x}^k_A(1) = \underset{1}{x}^k_A = \widehat{\widehat{x}}^k_A(1) = x^k_A(2)$, Lemma 2 yields

$$\breve{\ }w \equiv \int_0^2 \det|\breve{x}^k_B|\, \breve{t}_{ij}\, \breve{X}^A_j \frac{d\breve{x}^i_A}{d't}\, d't = 0. \tag{6.6}$$

But from Lemma 1

$$\begin{aligned} \int_0^1 \det|\breve{x}^k_B|\, \breve{t}_{ij}\, \breve{X}^A_j \frac{d\breve{x}^i_A}{d't}\, d't &= -\widehat{\ }w, \\ \int_1^2 \det|\breve{x}^k_B|\, \breve{t}_{ij}\, \breve{X}^A_j \frac{d\breve{x}^i_A}{d't}\, d't &= \widehat{\widehat{\ }}w. \end{aligned} \tag{6.7}$$

Combining (6.6) and (6.7) gives

$$0 = \breve{\ }w = \widehat{\widehat{\ }}w - \widehat{\ }w,$$

and hence the lemma. *q.e.d.*

Remark 2. *Suppose that we consider a given stress-configuration pair,* $\{\underset{0}{t}_{ij}, \underset{0}{x}^k_A\}$, *corresponding to a given representation* IV. *Then, by Lemma* 3, *we may define a function* $\widetilde{\Sigma}(x^i_A, X)$ *as follows: for each fixed* X, $\widetilde{\Sigma}('x^i_A, X)$ *is the value of the work density for any solution of* (3.5) *for which* $[\underset{0}{t}_{ij}, \underset{0}{x}^k_A](X)$ *constitute the initial conditions and for which the final values of the displacement gradients are* $'x^i_A$.

We cannot differentiate $\widetilde{\Sigma}$ with respect to x^i_A by ordinary means since $\widetilde{\Sigma}$ is defined by an integral whose integrand has not been shown to be a function of x^i_A and X. Nevertheless, we shall now prove

Lemma 4. *The partial derivatives of* $\widetilde{\Sigma}(x^i_A, X)$ *with respect to the displacement gradients exist and are given by*

$$\frac{\partial \widetilde{\Sigma}}{\partial x^i_A} = \det|x^k_B|\, t_{ij}\, X^A_j, \tag{6.8}$$

where, for given x^k_A, t_{ij} *has any value such that* $[t_{ij}, x^k_A]$ *is an allowable stress-displacement gradient pair at* X.

Proof. Let $[\underset{1}{t}_{ij}, \underset{1}{x}^k_A]$ be any allowable stress-displacement gradient pair at X. Then there exists a solution of (3.5) $[\widehat{t}_{ij}(t), \widehat{x}^k_A(t)]$, $0 \leqq t \leqq 1$, such that

$$[\widehat{t}_{\cdot j}(0), \widehat{x}^k_A(0)] = [\underset{0}{t}_{ij}, \underset{0}{x}^k_A](X),$$
$$[t_{ij}(1), x^k_A(1)] = [\underset{1}{t}_{ij}, \underset{1}{x}^k_A].$$

By definition

$$\widetilde{\Sigma}(x^k_A, X) = \int_0^1 \det|\widehat{x}^k_B|\, \widehat{t}_{ij}\, \widehat{X}^A_j \frac{dx^i_A}{dt}\, dt.$$

Let us extend the function $x^i_A(t)$ beyond $t=1$ in any one of the following eighteen ways; write

$$\widehat{x}^i_A(t) = \underset{1}{x}^i_A + \varepsilon(t-1)\,\delta^i_p\,\delta^L_A, \qquad 1 \leqq t \leqq 1+h, \tag{6.9}$$

where p and L each take *one* of the values 1, 2, 3, ε takes either the values $+1$ or -1, and h is some positive real number. Let $t_{ij}(t)$ be the corresponding solution of (3.5). Then

$$\begin{aligned}\widetilde{\Sigma}(\underset{1}{x}^i_A + \varepsilon\,\eta\,\delta^i_p\,\delta^L_A, X) - \widetilde{\Sigma}(\underset{1}{x}^i_A, X) &= \int_1^\eta \det|\widehat{x}^k_B(t)|\, \widehat{t}_{pj}(t)\, \widehat{X}^L_j(t)\, \varepsilon\, dt \\ &= \det|\widehat{x}^k_B(\tau)|\, \widehat{t}_{pj}(\tau)\, \widehat{X}^L_j(\tau)\, \varepsilon\,(\eta-1),\end{aligned} \tag{6.10}$$

where $1 < \eta \leqq 1+h$, and τ is some value between 1 and η, the last inequality following from the law of the mean for integrals. Using (6.9), (6.10) becomes

$$\frac{\widetilde{\Sigma}(\widehat{x}^i_A(\eta), X) - \widetilde{\Sigma}(\underset{1}{\widehat{x}}^i_A, X)}{x^p_L(\eta) - \underset{1}{x}^p_L} = \det|x^k_B(\tau)|\, \widehat{t}_{pj}(\tau)\, \widehat{X}^L_j(\tau), \qquad 1 < \tau < \eta. \tag{6.11}$$

Since the limit of the right-hand side of (6.10) exists as $\eta \to 1$, the limit of the left-hand side must also exist. Since $\widehat{x}^i_A(\eta) = \underset{1}{x}^i_A$ for $\eta \geqq 1$ unless $i=p$ and $A=L$, the limit of the left-hand side of (6.10) as $\eta \to 1$ represents the right or left-sided partial derivative of $\widetilde{\Sigma}$ with respect to x^p_L according to whether ε is $+1$ or -1. But both of these limits are equal and, in fact, are given by the right-hand side of (6.11) evaluated at $\tau = 1$, since solutions to (3.5) must be continuous in t. Hence the partial derivatives of $\widetilde{\Sigma}$ with respect to the displacement gradients exist and are given by (6.8), where t_{ij} is determined as in the hypotheses of Lemma 4. *q.e.d.*

With the help of our lemmas, Theorem IV follows immediately. From Lemma 4, in particular (6.8), and from $(2.5)_2$, a stress which will make $[t_{ij}, x^k_A]$ an allowable stress-displacement gradient pair at any given X, for a given representation IV, must satisfy

$$t_{ij} = [\det|x^l_L|]^{-1}\, x^j_A \frac{\partial \widetilde{\Sigma}(x^k_B, X)}{\partial x^i_A} = \frac{\varrho}{\varrho_0}\, x^j_A \frac{\partial \widetilde{\Sigma}(x^k_B, X)}{\partial x^i_A}, \tag{6.12}$$

and thus there can be but one such stress. Moreover, comparison of (6.11) with (2.13) shows that a material obeying the hypotheses of Theorem IV must be elastic in the sense of Green. Hence Theorem IV is established.

7. Isotropy

Consider a representation of a Cauchy-elastic material in which the material coordinates are one possible set of values of the spatial coordinates and are cartesian. Let O^A_B and O^A, $A, B=1, 2, 3$, be a set of constants such that

$$\delta_{AB}\, O^A_C\, O^B_D = \delta_{CD}.$$

Then

$$'X^A = O^A_B\, X^B + O^A \tag{7.1}$$

denotes an orthogonal transformation of material points so that

$$'x^i_A \equiv \frac{\partial x^i}{\partial\, 'X^A} = x^i_B\, O^B_A, \qquad 'X^A_i \equiv \frac{\partial\, 'X^A}{\partial x^i} = X^B_i\, O^A_B. \tag{7.2}$$

If in (2.8) we have

$$\hat{t}_{ij}('x^i_A, 'X^B) = \hat{t}_{ij}(x^i_A, X^B), \tag{7.3}$$

when X^A and $'X^A$ are related by (7.1), we say that the given Cauchy-elastic material is isotropic with respect to the given representation.

It is well known [1952] [1955, 3] that the above definition of isotropy requires that the stress t_{ij} be a uniform hydrostatic pressure when $x^i_A = \delta^i_A$. But the converse of this statement is not true, as can be verified by considering a Green-elastic material for which

$$\tilde{\Sigma} \equiv [(\delta_{kl}\, x^k_A\, x^l_B - \delta_{AB})\, H^{AB}]^2, \tag{7.4}$$

where $H^{11}=1$, $H^{22}=2$, $H^{33}=1$ and $H^{AB}=0$ if $A \neq B$. That (7.4) is consistent with the principle of isotropy of space may be checked using the last paragraph in § 2.

Using (2.13), the stress for (7.4) becomes

$$t^{ij} = 2\frac{\varrho}{\varrho_0}(\delta_{kl}\, x^k_A\, x^l_B - \delta_{AB})\, H^{AB}\, x^i_L\, H^{LM}\, x^j_M. \tag{7.5}$$

Consider the following two special cases of (2.1);

$$x^1 = X^1, \quad x^2 = 2X^2, \quad x^3 = X^3 \qquad \text{(case 1)}$$

and

$$x^1 = 'X^2, \quad x^2 = 2'X^1, \quad x^3 = 'X^3 \qquad \text{(case 2)}$$

which differ by the orthogonal transformation

$$'X^1 = X^2, \quad 'X^2 = X^1, \quad 'X^3 = X^3.$$

We obtain from (7.5)

$$t^{11} = 6, \quad t^{22} = 8, \quad t^{33} = 6, \quad t^{ij} = 0, \quad i \neq j \qquad \text{(case 1)}$$

$$t^{11} = 12, \quad t^{22} = 6, \quad t^{33} = 3, \quad t^{ij} = 0, \quad i \neq j \qquad \text{(case 2)}$$

so that the Green-elastic material given by (7.4) is not isotropic with respect to the given representation although from (7.5) it is readily seen that the stress vanishes, and hence is certainly a hydrostatic pressure, when $x^i_A = \delta^i_A$.

We shall now establish the following:

Theorem V. *Given a representation of a Cauchy-elastic material which is also hypo-elastic, this material is also isotropic with respect to this representation if and only if the stress is a uniform hydrostatic pressure when* $x^i_A = \delta^i_A$.

Proof. Necessity has been established elsewhere, as stated above. We have to prove sufficiency. Assume, then, that the stress is a uniform hydrostatic pressure when $x^i_A = \delta^i_A$.

Let (2.8) correspond to our representation and define

$$\hat{\hat{t}}_{ij}(x^k_A, X^C) \equiv \hat{t}_{ij}('x^k_A, 'X^C), \tag{7.6}$$

using (7.1) and (7.2). Then, by (7.2),

$$\hat{\hat{t}}_{ij}(x^i_A, X^C) = \hat{t}_{ij}(O^H_A\, x^i_H, O^C_H\, X^H + O^C), \tag{7.7}$$

and by substitution into (4.2) we find that $\hat{\hat{t}}_{ij}$ is a solution. But when $x^i_A = \delta^i_A$ we have $t_{ij} = -p\,\delta_{ij}$, where p is independent of X. Hence, using (2.11) and (2.12), we see that

$$-p\,\delta^{ij} = \hat{t}^{ij}(\delta^k_A, X^C) = \delta^i_A\, \delta^j_B\, \hat{T}^{AB}(\delta^K_p\, \delta^L_q\, \delta^{pq}, X^C) = \delta^i_A\, \delta^j_B\, \hat{T}^{AB}(\delta^{KL}, X^C), \tag{7.8}$$

from which

$$\hat{T}^{AB}(\delta^{KL}, X^C) = -p\,\delta^{AB} = T^{AB}(\delta^{KL}, 'X^C), \tag{7.9}$$

the last equality following since p is independent of X. Thus, putting $x^i_A = \delta^i_A$ into (7.6) and using (7.7), (7.8) and (7.9), we obtain

$$\begin{aligned} \hat{\hat{t}}^{ij}(\delta^k_A, X^C) &= \hat{t}^{ij}(\delta^k_B\, O^B_A, 'X^C) = \delta^i_R\, O^R_A\, \delta^j_S\, O^S_B\, \hat{T}^{AB}(\delta^M_p\, O^K_M\, \delta^N_s\, O^L_N\, \delta^{ps}, 'X^C) \\ &= \delta^i_R\, O^R_A\, \delta^j_S\, O^S_B\, \hat{T}^{AB}(\delta^{KL}, 'X^C) = -p\, \delta^i_R\, O^R_A\, \delta^j_S\, O^S_B\, \delta^{AB} \\ &= -p\, \delta^i_R\, \delta^j_S\, \delta^{RS} = -p\,\delta^{ij} = \hat{t}^{ij}(\delta^k_A, X^C). \end{aligned}$$

Since the two solutions of (4.2), $\hat{t}^{ij}$ and $\hat{\hat{t}}^{ij}$, coincide for one value of x^i_A at each X, they must, because of uniqueness of solutions to (4.2), coincide for all values of x^i_A at each X, *i.e.*,

$$\hat{t}^{ij}('x^k_A, 'X^C) = \hat{\hat{t}}^{ij}(x^k_A, X^C) = \hat{t}^{ij}(x^k_A, X^C),$$

and hence the theorem is established.

We remark, then, that the material (7.4) is elastic but not hypo-elastic, since if it were hypo-elastic it would have to be isotropic because of Theorem V, and it is not. Thus hypo-elasticity does not include all of elasticity.

References

1947 Eisenhart, L. P.: Differential Geometry, Princeton University Press, Princeton, N. J.

1952 Truesdell, C. A.: The mechanical foundations of elasticity and fluid dynamics. J. Rational Mech. Anal. **1**, 125—300.

1954 Schouten, J. A.: Tensor Analysis for Physicists. Oxford University Press, Oxford.

1955 1. Caprioli, L.: Su una criteria per l'esistenza dell'energia di deformazione. Boll. Un. Mat. Ital. (3) **10**, 481—483.
2. Noll, W.: On the continuity of the solid and fluid states. J. Rational Mech. Anal. **4**, 3—81.
3. Rivlin, R. S., & J. L. Ericksen: Stress-deformation relations in isotropic materials. J. Rational Mech. Anal. **4**, 323—425.
4. Thomas, T. Y.: On the structure of stress strain relations. Proc. Nat. Acad. Sci. **41**, 716—720.
5. Thomas, T. Y.: Kinematically preferred coordinate systems. Proc. Nat. Acad. Sci. **41**, 762—720.
6. Truesdell, C. A.: Hypo-elasticity. J. Rational Mech. Anal. **4**, 83—133.

1958 1. Bernstein, B., & J. L. Ericksen: Work functions in hypo-elasticity. Arch. Rational Mech. Anal. **1**, 396—409.
2. Noll, W.: A mathematical theory of the mechanical behavior of continuous media. Arch. Rational Mech. Anal. **2**, 197—226.
3. Toupin, R. A.: World invariant kinematics. Arch. Rational Mech. Anal. **1**, 181—211.

1960 Bernstein, B.: Relations between hypo-elasticity and elasticity. Trans. Society of Rheology **4** (in press).

U. S. Naval Research Laboratory
Washington, D. C.

(Received July 5, 1960)

Druck der Universitätsdruckerei H. Stürtz AG., Würzburg

No. 14

FOUNDATIONS OF LINEAR VISCO-ELASTICITY

B. D. Coleman & W. Noll

Reviews of Modern Physics, Volume 33, pp. 239-249 (1961).

The various theories of "small" deformation violate the principle of material indifference and hence cannot represent accurately the behavior of any material. A rational position for linearized elasticity is easily found: One has only to restrict attention to those deformations in which the strain and rotation from the natural state are small in order to derive, simply and rigorously, the stress-strain relation of the linearized theory as an approximation to the properly invariant stress-strain relation of finite elasticity. For BOLTZMANN's theory of infinitesimal viscoelasticity, no such status was known, and there was some doubt any existed, until the paper here reprinted was published. It is a meaningless ritual to say a theory is "approximate" unless the exact model being approximated is specified; an equation is not truly "approximate" until its error has been determined, and an approximation is not really satisfactory until a means of improving it, if need be, has been found.

In this paper COLEMAN & NOLL find a rational position for BOLTZMANN's theory as a first approximation to a simple material in the sense of NOLL (No. 12 in RMM). A simple material is one in which the stress at a particle is uniquely determined by the history of the deformation gradient at that particle. In addition, COLEMAN & NOLL adopt a postulate of fading memory, giving mathematical form to the assumption that long past events have less influence on the present stress than do recent past events, omitting events at a set of times of measure 0. For other consequences of this principle, see RMM, No. 15.

The norm (3.7) may be called the **recollection** of the deformation history **G**(s). According to (4.4) and the observations preceding it, a deformation that has always been sufficiently small has an arbitrarily small recollection. It is then shown quite simply that the stress relation of any simple material obeying the principle of fading memory is approximated arbitrarily closely by equations of BOLTZMANN's type, so long as the entire deformation history is small enough. Eq. (4.16) generalizes BOLTZMANN's equations to anisotropic materials slightly deformed from an arbitrarily stressed state.

In Section 5 similar methods are used to correct BOLTZMANN's theory when it is assumed only that the recollection is small; under this assumption the deformation need not have been small at times long past. The resulting constitutive equation (5.1) of "finite linear visco-elasticity" satisfies the principle of material indifference and thus may be set alongside the constitutive equations of finite elasticity and linear viscosity as affording a possible model for material behavior in arbitrary deformation processes.

In Section 6 a method of pushing the approximation one stage further is indicated, and the details are presented for the case of an incompressible fluid. One of the normal-stress differences in simple shearing flow is then shown to be specified in terms of the shear viscosity function, a rather unexpected result.

Reprinted from REVIEWS OF MODERN PHYSICS, Vol. 33, No. 2, 239–249, April, 1961
Printed in U. S. A.

Foundations of Linear Viscoelasticity*

BERNARD D. COLEMAN
Mellon Institute, Pittsburgh, Pennsylvania
AND
WALTER NOLL
Department of Mathematics, Carnegie Institute of Technology, Pittsburgh, Pennsylvania

1. INTRODUCTION

THE classical linear theory of viscoelasticity was apparently first formulated by Boltzmann[1] in 1874. His original presentation covered the three-dimensional case, but was restricted to isotropic materials. The extension of the theory to anisotropic materials is, however, almost immediately evident on reading Boltzmann's paper, and the basic hypotheses of the theory have not changed since 1874. Since that date, much work has been done on the following aspects of linear viscoelasticity: solution of special boundary value problems,[2a] reformulation[3,4] of the one-dimensional version of the theory in terms of new material functions (such as "creep functions" and frequency-dependent complex "impedances") which appear to be directly accessible to measurement, experimental determination[2b] of the material functions for those materials for which the theory appears useful, prediction of the form of the material functions from molecular models, and, recently, axiomatization[5,6] of the theory. In this article, instead of being concerned with these matters, we reexamine the fundamental hypotheses of linear viscoelasticity in the light of recent advances in nonlinear continuum mechanics.

The basic assumption of the classical linear theory of viscoelasticity is a constitutive equation relating stress tensor $T(t)$ at time t to the history of the infinitesimal strain tensor $E(t-s)$, $0\leq s<\infty$. This assumption asserts that if $E(t-s)$, taken relative to a natural reference configuration corresponding to zero equilibrium stress, is *small* in magnitude for *all s*, then

$$T(t)=\mathbf{\Omega}\{E(t)\}+\mathbf{\Phi}(0)\{E(t)\}+\int_0^\infty \dot{\mathbf{\Phi}}(s)\{E(t-s)\}ds, \tag{1.1}$$

where

$$\dot{\mathbf{\Phi}}(s)=(d/ds)\mathbf{\Phi}(s), \tag{1.2}$$

and $\mathbf{\Phi}$ is such that

$$\lim_{s\to\infty}\mathbf{\Phi}(s)=0. \tag{1.3}$$

Here $\mathbf{\Phi}(s)\{\ \}$ (for each s) and $\mathbf{\Omega}\{\ \}$ are linear transformations of the space of symmetric tensors into itself. As a function of time, $\mathbf{\Phi}$ has a simple physical significance and is called the "stress relaxation function." For if we consider a deformation history such that the material is kept in its natural reference configuration ($E=0$) for all times $t<0$ and has the strain E^* for all times $t\geq 0$, then for such a history Eq. (1.1) yields

$$T(t)=\begin{cases}0 & \text{if } t<0\\ \mathbf{\Phi}(t)\{E^*\}+\mathbf{\Omega}\{E^*\} & \text{if } t\geq 0.\end{cases} \tag{1.4}$$

In the familiar special case of an isotropic material, $\mathbf{\Phi}(t)$ is completely determined by two scalar-valued functions of time: the stress relaxation functions for shear and dilatation. The linear transformation $\mathbf{\Omega}$ characterizes the "linear equilibrium stress-strain law" of infinitesimal elasticity theory; i.e., Eqs. (1.3) and (1.4) yield

$$\lim_{t\to\infty}T(t)=\mathbf{\Omega}\{E^*\}. \tag{1.5}$$

For an isotropic solid, $\mathbf{\Omega}$ is determined by the two Lamé constants.

We refer to the classical linear theory based on Eqs. (1.1)–(1.3) as *infinitesimal viscoelasticity* because, roughly speaking, it can be applicable only to those situations in which the strain is small at all times.

In Sec. 4 we show how Eq. (1.1) must be modified when the reference configuration is arbitrary and not necessarily one in which the equilibrium stress is zero. In particular, in the case of a fluid, $T(t)$ should be replaced by $T(t)+p_rI$, where p_r is the equilibrium hydrostatic pressure corresponding to the reference configuration, and I denotes the unit (or identity) tensor. For a fluid $\mathbf{\Omega}$ is determined by the equilibrium compressibility.

It is often claimed that the theory of infinitesimal viscoelasticity can be derived from an assumption that on a microscopic level matter can be regarded as composed of "linear viscous elements" (also called

* This work was supported by the Air Force Office of Scientific Research under contract and by the National Science Foundation under Grant NSF-G5250.

[1] L. Boltzmann, Sitzber. Kaiserlich, Akad. Wiss. (Wien) Math.-Naturwiss. K1. 70, Sect. II, 275-306 (1874).
[2] (a) E. H. Lee, in *Viscoelasticity*, edited by J. T. Bergen (Academic Press, Inc., New York, 1960), p. 1; (b) J. D. Ferry and K. Ninomiya, *ibid.*, p. 55.
[3] B. Gross, *Mathematical Structure of the Theories of Viscoelasticity* (Hermann & Cie., Paris, 1953). A summary of relationships between those material functions which occur in the one-dimensional formulation of the theory is given in this reference and in reference 4.
[4] H. Leaderman, Trans. Soc. Rheol. 1, 213 (1957).
[5] E. R. Love, Australian J. Phys. 9, 1 (1956).
[6] H. Konig and J. Meixner, Math. Nachr. 19, 265 (1958).

"dashpots") and "linear elastic elements" (called "springs") connected together in intricate "networks."[7] The motivation behind some of the recent work on spring and dashpot networks appears to be the hope that the consideration of such readily visualized models will suggest a formalism for immersing viscoelasticity in a general thermodynamical theory of irreversible processes.

We feel that the physicist's confidence in the usefulness of the theory of infinitesimal viscoelasticity does not stem from a belief that the materials to which the theory is applied are really composed of microscopic networks of springs and dashpots, but comes rather from other considerations. First, there is the observation that the theory works for many real materials. But second, and perhaps more important to theoreticians, is the fact that the theory looks plausible because it seems to be a mathematization of little more than certain intuitive prejudices about smoothness in macroscopic phenomena. It is natural to assume that the dependence of the stress on the history of the deformation should be, in some sense, a *smooth dependence*. (Smoothness assumptions are usually so "natural" to physicists that they are seldom made explicit.) Since we know that in small neighborhoods smooth dependences are approximately *linear*, it is felt that if only small deformations are considered, the stress should be given by a linear functional of the deformation history, and that this functional should yield the form exhibited in Eqs. (1.1)–(1.3).

This article tries to make precise these observations about smoothness, and in so doing seeks to obtain a mathematical derivation of infinitesimal viscoelasticity from plausible macroscopic assumptions. To do this one must first presume a nonlinear theory of the mechanical behavior of materials with memory, and, if the undertaking is to be at all worthwhile, the presumed nonlinear theory must rest on constitutive equations based only on very general physical principles. Our development starts with the recently formulated general theory[8] of "simple materials" (i.e., materials for which the stress depends in an arbitrary way on the history of the first spatial gradient of the displacement). The theory of simple materials is outlined in Sec. 3.

To make precise the notion of smoothness we must introduce a topology into the space of functions characterizing the history of the deformation; i.e., we must have a way of knowing when two histories are close to each other. We do this by defining a *norm*. The particular norm used here is one of those considered in our paper on memory functionals.[9] This norm has two important properties: first, it makes our space of histories a Hilbert space; second, it places greater emphasis on the deformations which occurred in the recent past than on those which occurred in the distant past. We believe that this second property is essential if one is to formulate a smoothness assumption for macroscopic phenomena that is compatible with the everyday observation that memories are imperfect. The memory of a macroscopic object for its past deformations fades in the sense that deformations which occurred in the distant past have a smaller effect on the present forces than have more recent deformations.

We mathematize the notion of smoothness by assuming that the constitutive functionals which give the stress in a simple material are *Fréchet differentiable* in our Hilbert space of histories.

In considering finite deformations in simple materials, it is often convenient to take the present configuration as the reference configuration for describing the history of the deformation. Indeed, when dealing with a fluid, this is the natural thing to do, because a fluid has no preferred configurations. However, we can do this even for solids, provided we maintain in the constitutive equations a tensor parameter which tells how the present configuration is related to a preferred configuration.

The function space norm which we use has the property that the norm of a history is small if the deformations have been small at all times in the past; indeed, our derivation of infinitesimal viscoelasticity is a combination of this fact with our differentiability assumption. However, when one takes the present state as a reference, the deformation at the present time is zero, and if one further notes that the distant past is of little importance, it becomes clear that there are several ways in which a history can be small in norm. In particular, any history for which the motion has been *slow* in the recent past has a small norm. This observation has suggested to us the consideration of a new linear approximation for the general constitutive functionals of simple materials. We call the theory based on this new approximation *finite linear viscoelasticity*; it includes the classical infinitesimal theory as a special case, but has the advantage of being meaningful in situations involving finite deformations. The arguments presented in Secs. 3 and 5 show that finite linear viscoelasticity furnishes a complete first-order approximation to the theory of simple materials in the limit in which the history of the deformation, taken relative to the present configuration, is small in norm.

The smoothness considerations presented can be extended to obtain higher order approximations to the general constitutive equations of simple materials. In Sec. 6 we discuss a second-order theory of viscoelasticity for incompressible simple fluids.

2. KINEMATICS

We present a brief outline of the kinematics required for a discussion of simple materials. For a more complete

[7] D. R. Bland, *The Theory of Viscoelasticity* (Pergamon Press, New York, 1960), Chap. 2.
[8] W. Noll, Arch. Ratl. Mech. Anal. 2, 197 (1958).
[9] B. D. Coleman and W. Noll, Arch. Ratl. Mech. Anal. 6, 356 (1960).

presentation which goes back to first principles, see Noll.[8]

Consider a particular material point X of a body $\mathfrak{B}$. Suppose that X occupies the position $\mathbf{X}$ in Euclidean space $\mathcal{E}$ when $\mathfrak{B}$ is in a reference configuration. Let $\boldsymbol{\xi}$ be the position of X in $\mathcal{E}$ at time τ. For the dependence of $\boldsymbol{\xi}$ on $\mathbf{X}$ and τ, we write

$$\boldsymbol{\xi}=\boldsymbol{\chi}(\mathbf{X},\tau). \tag{2.1}$$

The gradient $F(\tau)$ of $\boldsymbol{\chi}(\mathbf{X},\tau)$ with respect to $\mathbf{X}$,

$$F(\tau)=\nabla\boldsymbol{\chi}(\mathbf{X},\tau), \tag{2.2}$$

is called the *deformation gradient* at the material point X at time τ. It is a tensor which possesses an inverse $F(\tau)^{-1}$. (Here the term "tensor" is used a synonym for "linear transformation of the three-dimensional Euclidean vector space into itself.") The value of $F(\tau)$ at each point of $\mathfrak{B}$ is affected not only by the configuration of $\mathfrak{B}$ at time τ but also by our choice of a reference configuration for $\mathfrak{B}$. This reference configuration may be chosen for convenience and need not necessarily be a configuration actually occupied by the body during its motion.

It is often useful to employ the configuration at the present time t, rather than a fixed configuration, as the reference. The corresponding deformation gradient is denoted by $F_t(\tau)$ and called the *relative deformation gradient*. The deformation gradients enjoy the following important property, which is a direct consequence of the chain rule for the differentiation of composite vector-valued functions:

$$F(\tau)=F_t(\tau)F(t), \tag{2.3}$$

where the indicated multiplication is the usual composition of linear transformations (matrix product).

An immediate consequence of the definition of $F_t(t)$ is that

$$F_t(t)=I, \tag{2.4}$$

where I is the unit (or identity) tensor. From Eq. (2.3) we obtain the relation

$$F_t(\tau)=F(\tau)F(t)^{-1}. \tag{2.5}$$

Let $\rho(\tau)$ give the mass density at X as a function of τ; it follows from a theorem of kinematics that

$$\det F_t(\tau)=\rho(t)/\rho(\tau). \tag{2.6}$$

If $F(\tau)$ is independent of X, we say that the configuration of $\mathfrak{B}$ at time τ and the reference configuration of $\mathfrak{B}$ are related by a *homogeneous deformation*. If $F=F(\tau)$ is orthogonal, i.e., if

$$F^TF=FF^T=I, \tag{2.7}$$

in which F^T denotes the transpose of F, then this "homogeneous deformation" represents a rigid rotation of the body. If F is symmetric positive-definite, then the body has been subjected to a *pure stretch*; in this case the proper vectors of F give the principal directions of stretch and the proper numbers of F are the principal stretch ratios.

A theorem of algebra, called the *polar decomposition theorem*, states that any invertible tensor F can be written in two ways as the product of a symmetric positive-definite tensor and an orthogonal tensor:

$$F=RU, \tag{2.8}$$

$$F=VR. \tag{2.9}$$

Furthermore, the orthogonal tensor R and the symmetric positive-definite tensors U and V in these decompositions are uniquely determined by F and obey the following relations:

$$U^2=F^TF\equiv C, \tag{2.10}$$

$$V^2=FF^T\equiv B, \tag{2.11}$$

$$U=R^TVR. \tag{2.12}$$

Equations (2.8) and (2.9) have the following significance in kinematics: Any homogeneous deformation with deformation gradient F may be regarded as being the result of a pure stretch U followed by a rigid rotation R, or a rigid rotation R followed by a pure stretch V. These interpretations uniquely determine the pairs R, U and R, V. The rigid rotations entering these two interpretations are the same; however, the pure stretches U and V can be different. It follows from Eq. (2.12) that although these stretches may have different principal directions, they must yield the same stretch ratios. We call the tensor R the *rotation tensor* and the tensors U and V, respectively, the *right* and *left stretch tensors*. The symmetric positive-definite tensors C and B, defined by Eqs. (2.10) and (2.11), are called, respectively, the *right* and *left Cauchy-Green tensors*; they obviously contain the same information as the corresponding stretch tensors, and their components are often easier to compute.

The rotation tensor, the stretch tensors, and the Cauchy-Green tensors computed from the relative deformation gradient F_t are denoted by R_t, U_t, V_t, C_t, and B_t. The modifier *relative* is used to indicate that the present configuration (time t) is used as the reference. For example, $C_t(\tau)$, is called the *relative right Cauchy-Green tensor*.

The following formulas are consequences of Eq. (2.4):

$$U_t(t)=V_t(t)=C_t(t)=B_t(t)=R_t(t)=I. \tag{2.13}$$

For simplicity we have emphasized the interpretation for *homogeneous deformations* of the tensors defined by Eqs. (2.8)–(2.11). These definitions obviously apply also to nonhomogeneous deformations, and similar interpretations can be given to them in the nonhomogeneous case if one merely first observes that the deformations considered in continuum mechanics are sufficiently smooth to be approximately homogeneous in small regions of $\mathfrak{B}$.

We note that there is no unique way to measure "the strain" corresponding to an arbitrary finite deformation.

We now establish the connection between the kinematics of *finite deformations* sketched in the foregoing and the more familiar kinematics of *infinitesimal deformations.*

The *magnitude* $|A|$ of a tensor A is defined by

$$|A|^2=\mathrm{Tr}(AA^T), \tag{2.14}$$

where Tr denotes the trace of a tensor. If Cartesian coordinates are used, then $|A|^2$ is the sum of the squares of the elements of the 3×3 matrix corresponding to A. We also use the definition (2.14) or magnitude when A is replaced by a linear transformation $\mathbf{\Gamma}$ of the six-dimensional space of symmetric tensors. In this case, the square of the magnitude $|\mathbf{\Gamma}|$ of $\mathbf{\Gamma}$ is the sum of the squares of the 6×6 matrix corresponding to $\mathbf{\Gamma}$.

Let a motion with deformation gradient $F=F(\tau)$ be given. We put

$$H=F-I \tag{2.15}$$

and

$$\epsilon=\sup_{\tau}|H(\tau)|. \tag{2.16}$$

H is the gradient of the displacement vector field. We say that the deformation corresponding to $F(\tau)$ is *infinitesimal at all times* τ if

$$\epsilon\ll 1. \tag{2.17}$$

The *infinitesimal strain tensor* $E=E(\tau)$ is defined by

$$E=\tfrac{1}{2}(H+H^T). \tag{2.18}$$

In the following we consider functions of τ which are determined by $H(\tau)$ and which have the property that for each τ their magnitude is less than $K\epsilon^n$, where K is a number independent of τ, the function $H(\tau)$, and ϵ. Any such function is denoted by the order symbol $O(\epsilon^n)$; i.e.,

$$|O(\epsilon^n)|<K\epsilon^n. \tag{2.19}$$

It is easy to show that

$$F=I+H=I+O(\epsilon), \tag{2.20}$$

$$F^{-1}=I-H+O(\epsilon^2)=I+O(\epsilon). \tag{2.21}$$

Also, it is not difficult to establish the following relations between the stretch tensors U, V and Cauchy-Green tensors C, B, on the one hand, and the infinitesimal strain tensor E, on the other hand:

$$U-I=E+O(\epsilon^2)=O(\epsilon), \tag{2.22}$$

$$V-I=E+O(\epsilon^2)=O(\epsilon), \tag{2.23}$$

$$C-I=2E+O(\epsilon^2)=O(\epsilon), \tag{2.24}$$

$$B-I=2E+O(\epsilon^2)=O(\epsilon). \tag{2.25}$$

Thus, if terms of order $O(\epsilon^2)$ can be neglected, the stretch tensors U, V and Cauchy-Green tensors C, B can be expressed in terms of E. For finite deformations, however, the infinitesimal strain tensor E is devoid of kinematical significance.

Finally, we note the following relations between the *infinitesimal rotation tensor* W, defined by

$$W=\tfrac{1}{2}(H-H^T), \tag{2.26}$$

and the finite rotation tensor R:

$$R=I+W+O(\epsilon^2)=I+O(\epsilon),$$
$$R^T=R^{-1}=I-W+O(\epsilon^2)=I+O(\epsilon). \tag{2.27}$$

In order to find an expression for the relative Cauchy-Green tensor $C_t(\tau)$, we first substitute Eqs. (2.20) and (2.21) into Eq. (2.5) and obtain

$$F_t(\tau)=I+H(\tau)-H(t)+O(\epsilon^2). \tag{2.28}$$

Equation (2.10), written for the relative tensors F_t and C_t, reads

$$C_t(\tau)=F_t(\tau)^TF_t(\tau). \tag{2.29}$$

Substitution of Eq. (2.28) into Eq. (2.29) and use of Eq. (2.18) yield

$$C_t(\tau)=I+2[E(\tau)-E(t)]+O(\epsilon^2)=I+O(\epsilon). \tag{2.30}$$

For finite deformations there is no simple relation between $C_t(\tau)$, $C(\tau)$, and $C(t)$.

3. FADING MEMORY

The theory of simple materials is based on the following physical assumption: *The present stress is given by a functional of the past history of the deformation gradient.*

Suppose the deformation gradient $F(\tau)$ is given (for all $\tau\leq t$) computed relative to a fixed reference configuration. The right Cauchy-Green tensor $C(t)$ and rotation tensor $R(t)$ corresponding to $F(t)$ are determined by Eqs. (2.8) and (2.10). On using Eqs. (2.5) and (2.29) we can compute the relative Cauchy-Green tensors $C_t(\tau)$ for all $\tau\leq t$. We now put

$$\bar{C}_t(\tau)=R^T(t)C_t(\tau)R(t). \tag{3.1}$$

If the material has always been at rest, we have, by Eqs. (2.13) and (3.1),

$$\bar{C}_t(\tau)\equiv I \quad \text{for } \tau\leq t. \tag{3.2}$$

The principle of material objectivity, which states that the properties of a material should appear the same to all observers, can be used to show that the general constitutive equation for simple materials reduces to the form

$$\bar{T}(t)\equiv R^T(t)T(t)R(t)=\underset{s=0}{\overset{\infty}{\mathfrak{R}}}(\bar{C}_t(t-s);C(t)), \tag{3.3}$$

where $T(t)$ is the stress tensor at time t and the symbol $\mathfrak{R}$ denotes a functional. [This may be compared with reference 8, Eq. (22.8). Here we use a somewhat more suggestive notation.]

It is useful to put Eq. (3.3) into a slightly different form by writing the right-hand side as the sum of an "equilibrium term" $\mathfrak{h}(C(t))$ and a term which vanishes when the material has always been at rest, i.e., when Eq. (3.2) holds:

$$\bar{T}(t)=\mathfrak{h}(C(t))+\overset{\infty}{\underset{s=0}{\mathfrak{F}}}(\bar{C}_t(t-s)-I;C(t)), \quad (3.4)$$

$$\overset{\infty}{\underset{s=0}{\mathfrak{F}}}(0;C(t))=0. \quad (3.5)$$

For present purposes it is sufficient to regard the constitutive equation (3.4) as the definition of a simple material.

We now add a new physical assumption: *The memory of a simple material fades in time.*

There is no unique way to give this statement a precise meaning. We consider a particular mathematical interpretation of it. For this purpose we first introduce the concept of an influence function which is used to characterize the rate at which the memory fades. (This definition of an influence function is slightly different and somewhat less technical than the one we gave in reference 9.) A function h is called an *influence function* of order $r>0$ if it satisfies the following conditions:

(a) $h(s)$ is defined for $0\leq s<\infty$ and has positive real values: $h(s)>0$.

(b) $h(s)$ decays to zero according to

$$\lim_{s\to\infty} s^r h(s)=0 \quad (3.6)$$

monotonically for large s. For example,

$$h(s)=(s+1)^{-p}$$

is an influence function of order r if $r<p$. An exponential

$$h(s)=e^{-\beta s}, \quad \beta>0$$

is an influence function of any order.

Any function $G(s)$, defined for $s\geq 0$ and with values which are symmetric tensors, is called a *history*. The argument function $G(s)=\bar{C}_t(t-s)-I$ of the functional $\mathfrak{F}$ of Eq. (3.4) is a history. The tensor $C(t)$ in Eq. (3.4) plays the role of a parameter.

Let an influence function $h(s)$ be given. We then define the norm $\|G(s)\|$ of a history $G(s)$ by

$$\|G(s)\|^2=\int_0^\infty |G(s)|^2 h(s)^2 ds, \quad (3.7)$$

where $|G(s)|$ is the magnitude of the tensor $G(s)$ defined by Eq. (2.14). The influence function $h(s)$ determines the influence assigned to the values of $G(s)$ in computing the norm $\|G(s)\|$. Since $h(s)\to 0$ as $s\to\infty$, the values of $G(s)$ for small s (recent past) have a greater weight than the values for large s (distant past).

The collection of all histories with finite norm (3.7) forms a Hilbert space $\mathfrak{H}$. A history $G(s)$ belongs to the space $\mathfrak{H}$ if it does not grow too fast as $s\to\infty$.

Consider now an influence function h and a functional

$$\overset{\infty}{\underset{s=0}{\mathfrak{F}}}(G(s))$$

which is defined on a neighborhood of the zero history in the Hilbert space $\mathfrak{H}$ corresponding to h and whose values are symmetric tensors. Assume that the value of $\mathfrak{F}$ for the zero history is zero, i.e., that

$$\overset{\infty}{\underset{s=0}{\mathfrak{F}}}(0)=0. \quad (3.8)$$

We say that $\mathfrak{F}$ is *Fréchet-differentiable* at the zero history if there is a continuous linear functional $\delta\mathfrak{F}$ such that

$$\overset{\infty}{\underset{s=0}{\mathfrak{F}}}(G(s))=\overset{\infty}{\underset{s=0}{\delta\mathfrak{F}}}(G(s))+\overset{\infty}{\underset{s=0}{\mathfrak{R}}}(G(s)), \quad (3.9)$$

where the "remainder" $\mathfrak{R}$ is of order $o(\|G(s)\|)$ in the sense that

$$\lim_{\|G(s)\|\to 0} \|G(s)\|^{-1}\overset{\infty}{\underset{s=0}{\mathfrak{R}}}(G(s))=0. \quad (3.10)$$

The linear functional $\delta\mathfrak{F}$ is called the *first variation* or *Fréchet differential* of $\mathfrak{F}$ at the zero history.

We now translate our physical assumption of fading memory into the following mathematical requirement:

(F) *There exists an influence function $h(s)$ of an order $r>\frac{1}{2}$ such that, for each value of the tensor parameter C, the functional $\mathfrak{F}$ of the constitutive equation* (3.4) *is Fréchet-differentiable at the zero history in the Hilbert space $\mathfrak{H}$ corresponding to $h(s)$.*

If we indicate the dependence on the tensor parameter C, Eq. (3.9) becomes

$$\overset{\infty}{\underset{s=0}{\mathfrak{F}}}(G(s);C)=\overset{\infty}{\underset{s=0}{\delta\mathfrak{F}}}(G(s);C)+\overset{\infty}{\underset{s=0}{\mathfrak{R}}}(G(s);C). \quad (3.11)$$

We now invoke the theorem of the theory of Hilbert spaces which states that every continuous linear functional may be written as an inner product. It follows from this theorem that the first variation $\delta\mathfrak{F}$ has an integral representation of the form

$$\overset{\infty}{\underset{s=0}{\delta\mathfrak{F}}}(G(s);C)=\int_0^\infty \mathbf{\Gamma}(s;C)\{G(s)\}ds. \quad (3.12)$$

Here $\mathbf{\Gamma}(s;C)\{\ \}$, for each s and each C, is a linear transformation of the space of symmetric tensors into itself with the property that

$$\int_0^\infty |\mathbf{\Gamma}(s;C)|^2 h(s)^{-2}ds<\infty, \quad (3.13)$$

where $|\mathbf{\Gamma}(s;C)|$ is the magnitude of $\mathbf{\Gamma}(s;C)$ as defined by Eq. (2.14). The property (3.13) shows that $\mathbf{\Gamma}(s;C)$ must approach zero at a faster rate than the influence function $h(s)$ as $s\to\infty$. Substitution of Eqs. (3.12) and (3.11) into Eq. (3.4) yields

$$\bar{T}=\mathfrak{h}(C)+\int_0^\infty \mathbf{\Gamma}(s;C)\{G(s)\}ds+\mathop{\mathfrak{R}}_{s=0}^{\infty}(G(s);C), \quad (3.14)$$

where

$$G(s)=\bar{C}_t(t-s)-I. \quad (3.15)$$

It is understood that the variables $\bar{T}$, C, and $G(s)$ depend on the present time t.

It seems natural to add to the requirement (*F*) the following two assumptions:

(F′) *The Fréchet-differentiability of* $\mathfrak{F}$ *postulated in* (*F*) *is uniform in the tensor parameter* C.

(D) *The tensor function* $\mathfrak{h}(C)$ *of* (3.14) *is continuously differentiable.*

By the assumption (F′) we mean that the first variation

$$\delta\mathop{\mathfrak{F}}_{s=0}^{\infty}(G(s);C)$$

depends continuously on C in the strong sense and that the convergence in Eq. (3.10) is uniform in C.

4. INFINITESIMAL VISCOELASTICITY

We first remark that any function of order $O(\epsilon^n)$ in the sense of Eq. (2.19) is also a function of order $O(\epsilon^n)$ with respect to the Hilbert-space norm (3.7); i.e., there is a constant $\bar{K}$, independent of ϵ, such that

$$\|O(\epsilon^n)\|<\bar{K}\epsilon^n. \quad (4.1)$$

In order to prove this inequality we substitute $O(\epsilon^n)$ for $G(s)$ in the definition (3.7) of the norm and use the inequality (2.19):

$$\|O(\epsilon^n)\|^2=\int_0^\infty |O(\epsilon^n)|^2h(s)^2ds<(K\epsilon^n)^2\int_0^\infty h(s)^2ds. \quad (4.2)$$

The requirement (F) of Sec. 3 ensures that the number r of Eq. (3.6) is greater than $\frac{1}{2}$. It follows that the integral $\int_0^\infty h^2(s)ds$ is finite and hence that the inequality (4.1) holds with

$$\bar{K}=K\left(\int_0^\infty h(s)^2ds\right)^{\frac{1}{2}}. \quad (4.3)$$

This remark shows that the order symbols in Eqs. (2.20)–(2.30) may be interpreted in terms of the convergence in the Hilbert space of histories defined in Sec. 3. This interpretation must be used to justify most of the subsequent considerations.

By combining Eqs. (3.1), (2.30), and (2.27), we find the following expression for the history

$$G(s)=\bar{C}_t(t-s)-I$$

which enters the constitutive equation (3.4) of a simple material:

$$G(s)=2[E(t-s)-E(t)]+O(\epsilon^2)=O(\epsilon). \quad (4.4)$$

On substituting Eq. (4.4) into Eq. (3.11) and using Eq. (3.10) and the linearity and continuity of the first variation $\delta\mathfrak{F}$, we obtain

$$\mathop{\mathfrak{F}}_{s=0}^{\infty}(G(s);C)=2\,\delta\mathop{\mathfrak{F}}_{s=0}^{\infty}(E(t-s)-E(t);C)+o(\epsilon), \quad (4.5)$$

where the order symbol $o(\epsilon)$ is used in the sense that

$$\lim_{\epsilon\to 0}\epsilon^{-1}|o(\epsilon)|=0. \quad (4.6)$$

It is not difficult to prove that the uniformity assumption (F′) of Sec. 3 implies that Eq. (4.5) remains valid if, on the right-hand side, the tensor $C=I+O(\epsilon)$ is replaced by the unit tensor I:

$$\mathop{\mathfrak{F}}_{s=0}^{\infty}(G(s);C)=2\,\delta\mathop{\mathfrak{F}}_{s=0}^{\infty}(E(t-s)-E(t);I)+o(\epsilon). \quad (4.7)$$

We now substitute the integral representation (3.12), for $C=I$, into Eq. (4.7), and obtain

$$\mathop{\mathfrak{F}}_{s=0}^{\infty}(G(s);C)=\int_0^\infty 2\mathbf{\Gamma}(s)\{E(t-s)\}ds-\int_0^\infty 2\mathbf{\Gamma}(s)ds\{E(t)\}+o(\epsilon). \quad (4.8)$$

On defining $\mathbf{\Phi}(s)$ by

$$\mathbf{\Phi}(s)=-2\int_s^\infty \mathbf{\Gamma}(\sigma)d\sigma,\quad \dot{\mathbf{\Phi}}(s)=\frac{d}{ds}\mathbf{\Phi}(s)=2\mathbf{\Gamma}(s), \quad (4.9)$$

we may rewrite Eq. (4.8) in the form

$$\mathop{\mathfrak{F}}_{s=0}^{\infty}(G(s);C)=\mathbf{\Phi}(0)\{E(t)\}+\int_0^\infty \dot{\mathbf{\Phi}}(s)\{E(t-s)\}ds+o(\epsilon), \quad (4.10)$$

where

$$\lim_{s\to\infty}\mathbf{\Phi}(s)=0. \quad (4.11)$$

Assumption (D) of Sec. 3 and Eq. (2.24) imply that the equilibrium term $\mathfrak{h}(C)$ of Eq. (3.4) has the form

$$\mathfrak{h}(C(t))=T_r+\mathbf{\Omega}\{E(t)\}+o(\epsilon). \quad (4.12)$$

Here, the linear transformation $\mathbf{\Omega}\{\ \}$ of the space of symmetric tensors is the gradient of the tensor function $\mathfrak{h}(C)$ at $C=I$. The tensor

$$T_r=\mathfrak{h}(I) \quad (4.13)$$

is the *residual stress*, i.e., the stress the material would sustain if it had been held in the reference configuration at all times in the past.

Substitution of Eqs. (4.10) and (4.12) into the constitutive equation (3.4) yields

$$\bar{T}(t)=T_r+[\mathbf{\Omega}+\mathbf{\Phi}(0)]\{E(t)\}+\int_0^\infty \dot{\mathbf{\Phi}}(s)\{E(t-s)\}ds+o(\epsilon). \quad (4.14)$$

Finally, going back to the definition (3.3) of $\bar{T}$ and using Eqs. (2.27), we obtain the following expression for the stress tensor $T(t)$:

$$T(t)-T_r=W(t)T_r-T_rW(t)+[\mathbf{\Omega}+\mathbf{\Phi}(0)]\{E(t)\}+\int_0^\infty \dot{\mathbf{\Phi}}(s)\{E(t-s)\}ds+o(\epsilon). \quad (4.15)$$

When ϵ, given by Eq. (2.16), is small enough, the remainder term $o(\epsilon)$ can be neglected in comparison with the other terms on the right-hand side of Eq. (4.15), which are of order $O(\epsilon)$. Thus, the *constitutive equation of infinitesimal viscoelasticity* reads

$$T(t)-T_r=W(t)T_r-T_rW(t)+[\mathbf{\Omega}+\mathbf{\Phi}(0)]\{E(t)\}+\int_0^\infty \dot{\mathbf{\Phi}}(s)\{E(t-s)\}ds. \quad (4.16)$$

When the reference configuration is a natural state, we have $T_r=0$, and Eq. (4.16) reduces to the classical equation (1.1). Equation (4.16), with $T_r\neq 0$, applies to infinitesimal deformations superposed on a large deformation from an unstressed natural state. In this case, the reference configuration is not the natural state but the deformed state with equilibrium stress T_r. If T_r is a hydrostatic pressure $T_r=-pI$, the terms involving $W(t)$ in Eq. (4.16), cancel. The stress relaxation function $\mathbf{\Phi}(s)$ depends not only on the material but also on the configuration which has been taken as the reference.

We remark that the special case $\mathbf{\Phi}(s)\equiv 0$ of Eq. (4.16) corresponds to the theory of infinitesimal elastic deformations superposed on large deformations. The special case $\mathbf{\Phi}(s)\equiv 0$ and $T_r=0$ corresponds to the classical theory of infinitesimal elasticity.

5. FINITE LINEAR VISCOELASTICITY

Motivation

Let us return to Eq. (3.14), which, under our hypothesis (F), is equivalent to the fundamental constitutive equation (3.4). It follows from Eq. (3.10) that the remainder term of Eq. (3.14) is small compared to the term involving the integral, provided the history $G(s)=\bar{C}_t(t-s)-I$ has a small Hilbert-space norm. Thus, the equation

$$\bar{T}=\mathfrak{h}(C)+\int_0^\infty \mathbf{\Gamma}(s;C)\{G(s)\}ds \quad (5.1)$$

approximates the general constitutive equation of a simple material in the limit

$$\|G(s)\|\to 0, \quad (5.2)$$

and the error approaches zero faster than $\|G(s)\|$. We call the theory based on Eq. (5.1) *finite linear viscoelasticity*.

One way of achieving the limit (5.2) is to let ϵ, defined by Eq. (2.16), go to zero. The discussion of Sec. 4 shows that, in this case, Eq. (5.1) reduces to the constitutive equation (4.16) of infinitesimal viscoelasticity.

When we consider, however, the definition (3.7) of the norm $\|G(s)\|$, we see that the limit (5.2) may be achieved even when ϵ does not approach zero. In order for $\|G(s)\|$ to be small, it is not necessary that the deformation (relative to the configuration at the present time t) be small at *all* past times $\tau<t$, but only that the deformation be small in the *recent* past. In particular, $\|G(s)\|$ is small for "slow" motions. To make this remark precise we consider a history $G(s)$ which has finite norm and corresponds to a deformation which makes no jump at the present, so that

$$\lim_{s\to 0} G(s)=0. \quad (5.3)$$

We then construct for each α, $0<\alpha\leq 1$, a "retarded" history

$$G_\alpha(s)=G(\alpha s). \quad (5.4)$$

It follows from Eq. (3.21) of reference 9 that

$$\lim_{\alpha\to 0}\|G_\alpha(s)\|=0, \quad (5.5)$$

i.e., that the limit (5.2) may be achieved by retardation of a given process.

Aside from the fact that the finite theory based on Eq. (5.1) applies to a much larger class of problems than the infinitesimal theory, there is a fundamental difference between the two theories. The infinitesimal theory is physically meaningless for finite deformations because it does not have the invariance properties required by the principle of material objectivity. The finite linear theory, on the other hand, enjoys the correct invariance. Thus, it is conceivable that there exists *some* material which obeys Eq. (5.1) for *arbitrary* finite deformations. The infinitesimal theory cannot possibly apply to *any* material when finite deformations are considered.

Finally, we remark that in the derivation of Eq. (5.1) no assumption has been made about the magnitude of the tensor parameter C. Hence, the finite theory based on Eq. (5.1) is applicable when the present and the reference configuration are related by an arbitrary large deformation.

Isotropic Materials

When dealing with isotropic materials it is convenient to take the reference configuration to be *undis-*

torted. (A precise definition of this term is given in reference 8.) Then the equilibrium stress is hydrostatic. Furthermore, the results in Sec. 22 of reference 8 show that the constitutive equation (5.1) reduces to

$$T=\mathfrak{h}(B)+\int_0^\infty \mathbf{\Gamma}(s;B)\{J(s)\}ds, \qquad (5.6)$$

where $B=B(t)$ is the left Cauchy-Green tensor, defined by Eq. (2.11), and the history $J(s)$ is given by

$$J(s)=C_t(t-s)-I. \qquad (5.7)$$

Furthermore, the tensor function $\mathfrak{h}$ and the linear functional given by the integral in Eq. (5.6) are *isotropic* in the sense that they obey the identities

$$Q\mathfrak{h}(B)Q^T=\mathfrak{h}(QBQ^T), \qquad (5.8)$$

$$Q\int_0^\infty \mathbf{\Gamma}(s;B)\{J(s)\}ds\, Q^T = \int_0^\infty \mathbf{\Gamma}(s;QBQ^T)\{QJ(s)Q^T\}ds \qquad (5.9)$$

for all orthogonal tensors Q. A fundamental theorem of the theory of isotropic tensor functions (for an elegant recent proof see reference 10, Sec. 59) states that $\mathfrak{h}$ has a representation

$$\mathfrak{h}(B)=h_0I+h_1B+h_2B^2, \qquad (5.10)$$

where h_0, h_1, and h_2 are scalar invariants of B. Also, it can be shown that the identity (5.9) implies the following representation for $\mathbf{\Gamma}$:

$$\mathbf{\Gamma}(s;B)\{J(s)\} = \mathfrak{k}_1(s;B)J(s) + J(s)\mathfrak{k}_1(s;B) \qquad (5.11)$$
$$+ \operatorname{Tr}[J(s)\mathfrak{k}_2(s;B)]I + \operatorname{Tr}[J(s)\mathfrak{k}_3(s;B)]B + \operatorname{Tr}[J(s)\mathfrak{k}_4(s;B)]B^2 .$$

Here, for each s, the tensor functions $\mathfrak{k}_i(s;B)$ are isotropic in the sense of Eq. (5.8) and hence have representations of the form (5.10). The proof of this result is too technical to be included here. Equations (5.10) and (5.11) and the representations for the $\mathfrak{k}_i$ may be used to render the constitutive equation (5.6) explicit. The resulting formula shows that in finite linear viscoelasticity the behavior of an isotropic material is determined by 15 independent scalar material functions; three of these depend on three variables and the remaining eight on four variables. The assumption of isotropy alone yields no further simplification. The special case $\mathbf{\Gamma}\equiv 0$ of Eq. (5.6) corresponds to the theory of finite (nonlinear) isotropic elasticity.

Fluids

We now consider materials which not only obey a constitutive equation of the form (5.1) but which are also *simple fluids* in the sense of the definition given in reference 8. (Coleman and Noll[11] give a summary of the general theory of simple fluids with emphasis on physical applications.) Such materials are isotropic, and hence Eqs. (5.6)–(5.9) apply. Moreover, the functions $\mathfrak{h}(B)$ and $\mathbf{\Gamma}(s;B)$ in Eq. (5.6) depend on B only through the determinant of B or, equivalently, only through the present density $\rho=\rho(t)$. Thus, for a fluid, Eq. (5.6) becomes

$$T=\mathfrak{h}(\rho)+\int_0^\infty \mathbf{\Gamma}(s;\rho)\{J(s)\}ds. \qquad (5.12)$$

The isotropy identities (5.8) and (5.9) may be written in the form

$$Q\mathfrak{h}(\rho)Q^T=\mathfrak{h}(\rho), \qquad (5.13)$$

$$\int_0^\infty Q[\mathbf{\Gamma}(s;\rho)\{J(s)\}]Q^T - \mathbf{\Gamma}(s;\rho)\{QJ(s)Q^T\}ds=0. \qquad (5.14)$$

Since Eq. (5.13) is valid for all orthogonal tensors Q, it follows that $\mathfrak{h}(\rho)$ must reduce to a scalar multiple of the unit tensor:

$$\mathfrak{h}(\rho)=-p(\rho)I. \qquad (5.15)$$

We call $p(\rho)$ the *equilibrium pressure*; it is the pressure the fluid would be supporting if it had remained at rest in its present configuration at all times in the past.

Equation (5.14) is valid for all orthogonal Q and for all possible histories $J(s)$ belonging to the Hilbert space $\mathcal{H}$. The only element of a Hilbert space which is orthogonal to all elements of the space is the zero element. This fact implies that the integrand in Eq. (5.14) must be identically zero. Hence, the transformation $\mathbf{\Gamma}(s;\rho)\{\ \}$ satisfies the identity

$$Q[\Gamma(s;\rho)\{J\}]Q^T = \Gamma(s;\rho)\{QJQ^T\} \qquad (5.16)$$

for all orthogonal tensors Q and all symmetric tensors J. In other words, for each s and ρ, $\mathbf{\Gamma}(\rho;s)\{\ \}$ is an *isotropic* linear transformation of the space of symmetric tensors. The representation theorem for such isotropic transformations [special case of the theorem embodied in Eq. (5.10) (see reference 10, Sec. 59)] states that $\mathbf{\Gamma}(s;\rho)\{J(s)\}$ must be of the form

$$\mathbf{\Gamma}(s;\rho)\{J(s)\}=\mu(s;\rho)J(s)+\lambda(s;\rho)(\operatorname{Tr} J(s))I, \qquad (5.17)$$

where $\mu(s;\rho)$ and $\lambda(s;\rho)$ are scalar functions of the time lapse s and the present density ρ. On substituting Eqs. (5.15) and (5.17) into Eq. (5.12), we obtain the following *constitutive equation of a simple fluid in the theory of finite linear viscoelasticity*:

$$T=-p(\rho)I+\int^\infty \mu(s;\rho)J(s)ds + \left[\int_0^\infty \lambda(s;\rho)\operatorname{Tr} J(s)ds\right]I. \qquad (5.18)$$

[10] J. Serrin, "Mathematical principles of classical fluid mechanics," in *Encyclopedia of Physics*, edited by S. Flügge (Springer-Verlag, Berlin, 1959), Vol. VIII/1.

[11] B. D. Coleman and W. Noll, Ann. N. Y. Acad. Sci. **89**, 672 (1961).

In this theory, the mechanical behavior of a fluid is determined by the three scalar material functions $p(\rho)$, $\mu(s;\rho)$, and $\lambda(s;\rho)$.

If the fluid under consideration is *incompressible*, certain modifications must be made in this analysis. In incompressible materials, the motion determines the stress only up to a hydrostatic pressure. In other words, the constitutive equation gives only the *extra stress*

$$T_e = T + pI, \tag{5.19}$$

where p is an indeterminate pressure. In the incompressible case, the two terms in Eq. (5.18) which are scalar multiples of the unit tensor I may be absorbed into the indeterminate pressure term pI. From these remarks we see that in finite linear viscoelasticity the stress in an incompressible fluid is given by the remarkably simple equation

$$T_e = T + pI = \int_0^\infty \mu(s) J(s) ds, \tag{5.20}$$

where, since the density is constant, $\mu(s)$ is a function of only the time lapse s.

The "relaxation function" $\phi(s)$ determined by rheologists from measurements of the decay of shearing tractions for simple (infinitesimal) shear in incompressible fluids is related to the material function $\mu(s)$ as follows:

$$\phi(s) = -2\int_s^\infty \mu(\sigma) d\sigma, \quad \mu(s) = \tfrac{1}{2}(d/ds)\phi(s). \tag{5.21}$$

Thus, the relaxation function $\phi(s)$ is sufficient to determine the mechanical behavior of incompressible fluids in the theory of finite linear viscoelasticity.

For simple fluids, the property (3.13) is equivalent to the conditions

$$\int_0^\infty |\mu(s;\rho)|^2 h(s)^{-2} ds < \infty, \qquad \int_0^\infty |\lambda(s;\rho)|^2 h(s)^{-2} ds < \infty. \tag{5.22}$$

These conditions relate the rate of decay of the influence function to the rate of decay of the material functions $\mu(s;\rho)$ and $\lambda(s;\rho)$ as $s \to \infty$.

6. SECOND-ORDER VISCOELASTICITY

In Sec. 3 we showed, on the basis of our assumption (F), that the (nonlinear) functional $\mathfrak{F}$ giving the stress in a simple material may be approximated by a *linear* functional. The error in this approximation approaches zero faster than the Hilbert-space norm $\|G(s)\|$ of the history (3.15). The analysis of Sec. 3 may be generalized if the assumption (F) is replaced by a stronger assumption which requires that the functional $\mathfrak{F}$ be not just once but n times Fréchet differentiable at the zero history. It is then possible to approximate $\mathfrak{F}$ by a *polynomial* functional of degree n with an error that approaches zero faster than the nth power of the norm $\|G(s)\|$. For example, when $n=2$, we find the following generalization of Eq. (3.14):

$$\bar{T} = \mathfrak{h}(C) + \int_0^\infty \mathbf{\Gamma}(s;C)\{G(s)\}ds + \mathop{\mathfrak{Q}}_{s=0}^{\infty}(G(s);C) + \mathop{\mathfrak{R}'}_{s=0}^{\infty}(G(s);C). \tag{6.1}$$

Here, $\mathfrak{Q}$ is a continuous *quadratic* functional depending on the tensor parameter C; the remainder $\mathfrak{R}'$ is of order $o(\|G(s)\|^2)$, i.e.,

$$\lim_{\|G(s)\|\to 0} \|G(s)\|^{-2}\mathfrak{R}'(G(s);C) = 0. \tag{6.2}$$

Relation (6.1) shows that the equation

$$\bar{T} = \mathfrak{h}(C) + \int_0^\infty \mathbf{\Gamma}(s;C)\{G(s)\}ds + \mathop{\mathfrak{Q}}_{s=0}^{\infty}(G(s);C) \tag{6.3}$$

approximates the general constitutive equation of a simple material in the limit $\|G(s)\| \to 0$, and the error approaches zero faster than $\|G(s)\|^2$. We call the theory based on Eq. (6.3) *second-order viscoelasticity*.

The quadratic functional $\mathfrak{Q}$ of Eq. (6.3) may be expressed in terms of a bounded symmetric operator on the Hilbert space of histories. It is not possible, in general, to represent $\mathfrak{Q}$ by integrals. However, an integral representation does exist if the operator corresponding to $\mathfrak{Q}$ is completely continuous. We consider only this special case.

Explicit forms of the constitutive equations for isotropic materials and for simple fluids in second-order viscoelasticity may be obtained by an analysis similar to the one given in Sec. 5 in finite linear viscoelasticity. The resulting formulas are too complicated to be included here in full. Without giving the details of the derivation, we state the *constitutive equation of an incompressible fluid in the second-order theory of viscoelasticity*:

$$T + pI = \int_0^\infty \mu(s)J(s)ds + \int_0^\infty \int_0^\infty [\alpha(s_1,s_2)J(s_1)J(s_2) + \beta(s_1,s_2)\{\operatorname{Tr} J(s_1)\}J(s_2)]ds_1 ds_2. \tag{6.4}$$

Here, p is an indeterminate pressure, $J(s)$ is the history given by Eq. (5.7), and $\mu(s)$, $\alpha(s_1,s_2)$ and $\beta(s_1,s_2)$ are scalar material functions. The function $\mu(s)$ is the same **As in Eq. (5.23). The function α is uniquely**

determined if and only if it is chosen to be symmetric, i. e.,

$$\alpha(s_1,s_2)=\alpha(s_2,s_1); \tag{6.5}$$

the function β need not be symmetric.

In order to illustrate the behavior predicted by Eq. (6.4), we consider a class of motions called *simple shearing motions*. These motions are defined by the property that the velocity field $\mathbf{v}(\mathbf{x})=\{v_x,v_y,v_z\}$, in some Cartesian coordinate system x, y, z, has the components

$$v_x=0, \quad v_y=v(x,t), \quad v_z=0. \tag{6.6}$$

It follows from Eqs. (5.6), (5.8), and (5.10) of reference 11 that the matrix function corresponding to the history $J(s)$ defined by Eq. (5.7) has the form

$$[J(s)]=\lambda_t(s)\begin{Vmatrix}0&1&0\\1&0&0\\0&0&0\end{Vmatrix}+\lambda_t(s)^2\begin{Vmatrix}1&0&0\\0&0&0\\0&0&0\end{Vmatrix}, \tag{6.7}$$

where

$$\lambda_t(s)=\int_0^s \frac{d}{dx}v(x,t-\sigma)d\sigma. \tag{6.8}$$

In order to obtain the components T_{xx}, T_{xy}, etc., of the stress tensor T, we substitute Eq. (6.7) into Eq. (6.4). After a simple calculation, we find

$$T_{xy}=\int_0^\infty \mu(s)\lambda_t(s)ds+\int_0^\infty\int_0^\infty \gamma(s_1,s_2) \times\lambda_t(s_1)^2\lambda_t(s_2)ds_1ds_2, \tag{6.9}$$

$$T_{xx}-T_{yy}=\int_0^\infty \mu(s)\lambda_t^2(s)ds+\int_0^\infty\int_0^\infty \gamma(s_1,s_2) \times\lambda_t(s_1)^2\lambda_t(s_2)^2ds_1ds_2, \tag{6.10}$$

$$T_{yy}-T_{zz}=\int_0^\infty\int_0^\infty \alpha(s_1,s_2)\lambda_t(s_1)\lambda_t(s_2)ds_1ds_2, \tag{6.11}$$

where

$$\gamma(s_1,s_2)=\alpha(s_1,s_2)+\beta(s_1,s_2). \tag{6.12}$$

Equations (6.9)–(6.11), together with Cauchy's equations of motion, lead to a rather complicated system of integro-differential equations.

We now consider the special case when

$$\epsilon=\sup_{s>0}|\lambda_t(s)| \tag{6.13}$$

is small. Physically, this case corresponds to shearing motions with the property that the configuration of the fluid at *all* past times differs from the present configuration only by a small deformation. Shearing vibrations of small amplitude have this property. It is clear from Eqs. (6.13) and (6.7) that the Hilbert space norm $\|J(s)\|$ is of order $O(\epsilon^2)$. But the terms involving double integrals in Eqs. (6.9) and (6.10) are of order $O(\epsilon^3)$ and $O(\epsilon^4)$, respectively. Therefore, for small ϵ, Eqs. (6.9) and (6.10) reduce to

$$T_{xy}=\int_0^\infty \mu(s)\lambda_t(s)ds, \tag{6.14}$$

$$T_{xx}-T_{yy}=\int_0^\infty \mu(s)\lambda_t^2(s)ds. \tag{6.15}$$

Equation (6.14) for the shearing stress T_{xy} is the same as the corresponding equation in the theory of infinitesimal viscoelasticity. The normal stress differences given by Eqs. (6.15) and (6.11), zero in the infinitesimal theory, do not vanish in the second-order theory. Equations (6.11) and (6.15) may be used, for example, for the interpretation of data on normal stresses obtained in experiments involving shearing vibrations of small amplitude. It is remarkable that the normal stress difference (6.15) depends only on the material function $\mu(s)$ or, equivalently, the shear relaxation function $\phi(s)$ given by Eq. (5.24).

These results on simple shearing motions can easily be generalized to motions that have a form similar to (6.6) in an appropriate curvilinear orthogonal coordinate system. (The method to be employed is analogous to the one used in Sec. 2 of reference 12.)

7. FINAL REMARKS

In our considerations in Secs. 3–6 we have used the relative right Cauchy-Green tensor C_t as a measure of strain. As we remarked at the end of Sec. 2, there is no unique "strain tensor" when finite deformations are considered. Instead of C_t we could also have used the relative right stretch tensor $U_t=(C_t)^{\frac{1}{2}}$, the inverse C_t^{-1}, $\log C_t$, or any other tensor related to C_t by a smooth one-to-one transformation. To different choices of the measure of strain correspond different theories of finite linear viscoelasticity. However, the difference of the stresses computed using two different such theories is of order $o(\|G(s)\|)$. Hence, since any finite linear theory can be expected to be accurate only when terms of order $o(\|G(s)\|)$ can be neglected, we can say that the various theories corresponding to the various measures of strain are equivalent.

To different choices of the measure of strain also correspond different theories of second-order viscoelasticity. These different theories are equivalent in the sense that the corresponding stresses differ only by terms of order $o(\|G(s)\|^2)$.

On the basis of a molecular model for certain incompressible fluids, Lodge[13] has derived a constitutive equation corresponding to Eq. (5.23) when $J(s)$ is

[12] B. D. Coleman and W. Noll, Arch. Ratl. Mech. Anal. 4, 289 (1959).

[13] A. S. Lodge, Trans. Faraday Soc. 52, 120 (1956).

Bemerkung zum geometrischen Grundgesetz der allgemeinen Kontinuumstheorie der Versetzungen und Eigenspannungen

EKKEHART KRÖNER

Vorgelegt von J. MEIXNER

In der vorliegenden Bemerkung, die als Ergänzung zu einer kürzlich erschienenen Arbeit [*1*] aufzufassen ist, soll begründet werden, daß die Einsteinschen Gleichungen $\Gamma^{ij} = B^{ij}$ eine vollständige Formulierung des geometrischen Grundgesetzes der obengenannten Theorie darstellen. Dieses Gesetz beinhaltet die Forderung nach der Kontinuität des verformten Körpers.

In der auf 9 funktionale Freiheitsgrade *beschränkten* Theorie, mit der *reine* Kontinua, d.h. solche ohne Fremd- oder Extramaterie behandelt werden, war das Grundgesetz früher in der linearisierten Form [*2, 3*]

$$\nabla \times \boldsymbol{\beta} - \boldsymbol{\alpha} = 0 \tag{1}$$

geschrieben worden. Hier ist $\boldsymbol{\beta}$ das Tensorfeld der Distorsion (= Deformation + Drehung) und $\boldsymbol{\alpha}$ das Tensorfeld der Versetzungsdichte. Die auch für endliche Verformungen geltende Formulierung lautet nach KONDO [*4*] sowie BILBY, BULLOUGH und SMITH [*5*] (Summationskonvention!)

$$\Gamma_{[ml]k} = A_{\varkappa k} (\partial_m A_l^\varkappa - \partial_l A_m^\varkappa)/2. \tag{2}$$

Hier ist $\Gamma_{[ml]k}$ der in m, l antisymmetrische Teil der affinen Konnexion Γ_{mlk}, die den natürlichen Zustand des Kontinuums in den Koordinaten x^k des Endzustands beschreibt, er repräsentiert die Versetzungsdichte. $A_{\varkappa k}$ ist die Transformation vom natürlichen in den deformierten Zustand, $A_l^\varkappa$ die dazu reziproke Transformation. Die letzte Gleichung entsteht aus der Beziehung

$$\Gamma_{mlk} = A_{\varkappa k}\, \partial_m A_l^\varkappa \tag{3}$$

durch Antisymmetrisierung bezüglich der Indizes m, l. Wie früher bemerkt ([*1*], S. 289), ist auch Gl. (3) eine Formulierung des Grundgesetzes. Es ist in der Differentialgeometrie wohlbekannt, daß eine Konnexion die Form (3) dann und nur dann hat, wenn der zugehörige Riemann-Christoffelsche Krümmungstensor Γ_{nmlk} verschwindet[1]. Da wir uns, wie früher begründet, auf metrische

[1] Das Verschwinden des Krümmungstensors Γ_{nmlk} in der beschränkten Theorie kommt schon bei BILBY, BULLOUGH und SMITH vor.

Kontinua beschränken, ist Γ_{nmlk} in l, k antisymmetrisch und kann somit vollständig durch den zugehörigen Einstein-Tensor Γ^{ij} ersetzt werden. Es folgt, daß die *homogenen* Einsteinschen Gleichungen

$$\Gamma^{ij} = 0 \tag{4}$$

eine weitere Formulierung des geometrischen Grundgesetzes in der beschränkten Theorie darstellen.

Hiernach darf geschlossen werden, daß die *inhomogenen* Einsteinschen Gleichungen

$$\Gamma^{ij} = B^{ij}, \tag{5}$$

in denen B^{ij} wegen der Bianchi-Identität 6 funktionale Freiheitsgrade besitzt, eine vollständige Formulierung des geometrischen Grundgesetzes der allgemeinen Theorie (15 Freiheitsgrade) darstellen, wobei die bei der Verformung hervorgerufenen Kontinuitätsstörungen in der regulären Materie durch die Fremdmaterie (B^{ij}) gerade kompensiert werden.

Wendet man dieselbe Schlußweise auf Gl. (1) an, so kommt man zu einem Gesetz

$$\nabla \times \boldsymbol{\beta} - \boldsymbol{\alpha} = \boldsymbol{\delta}, \tag{6}$$

in dem der die Fremdmaterie repräsentierende Tensor $\boldsymbol{\delta}$ 9 funktionale Freiheitsgrade zu haben scheint. Ziehen wir von Gl. (6) ihre halbe, mit dem Einheitstensor $\boldsymbol{I}$ multiplizierte Spur (Symbol I) ab, so bleibt unter Berücksichtigung des bekannten Zusammenhangs von Versetzungsdichte und Cosserat-Nyeschem Krümmungstensor $\boldsymbol{K}$

$$\nabla \times \boldsymbol{\beta} - \tfrac{1}{2}(\nabla \times \boldsymbol{\beta})_{\mathrm{I}} \boldsymbol{I} + \boldsymbol{K} = \boldsymbol{\delta} - \tfrac{1}{2}\boldsymbol{\delta}_{\mathrm{I}} \boldsymbol{I} \equiv \boldsymbol{\delta}. \tag{7}$$

Mit der früher bewiesenen Zerlegungsformel ([2], S. 29)

$$\boldsymbol{\beta} = \nabla \boldsymbol{s} + \nabla \times \boldsymbol{\iota} \times \nabla + \boldsymbol{I} \times \vec{\Theta}, \tag{8}$$

in der $\boldsymbol{s}$ und $\vec{\Theta}$ je ein Vektorfeld, $\boldsymbol{\iota}$ ein symmetrisches Tensorfeld ist, erhält man

$$\nabla \times (\nabla \times \boldsymbol{\iota} \times \nabla) - \vec{\Theta} \nabla + \boldsymbol{K} = \boldsymbol{\delta}'. \tag{9}$$

Nun entnehmen wir Gl. (9), daß im Fall $\boldsymbol{\delta}' = 0$ und $\boldsymbol{\iota} = 0$ der Krümmungstensor $\boldsymbol{K}$ die Form $\vec{\Theta} \nabla$ hat. Die Realisation erfolgt, wie wir wissen, durch den Angriff einer äußeren Drehmomentendichte. Andere äußere Einflüsse können nun keinesfalls eine Krümmung der gleichen Art, also etwa $\vec{\Theta}' \nabla$ hervorrufen, sie müßten sonst ebenfalls als äußere Drehmomente interpretiert werden (wir denken an unendlich ausgedehnte Medien). Hieraus folgt, daß $\boldsymbol{K}$ die Form

$$\boldsymbol{K} = \vec{\Theta} \nabla + \boldsymbol{\Phi} \times \nabla \tag{10}$$

mit einem noch beliebigen Tensorfeld $\boldsymbol{\Phi}$ hat. Infolgedessen verschwindet die linke Seite von Gl. (9) bei rechtsseitiger Divergenzbildung identisch, und es ist somit $\boldsymbol{\delta}' \cdot \nabla \equiv 0$, d.h. der Tensor $\boldsymbol{\delta}$ verliert 3 seiner funktionalen Freiheitsgrade. Man überzeugt sich leicht, daß andererseits die Gln. (9) bei rechtsseitiger Rotationsbildung in die linearisierten Einsteinschen Gleichungen (5) übergehen ($\boldsymbol{\delta}' \times \nabla \equiv \boldsymbol{B}$).

Damit ist die Gültigkeit unserer Behauptung, daß die Einsteinschen Gleichungen (5) ein vollständiger Ausdruck des geometrischen Grundgesetzes sind, auf anderem Wege bekräftigt worden. Hiermit werden insbesondere auch die in [*1*, *6*] zuweilen gebrauchten Bezeichnungen „Grundgleichungen der Eigenspannungsbestimmung" und „Drehmaterie" überflüssig.

Die Beschränkung von $\boldsymbol{\delta}$ auf 6 funktionale Freiheitsgrade bedeutet, daß die Zahl der Freiheitsgrade aller äußeren Einwirkungen nur 12 beträgt, im Gegensatz zu den statischen und geometrischen Zustandsgrößen, die je 15 Freiheitsgrade besitzen. Sind alle äußeren Einwirkungen gleich Null, so gibt es infolge der besonderen Struktur der Einsteinschen Gleichungen trotzdem von Null verschiedene Lösungen, es sind dies die zu den Eigenspannungen führenden Lösungen, als deren Quellen die Versetzungen auftreten. Die hierzu gehörigen Freiheitsgrade sind gerade die 3 überzähligen Freiheitsgrade der geometrischen und statischen Größen. Offensichtlich handelt es sich hier um Lösungen, die metastabile Zustände beschreiben, was in bester Übereinstimmung mit allem ist, was man heute über Versetzungen weiß.

Ich halte es für höchst wahrscheinlich, daß die Einsteinschen Gleichungen überhaupt die einzige vernünftige auf den Endzustand bezogene Formulierung des geometrischen Grundgesetzes der allgemeinen Theorie durch Differentialgleichungen sind, da sie Ableitungen sowohl der Deformationen als auch der Krümmungen enthalten. Darüber hinaus ist die enge Analogie zur allgemeinen Relativitätstheorie sehr ermutigend. Nach den ersten größeren Erfolgen zur Versetzungsdynamik des Kontinuums von Holländer [*7*] darf man hoffen, daß die Einsteinschen Gleichungen (5) auch bei Hinzunahme der 4. Dimension (der Zeit) gültig bleiben, wobei man jetzt die Indizes in (5) von 1 bis 4 laufen lassen sollte.

Literatur

[*1*] Kröner, E.: Allgemeine Kontinuumstheorie der Versetzungen und Eigenspannungen. Arch. Rational Mech. Anal. **4**, 273—334 (1960).

[*2*] Bilby, B. A.: Types of dislocation source, Defects in crystalline solids. Report of 1954 Bristol conference, S. 123—133. London: The Physical Society 1955.

[*3*] Kröner, E.: Kontinuumstheorie der Versetzungen und Eigenspannungen. Erg. angew. Math. **5**, 1—179 (1958).

[*4*] Kondo, K.: Memoirs of the Unifying Study of the Basic Problems in Engineering by Means of Geometry, Vol. I u. II. Tokyo: Gakujutsu Bunken Fukyu-Kai 1955 u. 1958.

[*5*] Bilby, B. A., R. Bullough & E. Smith: Continuous distributions of dislocations: a new application of the methods of non-Riemannian geometry. Proc. Roy. Soc. London, Ser. A **231**, 263—273 (1955).

[*6*] Kröner, E., & A. Seeger: Nicht-lineare Elastizitätstheorie der Versetzungen und Eigenspannungen. Arch. Rational Mech. Anal. **3**, 97—119 (1959).

[*7*] Holländer, E. F.: The basic equations of the dynamics of the continuous distribution of dislocations. Czech. J. Phys. B **10**, 409—418, 479—487, 551—560 (1960).

Institut für theoretische und angewandte Physik
Technische Hochschule Stuttgart
Wiederholdstraße 13